Encyclopedia of
Plant Physiology

New Series Volume 1

Editors
A. Pirson, Göttingen
M. H. Zimmermann, Harvard

Transport in Plants I
Phloem Transport

Edited by

M. H. Zimmermann and J. A. Milburn

Contributors

M. J. P. Canny J. Dainty A. F. G. Dixon W. Eschrich
D. S. Fensom D. R. Geiger W. Heyser W. Höll
J. A. Milburn T. R. F. Nonweiler M. V. Parthasarathy
J. S. Pate A. J. Peel S. A. Sovonick D. C. Spanner
P. M. L. Tammes M. T. Tyree J. Van Die H. Ziegler
M. H. Zimmermann

With 93 Figures

Springer-Verlag Berlin Heidelberg New York 1975

ISBN 3-540-07314-0 Springer-Verlag Berlin Heidelberg New York
ISBN 0-387-07314-0 Springer-Verlag New York Heidelberg Berlin

Library of Congress Cataloging in Publication Data. Main entry under title: Transport in plants I: phloem transport. (Encyclopedia of plant physiology; v. 1) Bibliography: p. Includes index. 1. Plant translocation. 2. Phloem. I. Zimmermann, Martin Huldrych, 1926— II. Milburn, John A., 1936— QK871.T73 582'.041 75-20178

Typesetting, printing and bookbinding: Universitätsdruckerei H. Stürtz AG, Würzburg.

Preface

When WILHELM RUHLAND developed his plan for an Encyclopedia of Plant Physiology more than three decades ago, biology could still be conveniently subdivided into classical areas. Even within plant physiology, subdivisions were not too difficult to make, and general principles could be covered sufficiently in the two introductory volumes of the Encyclopedia on the physical and chemical basis of cell biology. But the situation changed rapidly even during the 12-year publication period of the Encyclopedia (1955–1967). The new molecular direction of genetics and structural research on biopolymers had an integrating effect on all other biological fields, including plant physiology, and it became increasingly difficult to keep previously distinct areas separated.

RUHLAND's overall plan included 18 volumes and about 22,000 pages. It covered the entire field of plant physiology, in most cases from the very beginning. But, as each volume appeared, it was clear that its content would soon be outdated. Discussions between the publisher and plant physiologists were therefore initiated to determine if and how the series could be continued. A difficult question concerned the degree of independence of individual fields. Modern biologists, particularly cell biologists, have a tendency to generalize, particularly if their background is primarily in physics or chemistry. Indeed, many basic principles of biology can be considered today well proven for all organisms. On the other hand, nature is extremely diverse; any generalized information that has been obtained in the laboratory with "standard" organisms and *in vitro* systems has to be compared with results obtained with the wide variety of organisms in nature. In plant physiology, as in other fields, this apparent antagonism between general principles and diversity has a stimulating effect on research.

Life processes of green plants are being studied with all available methods of modern biology. Electron microscopy, penetrating more and more into the dimensions of molecules, shows increasing concern with the functional aspects of structure. One of the most fascinating ways of studying life processes is the study of their regulation. In this respect, plant physiology is particularly dependent upon the progress made in biochemistry and genetics. It will probably not be long before methods and principles of bacterial genetics can be applied to the much more complex eucaryotic organisms, including green plants with their specific genetic material.

Thus, on the one hand, new methods of studying regulation and adaptation break down old barriers between formerly separate fields such as genetics, physiology and ecology. On the other hand, certain areas have remained well defined, particularly those concerning functions of the organism as a whole, such as phloem transport.

Today it is impractical or impossible to merely issue supplementary volumes or a revised edition of the Encyclopedia of Plant Physiology. Even though there are still clearly-defined fields, too many of the boundaries have crumbled and new combinations of interests are developing. For this reason it was decided not to make subdivisions into predetermined areas in a grand overall publication plan, as it was done in the first edition, but to publish a "New Series" in a much more flexible way. New and expanding fields will be treated separately as the need arises. There will be no introductory volumes to discuss basic principles. Historical concepts, already treated in the old Encyclopedia, will be discussed only if they need to be reconsidered in the light of newer findings. As each volume is to be more or less self-contained, overlapping will become unavoidable in the long run. Such overlap is not too disadvantageous if similar chapters are written by different authors and if the publication dates of the respective volumes are reasonably far apart from each other. Furthermore, it is always desirable that in the case of controversial issues individual representatives can defend their own point of view.

The subject matter of larger individual fields will be covered in several volumes, each one however self-contained and complete in itself. Thus the first volumes of the New Series consist of a set of three, covering transport and exchange phenomena at three levels of organization: the whole plant, tissue and cells, and structures within cells.

The New Series differs not only in material from the old Handbook, but also in appearance. The individual volumes will be less extensive, and consequently probably also less costly. They will be written exclusively in English, the language now established as the most suitable for communication in the natural sciences. Moreover, once a manuscript is complete, it will be published within a shorter time than before, probably two or three volumes in the course of each year. These measures should greatly contribute towards distributing the New Series in greater number than the old Handbook, and to making it for years to come one of the most important literary references in plant physiological research.

We hope that within the next few years, the New Series will once again cover the whole field of plant physiology, although in a quite different way from the old Handbook.

A. Pirson
M.H. Zimmermann

Introduction

Research on long-distance transport in plants probably began with the work of MALPIGHI in the later 17th century, following the discovery of blood circulation in animals by HARVEY. But the fact that there are *two* separate long-distance transport channels, the xylem and the phloem, was not recognized until more than 100 years later. The significance of phloem transport remained unclear until the assimilation of carbon dioxide had been discovered by DE SAUSSURE in 1804. Outstanding experimental work early during the 19th century by COTTA, DE CANDOLLE and KNIGHT established the movement of carbohydrates from leaves into stems and roots and their storage in the form of starch. THEODOR HARTIG discovered the sieve tube in 1837 and described exudation from both xylem and phloem in 1860. Thus, a reasonably clear understanding of long-distance transport pathways had been reached by the mid-19th century, though the transport mechanisms were unknown. Toward the end of the last century, translocation research suffered from the somewhat dogmatic statement by the great plant physiologist SACHS that diffusion is the mechanism by which assimilates are distributed in plants. SACHS was undoubtedly an outstanding scientist, but his influence was decidedly negative in the field of translocation.

Interest in translocation research developed rather slowly at the beginning of the 20th century, possibly because SACHS' influence still lingered on and because interest in plant physiology moved away from whole-plant physiology towards problems at the tissue and cellular level. During the 1920s, phloem-transport research was re-established in a number of laboratories and for the first time it became quantitative. Mass-transfer studies by DIXON and his students (e.g. MASON) established beyond doubt that diffusion was inadequate, by several orders of magnitude, as a mechanism for assimilate distribution over long distances. The search began for a mechanism to explain the phenomenally efficient way in which plants transport solutes rapidly over long distances. The chapters of this volume show that this search has not yet ended to the satisfaction of everyone.

In 1926 MÜNCH proposed his pressure-flow hypothesis which was published in greater detail in his book in 1930 by GUSTAV FISCHER in Jena. It had a very profound and lasting effect on virtually all subsequent work. It was considered carefully by MASON and MASKELL and eventually supported by DIXON. Nevertheless, though MÜNCH's book is unquestionably the most-cited single literature report of phloem transport, it may equally well merit the reputation of the least-read book in the field, at least so far as the English-speaking scientific community is concerned.

Interest in the phenomenon of phloem transport has increased steadily during the past 50 years. The number of publications has multiplied annually and several books on the subject have appeared recently. These books, taken individually and all cited in various chapters of this volume, represent strongly the points of view of the particular authors, and thus each presents an individual view of the state of knowledge. During the month of August, 1974, a conference was held at Banff, Canada, on phloem transport, the proceedings of which may be published before the end of the year. In this, considerable emphasis was placed on recent research in structural aspects and on theoretical models of phloem transport. The present volume does not duplicate this effort. We have striven to produce a more text-book-like presentation with a good deal more emphasis on experimental work.

The subject matter for this volume and the chapter authors have been carefully selected to represent as balanced an overall coverage as possible. Naturally, this resulted in the presentation of widely varied opinions, a fact which some readers may find confusing. At the present stage of knowledge, this is unavoidable. It has been said that the mechanism of phloem transport is still a matter of faith. What appears perfectly clear and logical to one person, may seem incredible to another. This is largely the result of the authors' interpretation of certain experimental results. For example, a whole chapter is devoted to the proposal of electroosmotically driven transport. Yet, in another chapter (Chapter 16, p. 367) the authors state that they consider it so unlikely an explanation of transport that they refuse "to belabor the point any further". Some authors dismiss the concept of a flowing solution on the basis of experimental results which appear highly questionable to others. For proponents of the mass-flow concept it is difficult to believe in conclusions drawn from electronmicrographs of fixed plant material which appear to preclude mass-flow when in the same plant they can observe, for hours or days, exudation from a single tube through a severed aphid stylet at a rate which requires refilling of the sieve element three to ten times per second. What else but a flowing solution could do this? On the other hand it is often very healthy if established "facts" and dogmatic views are challenged.

Scientific endeavor is perhaps more often than we like in direct conflict with human nature. Once we have made a statement we have a natural reluctance to withdraw it. Too often our attitude is to do experiments and use arguments to prove our point, rather than to find out honestly how the plant works, at the risk of finding an answer contrary to our wishes. Phloem research has developed a mystique which seems in turn to produce a search for certainties. These can easily become dogmatic assertions, for example: that glutaraldehyde is the best fixative for phloem; that radio-active tracer profiles correspond with the *contents* of sieve tubes; that calcium is always "immobile" in the phloem; that all sieve tubes behave in unison at a given time; that sieve-tube sap is always alkaline; that sieve tubes are short-lived; that osmotic adjustments are always through changes in sugar concentration; that sieve tubes occupy 20% of the (non-fibrous?) phloem. Although the above statements are often correct, there are good reasons to challenge each one of them. We have cited them in the hope that they will produce a note of caution in future research.

In spite of the present disagreement about transport mechanisms, this volume shows that considerable progress *has* been made during recent years. Much of the research that accumulated this knowledge was stimulated by MÜNCH's controversial book and the apparent simplicity of his proposed mechanism. If the present volume has a similarly stimulating effect, it will have served its purpose well. We do not doubt that in spite of the present-day controversy, a more thorough understanding of how nutrients are transported over long distances throughout the plant is not too far distant. We are inclined to doubt that appreciable new advances will be made using conventional electronmicroscopy to elucidate structure alone. The need here is for *experimental* investigations into the structures seen in sieve tubes. Similarly we are convinced that the present trend towards quantification of the parameters must be the main avenue of future advances and this in turn depends on the development of better experimental techniques.

We would like to thank all our friends and colleagues who contributed to this book. Their collaboration is greatly appreciated. Those who delivered their chapter promptly had to bring it up to date one or more times before the volume was complete. We thank specifically the many authors who reviewed chapters other than their own. Many persons whose names do not appear elsewhere in the book also gave invaluable help during the course of production of individual chapters. This help ranged from discussing ideas, and in some cases assisting with experiments, to reviewing the text of the manuscripts. They are for Chapters 2, 4 and 10, Prof. RAY F. EVERT; Chapter 3, Dr. C.B. OSMOND; Chapter 6, Dr. J.M.S. FORREST; Chapters 9 and 15, Drs. R.G. THOMPSON and R.D. LEE; Chapters 11 and 17, Dr. ROBERT J. FELLOWS; Chapter 13, Dr. ENID A.C. MACROBBIE; Chapter 14, Prof. P.E. WEATHERLEY, F.R.S.; Chapter 19, Profs. BRIAN E.S. GUNNING and OWEN A.M. LEWIS, and Dr. PATRICK J. SHARKEY. We also thank Springer-Verlag for prompt publication and high quality production. Last but not least, we thank the many individuals in the publishing-house whose names never appear in books, but whose conscientious work makes it "their" book as well as "ours".

Petersham, Massachusetts and
Glasgow, Scotland
October 1975

MARTIN H. ZIMMERMANN
JOHN A. MILBURN

Contents

I. Structural Considerations in Phloem Transport

II. Nature of Substances in Phloem

III. Phloem Transport: Assessment of Evidence

List of Contributors

M.J.P. CANNY
Botany Department, Monash University, Clayton, Victoria 3168/Australia

J. DAINTY
Department of Botany, University of Toronto, Toronto M5S 1A1/Canada

A.F.G. DIXON
School of Biological Sciences, University of East Anglia, Norwich NR4 7TJ/Great Britain

W. ESCHRICH
Forstbotanisches Institut der Universität, 34 Göttingen-Weende, Büsgenweg 2/Federal Republic of Germany

D.S. FENSOM
Department of Biology, Mount Allison University, Sackville EOA 3CO, New Brunswick/Canada

D.R. GEIGER
Department of Biology, University of Dayton, Dayton, Ohio 45469/USA

W. HEYSER
Forstbotanisches Institut der Universität, 34 Göttingen-Weende, Büsgenweg 2/Federal Republic of Germany

W. HÖLL
Institut für Botanik und Mikrobiologie, Technische Universität, 8 München 2, Arcisstr. 21/Federal Republic of Germany

J.A. MILBURN
Department of Botany, University of Glasgow, Glasgow G 12 8QQ/Great Britain

T.R.F. NONWEILER
Department of Mathematics, Victoria University of Wellington, Wellington, C. 1/New Zealand

M.V. PARTHASARATHY
Division of Biological Sciences, Section of Genetics, Development and Physiology, Cornell University, Ithaca, N.Y. 14853/USA

J.S. PATE
Department of Botany, University of Western Australia, Nedlands, W.A. 6009/Australia

A.J. PEEL
Department of Plant Biology, University of Hull, Hull HU6 7RX/Great Britain

S.A. SOVONICK
Harvard University, Harvard Forest, Petersham, MA 01366/USA

D.C. SPANNER
Department of Botany, Bedford College, University of London, London NW1 4NS/Great Britain

P.M.L. TAMMES
Centrum voor Plantenfysiologisch Onderzoek, Bornsesteeg 47, Wageningen/The Netherlands

M.T. TYREE
Department of Botany, University of Toronto, Toronto M5S 1A1/Canada

J. VAN DIE
Botanical Laboratory of the University, Lange Nieuwstraat 106, Utrecht/The Netherlands

H. ZIEGLER
Institut für Botanik und Mikrobiologie, Technische Universität, 8 München 2, Arcisstr. 21/Federal Republic of Germany

M.H. ZIMMERMANN
Harvard University, Harvard Forest, Petersham, MA 01366/USA

I. Structural Considerations in Phloem Transport

1. Sieve-Element Structure

M.V. PARTHASARATHY

A. Introduction

Although it is now more than a hundred years since HARTIG (1837, 1860) first discovered sieve tubes, and associated solute transport with sieve elements, the structure of functioning sieve elements and the mechanism of phloem transport are still controversial issues. The extreme sensitivity of sieve elements to injury has made physiological and structural investigations of these elements very difficult. Nevertheless there has been a tremendous upsurge of interest in sieve-element structure and function for the past two decades, especially with the arrival of the electron-microscope as a biological tool. Inevitably, this increased interest in phloem has brought not only new insights to the problem but also some misconceptions. As ESAU (1971 b) has pointed out, a lack of familiarity with the previous observations made by botanists, and preconceived notions about sieve-element function have in some cases obscured the view of structure. Furthermore, there is a tendency among some physiologists to assume that the structure of sieve elements in all the groups of vascular plants is the same in every respect. This chapter is therefore aimed at familiarizing the reader with the salient structural features of sieve elements not only in angiosperms, but also in other vascular plants. The literature on structure and development of phloem from its beginnings up to the late 1960's has been comprehensively reviewed in a monumental volume by ESAU (1969). Thus, only the more recent literature will be reviewed here.

Phloem is morphologically and physiologically a complex tissue that is composed basically of sieve elements, several types of parenchyma cells, fibers, sclereids, and in some cases laticifers and other idioblasts. Since it is now generally accepted that the sieve element is the main conducting unit of phloem, a review of the structure of that element, rather than of all the phloem components, is the chief concern of this chapter. However, it should be borne in mind that sieve elements do not function in isolation but as components of a tissue.

B. Terminology, Sieve-Element Size and Shape

I. Terminology

The recent multidisciplinary interest in the structure and physiology of phloem has resulted in some confusing terminology in the literature with reference to sieve elements. The terminology suggested by CHEADLE and WHITFORD (1941) and emphasized by ESAU (1950, 1969) will be followed here. In brief the terms are:

1. Sieve areas: thin areas or pit-like recesses in the walls of sieve elements where pores with "connecting strands" are grouped. Sieve area is a more general term than the sieve plate and refers to various clusters of pores in sieve-element walls, regardless of the size and number of pores.

2. Sieve plate: a more restricted term referring to a wall or part of a wall bearing one or more highly differentiated sieve areas with conspicuous pores. If a sieve plate has only one sieve area it is termed a *simple sieve plate* and if it has more than one it is termed a *compound sieve plate.*

3. Lateral sieve areas: sieve areas that are less differentiated than sieve areas of sieve plates and that are located on the lateral walls of the sieve element.

4. Sieve-tube element or sieve-tube member: a cell in which certain sieve areas are more highly specialized than others, the specialized sieve areas being largely localized on end walls to form the sieve plates. Sieve-tube elements are typical of angiosperms.

5. Sieve tube: sieve-tube elements disposed end to end in a long series.

6. Sieve cell: a sieve element in which the sieve areas in all walls are of a similar degree of specialization and no wall regions that can be distinguished as sieve plates are present. Sieve cells are typical of gymnosperms and most vascular cryptogams.

7. Sieve element: a comprehensive term which includes both sieve cells and sieve-tube elements.

II. Sieve-Element Size and Shape

Sieve elements, like most cells of the vascular tissue, are longitudinally elongated, their length usually being several times their width. Variations in length and width can occur within the same plant and between species and genera. Sieve elements may be short or long depending on their position in the plant body. Nodal regions and small leaf veins in some plants, for example, have short sieve elements as compared to other parts of the plant. Dimensions of sieve elements in various groups have been well reviewed by ESAU (1969). Briefly, the length of sieve elements in secondary phloem can range from about 100 μ to more than 500 μ in dicotyledons (ZAHUR, 1959) and from about 1400 μ to 4850 μ or more in conifers (CHANG, 1954). Width of these elements varies from about 10 μ to 70 μ, the narrower ones usually belonging to conifer sieve cells. Dimensions of sieve elements in the metaphloem (primary phloem) of monocotyledons are also variable. The short and narrow sieve elements in the nodal regions of *Dioscorea* for example are about 100 μ long and 5–10 μ wide (BEHNKE, 1965) whereas those in some palms can be as long as 5 mm, and 400 μ wide (PARTHASARATHY, 1966).

Variations in the shape of sieve elements are usually determined by the degree of inclination of the end walls and have been graphically illustrated by ESAU (1960). Long sieve-tube elements with very oblique end walls tend to have compound sieve plates while short elements with transverse end walls normally have simple sieve plates. A comparative study of phloem in different organs of more than 200 species of monocotyledons by CHEADLE (1948) has shown that sieve elements in leaves, inflorescence axes, corms and rhizomes tend to be specialized, i.e. they have transverse or slightly oblique end walls with simple or compound sieve plates.

Roots on the other hand have less specialized sieve elements, i.e. elements with very oblique end walls and very large compound sieve plates. Sieve elements in the aerial stems occupy an intermediate position in terms of specialization.

C. Structure of Sieve Elements

Although evidence favoring the conduction of solutes in mature sieve elements, that is, elements which have undergone complex changes in the protoplast, is substantial, some investigators have suggested that conduction chiefly occurs in immature sieve elements in which the protoplast is relatively unchanged (e.g. KOLLMANN, 1965; WARK and CHAMBERS, 1965; SCHUMACHER, 1967). Such investigators have raised the question whether the mature sieve tube represents the current channel of transport or whether "like a dried-up river bed, its structural features indicate the places where flow once occurred" (STEWARD, 1964). A clear understanding of sieve-element structure at successive stages of development is thus of fundamental importance if one is to elucidate the mechanism of translocation in sieve tubes.

I. Angiosperms

Angiosperms typically have sieve-tube elements that are normally associated with nucleate cells in the form of companion cells.

1. Differentiating Sieve Elements

In the very early stages of sieve-element differentiation, it is often difficult to distinguish the sieve element from associated parenchyma cell. At this stage the sieve element contains all the organelles that are normally present in cells of a meristematic region. Soon, however, structural changes in the cell wall or protoplast become evident that enable one to follow the complete differentiation of a sieve element. The structural changes in various components of the sieve element will be considered before discussing the sequential structural changes in the sieve element.

a) Cell Wall, Plasmalemma. The cell wall of the sieve element may resemble that of associated parenchyma or possess a special thickening, termed nacreous thickening, that is discernible with a light microscope. The thickness of nacreous wall is variable, depending not only on the developmental stage of the sieve element, but also on the species (Figs. 1, 10). Generally the wall attains its maximum thickness immediately before its maturation. In some plants the nacreous walls can be so thick as to extend almost to the center of the cell (ESAU, 1969). Relatively few systematic studies have been done on the ultrastructure of sieve-element wall in general and nacreous walls in particular. The electronmicroscope reveals a distinct inner wall layer in sieve elements of most angiosperms that has been interpreted as the nacreous wall (BOUCK and CRONSHAW, 1965; O'BRIEN and THIMANN, 1967; ESAU and CRONSHAW, 1968). The nacreous wall was reported to have a predominantly fibrillar structure with netted and striated patterns (O'BRIEN and THIMANN, 1967; ESAU and CRONSHAW, 1968). More recent studies have shown that nacreous walls contain fibrils that are predominantly parallel in arrangement, and oriented at a right angle to the longitudinal axis of the cell (Fig. 10; BEHNKE, 1971a; SINGH and SRIVASTAVA, 1972; PARTHASARATHY, 1974a). The predominantly parallel arrangement of fibrils was suggested by BEHNKE (1971a) to be one of the reasons for the pearly luster of nacreous wall when viewed with the light microscope. PARTHASARATHY (1974a) suggested that the transverse orientation of the parallel fibrils in the nacreous walls of young palm sieve tubes was probably the reason why the walls exhibit strong birefringence when transverse sections were seen in polarized light. Histochemical tests have suggested that nacreous walls are composed chiefly of cellulose, polyuronides and pectins (O'BRIEN and THIMANN, 1967; BEHNKE, 1971a; SINGH and SRIVASTAVA, 1972). The classification of nacreous wall as a primary or secondary wall will have to wait until the existing confusion in the terminology of cell-wall layers is clarified (ESAU, 1969).

The plasmalemma has the typical triple-layered structure of a unit-membrane when seen in thin sections. The plasmalemma of immature sieve elements often appears wavy or undulated in thin sections (Figs. 1, 5, 10, 11), and may appear to have inclusions that are actually present between plasmalemma and cell wall (Fig. 10). It is not yet clear whether such inclusions and the wavy appearance of plasmalemma represent true structures or fixation artefacts.

b) Microtubules, Microfilaments. Microtubules are usually present in the cortical regions of the differentiating sieve elements. They disappear soon after the elongation of the sieve element is completed. Microfilaments 5–6 nm in width occur in bundles as cytoplasmic fibers in some differentiating sieve elements (PARTHASARATHY and MÜHLETHALER, 1972). The bundles of microfilaments are usually found in the peripheral regions of the cell and are oriented parallel to the long axis of the cell. The larger diameter of P-protein filaments and their random orientation easily distinguish P-protein filaments from microfilaments. The microfilaments disappear when cell elongation is completed.

c) Nucleus and Nucleolus. A majority of observations indicates that the nucleus in a differentiating sieve element typically degenerates during differentiation (ESAU, 1969). The breakdown normally begins with a lobed condition of the nucleus followed by gradual disappearance of chromatic contents (Fig. 5), and eventual rupture of the nuclear envelope (NORTHCOTE and WOODING, 1966; BEHNKE, 1969b; ESAU, 1972; ESAU and GILL, 1971, 1972; PARTHASARATHY, 1974b). In some sieve elements the nuclei degenerate but remain as entities in mature sieve elements (O'BRIEN and THIMANN, 1967; ESAU and GILL, 1973). Some investigators are of the opinion that the nuclei do not break down in certain differentiating sieve elements of angiosperms (EVERT et al., 1970 and literature cited therein; WALSH, 1973).

ESAU and GILL (1972) noticed that nuclei in sieve elements, even at the very early stages of differentiation in the roots of *Nicotiana tabacum*, contained nucleoli smaller than those in adjacent cells. According to the authors, such small compact nucleoli suggested a relatively low metabolic activity of the cells. Light microscopy observations have indicated that nucleoli are released from the disintegrating nuclei in sieve elements of several dicotyledons (ESAU, 1969). Such extruded nucleoli apparently persist in fully differentiated sieve elements and usually develop a peculiar external sculpture with protrusions. Structures interpreted as extruded nucleoli have revealed ordered arrays of fibrillar or tubular material when observed with the electronmicroscope (KOLLMANN, 1960; MISHRA and SPANNER, 1970). However, an investigation of immature and mature sieve elements of five dicotyledons by DESHPANDE and EVERT (1970) suggests that structures commonly interpreted as persistent, extruded nucleoli may in fact be a substance similar to P-protein that has no relationship with the nucleoli. Further studies on these structures are obviously needed.

d) Endoplasmic Reticulum. Young sieve elements possess mostly rough endoplasmic reticulum (ER) resembling that of normal nucleate cells (Figs. 1, 10). During the early stages of sieve element differentiation in some plants there is an apparent increase in the rough ER and ribosomes (SINGH and SRIVASTAVA, 1972; PARTHASARATHY, 1974a). During differentiation, the ribosomes accompanying the ER are apparently lost and smooth ER becomes predominant. A gradual shifting of the ER to the parietal position of the element soon becomes evident (Fig. 11). The ER during the later periods of differentiation becomes modified and assumes tubular, stacked, convoluted, lattice-like or vesiculated forms (ESAU, 1969; PARTHASARATHY, 1974b, c). The cisternae in all forms of ER are less electron-dense than the intercisternal spaces (Figs. 16, 19). The aggregations of modified ER have been referred to as "sieve-element reticulum" by some investigators (e.g. BOUCK and CRONSHAW, 1965; WOODING, 1967).

e) Dictyosomes, Plastids, Mitochondria. Dictyosomes are fairly abundant in young sieve elements (Figs. 1, 10). Very few are present at later stages of cell differentiation and none in mature sieve elements.

Sieve-element plastids may contain starch grains and/or crystals, filaments, or dense spherical bodies (BEHNKE, 1969a; ESAU, 1969). A recent cytochemical study at the ultrastructural level by PALEVITZ and NEWCOMB (1970) suggests that sieve-element starch is composed of highly branched molecules containing numerous α 1–6 linkages typical of amylopectin. Sieve-element plastids normally have sparse internal membranes and have a dense matrix in young cells (Fig. 12). During sieve-element maturation the plastid matrix becomes more electron-transparent so that its inclusions appear more prominent (Fig. 13). Plastids are normally retained in mature sieve elements. Sieve-element plastids apparently have distinct characteristics in broad taxonomic groups of angiosperms. Monocotyledons, for example, have sieve-element plastids that contain wedge-shaped, presumably proteinaceous inclusions (Figs. 12, 13), and the order Caryophyllales (dicotyledons) have sieve-element plastids that contain peripherally situated ring-shaped bundles of proteinaceous filaments (BEHNKE and TURNER, 1971; BEHNKE, 1972).

ESAU and GILL (1972) observed that most plastids in young protophloem sieve elements of tobacco root were localized near the end walls which separate given cells from the next older ones. The reason for such polarized distribution of plastids in the young sieve elements, but not in the surrounding parenchyma cells, is not clear.

Mitochondria appear normal in young sieve elements (Figs. 1, 10). During sieve-element differentiation they may be modified as compared with the mitochondria of associated parenchymatous cells (ESAU, 1969). Mitochondria with crystalline inclusions have been reported in differentiating sieve elements of the coconut palm, *Cocos nucifera* (PARTHASARATHY, 1974b) and of roots in the onion, *Allium cepa*

(ESAU and GILL, 1973). Mitochondria are normally retained in mature sieve elements but appear to degenerate as the sieve elements age (PARTHASARATHY, 1974a).

f) P-Protein. A proteinaceous component of the sieve-element protoplast formerly known as slime but recently renamed P-protein (phloem-protein) by ESAU and CRONSHAW (1967) appears early in the ontogeny of sieve elements of dicotyledons (Fig. 1). P-protein may occur in amorphous, tubular, filamentous or crystalline forms depending on the species and/or the stage of sieve-element differentiation. More than one form of P-protein may be synthesized in the same sieve element in certain dicotyledons (ESAU, 1969; ZEE, 1969).

Incidentally P-protein is not restricted to sieve elements but is also found in companion cells and parenchyma cells of some plants (see ESAU, 1969).

The occurrence of P-protein in the sieve elements of monocotyledons seems to be sporadic. It is reported to be present in the sieve elements of several monocotyledons (BEHNKE, 1965, 1969b, c, 1973; BEHNKE and DÖRR, 1967; CURRIER and SHIH, 1968; ERVIN and EVERT, 1967, 1970; RAASCH, 1971; ESAU and GILL, 1973; PARTHASARATHY, 1974a) but absent in others (EVERT et al., 1971; SINGH and SRIVASTAVA, 1972; PARTHASARATHY, 1974a; WALSH, 1973). In certain monocotyledons P-protein may be present in some sieve elements but absent in others within a given organ (ESAU and GILL, 1973; PARTHASARATHY, 1974a).

Since the various forms and chemical composition of P-protein are discussed in detail elsewhere in this volume (see Chapter 2), only a brief account of the more common tubular and fibrillar forms of P-protein will be presented here.

The tubular and fibrillar forms of P-protein have been studied by several investigators (TAMULEVICH and EVERT, 1966; NORTHCOTE and WOODING, 1966; WOODING, 1967; CRONSHAW and ESAU, 1967, 1968a; BEHNKE, 1969b, c; EVERT and DESHPANDE, 1969; PARTHASARATHY and MÜHLETHALER, 1969; STEER and NEWCOMB, 1969; ESAU, 1971a; ESAU and HOEFERT, 1971). Filamentous P-protein has been referred to as "plasmatic filaments" by some authors (e.g. BEHNKE and DÖRR, 1967; SCHUMACHER, 1967). At an early stage of sieve-element differentiation, P-protein usually appears in the form of discrete bodies in the cytoplasm which are referred to as "slime bodies" or P-protein bodies (Fig. 1). There may be one or more P-protein bodies per sieve element. The tubules that comprise a P-protein body range from 18 to 23 nm in diameter and usually exhibit a six-fold symmetry when viewed in transection (Figs. 2, 3). The tubules may be several microns long and it is probable that they run the entire length of the P-protein body. Other organelles are excluded from P-protein bodies but might surround them. The origin of P-protein tubules is as yet not very clear. However, there are strong indications that the tubules are assembled from a fine fibrous material that is often present in the cytoplasm before the P-protein tubules are differentiated (CRONSHAW and ESAU, 1968a; ESAU, 1971a). WOODING (1969) has suggested the possibility of ER being associated with the origin of P-protein in *Nicotiana* callus phloem. BEHNKE (1973) has suggested that ribosomes might participate in the synthesis of filamentous P-protein in the sieve elements of *Smilax*.

PARTHASARATHY and MÜHLETHALER (1969) investigated the substructure of P-protein tubules in differentiating sieve elements and suggested that the tubules are composed of subunits 6–7 nm in diameter, and that each tubule is a tightly-wound double helix (Figs. 3, 4). The concept of helical structure of P-protein in dicotyledons has received support from subsequent investigations by EVERT and DESHPANDE (1969), KOLLMANN et al. (1970), BEHNKE (1971 b), ESAU (1971 a), ESAU and HOEFERT (1971), and CRONSHAW, GILDER and STONE (1973).

During the later stages of sieve-element differentiation, the P-protein body begins to disperse in the cytoplasm and the disaggregated P-protein tubules often appear fibrillar, striated or beaded (Figs. 5, 6). The striated or beaded appearance of the tubules has been attributed to the loosening of the double helix during dispersal (PARTHASARATHY and MÜHLETHALER, 1969). It should also be pointed out that occurrences of P-protein bodies that do not disperse have been recorded in the sieve elements of some dicotyledons (see ESAU, 1969). In monocotyledons, P-protein if present, also has a helical or tubular structure (BEHNKE, 1969c; PARTHASARATHY, 1974a, c). The distribution of P-protein in mature sieve elements is discussed in Section *C.2*.

g) Vacuole. Immature sieve elements usually contain small vacuoles ranging from few to many. The vacuoles may or may not fuse to form larger vacuoles during differentiation. In root protophloem sieve elements of *Nicotiana tabacum*, for example, the vacuoles enlarge during differentiation but do not fuse (ESAU and GILL, 1972). In sieve elements of some monocotyledons on the other hand, vacuoles appear to fuse to form larger vacuoles (HEYSER, 1971; RAASCH, 1971; PARTHASARATHY, 1974a). The apparent origin of vacuoles by ER dilations has been well illustrated by RAASCH (1971) in differentiating sieve elements of roots in the date palm *Phoenix dactylifera*. Most investigations on the fate of vacuoles in differentiating sieve elements indicate that the tonoplast breaks down during the later stages of cell differentiation thus creating an apparent integration of cytoplasmic and vacuolar components (see ESAU, 1969). Despite such an integration, a thin layer of cytoplasm persists in parietal position close to the plasmalemma (Figs. 13, 14, 16).

h) Sieve-Plate Pore Development. Ultrastructural aspects of sieve-plate pore development attracted the attention of several investigators during the 1960's. The investigations of ESAU et al. (1962), ESAU and CHEADLE (1965), NORTHCOTE and WOODING (1966) were particularly useful in gaining a good understanding of sieve-plate pore development in dicotyledons. Subsequent investigations by BEHNKE (1969c), SINGH and SRIVASTAVA (1972), ESAU and GILL (1973), and PARTHASARATHY (1974b), of sieve-plate differentiation in monocotyledons suggest that pore development is basically the same in all angiosperms. At the earliest stage of sieve-plate differentiation, each pore site is penetrated by a single plasmodesma. Soon the pore site may be discerned from the appearance of a small deposit of callose, in the form of a disc still penetrated by a plasmodesma, called callose platelet (Figs. 7–9, 11). The callose platelet gradually penetrates deeper into the wall, replacing the cell wall. ER cisternae are commonly in close association with the plasmodesmata (Fig. 8), and remain applied to the pore site during differentiation of the pores (Figs. 8, 9). The perforation of a pore is usually initiated at the center of the pore site, starting at the plasmodesmatal connection in the middle lamella. The perforation further enlarges, resulting in the disappearance of the compound middle lamella and the fusion of the pair of callose platelets around the pore to produce a callose cylinder (ESAU, 1969; PARTHASARATHY, 1974b). Thus the sieve-plate pore is apparently lined with callose at its inception, although in mature sieve elements the pores may or may not be lined with callose, depending on the species and the method of fixation employed (EVERT and DERR, 1964; PARTHASARATHY, 1966, 1968; ESAU, 1969). Although some investigators (e.g. WARK and CHAMBERS, 1965) have suggested that the sieve-plate pores are fully differentiated prior to the degeneration of the nucleus, other investigators have suggested the opposite (see ESAU, 1969). A recent study by ESAU and GILL (1972) on the protophloem sieve elements of tobacco supports the view that the transformation of plasmodesmatal pore sites into pores and the disintegration of nuclei are concomitant phenomena.

i) Lateral Sieve Areas. The fine structure of lateral sieve areas has not received as much attention as that of sieve plates. Recent investigations, however, have contributed to a better understanding of the structure of lateral sieve areas (see ESAU, 1969; EVERT et al., 1971). The development of sieve-area pores is essentially similar to that reported in sieve-plate pores. The pores of the developing sieve areas are each traversed by a single plasmodesma which is generally associated with ER. Callose platelets soon appear on both sides of the pore sites beneath the plasmalemma, followed by the development of a small cavity, the median cavity, in the region of the middle lamella. The callose platelets continue to thicken, accompanied by a widening of the median cavity. Thus callose-lined canals are established on either side of an enlarged median cavity. The finer structural aspects of lateral sieve areas are often obscured by heavy wound-callose (Fig. 14).

Companion cells, and presumably other contiguous parenchyma cells, have characteristic connections with the sieve element (Fig. 15). Several plasmodesmatal branches occur on the companion cell side whereas a single, relatively large pore occurs on the sieve-element side. A median cavity is often present where the single pore connects the branched plasmodesmata (Fig. 15). Ultrastructural studies suggest a continuity of plasmalemma, ground substance and membranous material, presumably ER, between the sieve element and companion cell (ESAU, 1969). WOODING and NORTHCOTE (1965) have reported that the plasmodesmatal branches on the companion cell side develop during the ontogeny of the cells. Callose may be present, lining the pore on the sieve-element side but not on the companion-cell side.

Figs. 1–9. *Differentiating sieve elements in dicotyledons.* ▶

Fig. 1. Transverse section of a differentiating sieve element in *Nicotiana tabacum* showing the nucleus (*N*) and P-protein body (*PP*). *D* dictyosome; *M* mitochondrion. ×8,000. Fig. 2. Transverse section of a portion of P-protein body showing transectional view of P-protein tubules. ×100,000. Fig. 3. Reinforced image of a P-protein tubule in transection (A), and the same without image reinforcement (B). ×1,000,000. Fig. 4. Longitudinal view of P-protein tubules prior to dispersion. Tubule at the arrow exhibits a structure that can be interpreted as a double helix. ×60,000. Fig. 5. Oblique section of a differentiating sieve element showing the dispersal of P-protein (*PP*). Note the lobed nucleus (*N*) with the sparse chromatin matter. *M* mitochondrion. ×16,200. Fig. 6. Magnified view of dispersed P-protein with beaded appearance (arrows). ×50,000. Fig. 7. Face view of differentiating sieve plate pores in *Nicotiana tabacum*. Each pore-site is transversed by a plasmodesma (unlabeled arrow) and delimited by a callose platelet (*C*). Each callose platelet is lined with plasmalemma (*PM*). ×28,000. Fig. 8. Sectional view of a sieve-plate pore in *Cucurbita maxima* showing a plasmodesma (short arrow) and the application of ER cisternae (long arrows) to the pore site. ×20,000. Fig. 9. Longitudinal section of a portion of a differentiating sieve-plate in *Nicotiana tabacum* showing the close association of ER cisternae (large arrows) with pore sites. Small arrows indicate plasmodesmata. Note that the large vacuoles (*V*) are still intact. *D* dictyosome; *ER* endoplasmic reticulum. ×10,000. (Figs. 1 and 3 from PARTHASARATHY and MÜHLETHALER, 1969)

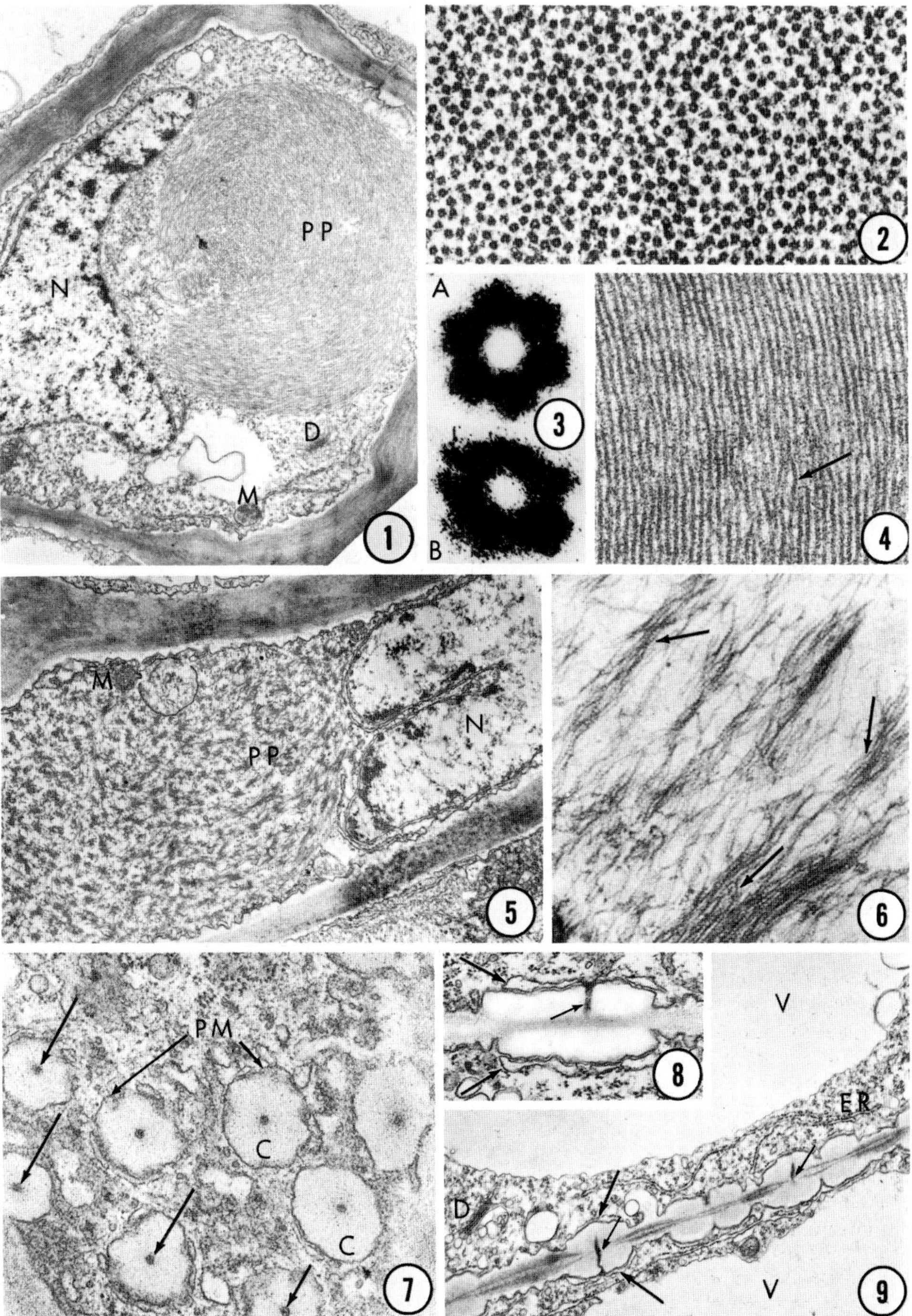

Figs. 1–9. Differentiating sieve elements in dicotyledons. For detailed legend see opposite page

2. Mature Sieve Elements

The structure of mature sieve elements has received by far the most attention from investigators because of evidence implicating mature sieve elements (rather than immature ones) in long distance transport (see ESAU, 1969; CRAFTS and CRISP, 1971). The sensitivity of mature sieve elements to injury has led some workers to investigate the structure of live, presumably functioning sieve elements with the light microscope instead of fixed elements (e.g. THAINE, 1964; PARKER, 1964; THAINE et al., 1967; LEE et al., 1971). Although such observations have yielded valuable data, the limited resolution of the light microscope, in combination with the thickness of material used in such studies, has not revealed all aspects of sieve-element structure. Thus the structure of mature sieve elements discussed here is chiefly of fixed cells although relevant observations made on fresh live sieve elements have also been included (see also Chapter 15).

a) Cell Wall and Plasmalemma. The thick nacreous walls of primary phloem sieve elements usually become thinner as the cell ages, whereas the thickening of the walls in the elements of secondary phloem is variable depending on the species (ESAU, 1969). The general assumption is that a loss of water leads to the shrinking of walls in older sieve elements (ESAU, 1969).

The persistent plasmalemma may be closely appressed to the cell wall or appear somewhat wavy depending on the quality of fixation. The concept of plasmalemma forming a type of "brush-border" by penetrating the cell wall in a radial direction has been forwarded by SPANNER and JONES (1970). Other investigators have not confirmed the presence of such "brush-borders" although a highly modified ER adjacent to the plasmalemma might in some sectional views present such a shape. As ESAU (1972) has indicated, it is likely that the "brush-border" effect is caused as a result of oblique sectioning of an uneven sieve-element wall and adjacent protoplast.

Figs. 10–16. *Differentiating sieve elements in palms (monocotyledons).* ▶

Fig. 10. Transverse section of a young sieve element in *Chamaedorea elegans* showing the nacreous wall (*CW*), nucleus (*N*) and the cytoplasm rich with organelles. *D* dictyosomes; *ER* endoplasmic reticulum; *M* mitochondrion; *P* plastid. ×12,500. Fig. 11. Longitudinal section of a differentiating sieve plate (*SP*) in the same species. Unlabeled arrows indicate developing pores. Callose that had originally been deposited as platelets are now fused across the wall to form cylinders enclosing the enlarging plasmodesmata. The cytoplasm is rich in ribosomes, and the ER cisternae (*ER*) have begun to occupy a parietal position in the cell. *M* mitochondrion; *P* plastid; *V* vacuole. ×14,000. Fig. 12. Plastid with cuneate crystalline inclusions in a differentiating sieve element of the same species. Except for a few vesiculate structures there are no internal membranes. ×30,000. Fig. 13. Plastids in a recently mature sieve element of *C. oblongata.* Note the relatively electron-transparent matrix of plastids and the cuneate inclusions. ER and mitochondria are parietal in position (arrows). ×11,000. Fig. 14. Lateral sieve area in a recently mature sieve element of *Cocos nucifera.* ER is present on both sides of the sieve area. Heavy deposits of callose have apparently constricted the pore connections. *CW* cell wall. ×20,000. Fig. 15. Sieve-area pit field connection in the stem of *Chamaedorea elegans.* Note the median nodule (arrow). *CC* companion cell; *SE* sieve element. ×25,000. Fig. 16. Stacked and vesiculate cisternae of ER in a recently mature sieve element of *Arenga englri. ER* endoplasmic reticulum. ×23,000. (All figures from PARTHASARATHY, 1974a, b, c)

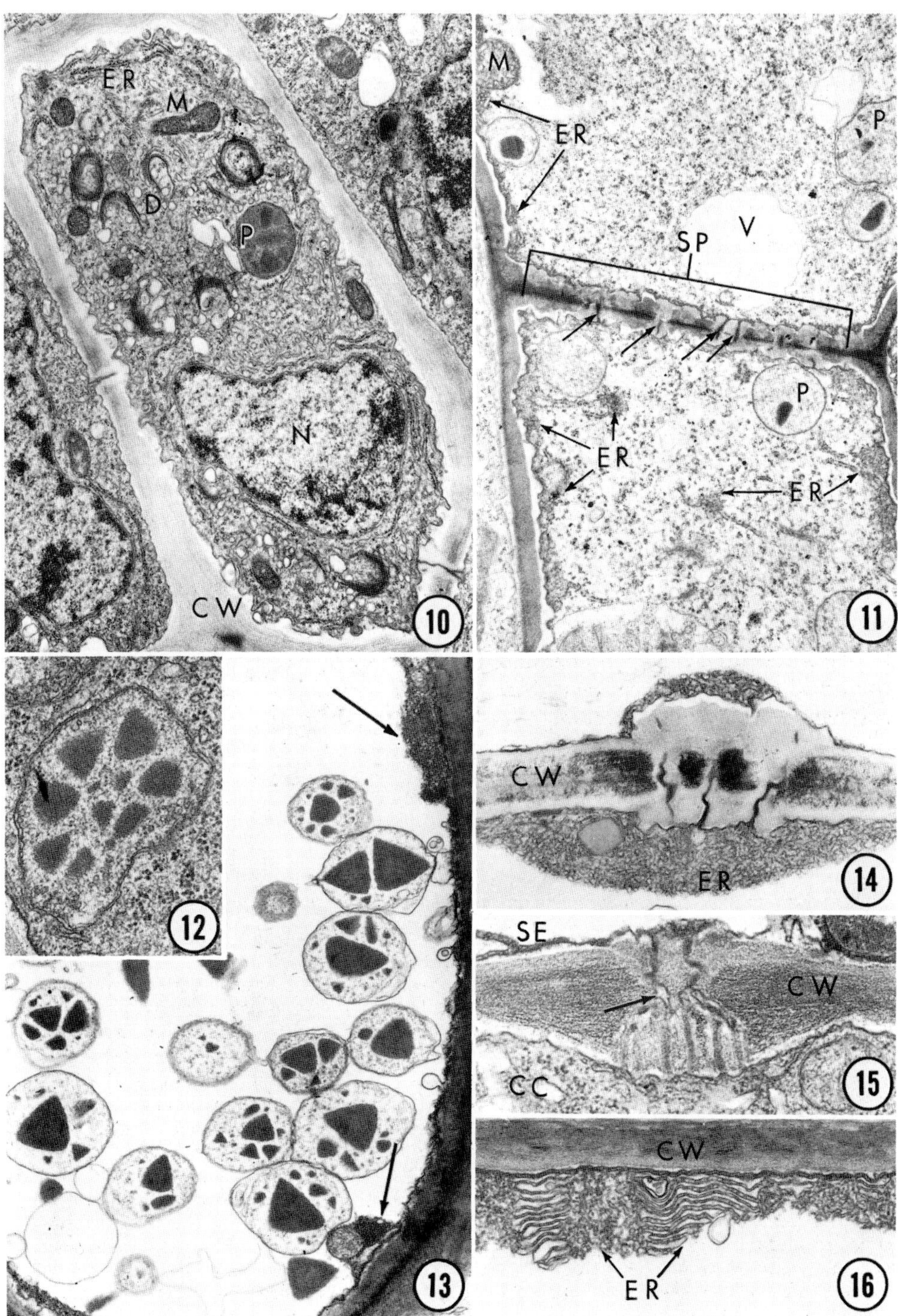

Figs. 10–16. Differentiating sieve elements in palms (monocotyledons). For detailed legend see opposite page

b) Enucleate Condition. Observations supporting the enucleate condition of mature sieve elements are impressive (see ESAU, 1969). Details of nuclear degeneration in differentiating sieve elements have been further documented by several recent studies (e.g. ZEE and CHAMBERS, 1968; BEHNKE, 1969b; ESAU, 1972; ESAU and GILL, 1971, 1972, 1973; SINGH and SRIVASTAVA, 1972; PARTHASARATHY, 1974b). However EVERT and his associates have recently recorded apparently normal nuclei in mature sieve elements of some angiosperms (EVERT et al., 1969; ERVIN and EVERT, 1970; EVERT et al., 1970). Since the above observations on persistent nuclei were done with the limited resolution of the light microscope, the exact structural integrity of such nuclei is yet to be determined. EVERT et al. (1970) speculate that the commonly observed enucleate condition of mature sieve elements might be due to the disruption of the fragile nucleus during the preparation of material for microscopy. However, recent investigations on sieve elements by ESAU and GILL (1972, 1973), documented by a remarkable series of electronmicrographs showing the nuclear degeneration in distinctly graded steps, do not support such a speculation. Although nuclei may not disintegrate in occasional sieve elements (ESAU, 1969), there is overwhelming evidence that mature sieve-tube elements are typically enucleate.

c) Parietal Cytoplasm. The degeneration or disintegration of the nucleus followed by the apparent breakdown of the tonoplast results in a mature sieve element that has a more or less clear lumen and a thin layer of parietal cytoplasm (Figs. 14, 16, 17). How a thin layer of cytoplasm could persist in spite of the apparent integration of cytoplasmic and vacuolar component is not clear. Not all investigators, however, agree that the tonoplast breaks down in a differentiating sieve element. Limiting membranes interpreted as tonoplasts have been reported in mature sieve elements by TAMULEVICH and EVERT (1966); EVERT et al. (1966), EVERT et al. (1969), and WALSH (1973). TAMULEVICH and EVERT have suggested that the apparent absence of tonoplast in mature sieve elements observed by other investigators was due to the disruption of the fragile vacuole during preparation for microscopy. Although a majority of observations seem to indicate the lack of tonoplast in mature sieve elements (see ESAU, 1969; BEHNKE, 1969b, c; PARTHASARATHY, 1964b, c), the presence or absence of tonoplast in mature sieve elements has not been unequivocally demonstrated.

The parietal cytoplasm consists chiefly of highly modified ER, mitochondria, plastids, and P-protein in species where it occurs (Figs. 13, 14, 16, 19). Microfilaments, microtubules, dictyosomes and ribosomes are absent in mature sieve elements. Stacked, convoluted, lattice-like, or tubular forms of modified ER are present along the parietal and end walls of mature sieve elements appressed to the plasmalemma (Figs. 16, 19). The stacked form of ER, and the amount of ER itself might diminish as the mature element ages (ESAU and GILL, 1972; PARTHASARATHY, 1974c). The intercisternal spaces in all forms of ER normally contain an electron-dense substance (Figs. 16, 19). The nature of the electron-dense substance is not clear. It has been speculated to be a form of membrane modification or protein (ESAU and GILL, 1971; PARTHASARATHY, 1974c), or a source of enzymes (ESAU and GILL, 1972).

d) P-Protein. The question as to what constitutes the normal form and distribution of P-protein in mature sieve elements has perhaps been the most controversial aspect of sieve-element structure. Helical, filamentous P-protein appears to be the most common form found in mature sieve elements (Figs. 17, 18), although there are some exceptions (see ESAU, 1969). Some investigators have suggested that P-protein occurs in the form of a fixed network throughout the sieve-element lumen (e.g. WOODING, 1967, 1969; CRONSHAW and ANDERSON, 1971) while others observed that the network of P-protein is normally parietal in distribution (EVERT et al., 1969; EVERT and DESHPANDE, 1969). Transcellular strands that were continuous from one sieve element to the next were visualized by yet others (e.g. THAINE, 1969; THAINE and DE MARIA, 1973). Using Nomarski interference optics and electronmicroscopy, LEE et al. (1971), and ROBIDOUX et al. (1973) reported that transcellular strands in the sieve tubes of *Heracleum* were apparently made up of P-protein. The strands appeared to pass through sieve-plate pores from one sieve element to another. The problem of P-protein distribution has been further complicated by the fact that under certain conditions, filaments resembling P-protein can also occur in sieve elements that normally *do not* contain P-protein. For example, when organelles are severely disrupted during the preparation of material, filaments can be formed from crystalline inclusions of broken-down plastids, and disorganized membrane systems (Figs. 24, 26, 27). HEYSER (1971) has suggested that filamentous P-protein in the sieve elements of *Tradescantia albiflora* is produced by ribosomes and polyribosomes during the final stages of cell differentiation, since he could not detect any P-protein in immature sieve elements. Another difficulty confronting the students of phloem is that observations on living sieve elements (e.g. LEE et al., 1971) have not yet been properly correlated with results of studies with the electronmicroscope. One fundamental problem with light microscopy investigation is the difficulty of determining the nature of the cytoplasmic or "transcellular strands". Although the nature and distribution of P-protein in mature sieve elements is yet to be determined, some recent investigations made with special precautions to reduce sudden pressure release in sieve tubes during preparation for microscopy suggest that P-protein occupies as parietal position in intact sieve elements of some plants (EVERT et al., 1973; PARTHASARATHY, 1974c). The evidence for and against the presence of P-protein in sieve-plate pores is discussed in the following section.

e) Sieve-Plate Pores. As noted earlier, the final opening of the pores takes place at about the same time that the nucleus has more or less completely degenerated. The opening of the pore is accomplished by the enlargement of the plasmodesmatal canal up to almost the entire diameter of the original callose platelets that delimited the pore site. The sieve-plate pore diameter in angiosperms ranges from less than a micron to about 14 μ depending on the species (ESAU and CHEADLE, 1959). Fully differentiated sieve-plate pores in some plants are lined with ER that may be continuous through pores *without* occluding them (ESAU, 1969; BEHNKE, 1971b; EVERT et al., 1973). The amount of callose lining the pores is variable depending on the species and/or the method of fixation. When present, callose is always deposited between plasmalemma and the cell wall (Figs. 20, 28). Fixation methods designed to kill phloem rapidly suggest that little or no callose lines the pores of functioning sieve elements (EVERT and DERR, 1964; PARTHASARATHY, 1966, 1968; ANDERSON and CRONSHAW, 1969; CRONSHAW and ANDERSON, 1969).

The nature of the contents of sieve plate pores is yet another aspect of sieve element structure that needs to be resolved. Almost all investigators agree that the pores are lined with plasmalemma, and variable amounts of callose or none, depending on the fixation. But there is no general agreement beyond that point. Images of sieve-plate pores may show the pores almost completely occluded by P-protein or other material (Figs. 20, 21, 24, 25) or may show the pores to be free of any occlusion (Figs. 22, 23, 28). The question as to which of these images represents the true structure of sieve-plate pores *in vivo* has been a source of constant debate among physiologists and structural botanists. ESAU (1969) has summarized the results of various studies done up to 1968 on this aspect of sieve-element structure. More recent studies have in no way clarified the issue of pore contents. Several investigators believe that the plugged condition of sieve-plate pores similar to the one illustrated in Fig. 20 is the normal state of functioning sieve elements (MISHRA and SPANNER, 1970; SIDDIQUI and SPANNER, 1970; SPANNER and JONES, 1970), while others have suggested that the plugged condition of the pores is an artefact created by the sudden release of pressure in sieve tubes when severing the tissue for histological preparation (ANDERSON and CRONSHAW, 1969, 1970; CRONSHAW and ANDERSON, 1969, 1971; EVERT et al., 1973; PARTHASARATHY, 1974c). They contend that the pores are not occluded in undisturbed sieve elements as illustrated in Figs. 22, 23, 28. Still others have illustrated loosely organized P-protein extending through the pores without plugging them (CURRIER and SHIH, 1968; JOHNSON, 1968; BEHNKE, 1971b). Since a knowledge of the nature of the pore contents is fundamental to an understanding of the mechanism of long-distance transport in phloem, it is discussed here in some detail.

Investigators who believe that pores are plugged in intact sieve elements point out that a majority of the studies has shown the pores to be plugged with P-protein, or some membranous material. Furthermore, a symmetrical arrangement of P-protein filaments in the pores, as shown in Fig. 20, cannot be interpreted as plugging caused by a sudden release of turgor pressure. Such plugging can usually be judged by the unequal displacement of sieve-element contents on either side of a sieve plate (Figs. 21, 25). It should also be borne in mind that loosely organized P-protein filaments in the pores can be compacted by callose deposition during fixation to present an image as in Fig. 20. Investigations by JOHNSON (1968, 1973) on sieve-plate pore contents of the water plant *Nymphoides peltata* are of interest. He examined sieve tubes that were frozen before being cut from plants, and were prepared for electronmicroscopy by freeze etching. Such a method of investigation has the advantage of using no harsh chemicals for the preparation of the tissue, and at the

---

Figs. 17–23. *Mature sieve elements in dicotyledons.* ▶

Fig. 17. Net work of dispersed, helical P-protein filaments in *Salix alba*. ×49,000. Fig. 18. Magnified view of P-protein filaments showing the helical structure (arrows). ×105,000. Fig. 19. Stacked and reticulate forms of ER. Note the electron-dense intercisternal regions (arrow). ×46,000. Fig. 20. Two sieve-plate pores plugged with P-protein. The amorphous appearance of P-protein in the pore might be due to the compacting of filaments as result of callose deposition (*C*). ×20,000. Fig. 21. Sieve-plate pores plugged due to pressure release in the sieve tubes of *Cucurbita maxima*. The sieve plate was located near the cut end of the material. ×15,500. Fig. 22. One of the several sieve plates that were free of occlusions in a region well away from the cut end of the material. The fixative was first injected into the intact hollow petiole and the material was cut into long slivers for further fixation before preparing them for microscopy. ×12,500. Fig. 23. Face view of a portion of unoccluded sieve plate in the hypocotyl of *C. maxima* showing ER and P-protein at the margins of the pores. The material was specially treated for reducing hydrostatic pressure in sieve tubes prior to fixation (see text). ×15,500. (Fig. 23. from EVERT et al., 1973)

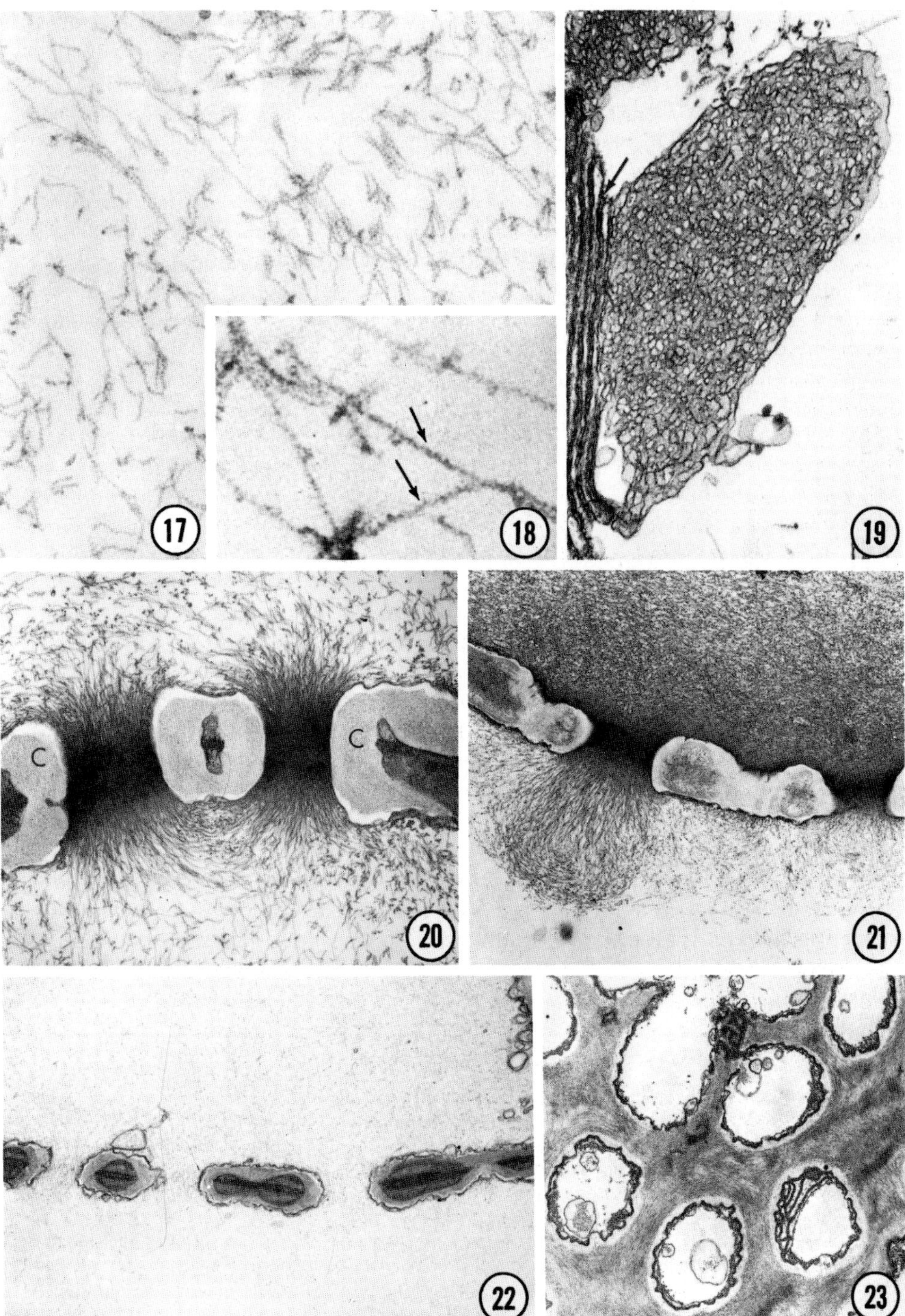

Figs. 17–23. Mature sieve elements in dicotyledons. For detailed legend see opposite page

same time avoids the sudden pressure release that follows when sieve tubes are severed. In a more recent study the same author (JOHNSON, 1973) made sure that the vascular bundles to be examined by the freeze-etching method were translocating ^{14}C just before they were frozen. This would prove that he was examining the sieve-plate pores of elements that were actually translocating. Considering the tremendous technical difficulties involved in freeze-etching of such material, his illustrations are impressive. JOHNSON's conclusion is that filaments are present in the pores of functioning sieve elements. Unfortunately it is difficult to decide from his illustrations whether structures identified as filaments are artefacts created by surrounding ice crystals, or whether they are P-protein filaments. It thus appears that one cannot as yet unequivocally claim that functioning sieve elements have pores that are filled with filaments.

Proponents of open sieve-plate pores, however, point out that when phloem material is fixed by methods whereby there is little or no pressure release in the sieve elements, a large number of sieve-plate pores do not indicate any plugging. An increase in the number of open sieve-plate pores has been demonstrated by fixing long slivers of material and examining the sieve elements in the mid-region of the slivers (e.g. PARTHASARATHY, 1974c), by rapidly fixing thin segments of plants (ANDERSON and CRONSHAW, 1970), by fixations preceded by rapid freezing of the material (CRONSHAW and ANDERSON, 1969), or by wilting the plant prior to fixation so as to reduce the high hydrostatic pressure within sieve tubes (ANDERSON and CRONSHAW, 1970). Recently, EVERT et al. (1973) found that more than 90% of the sieve-plate pores examined in the bicollateral bundles of the hypocotyls of *Cucurbita maxima* were free of any filamentous or amorphous contents (Fig. 23) when 16-day-old plants were fixed after the cotyledons and the first foliage leaves had been removed two days earlier. The purpose of the removal of the cotyledons and the foliage leaves before fixation was to reduce the solute concentration in the sieve tubes of the hypocotyls, and consequently to lower the hydrostatic pressure in them before severing the phloem for histological preparation.

It should also be mentioned that sieve-plate pores of the extrafascicular sieve elements of *Cucurbita* that normally contain undispersed P-protein remain relatively unobstructed even when special precautions to avoid pressure release are not taken (CRONSHAW and ESAU, 1968b). It is the sieve elements of the bicollateral bundles containing dispersed P-protein that appear to be more sensitive to injury.

Figs. 24–28. *Mature sieve elements in palms (monocotyledons).* ▶

Fig. 24. Longitudinal section of a disturbed sieve element (SE_1) and a relatively undisturbed sieve element (SE_2) in *Chamaedorea elegans*. Note that SE_1 is almost devoid of membranous material and has large amounts of filaments. Unlabeled arrows indicate crystalline structures that have been released from plastids. By contrast SE_2 has few filaments and relatively intact parietal *ER*. Some amorphous material is present in the pores (*PO*) presumably as a result of injury to SE_1. ×15,000. Fig. 25. Sieve-plate pores plugged with a filamentous material in a disturbed sieve tube of *C. oblongata*. The plugging of pores is apparently due to a sudden pressure release in the sieve tube. Note the cuneate crystalloids that have been displaced from plastids. ×35,000. Fig. 26. Helical filaments similar to those in Fig. 25. apparently being formed by the breakdown of the crystalloids (arrow) in a disturbed sieve element of *Phoenix canariensis*. ×130,000. Fig. 27. Helical filaments associated with tubular form of ER (arrows) in a disturbed sieve element of *C. oblongata*. ×60,000. Fig. 28. Portion of a compound sieve plate at the basal part of stem in *Cocos nucifera*. The material was cut into long slivers prior to fixation (see text). The pores are free of occlusions. ×9,000. (All figures from PARTHASARATHY, 1974c)

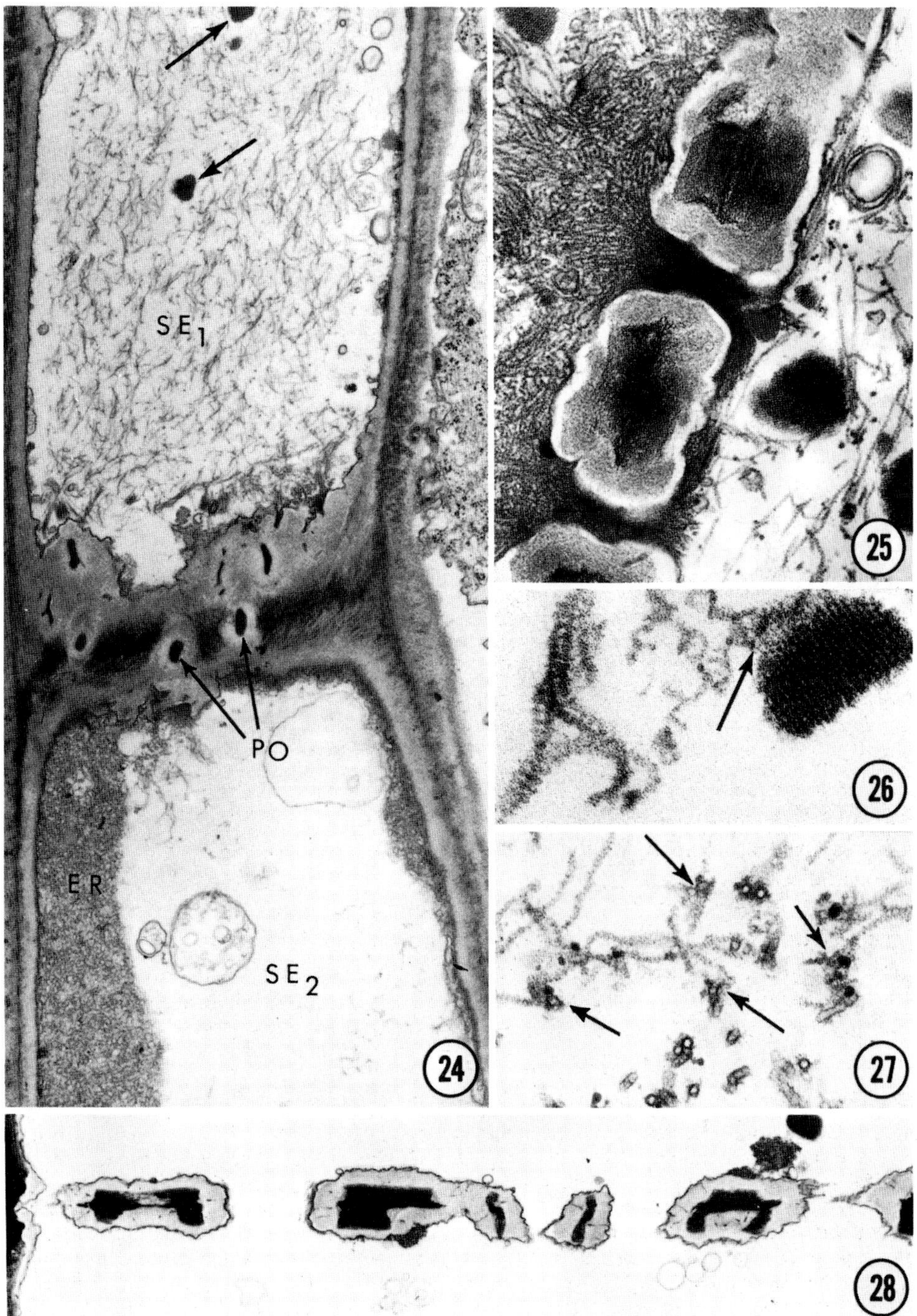

Figs. 24–28. Mature sieve elements in palms (monocotyledons). For detailed legend see opposite page

Sieve-plate pores that were filled with ER which was continuous from cell to cell have been recorded in a few sieve elements of palms (PARTHASARATHY, 1974b, c) and in the sieve elements in leaf veins of *Hordeum vulgare* (EVERT et al., 1971). It is not clear whether such sieve-plate pores are restricted to parts of certain organs in some species, or whether they occur more commonly in many plants.

It is obvious that the question of what is in the sieve-plate pores between translocating sieve elements of angiosperms is not yet completely answered. There is, however, a growing body of literature which suggests that sieve-plate pores are not occluded *in vivo*.

f) Lateral Sieve Areas. Lateral sieve areas between mature sieve elements are lined by the plasmalemma and variable amounts of callose. However, the median nodules are not lined with callose. Membranous material that is often present in the pore canals has been interpreted to be ER (see ESAU, 1969). After investigating the secondary phloem of seven species of woody dicotyledons, EVERT et al. (1971) concluded that the pores of the lateral sieve areas were similar to those of the sieve plates, differing from them primarily in size. According to the authors, most sieve-area and sieve-plate pores lacked ER, but many contained P-protein. Further investigations are needed to determine the exact nature of the sieve area in angiosperms.

3. Sequential Structural Changes in a Sieve Element

Based on the reports of various investigators on the phloem of angiosperms, the typical, sequential structural changes of a sieve element from its inception to its morphological maturity can be summarized as follows:

a) The young sieve element is rich in organelles; plastid inclusions start to differentiate.

b) During cell elongation the nucleus may become lobed; cortical microtubules are frequently present; plasmodesmata are present in both lateral and end walls; P-protein begins to appear in species where it is normally present.

c) Callose platelets that delimit the future pore sites are formed; stacking of ER becomes apparent.

d) There is a gradual loss of chromatin matter or an aggregation of chromatin in the nucleus shifting of the ER stacks towards the periphery of the cell becomes evident; ribosomes of the rough ER apparently become free so that the sieve element has mostly smooth ER. P-protein, if present, begins to disperse in the cytoplasm; the previously ameboid plastids assume an ovoid or spherical shape. Callose platelets of a pair become joined by removal of wall material.

e) Mitochondria and plastids also assume a parietal position along with the ER aggregates; microtubules and dictyosomes disappear; beginnings of sieve-plate pore enlargement are apparent at the middle lamella; the nucleus becomes almost electron transparent due to loss of chromatin and finally disintegrates, in a few species the chromatin is converted into an amorphous mass and is retained in the sieve element; the tonoplast breaks down and the cytoplasm is uniformly spread in the lumen, resulting in a dispersal of ribosomes throughout the cell.

f) Concomitant with nuclear degeneration and the breakdown of the tonoplast, the sieve-plate pore enlargement is completed; the parietal ER aggregates along with mitochondria, and plastids appear relatively intact; ribosomes disappear; P-protein, if present, may occupy the otherwise empty lumen, or may assume a parietal position.

The above sequence of structural changes will no doubt differ slightly from one species to another, and possibly in different sieve elements of the same species.

II. Gymnosperms

Studies on the structure of sieve elements in gymnosperms have been chiefly of secondary phloem. Among gymnosperms, the conifers have received more attention than other groups in terms of sieve-element structure. The gymnosperms typically have sieve cells. The general information on the phloem of this taxon has been well summarized by ESAU (1969).

As in the sieve elements of angiosperms, immature sieve cells resemble the surrounding nucleate cells and possess all the usual organelles. The walls of sieve cells vary in thickness depending on the species or family. In the Pinaceae the walls are thick and are interpreted as having a secondary thickening (ABBE and CRAFTS, 1939). Sieve-cell walls in the leaf veins of *Welwitschia* are also thick but lack a distinct secondary wall (EVERT et al., 1973a). Secondary walls have been reported only in the sieve cells of Pinaceae. The microfibrillar arrangement for the thickened sieve-cell walls of *Pinus strobus* was investigated by SRIVASTAVA (1969) who envisaged a wall composed of lamellae in which microfibrils were aligned at an angle to both horizontal and vertical axes of the cell. Recently CHAFE and DOOHAM (1972) investigated the same material and have demonstrated that, contrary to SRIVASTAVA's concept, the microfibrils are always oriented parallel to the plane of the cell wall.

Unlike the nuclei in most sieve elements of the angiosperms, those in the sieve cells of many conifers do not completely disintegrate as the cells become mature. As sieve-cell differentiation progresses, the nucleus increases in density and stainability, with concomitant decrease in volume in some species. The nuclei, in one form or other, have been identified in mature cells of conifers with the electronmicroscope (MURMANIS and EVERT, 1966; SRIVASTAVA and O'BRIEN, 1966; WOODING, 1966, 1968; NEUBERGER, 1973), as well as with the light microscope (EVERT and ALFIERI, 1965; EVERT et al., 1970). Nuclei at various stages of degeneration have also been reported in mature sieve cells of Gnetales (EVERT et al., 1973a; BEHNKE and PALIWAL, 1973) and cycads (PARTHASARATHY, unpublished data). A close special relationship between mitochondria and the degenerating nucleus has been reported in the sieve cells of *Welwitschia* (EVERT et al., 1973a). There is some controversy as to the integrity of the so called "persistent" nuclei in mature sieve cells of gymnosperms (see EVERT et al., 1970). However, published electronmicrographs indicate that such nuclei are typically necrotic (e.g. Fig. 29).

The sieve-cell plastids are among the first organelles to indicate structural changes during cell differentiation. Crystalloids, starch granules, filamentous material, or osmiophilic globules may be formed in plastids depending on the species (Figs. 29, 30). For example, all four types of inclusions may be found in the sieve cell plastids of *Pinus* (SRIVASTAVA and O'BRIEN, 1966; MURMANIS and EVERT, 1966; WOODING, 1966; PARAMESWARAN, 1971) and *Picea abies* (TIMELL, 1973). However, in *Metasequoia* (KOLLMANN and SCHUMACHER, 1961, 1964), *Welwitschia* (EVERT et al., 1973a),

Gnetum and *Ephedra* (BEHNKE and PALIWAL, 1973) the sieve-cell plastids contain only starch granules. The matrix of plastids becomes more and more electron-transparent as cell differentiation progresses.

Mitochondria undergo relatively less change in structure although in most mature sieve cells the mitochondrial cristae may appear somewhat swollen. In the sieve cells of *Welwitchia* the mitochondria become closely associated spatially with the nucleus during cell differentiation (EVERT et al., 1973a). Structures interpreted as slime or P-protein have been observed with the light microscope in the sieve cells of several coniferous species (EVERT and ALFIERI, 1965) and in *Ephedra californica* (ALOSI and ALFIERI, 1972). Observation of sieve cells with the electron-microscope, however, has produced conflicting results with regard to P-protein. MURMANIS and EVERT (1966), PARAMESWARAN (1971), CAMPBELL (1972) and HARRIS (1972) have reported the presence of P-protein in the sieve cells of *Pinus* whereas the investigations of WOODING (1966, 1968), SRIVASTAVA and O'BRIEN (1966), NEUBERGER (1973), and NEUBERGER and EVERT (1974) indicate that P-protein is absent in that genus. P-protein is also reported to be absent in sieve cells of *Metasequoia glyptostroboides* (KOLLMANN, 1964), *Picea abies* (TIMELL, 1973), *Welwitchia mirabilis* (EVERT et al., 1973a), *Ephedra campylopoda, Gnetum gnemon* (BEHNKE and PALIWAL, 1973) and the cycad *Zamia pseudoparasitica* (PARTHASARATHY, unpublished data). A careful study of the published electronmicrographs of the structures interpreted as P-protein in conifer sieve cells suggests that in some cases poorly fixed or degenerating nuclei have been misidentified as slime or P-protein (e.g. MURMANIS and EVERT, 1966; PARAMESWARAN, 1971; HARRIS, 1972). Similarly, the fibrous P-protein observed by CAMPBELL (1972) and HARRIS (1972) in *Pinus* sieve cells appears to be plastid filaments that were displaced into the cell lumen after rupture of the plastid envelope when tissue was prepared for microscopy (see PARAMESWARAN, 1971). Observations of "slime" in sieve cells with the light microscope (e.g. EVERT and ALFIERI, 1965; ALOSI and ALFIERI, 1972) cannot be considered to be a positive method of identification of P-protein due to the limited resolution of the light microscope. In summary it seems that P-protein has not been clearly demonstrated in any of the gymnosperms.

As in angiosperms, the ER in gymnosperm sieve cells also undergoes elaborate modification (see ESAU, 1969). During cell differentiation, aggregates of smooth ER begin to appear throughout the cytoplasm. Such aggregates of ER may be tubular (Figs. 29, 30), reticulate, or convoluted in form.

Dictyosomes and microtubules that are present in differentiating sieve elements disappear in mature sieve elements along with ribosomes. The tonoplast also apparently breaks down. Thus a mature gymnosperm sieve cell contains plasmalemma, plastids, mitochondria, highly modified ER, and either lacks a nucleus or has a necrotic nucleus. All the organelles in a mature sieve cell normally occupy a parietal position. The cell lumen appears empty and is devoid of any transcellular strands.

Sieve areas in gymnosperms are normally present on the radial face of the sieve cell walls (ESAU, 1969). The formation of sieve areas is quite similar to that of lateral sieve areas in angiosperms (ESAU, 1969, and literature cited therein). The sieve-area pores are joined in the middle of the cell wall by a median cavity. The median cavity normally contains membranous material that appears to be continuous with ER on either side of the sieve area (Fig. 30). Although fully developed pores are normally lined with a variable amount of callose (depending on the fixation), association of callose platelets with developing pores has not been

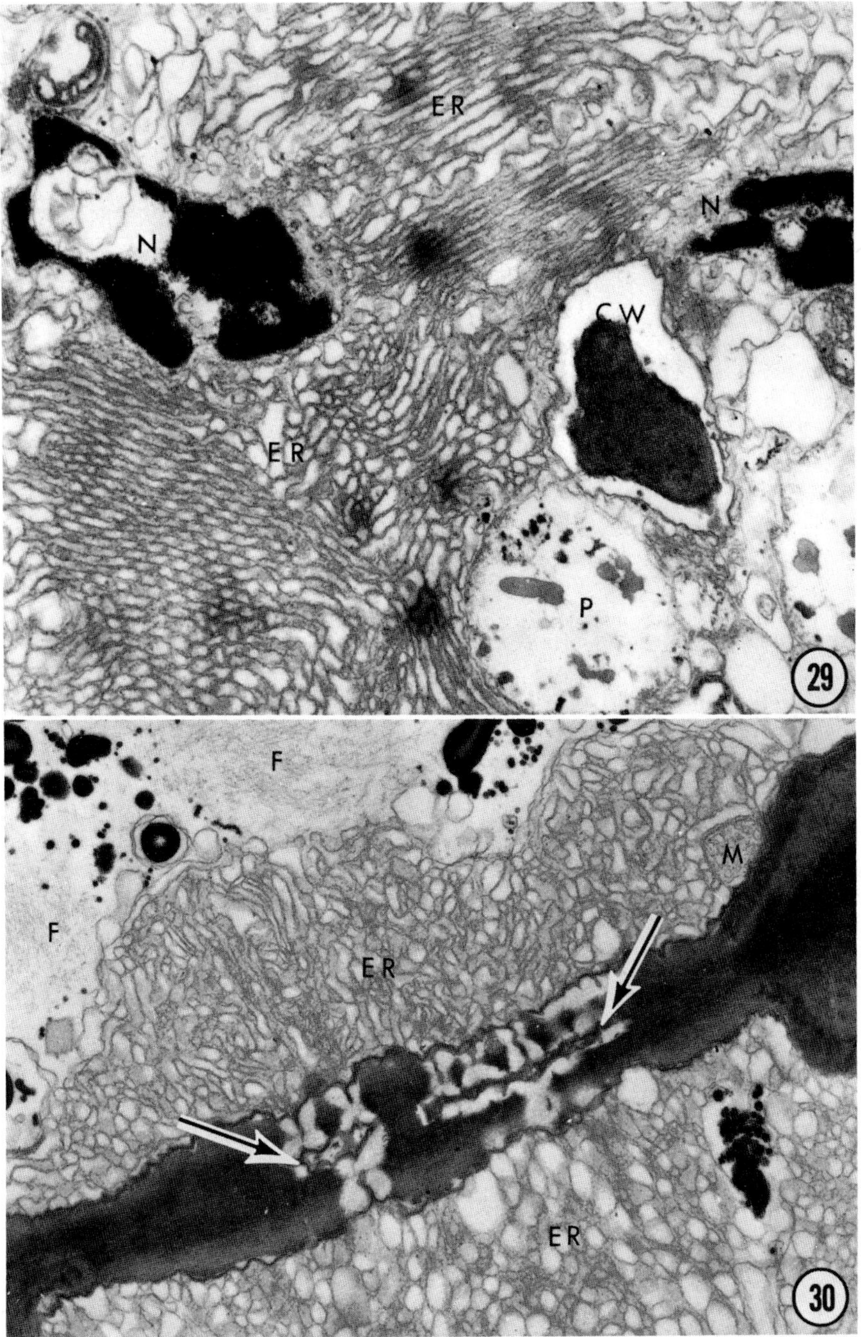

Figs. 29–30. *Sieve cells of gymnosperms.*
Fig. 29. A sieve cell in *Gnetum gnemon* at a late stage of cell differentiation. Note fragments of the electron-dense necrotic nucleus (*N*) and the stacks of modified tubular ER (*ER*). Plastids (*P*) with starch granules, and a fragment of cell wall (*CW*) are also seen. ×16,000. Fig. 30. Sieve area of a mature sieve cell in *Pinus silvestris*. Note the large amount of tubular and vesicular forms of ER cisternae (*ER*) on either side of the sieve-area pores. Plastid filaments (*F*) and electron-dense starch granules are also present. *M* mitochondrion. ×12,500. (Fig. 29 from Behnke and Paliwal, 1973. Fig. 30 from Parameswaran, 1971)

reported. Aggregates of ER normally occurring on both sides of sieve areas in mature sieve cells, apparently interconnected by elements of ER traversing the sieve pores, have been reported in the phloem of conifers (KOLLMANN and SCHUMACHER, 1964; MURMANIS and EVERT, 1966; SRIVASTAVA and O'BRIEN, 1966; WOODING, 1966, 1968; PARAMESWARAN, 1971; NEUBERGER, 1973), Gnetales (BEHNKE and PALIWAL, 1973; EVERT et al., 1973b) as well as cycads (PARTHASARATHY, unpublished). It is of interest to note that in contrast with the literature on the nature of sieve-plate pores in angiosperms, there is general agreement among the investigators with regard to the nature of sieve-area pores in conifers. Thus the sieve pores of sieve cells in gymnosperms do not appear as free, unobstructed channels for solute flow.

Sieve cells may also be connected to contiguous parenchymatous cells. On the sieve-cell side of the wall, these connections are similar to sieve-area pores; on the parenchyma side, similar to plasmodesmata (ESAU, 1969).

III. Vascular Cryptogams

The phloem of vascular cryptogams has received very little attention until recently as compared with the phloem of angiosperms and conifers. With the exception of some of the sieve elements in *Equisetum,* the sieve elements of lower vascular plants are apparently sieve cells (LAMOUREUX, 1961, and literature cited therein).

Although the sieve-element walls are frequently thicker than those of adjacent parenchyma cells, they may not be nacreous when viewed with the light microscope. True, nacreous walls are reported to occur in some species of *Hymenophyllaceae* and *Polypodiaceae* (LAMOUREUX, 1961). The presence or absence of nacreous walls might also depend on the type of organ, the age of sieve elements and the environment (HEBANT, 1969). An ultrastructural study of the nacreous wall in *Polypodium* has revealed a distinct outer, wide region consisting of a loose fibrillar mesh work, and an inner, narrow region consisting of a compact fibrillar mesh work (EVERT and EICHHORN, 1973).

Details of the ontogeny of sieve elements in vascular cryptogams are few (see ESAU, 1969). Ultrastructural details of very young sieve elements differ little from those of other young nucleate cells. As the sieve element differentiates, wall thickenings may become prominent in some species (EVERT and EICHHORN, 1973; PERRY, 1973; WARMBRODT, 1973). The nucleus begins to degenerate and either completely disintegrates by the time the sieve elements become mature, or persists in a degenerated state depending on the species (MAXE, 1966; ESAU, 1969; KRUATRACHUE, 1973). The sieve-element nuclei of certain species of ferns are reported to have crystalline inclusions that are liberated into the cytoplasm when the nucleus disappears (HÉBANT, 1969).

P-protein has not been recorded at both light and electronmicroscopy levels at any stage of sieve-element differentiation in the vascular cryptogams so far investigated (ESAU, 1969; LIBERMAN-MAXE, 1971; BURR and EVERT, 1973; EVERT and EICHHORN, 1973; KRUATRACHUE, 1973; PERRY, 1973; WARMBRODT, 1973; KRUATRACHUE and EVERT, 1974; WARMBRODT and EVERT, 1974). However, accumulations of crystalline and fibrillar material in intracisternal spaces of the rough ER, and in the vacuoles have been recorded in differentiating sieve elements of *Isoetes* and

Selaginella respectively (BURR and EVERT, 1973; KRUATRACHUE and EVERT, 1974). Such proteinaceous material cannot be considered as homologous to the P-protein of higher plants (see ESAU, 1969).

Very little is known about plastids and mitochondria in the sieve elements of vascular cryptogams. Plastids and mitochondria have been reported to occur in small numbers in mature sieve elements of some species (LIBERMAN-MAXE, 1971; KRUATRACHUE, 1973; PERRY, 1973; WARMBRODT, 1973). LIBERMAN-MAXE (1971) has reported that the number of mitochondria in mature sieve cells of *Polypodium vulgare* is fewer than in younger sieve cells. Mitochondria are apparently absent in mature sieve cells of *P. schraderi* (EVERT and EICHHORN, 1973). Sieve elements of vascular cryptogams characteristically contain highly refractive granules that were reported to be pectic, mucilaginous, or proteinaceous in nature (see ESAU, 1969). Recent studies on these refractive granules (also known as refractive spherules) in the phloem of *Microsorium* and *Psilotum* suggest that the spherules are chiefly proteinaceous (SAKAI and LAMOUREUX, 1973). The spherules appear as electron-dense regions surrounded by a unit membrane (Fig. 31). The spherules have been reported to develop from dilated tips of ER during sieve-element differentiation (LIBERMAN-MAXE, 1971; SAKAI and LAMOUREUX, 1973).

The ER apparently becomes modified as in other vascular plants, and stacked, tubular or vesicular aggregations of smooth ER are commonly seen in mature

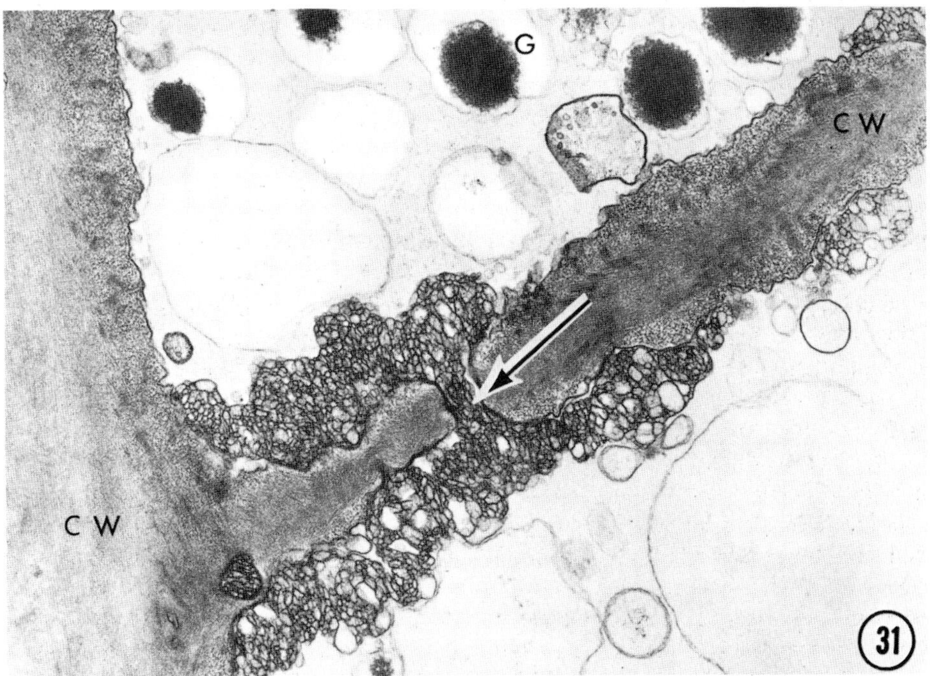

Fig. 31. Mature sieve cell of a vascular cryptogam, *Psilotum nudum*. The pore is filled with ER (arrow) and is free of callose. Round, electron-dense proteinaceous bodies bound by a membrane are granules (*G*) or refractive spherules that are characteristic of sieve elements in most vascular cryptogams. ×26,000. (Figure courtesy of Mr. J.W. PERRY, Botany Department, University of Wisconsin, Madison, Wisconsin)

sieve elements (LIBERMAN-MAXE, 1971; BURR and EVERT, 1973; PERRY, 1973). The mature sieve element typically lacks a nucleus (or has a necrotic one), tonoplast, dictyosomes and ribosomes and has a thin parietal cytoplasm that is composed of plasmalemma, modified ER, refractive spherules, and a few mitochondria and plastids. No transcellular strands have been recorded in the sieve elements.

Since the sieve-area pores are a fraction of a micron in diameter in most lower vascular plants (LAMOUREUX, 1961; ESAU, 1969), very little was known about the nature of the pores in these taxa until the arrival of the electronmicroscope. As in the sieve elements of other vascular plants, each pore site is associated with a single plasmodesma (LIBERMAN-MAXE, 1971; WARMBRODT and EVERT, 1974). Callose platelets were not associated with developing pores in the sieve elements of *Lycopodium* (WARMBRODT and EVERT, 1974). Mature pores are lined with plasmalemma and may or may not contain callose depending on the genera (ESAU, 1969). The pore contents appear to be quite variable. In some genera the pores are traversed by ER (Fig. 31; MAXE, 1966; EVERT and EICHHORN, 1973; PERRY, 1973). In others the pores may be unoccluded or occluded with vesicles and/or membranous material (WARMBRODT and EVERT, 1974). In the sieve elements of *Selaginella* and *Isoetes* the pores are often occluded with fibrillar material released by the rupture of vacuoles and dilated ER cisternae respectively (BURR and EVERT, 1973; KRUATRACHUE and EVERT, 1974).

It must be emphasized that the fine structure of sieve-area pores has been reported so far in only about half a dozen species of this heterogeneous group of plants. Further investigations on the fine structure of phloem in vascular cryptogams that are being conducted in the laboratory of Dr. R.F. EVERT, at the University of Wisconsin will be awaited with interest.

D. Longevity of Sieve Elements

The various signs of the inactive state of sieve elements can readily be detected even at the level of light microscopy (see ESAU, 1969). The sieve areas may initially become blocked by massive deposits of definitive callose and later become entirely free of it. The sieve elements may also appear free of any contents. Inactive sieve elements may be obliterated due to complex growth adjustments of the surrounding cells. Nonfunctioning sieve tubes may become filled with tylosoids (proliferations from contiguous parenchyma cells) in some plants (ESAU, 1969).

Because the sieve elements have been investigated largely in dicotyledons and conifers which renew vascular tissue by secondary growth, the elements are commonly regarded as having a short conducting life. The enucleate condition of the sieve elements with their highly specialized cytoplasm may perhaps support such a notion. However, most perennial monocotyledons which do not renew vascular tissues (e.g. palms), have enucleate sieve elements that apparently function throughout the life of the plant (TOMLINSON, 1964; PARTHASARATHY and TOMLINSON, 1967).

In most dicotyledons and conifers, the sieve elements appear to function for one or two growing seasons (ESAU, 1969). However, sieve tubes in *Tilia* have been reported to function up to a decade (HUME, 1912; EVERT, 1962). Very little is known about the longevity of sieve elements in woody dicotyledons of the tropical regions.

The longevity of sieve tubes in palms and other perennial monocotyledons has recently received some attention. PARTHASARATHY and TOMLINSON (1967) reported the absence of definitive callose in the metaphloem of vascular bundles in the stems of palms except when disconnected by leaf fall. The authors also showed that in the palm *Sabal palmetto* functional enucleate sieve elements were about 50 years old. Recently PARTHASARATHY (1974c) investigated the fine structure of palm sieve tubes estimated to be more than two decades old and found that the enucleate elements had intact plasmalemma, ER and plastids, and more or less unoccluded sieve-plate pores that were lined with callose and plasmalemma. Documented cases of royal palms (*Roystonea*) which have reached an age of more than 100 years suggest that the sieve elements in the basal parts of such palms must remain functioning for at least a century (ZIMMERMANN, 1973). ERVIN and EVERT (1970) found enucleate sieve elements that were apparently functioning for eight years or more in the rhizomes of several perennial monocotyledons. HEYSER et al. (1969) demonstrated with the help of autoradiography and electronmicroscopy that 15-month-old enucleate sieve elements in *Tradescantia albiflora* were functional.

Among lower vascular plants which perennate without secondary vascular tissue, long-lived sieve cells may also be expected to occur. HUME (1912) has reported a functional life of 5 years or more for sieve cells in *Pteridium aquilinum*. Recent investigations on the structure of primary phloem in the basal parts of a 12-year-old tree fern, *Alsophila stipularis* suggest that sieve elements in such ferns remain functioning for more than a decade (PARTHASARATHY, unpublished data).

In summary, despite the recent assertion "one common feature is that the sieve element is short lived" (CANNY, 1973, p. 125), there is little doubt that some groups of plants have long-lived, enucleate sieve elements. Investigations on the structure of long-lived sieve elements have not indicated any obvious difference from that of the short-lived elements. Factors that contribute to the longevity of such sieve elements are not known.

E. Structure of Sieve Elements and Translocation

The structure of the sieve element and its relation to function has been reviewed recently by several investigators (e.g. NORTHCOTE and WOODING, 1968; WEATHERLEY and JOHNSON, 1968; ESAU, 1969; MACROBBIE, 1971). This part of the chapter will be devoted chiefly to two aspects of sieve element structure and function: 1. at what stage of cell differentiation does a sieve element participate in long distance transport, and 2. how is the structure of the sieve element related to some possible mechanisms of translocation?

I. Are Undifferentiated Sieve Elements the Channels for Long-Distance Transport?

The concept of young sieve elements with intact nuclei being involved in translocation rather than mature, enucleate elements was chiefly forwarded by KOLLMANN (1964), KOLLMANN and SCHUMACHER (1964), KOLLMANN (1965), KOLLMANN and DÖRR

(1966), and WILLENBRINK and KOLLMANN (1966), as a result of their investigations on the sieve cells of gymnosperms. WARK and CHAMBERS (1965) investigated the sieve elements of *Pisum* and came to a similar conclusion. Experimental evidence for such a conclusion came from the fact that assimilates labeled with ^{14}C accumulated in the region of the youngest sieve cells between the cambium and the first band of bast fibers in the phloem of *Metasequoia* and *Juniperus*, and that aphids also pierced such young sieve cells with their stylets (KOLLMANN, 1965; KOLLMANN and DÖRR, 1966). From a structural point of view it is difficult to conceive how sugar solutions can move first through the cytoplasm and then across the undifferentiated sieve areas (i.e. plasmodesmata) at the velocities of more than 50 cms an hour recorded in many plants (see CANNY, 1973). Furthermore, recent anatomical and experimental evidence proves that mature enucleate sieve elements in the metaphloem of perennial monocotyledons that lack secondary growth constitute the functional conduit (see Section E. II). Although immature sieve elements may be capable of transporting solutes for short distances and at low velocities (which could explain the accumulation of assimilates labeled with ^{14}C in some young sieve elements), there is now overwhelming evidence that mature sieve elements are the main conduit for long distance transport in phloem (GEIGER et al., 1969; ESAU, 1969; CRAFTS and CRISP, 1971).

II. Sieve-Element Structure in Relation to Possible Mechanisms of Transport

This part of the review is an attempt to relate sieve element structure to the three commonly proposed mechanisms of translocation: 1. pressure driven mass flow; 2. electroosmotic flow, and 3. streaming mechanisms or activated mass flow.

1. Pressure Driven Mass Flow

The conditions required for this type of mechanism to operate in sieve elements have been dealt with in detail elsewhere in this volume (see Chapter 14). As far as structure of the sieve element is concerned, the pressure-flow mechanism requires a conduit of low resistance. This would mean that the sieve element should have a lumen relatively free of cytoplasm and the sieve-plate pores must offer little resistance to longitudinal solute flow. Obviously such a condition is possible only if the pores are free of any occlusions. It is now generally agreed that massive deposits of callose are formed mainly as a wound response in functioning sieve elements (see Chapter 2). Thus callose is no longer considered to be an obstruction to solute flow in intact sieve tubes. The controversy regarding the presence of filamentous or membranous material in the sieve-plate pores has already been discussed. If we assume that pores are free of any occlusions in functioning sieve elements, as some of the recent investigations suggest, then a pressure-driven mass flow is the most likely mechanism of translocation in angiosperms. It also seems conceivable that P-protein filaments can traverse sieve-plate pores without actually plugging them. As suggested by WOODING (1967), the tight packing of P-protein in the sieve-plate pores illustrated in many electronmicrographs (e.g. Fig. 20) might be due to the formation of callose as a response to wounding at the time of tissue preparation. It is thus likely that the filaments are more loosely arranged in the pores *in vivo* (see also BEHNKE, 1971b).

WEATHERLEY (1972) has pointed out that pressure flow in sieve tubes is possible even if some obstruction is offered by the sieve-plate pores, provided that the obstruction is not too great. According to WEATHERLEY's calculations the pressure-flow theory is compatible with a system of parallel filaments running through sieve-plate pores provided they are at least 100 nm apart for low velocities of translocation or at least 200 nm apart for high velocities. It will be of interest to see if future investigations of sieve-plate pores in carefully fixed sieve elements reveal such widely spaced filaments in the pores.

Indirect evidence in support of a relatively unplugged condition of the sieve-plate pores has come from the studies of plant diseases associated with mycoplasma-like organisms. Mycoplasma-like organisms up to a diameter of 1 μ have been observed in the sieve elements of angiosperms affected by the yellows diseases (see MARAMAROSCH et al., 1970). The typical rate and spread of disease symptoms thought to be caused by these microorganisms indicate that they are translocated along with the photosynthates in the sieve tubes. Although the extreme plasticity of mycoplasma-like organisms might enable them to squeeze through openings considerably smaller than the diameter of the microorganisms themselves (LEMCKE, 1971; RAZIN, 1969), it would be difficult to explain their passage through plugged pores as in Fig. 20. Furthermore, mycoplasma-like organisms in sieve elements are good indicators of a sudden pressure release, since they distort easily when they are flushed. A recent investigation by WORLEY (1973) on sieve elements of corn infected with corn stunt disease has shown that sieve-plate pores contain mycoplasma-like organisms 200 nm in diameter without signs of distortion. No obvious evidence of pressure release in the sieve elements containing the organisms was present.

Since the pressure-flow hypothesis does not require the presence of P-protein, what then is the function of P-protein filaments in angiosperm sieve tubes? It is probable that P-protein is involved in the rapid sealing response after injury (MILBURN, 1971). Initial plugging of sieve-plate pores with displaced P-protein filaments followed immediately by a constriction of pores by callose deposition could be an excellent sealing system in injured sieve elements (see also Chapter 2). P-protein, if present in the form of a network, might also help in keeping plastids and mitochondria away from the sieve-plate pores (WOODING, 1969).

A majority of physiological data (CRAFTS and CRISP, 1971) along with the growing body of literature which suggests that sieve-plate pores are open (or not completely occluded) *in vivo*, strongly supports the pressure-flow hypothesis. However, structural evidence indicates that the pressure-flow mechanism might be applicable only to the sieve tubes in angiosperms, and *not* to sieve cells in gymnosperms and many vascular cryptogams. As noted earlier, the sieve-area pores in conifers are filled with ER or other membranous material. Clearly, a pressure-flow mechanism as currently defined (see Chapter 14) cannot operate in such sieve cells at velocities that exceed 50 cms h (see WILLENBRINK and KOLLMANN, 1966). If such high velocities of translocation are proved to be correct in conifer phloem, the possible presence of some type of metabolic pump in the sieve areas must not be ruled out (see other hypotheses below).

It is also noteworthy that mycoplasma-like organisms have so far not been reported in the sieve cells of gymnosperms and vascular cryptogams.

A discussion of the physiological evidence in favor of or against the pressure-flow hypothesis is obviously beyond the scope of this chapter. But it is pertinent to note that the hypothesis does not explain simultaneous, bidirectional flow within a given sieve tube (WEATHERLEY and JOHNSON, 1968). However, ZIMMERMANN (1971) is of the opinion that simultaneous, bidirectional transport of material within a given sieve tube has not been unequivocally demonstrated (see also Chapter 10).

2. Electroosmotic Flow

The electroosmotic flow theory involves a metabolically driven circulation of ions in the area of sieve plates (SPANNER, 1958). The ions, probably potassium, are swept along the upstream side of sieve plate and removed on the down stream side to be recycled back to the upstream side *via* contiguous parenchyma cells. The electrically polarized sieve plates would then cause an electro-osmotic flow of solution through the sieve-plate pores (for details see Chapter 13). The electroosmotic theory requires that the pores be filled with some cytoplasmic material for the electroosmotic forces to be able to develop in the interstices between the fibrils of cytoplasmic material (SPANNER, 1958). As discussed in Section C, proponents of electroosmotic theory have maintained that the plugged condition of the sieve-plate pores is indicative of the normal state of pores in functioning sieve elements (e.g. MISHRA and SPANNER, 1970; SIDDIQUI and SPANNER, 1970). It is not clear how wide the interstices between fibrils in the sieve-plate pores visualized by SPANNER (1958) should be. MISHRA and SPANNER (1970) suggested that "loose" plugging of the pores can be considered to be normal for functioning sieve elements. If the interstices between P-protein filaments are wider than 100 nm, an electroosmotic pump need not even be necessary according to WEATHERLEY'S (1972) calculations. Furthermore, P-protein is absent in the sieve elements of some monocotyledons, and the plugged condition of the sieve-plate pores might not be a normal phenomenon in some angiosperms (see Section C. 2). The theory, however, might be compatible with the structure of sieve cells in gymnosperms where the narrow sieve-area pores traversed by ER or other membranous material could offer the required interstices to develop electroosmotic forces. But several physiologists have objected to electroosmotic flow on the basis that it has too many theoretical difficulties (see WEATHERLEY and JOHNSON, 1968; MACROBBIE, 1971; CANNY, 1973).

3. Activated Mass Flow or Streaming Mechanisms

The intracellular macroscopic transcellular strands described by THAINE (e.g. 1964, 1969) and others in mature sieve elements of some plants, and the rapid, bouncing movements of plastids and other organelles observed by LEE et al. (1971) in functioning sieve tubes of *Heracleum* have raised the possibility that some type of streaming mechanism is involved in translocation. The membrane-bound cytoplasmic strands 0.2–5 μ in diameter visualized by THAINE and his associates (1967, 1973) have not been substantiated by studies at the ultrastructural level, and hence will not be discussed here (see also JOHNSON, 1973). WEATHERLEY and JOHNSON (1968), MACROBBIE (1971) and FENSOM (1972) have suggested that P-protein filaments could be organized to form motile systems in sieve elements. WEATHERLEY and JOHNSON suggested that fluid in the sieve tubes might be propelled by some kind of movement of P-protein filaments. MACROBBIE speculated that activated mass flow by a mechanism similar to that involved in protoplasmic streaming might exist in sieve tubes and that P-protein filaments could be responsible for the production of motive force. FENSOM suggested that P-protein occurs as organized, axially oriented microtubules and that these extend from one sieve element to the next through the sieve-plate pores. He visualized microperistaltic movement of the tubules as being responsible for the production of motive force (see Chapter 15 for further details).

The association of streaming with microfilaments 5–7 nm in diameter in cells of the alga *Nitella* (KAMIYA, 1959; NAGAI and REHBAN, 1966) and the slime mould *Physarum polycephalum* (WOHLFARTH-BOTTERMAN, 1964; KAMIYA, 1968) is now well known. In streaming *Nitella* cells the microfilaments occur in bundles 0.1–0.15 μ in diameter and are always oriented parallel to the direction of streaming (NAGAI and REHBUN, 1966). Bundles of microfilaments oriented predominantly parallel to the long axis of the cell have also been recently recorded in the peripheral regions of elongating and/or streaming nucleate cells of several vascular plants (PARTHASARATHY and MÜHLETHALER, 1972 and literature cited therein). MACROBBIE (1971) suggests that a streaming mechanism similar to that in *Nitella* might be adequate for translocation in sieve tubes. If so, one would expect the P-protein filaments to be predominantly axial in orientation. A majority of studies done at the ultrastructural level do not indicate any preferred orientation for P-protein filaments in mature sieve elements (ESAU, 1969). EVERT and DESHPANDE (1969) and EVERT et al. (1969) concluded that longitudinally oriented P-protein strands are formed upon the fixation of sieve tubes. Using DMSO (dimethyl sulphoxide) with glutaraldehyde for a faster penetration of the fixative ROBIDOUX et al. (1973) observed that P-protein filaments (interpreted by the authors as being tubular) were oriented longitudinally in the sieve elements of *Heracleum*. The authors claimed that, because of the superior fixative used in the study, the images they obtained of the sieve elements reflected the proper distribution and orientation of P-protein in undisturbed sieve elements. However, their electronmicrographs indicate that such a claim might be somewhat exaggerated. Their Plate 2B for example, illustrates an "undisturbed" sieve element that contains free starch granules in the lumen (referred to by the authors as "marker-particles"). It is well known that starch granules are commonly displaced from plastids as a result of damage to sieve elements. The orientation of P-protein filaments in the lumen of mature, intact sieve elements is, therefore, still a moot question.

A second possibility, according to MACROBBIE (1971), would be an arrangement of P-protein similar to that in slime moulds which exhibit high rates of streaming. MACROBBIE speculates that P-protein filaments might produce "local pressure gradients within the sieve elements, probably as a consequence of the generation of shearing forces" at the filaments. In the slime moulds an oscillatory flow is evident between two protoplasmic masses in which the density and degree of organization of the fibrillar material vary periodically (KAMIYA, 1968). In attempting to translate this into the phloem, MACROBBIE theorizes that waves of the cycle of P-protein polymerization/depolymerization travelling down the sieve elements, or waves of a factor which affects this transition, could create a solute flow of required velocities in phloem. The difference between the *Nitella*-type of model and the *Physarum*-type of model is in the relative permanence of the fibrillar arrangement. The *Nitella*-type model requires a constant distribution and orientation of fibrillar material whereas in the *Physarum*-type model, changes in distribution of the organized fibrillar material with time is envisaged (MACROBBIE, 1971). All theories that are based on the active participation of P-protein filaments in translocation assume that the filaments have contractile properties. Microfilaments thought to be responsible for streaming in slime moulds have actin-like properties (e.g. HATANO and TAZAWA, 1968; NACHMIAS et al., 1970). Evidence on the question of contractility of filamentous P-protein, however, is conflicting.

The substructural features of P-protein filaments in negatively stained preparations (KOLLMANN et al., 1970) and some of the chemical reactions of the solubilized phloem protein (KLEINIG et al., 1971; KLEINIG et al., 1971) seem to indicate a possible relationship between actin-like proteins and the P-protein. However, absence of any binding capacity for ATP, GTP and colchicine recorded in P-protein isolated from sieve-tube sap along with other dissimilarities with actin-like proteins have also been reported (KLEINIG et al., 1971; WILLIAMSON, 1972; SABNIS and HART, 1973).

Perhaps the strongest evidence in support of contractile properties of P-protein comes from the recent cytochemical studies of GILDER and CRONSHAW (1973a, b) on the distribution of ATPase activity in differentiating phloem cells of *Cucurbita* and *Nicotiana*. With the aid of high quality electronmicrographs the authors have been able to demonstrate ATPase activity associated with the dispersed P-protein filaments in mature sieve elements. It is interesting to note that ATPase activity was associated only with dispersed P-protein filaments, and not with the undispersed P-protein bodies that were present in young sieve elements and parenchyma cells. ATPase activity was also found in dictyosomes, mitochondria, plasmalemma and some regions in the cell wall. More information on the composition of P-protein is obviously needed if one is to understand the role of these filaments, if any, in phloem translocation (see also Chapter 2).

The attractive aspect of a translocation mechanism mediated by P-protein filaments is that it can also explain bidirectional flow within a single sieve tube (see MACROBBIE, 1971, for details), and assign a function for P-protein filaments. However, if one assumes that an activated mass flow with the help of P-protein is theoretically possible, it can occur only in angiosperms since P-protein seems to be absent in gymnosperms and vascular cryptogams. It should also be noted that extrafascicular sieve elements in stems and petiole of *Cucurbita,* in which P-protein fails to disperse, have been demonstrated to translocate ^{14}C (WEBB and GORHAM, 1964).

F. Conclusion

Although a profoundly altered protoplast structure is a feature shared by mature sieve elements of all vascular plants, the nature of pores and the occurrence of P-protein, both of which can affect translocation, are not the same in all plants. Thus any hypothetical mechanism of translocation that relies heavily on the presence of P-protein in sieve elements will not be applicable to gymnosperms and vascular cryptogams. All the physiological data indicate that a Münch-type pressure-flow mechanism is the most likely one to be involved in translocation (CRAFTS and CRISP, 1971). Pressure-flow is also compatible with sieve-tube structure in angiosperms if we assume that the sieve-plate pores are relatively free of any obstruction in intact phloem.

However, it will be difficult to explain such a type of mechanism in the sieve cells of many lower vascular plants where the narrow pores that are traversed by ER will offer considerable resistance to flow. One is therefore forced to the conclusion either that there is more than one type of translocating mechanism present in vascular plants, or that there is an inconsistency between accepted facts of physiology and structure. More information on the energy required in translocation, and improved preparations of phloem for structural studies combined with a comparative study of translocation velocities in different groups of plants may be useful in elucidating the mechanism(s) of translocation. As emphasized earlier, the close relationship between sieve elements and surrounding cells including xylem should also not be overlooked when considering sieve-element function.

References

ABBE, L.B., CRAFTS, A.S.: Phloem of white pine and other coniferous species. Botan. Gaz. **100**, 695–722 (1939).

ALOSI, M.C., ALFIERI, F.J.: Ontogeny and structure of the secondary phloem of *Ephedra*. Am. J. Bot. **59**, 818–827 (1972).

ANDERSON, R., CRONSHAW, J.: The effects of pressure release on the sieve-plate pores of *Nicotiana*. J. Ultrastruct. Res. **29**, 50–59 (1969).

ANDERSON, R., CRONSHAW, J.: Sieve-plate pores in tobacco and bean. Planta **91**, 173–180 (1970).

BEHNKE, H.-D.: Über das Phloem der *Dioscoreaceen* unter besonderer Berücksichtigung ihrer Phloembecken. II. Elektronenoptische Untersuchungen zur Feinstruktur des Phloembeckens. Z. Pflanzenphysiol. **53**, 214–244 (1965).

BEHNKE, H.-D.: Die Siebröhren-Plastiden der Monocotyledonen. Vergleichende Untersuchungen über Feinbau und Verbreitung eines charakteristischen Plastidentyps. Planta **84**, 174–184 (1969a).

BEHNKE, H.-D.: Aspekte der Siebröhren-Differenzierung bei Monocotylen. Protoplasma **68**, 289–314 (1969b).

BEHNKE, H.-D.: Über den Feinbau und die Ausbreitung der Siebröhrenplasmafilamente und über Bau und Differenzierung der Siebporen bei einigen Monocotylen und bei *Nuphar*. Protoplasma **68**, 377–402 (1969c).

BEHNKE, H.-D.: Über den Feinbau verdickter (nacré) Wände und der Plastiden in den Siebröhren von *Annona* und *Myristica*. Protoplasma **72**, 69–78 (1971a).

BEHNKE, H.-D.: The contents of the sieve-plate pores in *Aristolochia*. J. Ultrastruct. Res. **36**, 493–498 (1971b).

BEHNKE, H.-D.: Sieve-tube plastids in relation to angiosperm systematics—an attempt towards a classification by ultrastructural analysis. Botan. Rev. **38**, 155–197 (1972).

BEHNKE, H.-D.: Plastids in sieve elements and their companion cells. Investigations on monocotyledons, with special reference to *Smilax* and *Tradescantia*. Planta **110**, 321–328 (1973).

BEHNKE, H.-D., DÖRR, I.: Zur Herkunft und Struktur der Plasmafilamente in Assimilatleitbahnen. Planta **74**, 18–44 (1967).

BEHNKE, H.-D., PALIWAL, G.S.: Ultrastructure of phloem and its development in *Gnetum gnemon*, with some observations on *Ephedra campylopoda*. Protoplasma **78**, 305–319 (1973).

BEHNKE, H.-D., TURNER, B.L.: On specific sieve-tube plastids in Caryophyllales. Further investigations with special reference to the Bataceae. Taxon **20**, 731–737 (1971).

BOUCK, Y.B., CRONSHAW, J.: The fine structure of differentiating sieve tube elements. J. Cell Biol. **25**, 79–96 (1965).

BURR, F.A., EVERT, R.F.: Some aspects of sieve-element structure and development in *Selaginella kraussiana*. Protoplasma **78**, 81–97 (1973).

CAMPBELL, R.: Electronmicroscopy of the development of needles of *Pinus nigra* var. *maritima*. Ann. Botany (London) **36**, 711–720 (1972).

CANNY, M.J.: Phloem Translocation. London: Cambridge University Press 1973.
CHAFE, S.C., DOOHAN, M.E.: Observations on the ultrastructure of the thickened sieve cell in *Pinus strobus* L. Protoplasma **75**, 67–78 (1972).
CHANG, B.: Anatomy of common North American pulpwood bark. Tappi Monogr. Ser. No. 14 (1954).
CHEADLE, V.I.: Observations on the phloem in the Monocotyledoneae. II. Additional data on the occurrence and phylogenetic specialization in structure of the sieve tubes in the metaphloem. Am. J. Bot. **35**, 129–131 (1948).
CHEADLE, V.I., UHL, N.W.: The relation of metaphloem to the types of vascular bundles in the Monocotyledoneae. Am. J. Bot. **35**, 578–583 (1948).
CHEADLE, V.I., WHITFORD, N.B.: Observations on the phloem in the Monocotyledoneae. I. The occurrence and phylogenetic specialization in structure of the sieve tubes in the metaphloem. Am. J. Bot. **28**, 623–627 (1941).
CRAFTS, A.W., CRISP, C.E.: Phloem transport in plants. San Francisco: W.H. Freeman and Co. 1971.
CRONSHAW, J., ANDERSON, R.: Sieve plate pores of *Nicotiana*. J. Ultrastruct. Res. **27**, 134–148 (1969).
CRONSHAW, J., ANDERSON, R.: Phloem differentiation in tobacco pith culture. J. Ultrastruct. Res. **34**, 244–259 (1971).
CRONSHAW, J., ESAU, K.: Tubular and fibrillar components of mature and differentiating sieve elements. J. Cell Biol. **34**, 801–816 (1967).
CRONSHAW, J., ESAU, K.: P-protein in the phloem of *Cucurbita*. I. The development of P-protein bodies. J. Cell Biol. **38**, 25–39 (1968a).
CRONSHAW, J., ESAU, K.: P-protein in the phloem of *Cucurbita*. II. The P-protein of mature sieve elements. J. Cell Biol. **38**, 292–303 (1968b).
CRONSHAW, J., GILDER, J., STONE, D.: Fine structural studies of P-proteins in *Cucurbita, Cucumis,* and *Nicotiana*. J. Ultrastruct. Res. **45**, 192–205 (1973).
CURRIER, H.B., SHIH, C.Y.: Sieve tubes and callose in *Elodea* leaves. Am. J. Bot. **55**, 145–152 (1968).
DESHPANDE, B.P., EVERT, R.F.: A re-evaluation of extruded nucleoli in sieve elements. J. Ultrastruct. Res. **33**, 483–494 (1970).
ERVIN, E.L., EVERT, R.F.: Aspects of sieve-element ontogeny and structure in *Smilax rotundifolia*. Botan. Gaz. **128**, 138–144 (1967).
ERVIN, L.E., EVERT, R.F.: Observations on sieve elements in three perennial monocotyledons. Am. J. Bot. **57**, 218–224 (1970).
ESAU, K.: Development and structure of the phloem tissue. II. Botan. Rev. **16**, 67–114 (1950).
ESAU, K.: Plant anatomy. New York: John Wiley and Sons, Inc. 1960.
ESAU, K.: The Phloem. In: Handbuch der Pflanzenanatomie, Bd. V, Teil 2. (eds. ZIMMERMANN, W., OZENDA, P., and WULFF, H.D. Berlin: Gebrüder Borntraeger 1969.
ESAU, K.: Development of P-protein in sieve elements of *Mimosa pudica*. Protoplasma **73**, 225–238 (1971a).
ESAU, K.: The sieve element and its immediate environment: Thoughts on research of the past fifty years. J. Indian Bot. **502** Golden Jubiles Vol. 50A, 115–129 (1971b).
ESAU, K.: Changes in the nucleus and the endoplasmic reticulum during differentiation of a sieve element in *Mimosa pudica* L. Ann. Botany (London) **36**, 703–710 (1972).
ESAU, K., CHEADLE, V.I.: Size of pores and their contents in sieve elements of dicotyledons. Proc. Natl. Acad. Sci. U.S. **45**, 156–162 (1959).
ESAU, K., CHEADLE, V.I.: Cytologic studies on phloem. Univ. Calif. (Berkeley) Publ. Botany **36**, 253–344 (1965).
ESAU, K., CHEADLE, V.I., RISLEY, E.B.: Development of sieve-plate pores. Botan. Gaz. **123**, 233–243 (1962).
ESAU, K., CRONSHAW, J.: Tubular components in cells of healthy and tobacco mosaic virus-infected *Nicotiana*. Virology **33**, 26–35 (1967).
ESAU, K., CRONSHAW, J.: Endoplasmic reticulum in the sieve element of *Cucurbita*. J. Ultrastruct. Res. **23**, 1–14 (1968).
ESAU, K., GILL, R.H.: Aggregation of endoplasmic reticulum and its relation to the nucleus in a differentiating sieve element. J. Ultrastruct. Res. **34**, 144–158 (1971).
ESAU, K., GILL, R.H.: Nucleus and endoplasmic reticulum in differentiating root protophloem of *Nicotiana tabacum*. J. Ultrastruct. Res. **41**, 160–175 (1972).

ESAU, K., GILL, R.H.: Correlation in differentiation of protophloem sieve elements of *Allium cepa* root. J. Ultrastruct. Res. **44**, 310–328 (1973).
ESAU, K., HOEFERT, L.L.: Composition and fine structure of minor veins in *Tetragonia* leaf. Protoplasma **72**, 237–253 (1971).
EVERT, R.F.: Some aspects of phloem development in *Tilia americana*. Am. J. Bot. **49**, 659 (1962).
EVERT, R.F., ALFIERI, F.J.: Ontogeny and structure of coniferous sieve cells. Am. J. Bot. **52**, 1058–1066 (1965).
EVERT, R.F., BORNMAN, C.H., BUTLER, V., GILLILAND, M.G.: Structure and development of the sieve-cell protoplast in leaf veins in *Welwitschia*. Protoplasma **76**, 1–21 (1973a).
EVERT, R.F., BORNMAN, C.H., BUTLER, V., GILLILAND, M.G.: Structure and development of sieve areas in leaf veins of *Welwitschia*. Protoplasma **76**, 23–34 (1973b).
EVERT, R.F., DAVIS, J.D., TUCKER, C.M., ALFIERI, F.J.: On the occurrence of nuclei in mature sieve elements. Planta **95**, 281–296 (1970).
EVERT, R.F., DERR, W.F.: Callose substance in sieve elements. Am. J. Bot. **51**, 552–559 (1964).
EVERT, R.F., DESHPANDE, B.P.: Electronmicroscope investigation of sieve-element ontogeny and structure in *Ulmus americana*. Protoplasma **68**, 403–432 (1969).
EVERT, R.F., DESHPANDE, B.P., EICHHORN, S.E.: Lateral sieve-area pores in woody dicotyledons. Can. J. Botany **49**, 1509–1515 (1971).
EVERT, R.F., EICHHORN, E.: Some aspects of sieve-cell ultrastructure in *Polypodium schraderi*. Am. J. Bot. **60**, 38 (1973).
EVERT, R.F., ESCHRICH, W., EICHHORN, S.E.: Sieve-plate pores in leaf veins of *Hordeum vulgare*. Planta **100**, 262–267 (1971).
EVERT, R.F., ESCHRICH, W.: P-protein distribution in mature sieve elements of *Cucurbita maxima*. Planta **109**, 193–210 (1973).
EVERT, R.F., MURMANIS, L., SACHS, I.B.: Another view of the ultrastructure of *Cucurbita* phloem. Ann. Botany N.S. **30**, 563–581 (1966).
EVERT, R.F., TUCKER, C.M., DAVIS, J.D., DESHPANDE, B.P.: Light microscope investigation of sieve-element ontogeny and structure in *Ulmus americana*. Am. J. Bot. **56**, 999–1017 (1969).
FENSOM, D.S.: A theory of translocation in phloem of *Heracleum* by contractile protein microfibrillar material. Can. J. Botany **50**, 479–497 (1972).
GEIGER, D.R., SAUNDERS, M.A., CATALDO, D.A.: Translocation and accumulation of translocate in sugar-beet petiole. Plant Physiol. **44**, 1657–1665 (1969).
GILDER, J., CRONSHAW, J.: Adenosine triphosphatase in the phloem of *Cucurbita*. Planta **110**, 189–204 (1973a).
GILDER, J., CRONSHAW, J.: The distribution of adenosine triphosphatase activity in differentiating and mature phloem cells of *Nicotiana tabacum* and its relationship to phloem transport. J. Ultrastruct. Res. **44**, 388–404 (1973b).
HARRIS, W.M.: Ultrastructural observations on Pinaceae leaf phloem. I. The spring condition. New Phytologist **71**, 169–173 (1972).
HARTIG, T.: Vergleichende Untersuchungen über die Organisation des Stammes der einheimischen Waldbäume. Jahresber. Fortschr. Forstwiss. und Forstl. Naturk. **1**, 125–168 (1837).
HARTIG, T.: Beiträge zur physiologischen Forstbotanik. Allgem. Forst- u. Jagdz. **36**, 257–261 (1860).
HATANO, S., TAZAWA, M.: Isolation, purification and characterization of myosin B from myxomycete plasmodium. Biochem. Biophys. Acta **154**, 507–519 (1968).
HÉBANT, C.: Observations sur le phloème de quelques filicinées tropicales. Naturalia monspeliensia, série Bot. **20**, 135–196 (1969).
HEYSER, W.: Phloemdifferenzierung bei *Tradescantia albiflora*. Cytobiol. **4**, 186–197 (1971).
HEYSER, W., ESCHRICH, W., EVERT, R.F.: Translocation in perennial monocotyledons. Science **164**, 572–574 (1969).
HUME, E.M.M.: The histology of the sieve tubes of *Pteridium aquilinum*, with some notes on *Marsilea quadrifolia* and *Lygodium dichotomum*. Ann. Botany (London) **26**, 573–587 (1912).
JOHNSON, R.P.C.: Microfilaments in pores between frozen-etched sieve elements. Planta **81**, 314–332 (1968).
JOHNSON, R.P.C.: Filaments but no membranous transcellular strands in sieve pores in freeze-etched, translocating phloem. Nature **244**, 464–466 (1973).

KAMIYA, N.: Protoplasmic streaming. Protoplasmatalogia **8** (3a), 1–99 (1959).

KAMIYA, N.: The mechanism of cytoplasmic movement in myxomycete plasmodium. Symp. Soc. Exptl. Biol. **22**, 199–214 (1968).

KLEINIG, H., DÖRR, I., KOLLMANN, R.: Vinblastine-induced precipitation of phloem proteins *in vitro*. Protoplasma **73**, 293–302 (1971).

KLEINIG, H., DÖRR, I., WEBER, C., KOLLMANN, R.: Filamentous proteins from plant sieve tubes. Nature New Biol. **229**, 152–153 (1971).

KOLLMANN, R.: Untersuchungen über das Protoplasma der Siebröhren von *Passiflora coerulea*. II. Elektronenoptische Untersuchungen. Planta **55**, 67–107 (1960).

KOLLMANN, R.: On the fine structure of the sieve-element protoplast. Phytomorphology **14**, 247–264 (1964).

KOLLMANN, R.: Zur Lokalisierung der funktionstüchtigen Siebzellen in sekundären Phloem von *Metasequoia glyptostroboides*. Planta **65**, 173–179 (1965).

KOLLMANN, R., DÖRR, I.: Lokalisierung funktionstüchtiger Siebzellen bei *Juniperus communis* mit Hilfe von Aphiden. Z. Pflanzenphysiol. **55**, 131–141 (1966).

KOLLMANN, R., DÖRR, I., KLEINIG, H.: Protein filaments—structural components of the phloem exudate. I. Observations with *Cucurbita* and *Nicotiana*. Planta **95**, 86–94 (1970).

KOLLMANN, R., SCHUMACHER, W.: Über die Feinstruktur des Phloems von *Metasequoia glyptostroboides* und seine jahreszeitlichen Veränderungen. I. Das Ruhephloem. Planta **57**, 583–607 (1961).

KOLLMANN, R., SCHUMACHER, W.: Über die Feinstruktur des Phloems von *Metasequoia glyptostroboides* und seine jahreszeitlichen Veränderungen. V. Die Differenzierung der Siebzellen im Verlaufe einer Vegetationsperiode. Planta **63**, 155–190 (1964).

KRUATRACHUE, M.: Ultrastructure of sieve elements in the leaf of *Isoetes muricata*. Am. J. Bot. **60**, 39 (abst.) (1973).

KRUATRACHUE, M., EVERT, R.F.: Structure and development of sieve elements in the leaf of *Isoetes muricata*. Am. J. Bot. **61**, 253–266 (1974).

LAMOUREUX, C.H.: Comparative studies on phloem of vascular cryptogams. Ph. D. Diss., Univ. of Calif. (1961).

LEE, D.R., ARNOLD, D.C., FENSOM, D.S.: Some microscopical observations of functioning sieve tubes of *Heracleum* using Nomarski optics. J. Exptl. Botany **22**, 25–38 (1971).

LEMCKE, R.M.: Sizing small organisms. Nature **229**, 492–493 (1971).

LIBERMAN-MAXE, M.: Étude cytologique de la différenciation des cellules criblées de *Polypodium vulgare*. (Polypodiacée). J. Microscopie **12**, 271–288 (1971).

MACROBBIE, E.A.C.: Phloem translocation. Facts and mechanisms: a comparative survey. Biol. Rev. **46**, 429–481 (1971).

MARAMAROSCH, K., GRANADOS, R.R., HIRUMI, H.: Mycoplasma diseases of plants and insects. Advan. Virus Res. **16**, 135–193 (1970).

MAXE, M.: Étude de la dégénerescence nucléaire dans les cellules criblées de *Polypodium vulgare* (Polypodiacée). Compt. Rend. **262**, 2211–2214 (1966).

MILBURN, J.A.: An analysis of the response in phloem exudation on application of massage to *Ricinus*. Planta **100**, 143–154 (1971).

MISHRA, U., SPANNER, D.C.: The fine structure of the sieve tubes of *Salix caprea* L. and its relation to the electroosmotic theory. Planta **90**, 43–56 (1970).

MURMANIS, L., EVERT, R.F.: Some aspects of sieve-cell ultrastructure in *Pinus strobus*. Am. J. Bot. **53**, 1065–1078 (1966).

NACHMIAS, V.T., HUXLEY, H.E., KESSLER, D.: Electronmicroscope observations on actomyosin and actin preparations from *Physarum polycephalum* and on their interaction with heavy meromyosin subfragments I from muscle myosin. J. Mol. Biol. **50**, 83–90 (1970).

NAGAI, R., REBHUN, L.I.: Cytoplasmic microfilaments in streaming *Nitella* cells. J. Ultrastruct. Res. **14**, 571–589 (1966).

NEUBERGER, D.S.: Sieve-cell ultrastructure in the hypocotyl of *Pinus resinosa*. Am. J. Bot. **70**, 40 (abst.) (1973).

NEUBERGER, D.S., EVERT, R.F.: Structure and development of the sieve-element protoplast in the hypocotyl of *Pinus resinosa*. Am. J. Bot. **61**, 360–374 (1974).

NORTHCOTE, D.H., WOODING, R.B.P.: Development of sieve tubes in *Acer pseudoplatanus*. Proc. Roy. Soc. (London), Ser. B **163**, 524–537 (1966).

NORTHCOTE, D.H., WOODING, F.B.P.: The structure and function of phloem tissue. Sci. Progr. Oxford **56**, 35–58 (1968).

O'Brien, T.P., Thimann, K.V.: Observations on the fine structure of the oat coleoptile. III. Correlated light and electronmicroscopy of the vascular tissues. Protoplasma **63**, 443–478 (1967).

Palevitz, B.A., Newcomb, E.H.: A study of sieve-element starch using sequential enzymatic digestion and electronmicroscopy. J. Cell Biol. **45**, 383–398 (1970).

Parameswaran, N.: Zur Feinstruktur der Assimilatleitbahnen in der Nadel von *Pinus sylvestris*. Cytobiol. **3**, 70–88 (1971).

Parker, J.: Transcellular strands and intercellular particles. Movement in sieve tubes of some common tree species. Naturwissenschaften **51**, 273–274 (1964).

Parthasarathy, M.V.: Studies on metaphloem in petioles and roots of Palmae. Ph. D. Diss., Cornell University (1966).

Parthasarathy, M.V.: Observations on metaphloem in the vegetative parts of palms. Am. J. Bot. **55**, 1140–1168 (1968).

Parthasarathy, M.V.: Ultrastructure of phloem in palms. I. Immature sieve elements and parenchymatic elements. Protoplasma **79**, 59–91 (1974a).

Parthasarathy, M.V.: Ultrastructure of phloem in palms. II. Structural changes and fate of the organelles in differentiating sieve elements. Protoplasma **79**, 93–125 (1974b).

Parthasarathy, M.V.: Ultrastructure of phloem in palms. III. Mature phloem. Protoplasma **79**, 265–315 (1974c).

Parthasarathy, M.V., Mühlethaler, K.: Ultrastructure of protein tubules in differentiating sieve elements, Cytobiol. **1**, 17–36 (1969).

Parthasarathy, M.V., Mühlethaler, K.: Cytoplasmic microfilaments in plant cells. J. Ultrastruct. Res. **38**, 46–62 (1972).

Parthasarathy, M.V., Tomlinson, P.B.: Anatomical features of metaphloem in stems of *Sabal, Cocos* and two other palms. Am. J. Bot. **54**, 1143–1151 (1967).

Perry, J.W.: Ultrastructural observations on the phloem in aerial shoots of *Psilotum nudum*. Am. J. Bot. **60**, 40 (abst.) (1973).

Raasch, H.-D.: Zur feinstrukturellen Differenzierung des Phloems bei Palmen. Ph. D. Diss., Rheinischen Friedrich Wilhelms-Universität, Bonn (1971).

Razin, Ś.: Structure and function in mycoplasma. Ann. Rev. Microbiol. **23**, 317–356 (1969).

Robidoux, J., Sandborn, E.B., Fensom, D.S., Cameron, M.L.: Plasmatic filaments and particles in mature sieve elements of *Heracleum sphondylium* under the electronmicroscope. J. Exptl. Bot. **24**, 349–359 (1973).

Sabnis, D.D., Hart, J.W.: P-protein in sieve elements. I. Ultrastructure after treatment with vinblastine and colchicine. Planta **109**, 127–133 (1973).

Sakai, W.S., Lamoureux, C.H.: Refractive spherules in phloem of *Microsorium scolopendria* and *Psilotum nudum*. Protoplasma **77**, 221–229 (1973).

Schumacher, W.: Die Fernleitung der Stoffe im Pflanzenkörper. In: Handbuch der Pflanzenphysiologie, Bd. XIII, S. 61–177. Berlin-Heidelberg-New York: Springer 1967.

Siddiqui, A.W., Spanner, D.C.: The state of the pores in functioning sieve plates. Planta **91**, 181–189 (1970).

Singh, A.P., Srivastava, L.M.: The fine structure of corn phloem. Can. J. Botany **50**, 839–846 (1972).

Spanner, D.C.: The translocation of sugar in sieve tubes. J. Exptl. Bot. **9**, 332–342 (1958).

Spanner, D.C., Jones, R.L.: The sieve-tube wall and its relation to translocation. Planta **92**, 64–72 (1970).

Srivastava, L.M.: On the ultrastructure of cambium and its vascular derivatives. III. The secondary walls of the sieve elements of *Pinus strobus*. Am. J. Bot. **56**, 354–361 (1969).

Srivastava, L.M., O'Brien, T.P.: On the ultrastructure of cambium and its vascular derivatives. II. Secondary phloem of *Pinus strobus* L. Protoplasma **61**, 277–296 (1966).

Steer, M.W., Newcomb, E.H.: Development and dispersal of P-protein in the phloem of *Coleus blumei* Benth. J. Cell Sci. **4**, 155–169 (1969).

Steward, F.C.: Plants at work. A summary of plant physiology. Addison-Wesley Publishing Co. 1964.

Tamulevich, S.R., Evert, R.F.: Aspects of sieve element ultrastructure in *Primula obconica*. Planta **69**, 319–337 (1966).

Thaine, R.: Protoplast structure in sieve-tube elements. New Phytologist **63**, 236–243 (1964).

Thaine, R.: Movement of sugars through plants by cytoplasmic pumping. Nature **222**, 873–874 (1969).

THAINE, R., DE MARIA, M.E.: Transcellular strands of cytoplasme in sieve tubes of squash. Nature **245**, 161–163 (1973).

THAINE, R., PROBINE, M.C., DYER, P.Y.: The existence of transcellular strands in mature sieve elements. J. Exptl. Bot. **18**, 110–127 (1967).

TIMELL, T.E.: Ultrastructure of dormant and active cambial zones and the dormant phloem associated with the formation of normal and compression woods in *Picea abies* (L.) Karst. State Univ. Coll. Environ. Sci. and For., Tech. Pub. No. 96 (1973).

TOMLINSON, P.B.: Stem structure in arborescent monocotyledons. Formation of Wood in Forest Trees, p. 85–86. New York: Academic Press, Inc. 1964.

WALSH, M.A.: The ultrastructure of the phloem in *Zea mays* L. Am. J. Bot. **60**, 41 (abst.) (1973).

WARK, M.C., CHAMBERS, T.C.: Fine structure of the phloem of *Pisum sativum*. I. The sieve-element ontogeny. Australian J. Botany **13**, 171–183 (1965).

WARMBRODT, R.D.: Ultrastructure of the phloem in the stem of *Lycopodium lucidulum* Michx. Am. J. Bot. **60**, 41–42 (abst.) (1973).

WARMBRODT, R.D., EVERT, R.F.: Structure and development of the sieve element in the stem of *Lycopodium lucidulum*. Am. J. Bot. **61**, 267–277 (1974).

WEATHERLEY, P.E.: Translocation in sieve tubes. Some thoughts on structure and mechanism. Physiol. Vég. **10**, 731–742 (1972).

WEATHERLEY, P.E., JOHNSON, R.P.C.: The form and function of the sieve tube: a problem in reconciliation. Intern. Rev. Cytol. **24**, 149–192 (1968).

WEBB, J.A., GORHAM, P.R.: Translocation of photosynthetically assimilated C^{14} in straight-necked squash. Plant Physiol. **39**, 663–672 (1964).

WILLENBRINK, J., KOLLMANN, R.: Über den Assimilattransport in Phloem von *Metasequoia*. Z. Pflanzenphysiol. **55**, 42–53 (1966).

WILLIAMSON, R.E.: An investigation of the contractile protein hypothesis of phloem translocation. Planta **106**, 149–157 (1972).

WOHLFARTH-BOTTERMANN, K.E.: Differentiations of the ground cytoplasm and their significance for the generation of the motive force of amaeboid movement. In: Primitive motile systems in cell biology (R.D. Allen and N. Kamiya), p. 79–109. New York: Academic Press. 1964.

WOODING, F.B.P.: The development of the sieve elements in *Pinus pinea*. Planta **69**, 230–243 (1966).

WOODING, F.B.P.: Fine structure and development of phloem sieve tube content. Protoplasma **64**, 315–324 (1967).

WOODING, F.B.P.: Fine structure of callus phloem in *Pinus pinea*. Planta **83**, 99–110 (1968).

WOODING, F.B.P.: P-protein and microtubular systems in *Nicotiana* callus phloem. Planta **85**, 284–298 (1969).

WOODING, F.B.P., NORTHCOTE, D.H.: The fine structure and development of the companion cell of the phloem of *Acer pseudoplatanus*. J. Cell Biol. **24**, 117–128 (1965).

WORLEY, J.F.: Evidence in support of "open" sieve tube pores. Protoplasma **76**, 129–132 (1973).

ZAHUR, M.S.: Comparative study of secondary phloem of 423 species of woody dicotyledons belonging to 85 families. Cornell Univ. Agr. Expt. Sta. Mem. **358** (1959).

ZEE, S.Y.: Fine structure of the differentiating sieve elements of *Vicia faba*. Austral. J. Bot. **17**, 441–456 (1969).

ZEE, S.Y., CHAMBERS, T.C.: Fine structure of the primary root phloem of *Pisum*. Austral. J. Bot. **16**, 37–47 (1968).

ZIMMERMANN, M.H.: Transport in phloem. In: ZIMMERMANN, M.H., BROWN, C.L., Trees. Structure and function, p. 221–279. Berlin-Heidelberg-New York: Springer 1971.

ZIMMERMANN, M.H.: The moncotyledons: Their evolution and comparative biology. IV. Transport problems in arborescent monocotyledons. Quart. Rev. Biol. **48**, 314–321 (1973).

2. Sealing Systems in Phloem

W. Eschrich

A. Introduction

Callose and slime plugs in general constitute prominent parts of sieve-tube content. It is common procedure to stain sections with either resorcin blue (for callose) or amidoblack (for slime plugs) to facilitate localization of sieve tubes under the light microscope.

Although research on both components dates back to the time of early phloem investigation, no definitive explanations of their functions has yet been given.

Since sieve tubes are food-conducting channels of considerable length, it is assumed that "security valves" exist to prevent bleeding when the system is severed and can regulate and stop the flow of sap when necessary. This function has been ascribed to both callose and sieve-tube slime. Both components are considered to function as sealing systems. However, convincing evidence for solely this function is still wanting, and the title of this chapter could perhaps rather be presented as a question.

B. Callose

(For biochemical aspects of synthesis and hydrolysis of callose see Chapter 4).

I. Identification and Distribution

Callose is characterized histologically by its staining reactions with either resorcin blue as diachrome, or alkaline aniline blue as fluorochrome (Eschrich and Currier, 1964). It may occur in all types of living plant cells, at least in the form of "pit" callose (Currier and Strugger, 1956). The location of major callose deposits has been reviewed by Eschrich (1956) and Currier (1957).

Callose is secreted outside the plasmalemma, either in contact with or isolated from (plasmolysis callose, Eschrich, 1957) the wall. In general, callose deposits appear as homogenous layers, distinct from the cellulosic portion of the wall. It has been reported that layers of callose in pollen-tube walls contain some cellulose (Müller-Stoll and Lerch, 1957).

Among the many sites of callose deposition, some are associated consistently with certain developmental phenomena, others with specific cell types or structures.

Ephemeral "walls" of callose occur regularly during development of female (Esser, 1963; Rodkiewicz and Gorska-Brylass, 1968; Jalouzot, 1970) and male

(GORSKA-BRYLASS, 1967, 1968, 1969, 1970) gametophytes of both phanerogams and cryptogams (HESLOP-HARRISON, 1972, and literature cited therein). In male flowers of *Cucurbita ficifolia,* the special wall of callose of the pollen mother cell is formed prior to meiosis, and is retained until the pollen grains are released. Such callose envelopes are deposited and hydrolyzed within a period of 48 h (ESCHRICH, 1961, 1965).

Sieve-tube callose, which may be regarded as a consistent component of sieve tubes, varies in quantity, depending on certain environmental and physiological conditions.

Common sites of callose deposition are the connections that unite the protoplasts of contiguous cells, ranging from single plasmodesmata to sieve-plate pores (Fig. 1). The simplest of connections are plasmodesmata (A). Sometimes plasmodesmata are clustered in shallow portions of the wall called primary pit-fields. Callose occurring in such regions borders the primary pit-field as a rim on both sides of the wall. The amount of callose may differ on either side of the cell wall (B). Some primary pit-fields contain median cavities which may arise through dissolution of the middle lamella (C). Sometimes the cavities are so large that all the plasmodesmata merge in the region of the middle lamella. Numerous membranes, probably endoplasmic reticulum, occur in such cavities. The sieve areas of conifers (D) (KOLLMANN

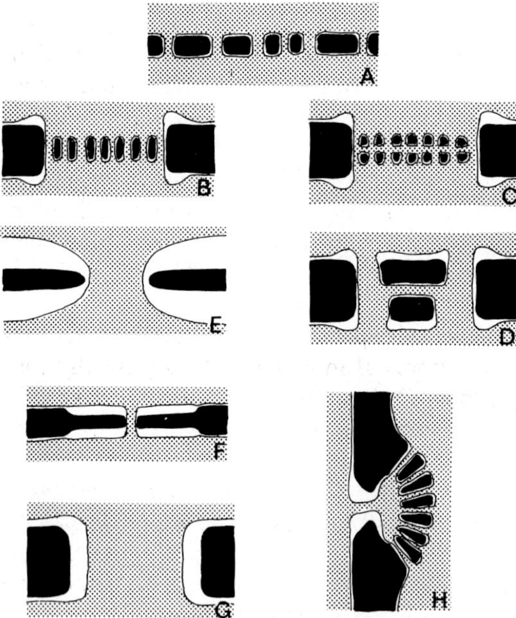

Fig. 1A–H. Relation between callose deposition and types of cytoplasmic connections through walls of plant cells. (A) Plasmodesmata distributed irregularly in a developing cell wall. (B) Clustered plasmodesmata forming a primary pit-field. Callose borders the pit-field as a rim. (C) Primary pit-field with median cavity. (D) Enlarged median cavities as occurring in sieve areas of conifers. (E) Large perforation of partition walls of pollen mother cells. (F) Single plasmodesma in a differentiating sieve area pore of angiosperms. (G) Sieve pore of angiosperms. (H) Connection between sieve-element (left) and companion cell (right). Walls, black; callose, white; cytoplasma, stippled

and SCHUMACHER, 1962; EVERT et al., 1973; BEHNKE and PALIWAL, 1973) are essentially elaborations of such wall areas. Callose is commonly associated with the types of connections illustrated in C and D of Fig. 1, where it often lines the outer portion of the cell wall. In the sieve areas of conifers (D), huge deposits of callose may occlude the pores, enclosing the membranous material of the median cavity.

It has been clearly shown that sieve-area pores differentiate by enlargement of plasmodesmata (F, G) (ESAU et al., 1962; ESAU, 1969, Fig. 14; see also Figs. 7–9 and 11, in Chapter 1). Perforations of similar size occur in partition walls of pollen mother cells (E) (ESCHRICH, 1963a; WEILING, 1965; HESLOP-HARRISON, 1966), but stages of development of these pores have not been described. They may also arise through enlargement of plasmodesmata. The pores between pollen mother cells are traversed by cytoplasmic strands and are lined by callose, which is continuous with the callose envelopes of the undifferentiated pollen cells.

The development of a sieve pore is initiated with the deposition of pairs of callose platelets at the pore site. The platelets encircle the plasmodesma, and are separated from one another by the middle lamella and thin layers of primary wall. Later, wall material is removed centrifugally from the site of the plasmodesma. The merging callose retracts and an enlarged cytoplasmatic strand is formed. Since deposition of the callose platelets occurs in fully-expanded sieve elements, removal of wall material and enlargement of the connections cannot be related merely to passive enlargement by lateral growth of the sieve area. It must include active processes of wall dissolution. The differentiation of the sieve pore in angiosperms, which is initially associated with callose platelets and the formation of the median cavities of gymnospermous sieve areas may involve different developmental phenomena.

The connections between sieve elements and companion cells (H) (see Fig. 15 in Chapter 1) exhibit a single pore on the sieve-element side, and several plasmodesmata on the side of the companion cell. The pore on the sieve-element side often appears slightly bordered while the wall on the companion-cell side is commonly considerably thickened, and bulges into the lumen of the cell. The differentiation of such heterogenous connections is not well understood.

Although the amount of callose associated with pores depends greatly on environmental and physiological factors, the sieve pores of monocotyledons generally contain less callose than those of dicotyledons. Callose also occurs in the sieve cells of pteridophytes and in the sieve tubes of certain brown algae (*Macrocystis* and *Nereocystis*).

In addition, it occurs in assimilate conducting elements of lower cryptogams, which have plasmodesmata instead of pores in the cross walls; for example, the trumpet hyphae of *Laminaria* species (ZIEGLER and RUCK, 1967; STEINBISS and SCHMITZ, 1973; VAN WENT and TAMMES, 1973; VAN WENT et al., 1973), and the leptoids of *Polytrichum* (ESCHRICH and STEINER, 1968; HÉBANT, 1970).

II. Structure and Properties

Sieve-plate callose of *Vitis vinifera* was isolated by a laborious procedure by KESSLER (1958), who eventually found that callose is a β-(1$\rightarrow$3)-glucan, yielding mainly glucose and a small amount of uronic acids (1.9%) when hydrolysed. Air-dried callose from pollen mother cells of *Cucurbita ficifolia* swells to 6 times its volume in water. A column of this hydrated callose is practically impermeable to water and aqueous solutions of non-electrolytes. Addition of boric acid (1 M) or KCl (10^{-2} M) does not change this property. However, addition of $CaCl_2$ (7×10^{-4} M) causes a rapid flow of aqueous solutions through the packed callose, forced by either gravity or slight suction (ESCHRICH and ESCHRICH, 1964). The impermeability of callose to organic molecules was demonstrated by KNOX and HESLOP-HARRISON (1970). Fluoresceine diacetate, a non-fluorescing compound, is accumulated in pollen mother cells as long as their callose envelopes are missing or incomplete. The diester is split in the cells, obviously by action of esterases. Thus, uptake of the non-fluorescing compound is indicated by fluorescence after enzymic cleavage.

Cells with complete callose envelopes show no fluorescence when fluoresceine diacetate is added to the surrounding medium.

Native callose is isotropic. By complete dehydration it shows anisotropy with a sign opposing that of cellulose (SITTE, 1963). When callose is vacuum-dried it forms a xerogel, which shows a period of structural identity in the X-ray diagram of about 15 Å. By potential energy calculations from energy contour diagrams, SATHYANARAYANA and RAO (1971) came to the conclusion that β-D-(1$\rightarrow$3)-glucans could have four types of hydrogen bonds. Such glucans may occur therefore in both wide and extended helical conformations. In addition, both right- and left-handed helical conformations are possible. Native callose has a density of 1.62, similar to starch (1.60–1.63) but dissimilar to cellulose (1.55) (FREY-WYSSLING et al., 1957).

The chemical isolation of relatively large quantities of callose from pine bark (*Pinus sylvestris*) was described by FU et al. (1972). The soft inner bark of pine trees, felled in late spring (a period of low starch content) was boiled in methanol, dried, ground, and extracted with ethanol-benzene. Lignin and other phenolic compounds were removed with acid chlorite yielding a holocellulose fraction (65%) and a polysaccharide fraction dissolved in the chlorite liquor (6%). The latter fraction and extracts of the holocellulose with water and 0.5% ammonium oxalate were combined and treated with α-amylase. The insoluble residue was freed of remnants of starch by boiling in water, yielding pure callose. This material gave specific rotations in aqueous alkali from $[\alpha]_D = -19°$ to $+7.7°$. Hydrolysis yielded glucose and 1.6% uronic acids. Enzymic digestion resulted in glucose, laminaribiose and its polymeric homologs.

Callose obtained by this procedure was completely insoluble in water, anhydrous formamide, dimethyl formamide, dimethylsulfoxide, pyridine and liquid ammonia. Once isolated in a solid state, this callose is only to a small extent soluble in aqueous alkali. In this respect it is unlike other β-(1$\rightarrow$3)-glucans such as pachyman (HOFFMANN et al., 1971) or the acidic laricinan (HOFFMANN and TIMELL, 1970).

III. Changes of Callose Content

1. Seasonal Changes

As a sieve element ages, it accumulates callose on its sieve plates. In annual plants, sieve tubes of the primary phloem generally form large quantities of callose before they become obliterated. The same is true for sieve tubes of the secondary phloem. Callose deposits of this kind are called definitive. In perennials, deposits of definitive callose are removed sooner or later from the dead cells.

In many perennials cambial activity produces sieve elements over a considerable period of the growing season. Thus, sieve elements of varying ages enter the winter season. Sieve plates of early-formed sieve elements are generally occluded with definitive callose. Such sieve tubes become nonfunctional. More recently formed sieve elements also develop callose. However, it is called "dormancy" callose, when thin threads of cytoplasmic material are discernible in the callose plugging of the pores (ESAU, 1948). Dormancy callose is dissolved during reactivation in early spring (ESAU, 1964). Phloem exudate of *Tilia tomentosa* and *Acer platanoides*, collected four weeks (1. March) before xylem-sap flow could be detected (26. March) had pH's of 4.8 and 5.0, respectively.

This agrees fairly well with the pH optimum of β-(1$\rightarrow$3)-glucanase of higher plants (ESCHRICH, 1961). The last-formed sieve elements of a given year show much less callose in winter than those formed earlier in the previous growing season. In *Tilia*, for instance, a gradual decrease of callose deposition can be seen in radial sections, if followed, centripetally. The sieve elements of some other woody plants may overwinter in an undifferentiated state (ALFIERI and EVERT, 1973).

2. Artifacts Caused by Preparation

Since sieve elements of deciduous trees are inactive in winter, collection of bark samples at that time generally does not result in formation of wound callose. However, storage of unfixed bark samples at room temperature can bring about reactivation, and such reactivated sieve elements will respond to wounding.

The response to wounding and to chemical stimulation caused by fixatives constitutes the most serious problem in determinations of the normal callose content of sieve tubes. It seems impossible to record minor changes in callose content in active sieve tubes with certainty.

Sieve tubes prepared for *in vivo* observation respond to wounding with deposition of wound callose. Changes in the amount of sieve-tube callose therefore can only be recorded by comparison with similarly fixed material. Fixation, however, means stimulation. Once again, only relative results can be obtained.

Since methods for quantitative extraction of callose are not available, the estimation of the callose content must be based on microscopic evaluations, which include subjective errors.

Sieve tubes also respond to mechanical stimulation other than wounding. Treatment with ultrasound can cause heavy callose deposition (CURRIER and WEBSTER, 1964). Transport of ^{14}C-assimilates in *Vicia faba* was also reduced when the plant was shaken or moved with an electric fan (FERREIRA, (unpublished data), personal communication by H.B. CURRIER). Plants, when carried from the field or greenhouse to the laboratory for fixation probably respond with the deposition of wound callose in sieve tubes prior to fixation.

The *in situ* fixation method described by ESAU and CHEADLE (1961) can be applied only to plants with hollow petioles or stems, because the fixative has to be injected into such cavities. With this method critical fixation can be obtained for electron microscopy. It has been shown, however, that only the internal phloem, where present, is fixed quickly enough to prevent callose deposition (Eschrich, 1963b).

For an estimation of callose content by light microscopy, the freeze-fixation method (Eschrich and Currier, 1964; Eschrich et al., 1965) has been found most reliable. This method has also been adapted for evaluations with the electron-microscope (Cronshaw and Anderson, 1969). The entire intact plant is frozen with crushed dry ice without removing it from its normal environment. Pieces of the frozen material are transferred to ethanol, acetone, acrolein or another fixative previously cooled with dry ice. After thawing at about 2° C, vacuum infiltration is followed by heating (to 65° C, if ethanol is used) for about 10 min. Such inactivated material can be processed to microscopic preparations without danger of artificial callose formation.

When cryostat sections of freshly frozen and unfixed material are used to estimate the callose contents in sieve tubes, the possibility of postmortal callose synthesis cannot be excluded. Sieve-tube exudate of *Yucca flaccida,* which had been stored frozen for two years, was still able to catalyze callose synthesis (Eschrich et al., 1972).

3. Callose-Free Sieve Tubes

Some investigations have been conducted to determine whether sieve-plate callose is a normal cellular constituent or whether it is absent in undisturbed sieve tubes. Zimmermann (1960) reported that conducting sieve tubes of trees had no detectable callose during summer months when fresh samples of bark were sectioned immediately.

Evert and Derr (1964) also found sieve elements in active phloem, which did not give callose reactions in 6 species of deciduous trees. The bark samples were removed in July, and quick-killed tissue (25 sec or less) was compared with delay-killed tissue (15 min after removal from the tree). Samples were frozen in liquid nitrogen and freeze-substituted, or directly fixed with various fixation mixtures. In quick-killed tissues of all species investigated functional sieve elements without callose were found besides some with callose. In delay-killed tissues *all* sieve elements gave bright callose fluorescence, when stained with aniline blue.

Engleman (1965) used several methods to kill the stem of *Impatiens sultani* plants as quickly as possible, he reported that the most effective technique was to press the stem between two blocks of heated aluminum. He estimated that, if callose were to form anew, it would have to be deposited within 4 sec. Engleman found that sieve-plate callose was always present. However, he did not report whether the plants had been transported to the laboratory prior to killing, which could have induced callose formation.

Comparing a variety of killing agents, Eschrich (1963b) found that OsO_4/chromic acid mixtures were the most rapid killing fluids when injected into the hollow petiole of leaves of *Cucurbita ficifolia.* Termination of fixation was indicated by bending of the petiole under the weight of the leaf blade. This occurred 7 to 10 min after injection. Plants growing in a 13-h day in the greenhouse showed no variation in the amount of sieve-tube callose, regardless of whether the petioles were fixed in the morning, at noon, or at night.

It was found that the internal phloem, which is situated next to the killing fluid, showed less callose than the external phloem. Darkening the leaf blade for 16 h or more caused heavy callose deposition in the internal phloem. When a plant was exposed to continuous light for 3 days, no callose occurred in the internal phloem; the external phloem, however, showed callose deposits.

The complete absence of both sieve-plate callose and pit callose in healthy attached leaves of *Elodea* was demonstrated by CURRIER and SHIH (1968), who used the freeze-fixing method. Even at the electron microscopic level no callose was detected lining the sieve pores. The authors were able to show that practically all solutions of dyes and buffers used for vital staining in microscopy cause deposition of callose.

Although callose is present during differentiation of sieve elements in the form of callose platelets, it is possible that all the callose is removed after perforation is completed. It is uncertain, however, whether callose-free sieve plates occur only under abnormal or "super-optimal" conditions (continuous illumination), or whether complete removal of callose is an indication of normal vigorous growth. Under the latter assumption, callose deposition in active sieve elements would be induced solely by mechanical injury or other kinds of stimulation. It also appears that herbaceous plants are more sensitive to such stimulation than trees with active secondary phloem. The response to callose-producing stimulations obviously occurs quickly, probably within one minute or less. This is confirmed by observations on plasmolyzed epidermal cells of *Allium cepa* bulb scales, in which the first fluorescing plasmolysis callose was detected by fluorescence only 30 sec after plasmolysis (ESCHRICH, 1965).

IV. Sieve-Tube Callose in Relation to Transport

Exposure to heat seems to be a reliable method to induce reversible callose formation. WEBSTER and CURRIER (1965, 1968) heated 1 cm parts of cotyledonary petioles of light-grown cotton seedlings for 15 min with warm water. They found significant deposition of sieve-tube callose at 45°–50° C, slight at 60°, and slight or not reproducible at 43° C and below. The newly-formed callose disappeared after approximately one day. Plants previously darkened for 16 h or more, did not respond to such stimulation with callose formation. When ^{14}C-urea was applied to the blade of the cotyledon, lateral transport in the heated region was inhibited, but longitudinal transport of label appeared as normal as in untreated control plants. Later, however, McNAIRN and CURRIER (1968) reported that translocation of ^{14}C-labeled assimilates was blocked when a 4 cm portion of the hypocotyl of a young cotton plant was heated to 45° C. Obviously, a 1 cm portion of heated translocation path can be bridged, but a heated 4 cm portion can not. Electronmicroscopy of equivalent plants has shown that extra callose promoted by heating constricted the sieve pores almost completely (SHIH and CURRIER, 1969). 65% of the sieve plates were heavily callosed in the treated region and, within 1 or 2 days after the heat treatment, callose deposits returned to normal. However, an acceleration of transport was recorded 6 h after heating, i.e. through the region where sieve-plate callose must have been still present in heavy amounts. The authors explained this effect by an increased turgor gradient, which may have built up in the sieve tubes above the heated region during the

6 h of blockage. This explanation implies that phloem loading and assimilate transport can be independent of each other. Also the sealing capability of callose is suspect.

Interesting results, obtained with field-grown cotton plants were reported by MCNAIRN (1972). These experiments were carried out in the central valley of California, where the afternoon temperature (3 pm) rose to 44° C. The rate of translocation decreased from morning to afternoon and continued to decline toward evening. The water stress was generally proportional to diurnal radiation. Thus, water stress could not be the critical factor causing the steady decline in translocation rate toward evening. Callose ratings, taken from the hypocotyl, sectioned in a cryostat, reflected in a reverse sense the translocation rate, i.e. at the times of lowest translocation rate, the callose content was highest. MCNAIRN concluded that callose was deposited in response to heat with a maximum at 3 pm. 30° C at 9 am and 3 pm induced much less callose than 30° C at 8 pm (Fig. 2). Possibly callose synthesized during the hottest time of day (3 pm) can only be removed slowly. Thus, a high amount of callose in the evening (8 pm) reflects its synthesis during a hot afternoon. By morning, callose was at a minimum, regardless of how high the temperature had been on the previous day.

The influence of boron accumulation on the synthesis of pit callose in mesophyll cells of *Phaseolus vulgaris*, as observed by MCNAIRN and CURRIER (1965), prompted an investigation in which boric acid was used to evoke deposition of sieve-plate callose (ESCHRICH et al., 1965).

A 5×10^{-5} M solution of boric acid was injected into a hollow petiole of a *Cucurbita maxima* plant. 34% of the sieve tubes in the lower portion of the petiole showed thick callose deposits, whereas control plants injected with water had only 5.4% of the sieve plates heavily callosed. When ^{14}C-labeled assimilates moved from the blade through the petiole of the treated leaf, the translocation rate appeared somewhat greater in boron-treated plants than in control plants. Similarly, 30% heavily callosed sieve plates were found after injection of a 1.5×10^{-4} M $CaCl_2$ solution, and no difference in translocation rate from control plants could be detected. Callose ratings were recorded microscopically on paraffin sections prepared according to the freeze-fixation method (see p. 44).

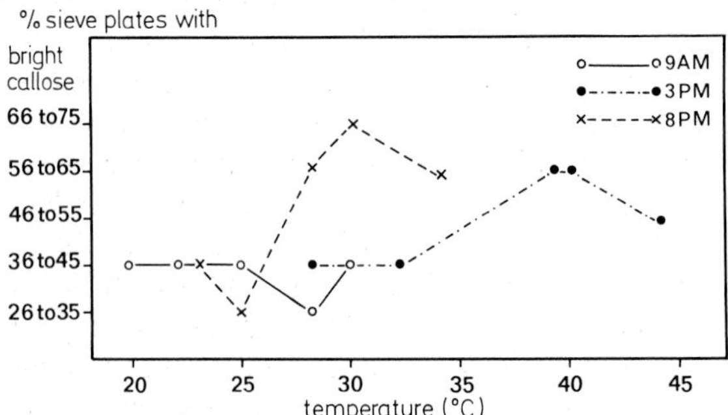

Fig. 2. Callose ratings of hypocotyl sieve plates of fieldgrown cotton plants. Values were taken during morning, afternoon and evening on various days over the course of two summers. Each datum is the mean for five plants and at least 100 sieve plates per plant. (From MCNAIRN, 1972)

Internal phloem was less callosed than external phloem in both boron and $CaCl_2$ treated petioles. K-fluorescein, which was utilized in addition to ^{14}C-labeled assimilates, was exported from the blade equally in both external and internal phloem. In the boron-treated region of the petiole, the internal phloem seemed to be used preferably for export. These results indicate that 34% heavily callosed sieve plates caused no decrease in translocation rate.

Since sieve tubes of the internal phloem showed less callose deposition, transport of assimilates may have been detoured in part from external to internal phloem. However, the passage of label also occurred in sieve tubes with heavily callosed sieve plates, as was shown by microautoradiographs.

V. Conclusions

Callose deposits are associated with connections between cells, ranging from plasmodesmata to sieve-plate pores. Its occurrence is restricted to living cells, which emphasizes its relation to symplastic connections. The amount of pit callose as well as sieve-plate callose can vary depending on environmental and physiological conditions. Increasing amounts of callose lead to constriction of the symplastic connection. By this, diffusional and active movements of both solutes and larger particles should be slowed down, movement induced by pressure or suction should be accelerated, until frictional resistance matches hydraulic forces. Thus, callose can be regarded as a substance which controls flow rate and movements through symplastic connections.

However, the assumption that callose slows down or stops transport by narrowing or sealing sieve pores is based on anatomical observations. Physiological experiments recording tracer movements through phloem bundles with more or less callosed sieve plates do not support unequivocally the sealing function of callose. This uncertainty also extends to the commonly accepted sealing function of dormancy callose in perennials. Anatomically, huge masses of callose cover the sieve plates. It is, however, not known which is first, blockage by callose or cessation of transport.

Callose is an excretion deposited outside the protoplast, normally between plasmalemma and cell wall. If solute transport takes place in the sieve-tube symplast, callose may participate in transport processes simply by controlling the water balance. Its property of limited swelling in water may counteract osmotic water uptake by sieve elements. In addition, bound water is kept or released by K^+ and Ca^{++}, respectively. Considering these facts, a hypothesis on a possible function of sieve-tube callose was advanced (ESCHRICH, 1965), which basically regards callose as a mechanical substitute for the vacuole in respect to water balance. This hypothesis is supported by the results obtained by ESCHRICH et al. (1965), in which a local release of assimilates into the surrounding tissue was found to be accompanied by deposition of callose.

It seems obvious that callose can replace cellulose when the wall is of transient function. Examples are the pairs of callose platelets at sites of future sieve pores and callose walls between cells of the micro- and macroprothallia in phanerogams. In these cases callose masks partition walls or parts of them, preventing further deposition of cellulose. Callose can function in this way, because of its amorphous structure, hydrolyzability (by β-(1$\rightarrow$3)-glucanases which do not affect cellulose), ability to absorb water edemically (swelling forces) or its (im)permeability. Thus, callose can also be regarded as a substance preventing apposition of cellulose.

C. Sieve-Tube Slime

(The biochemical aspects of sieve-tube proteins are reviewed in Chapter 4).

I. General Considerations

The term "sieve-tube slime" dates back to the earliest work on phloem anatomy (NÄGELI, 1861, see ESAU, 1969). The term "slime" is normally used for certain polysaccharides. Sieve-tube "slime" however does not give polysaccharide reactions, but is mainly proteinaceous and the term "P-protein" (for phloem protein; ESAU and CRONSHAW, 1967) has been widely adopted as a more appropriate term.

Attention has been focused on P-protein recently and its filamentous appearance in electron micrographs has prompted a variety of hypotheses on its function. The term "filament" is used in this Chapter as proposed by BEHNKE and DÖRR (1967) to cover all types of fibrillar, filamentous or tubular P-protein components, smooth-surfaced or striated, within the range of 9–24 nm in diameter. The interest in P-protein is reflected by the great number of electron micrographs of sieve plates, starting with the electron micrographs of HEPTON et al. (1955) showing heavily plugged sieve pores, and leading to ANDERSON and CRONSHAW's (1970) open-pore picture, which was chosen by CRAFTS and CRISP (1971) for the cover of their book.

The proposed sealing function of sieve-tube slime, to which the discussion is restricted in this chapter, relates to common light-microscopic observations. Sieve tubes, cut prior to sectioning or fixation commonly exhibit accumulations of dense material lodged against the side of the sieve plate away from the cut surface. This material stains readily with amido black and other protein dyes. It forms a "Schleimpfropf" (slime plug) (DE BARY, 1877), situated inside the "Schlauchkopf" (cytoplasm) (HARTIG, 1854), a somewhat extended end of the constricted protoplast. The slime plug is composed of the protoplasmic contents that surge against the sieve plate when the high turgor pressure is released on cutting the sieve tube. It may also include material sucked or rapidly secreted from companion cells and adjacent phloem parenchyma (LEHMANN, 1973).

Certainly, sieve pores plugged by such material are sealed. It is, however, questionable whether the intact sieve-tube system uses this sealing system to regulate assimilate distribution.

II. Distribution and Origin

Plugged sieve pores can be found in all vascular plants. The plugs may differ in appearance, especially when investigated with the electron microscope. In dicotyledons, cloudy masses of slime or typical slime sacs (EVERT and DESHPANDE, 1969, Fig. 16; CRONSHAW and ANDERSON, 1969, Fig. 8; CRONSHAW and ESAU, 1968, Fig. 10) can be seen in mature sieve elements. Such slime sacs have not been recorded in monocotyledons. In the latter the filamentous contents of the pores fray out like a "dry brush" into one or both lumina of the adjacent sieve elements. Slime plugs of similar appearance also occur in sieve elements of dicotyledons (ESAU, 1969, Plate 1).

Electronmicroscopy has demonstrated that the brush-like plugs consist of bundles of filaments. Whereas the slime sacs may appear to be composed of granular material. The granular material is derived from degraded filaments. In some monocotyledons, like *Hordeum* (EVERT et al., 1971), and in a number of gymnosperms (KOLLMANN and SCHUMACHER, 1962; EVERT et al., 1973; BEHNKE and PALIWAL, 1973) and Pteridophytes (LIBERMAN-MAXE, 1971) the sieve pores appear to be occluded by membranes similar to endoplasmic reticulum (ER) (see Fig. 30 in Chapter 1). P-protein is apparently absent in most of these plants. Therefore, from a structural aspect, sieve pores may be occluded, either by P-protein, which may be amorphous or filamentous in appearance; or ER.

Relatively little information is available on the development of sieve elements with pores containing solely ER. In addition, ER is a well defined cytoplasmic structure and may have nothing to do with sealing mechanisms.

Some ER may traverse the sieve pores of both monocotyledons and dicotyledons. It has been suggested that ER thins out to filaments when entering the sieve pore (SCHUMACHER, 1967, Fig. 16A). However, BEHNKE (1973) has shown convincingly that the filaments and the ER are distinct entities with different origins.

It is well known that the P-protein filaments of sieve elements of many dicotyledons are derived from slime bodies or P-protein bodies. P-Protein filaments vary in appearance. For example, NORTHCOTE and WOODING (1966) found a meshwork of small filaments (90–100 Å) and slime tubules of 180–240 Å diameter in the same sieve element of *Acer pseudoplatanus*.

The sieve elements of Leguminosae develop crystalline P-protein bodies which either persist until obliteration of the sieve tube (PALEVITZ and NEWCOMB, 1971) or disperse (WERGIN and NEWCOMB, 1970; LAFLÈCHE, 1966), in which case they may plug a sieve plate.

The formation of P-protein is not restricted to the cytoplasm. EVERT and DESHPANDE (1970) have shown that P-protein filaments also occur in nuclei of young sieve elements of *Tilia americana*, and undergo developmental changes similar to those of the cytoplasmic P-protein. Other filamentous structures occur in the sieve-element plastids of some plants, but these should not be confused with P-protein or slime. One example is found in the Caryophyllales (BEHNKE, 1969), where the filaments form a ring-like structure in the plastid (FALK, 1964; ESAU, 1965). If the plastids are ruptured, the filamentous ring can contribute to pore plugging (BEHNKE, 1969). A similar phenomenon is exhibited by certain gymnosperms with filament-forming plastids (NEUBERGER and EVERT, 1974).

In monocotyledons, P-protein filaments apparently arise in the parietal layer of cytoplasm of the sieve element without forming discrete slime bodies. Plastids with angular protein bodies (crystalloids) occur in almost all monocotyledonous species (BEHNKE, 1972), but are apparently unrelated to P-protein. If such plastids are ruptured, the crystalloids may end up in the pores of the sieve plates.

This brief survey, although incomplete, shows that filamentous structures found in sieve elements of angiosperms and some gymnosperms can differ in origin. Since all types of filaments (smooth-surfaced or striated tubules, fibrils) are obviously proteinaceous in nature, ribosomes are required for synthesis. If proteins are synthesized in the sieve element this synthesis may take place as long as ribosomes are present, either in the cytoplasm or in the protein-forming plastids of the differentiating cell.

The occurrence of transient or permanent protein deposits, like slime bodies or protein crystals, indicates that excess protein has been synthesized prior to breakdown of the nucleus and the ribosomes. Thus, sieve elements, especially those of monocotyledons, enter their functional stage provided with a stock of storage protein.

III. Position of Phloem Filaments

Most workers agreed that the P-protein filaments of sieve elements are continuous through the sieve pores from one cell to the next. Numerous publications show the filaments as branched entities forming a network, which loosely fills the lumen of the sieve element. Such a filament reticulum would have to be stationary, because the sieve plate would rupture it during transport. Since filamentous reticula, as well as stranded networks, can be seen in carefully fixed light-microscopic preparations (EVERT et al., 1969; JARVIS et al., 1973), and since filaments occur in sieve-tube exudates (ESCHRICH, 1963c; KOLLMANN et al., 1970; WALKER and THAINE, 1971; ESCHRICH et al., 1971), it seems that the filaments are extremely labile structures. This is confirmed by results of EVERT et al. (1973) obtained with *Cucurbita* plants, which were defoliated and kept well supplied with water with the epicotyl darkened for 2 days. (Compare Fig. 23 in Chapter 1). 90% of the investigated sieve tubes of the hypocotyl showed the filaments firmly attached to the parietal layer of cytoplasm, but continuous with plasmalemma and ER through the open sieve pores, which were scarcely callosed.

Other treatments prior to fixation for electronmicroscopy are few. GIAQUINTA and GEIGER (1973) compared chilled (30 min at 0° C) and non-chilled phloem tissues of petioles of *Phaseolus vulgaris*. The electron micrographs show sieve pores occluded with decomposed filaments in the chilled specimens and open pores and filaments attached to the parietal cytoplasm in the control plants. However, surging, as deduced from the position of the single persistent slime body, was less in sieve tubes of the chilled petioles than in those cut at 25° C.

ANDERSON and CRONSHAW (1970) fixed wilted tobacco plants for electron microscopy in the hope that surging would be reduced if sieve tubes were flaccid. In some preparations the sieve pores appeared unplugged by P-protein and lined by only small amounts of callose. SIDDIQUI and SPANNER (1970) however, found only densely plugged sieve pores in wilted *Helianthus* and *Saxifraga* plants.

The experiments of EVERT et al. (1973) and ANDERSON and CRONSHAW (1970) were all designed to reduce sieve-tube turgor, in order to reduce surging of the sieve-tube contents. In one case (EVERT et al., 1973), it was concluded that removal of sources of assimilates in combination with low water potential (xylem-sap pressures around zero) would reduce solute concentration inside the sieve tubes, in the other (ANDERSON and CRONSHAW), that reduction of turgor in the whole plant might reduce phloem loading. The solute concentration in sieve tubes, however, seems to rise in wilted plants. It has been frequently observed that aphids feeding on wilting leaves continue to produce honey dew until the leaf blade appears dry and brittle, showing that turgor pressures are still probably positive. The osmotic value of sieve-tube exudate of *Cucurbita maxima* was determined cryoscopically (ESCHRICH et al., unpublished data). Exudate collected from well-watered plants gave values of about 7 atm. When the plants were not watered for several days, the osmotic value of the exudate rose continually and gave values up to 12 atm, when the leaves started to wilt.

It is commonly accepted that surging of the sieve-tube content is caused by sudden turgor release, for instance, by cutting the bundle. Contents of sieve elements then appear pressed against the sieve plates in the direction of the cut surface. If a piece of stem is cut transversely with two cuts carried out simultaneously, sieve-element contents then surge towards the nearest cut, and sieve elements situated in the middle should show surging in both directions. The unilateral displacement of slime can be seen in most light microscope slides of phloem tissue. Sometimes,

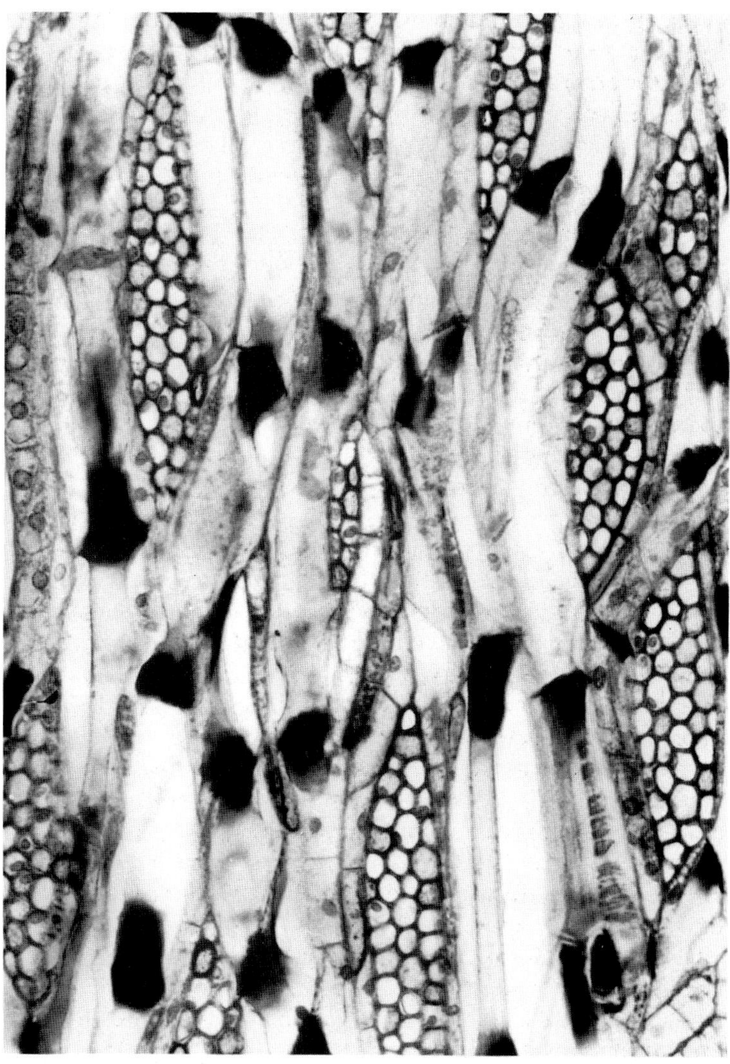

Fig. 3. Tangential section through secondary phloem of FAA-fixed bark of *Ulmus americana*. Accumulation of sieve-tube slime (black masses) in opposite directions in different rows of sieve elements. ×240. (Courtesy of Dr. RAY F. EVERT, Madison)

however, single sieve tubes show slime displacement in the opposite direction. This occurs preferably in radial sections (ESCHRICH, 1965, Fig. 6; DAVIS et al., 1972, Fig. 2), where each sieve tube is of different age. Fig. 3 shows a tangential section of the secondary phloem of *Ulmus americana,* in which all sieve tubes are of the same age. Sieve tubes show slime displacement in opposite directions. This suggests that surging may occur not only in response to turgor release by cutting, but also in an intact sieve tube in response to some other factor.

IV. Conclusions

The sealing of sieve pores by slime seems to occur only once per sieve element, and in response to injury. When the amount of exudate obtained after cutting a plant is regarded as a measure for the effectiveness of the sealing mechanism, great differences seem to occur.

Most dicotyledons yield no sieve-tube exudate. The Cucurbitaceae give small amounts of exudate. Phloem exudate can be obtained from *Ricinus* (MILBURN, 1972) and *Robinia* (ZIEGLER, 1956). Among the monocotyledons *Yucca flaccida* (cf Chapter III.8 of this volume) and certain palms (TAMMES, 1933) give high yields of sieve-tube exudate. Interestingly, the highest yields exude from cut inflorescence stalks, whereas exudate from cut leaves is negligible. It is not known whether the sieve elements of inflorescence stalks have less slime than those of leaves.

The sealing process in sieve tubes is paralleled by observations on certain Siphonales (BURR and EVERT, 1972), where special protein bodies are able to seal a small hole in the wall of the giant cell.

If angiosperms had developed sieve-tube slime or P-protein only to seal the sieve pores, their production and appearance would apparently be simpler than it is.

Slime plugging and subsequent deposition of callose might be explained if the precursors and catalysts for callose synthesis are released during the plugging process. In this case, less callose would occur in sieve tubes which have minimal amounts of slime, a correlation which has not been investigated.

However, this phenomenon would not explain why callose is also present in unplugged sieve pores. Nor does it explain the filamentous appearance of the plugging material. Therefore, it must be concluded that P-protein may have functions which are still unknown.

References

ALFIERI, F.J., EVERT, R.F.: Structure and seasonal development of the secondary phloem in the Pinaceae. Botan. Gaz. **134**, 17–25 (1973).

ANDERSON, R., CRONSHAW, J.: Sieve-plate pores in tobacco and bean. Planta **91**, 173–180 (1970).

BEHNKE, H.D.: Über Siebröhren-Plastiden und Plastidenfilamente der Caryophyllales. Planta **89**, 275–283 (1969).

BEHNKE, H.D.: Sieve-tube plastids in relation to angiosperm systematics—An attempt towards a classification by ultrastructural analysis. Botan. Rev. **38**, 155–197 (1972).

BEHNKE, H.D.: Strukturänderungen des endoplasmatischen Reticulums und Auftreten von Proteinfilamenten während der Siebröhrendifferenzierung bei *Smilax excelsa*. Protoplasma **77**, 279–289 (1973).

BEHNKE, H.D., DÖRR, I.: Zur Herkunft und Struktur der Plasmafilamente in Assimilatleitbahnen. Planta **74**, 18–44 (1967).

BEHNKE, H.D., PALIWAL, G.S.: Ultrastructure of phloem and its development in *Gnetum gnemon*, with some observations on *Ephedra campylopoda*. Protoplasma **78**, 305–319 (1973).

BOUCK, G.B., CRONSHAW, J.: The fine structure of differentiating sieve-tube elements. J. Cell Biol. **25**, 79–96 (1965).

BURGESS, J.: Observations on structure and differentiation in plasmodesmata. Protoplasma **73**, 83–95 (1971).

BURR, F.A., EVERT, R.F.: A cytochemical study of the wound-healing protein in *Bryopsis hypnoides*. Cytobios **6**, 199–215 (1972).

CRAFTS, A.S.: Problem of sieve-tube slime. Science **160**, 325–327 (1968).

CRAFTS, A.S., CRISP, C.E.: Phloem transport in plants. San Francisco: W.H. Freeman and Company 1971.

CRONSHAW, J., ANDERSON, R.: Sieve-plate pores of *Nicotiana*. J. Ultrastruct. Res. **27**, 134–148 (1969).

CRONSHAW, J., ESAU, K.: Tubular and fibrillar components of mature and differentiating sieve elements. J. Cell Biol. **34**, 801–816 (1967).

CRONSHAW, J., ESAU, K.: P-protein in the phloem of *Cucurbita*. II. The P-protein of mature sieve elements. J. Cell Biol. **38**, 292–303 (1968).

CURRIER, H.B.: Callose substance in plant cells. Am. J. Bot. **44**, 478–488 (1957).

CURRIER, H.B., SHIH, C.Y.: Sieve tubes and callose in *Elodea* leaves. Am. J. Bot. **55**, 145–152 (1968).

CURRIER, H.B., STRUGGER, S.: Aniline blue fluorescence microscopy of callose in bulb scales of *Allium cepa* L. Protoplasma **45**, 552–559 (1956).

CURRIER, H.B., WEBSTER, D.H.: Callose formation and subsequent disappearance: Studies in ultrasound stimulation. Plant Physiol. **39**, 843–847 (1964).

DAVIS, J.D., SAIGO, R., EVERT, R.F.: Some effects of *Ceratocystis ulmi* on the phloem and vascular cambium of *Ulmus americana*. Can. J. Botany **50**, 1009–1011 (1972).

DE BARY, A.: Vergleichende Anatomie der Vegetationsorgane der Phanerogamen und Farne. Leipzig: Wilhelm Engelmann 1877.

ENGLEMAN, E.M.: Sieve element of *Impatiens sultanii*. Wound reaction. Ann. Botany (London) **29**, 83–101 (1965).

ESAU, K.: Phloem structure in the grapevine, and its seasonal changes. Hilgardia **18**, 217–296 (1948).

ESAU, K.: Aspect of ultrastructure of phloem. In: ZIMMERMANN, M.H., Formation of wood in forest trees. New York-London: Academic Press 1964.

ESAU, K.: Fixation images of sieve-element plastids in *Beta*. Proc. Natl. Acad. Sci. U.S. **54**, 429–437 (1965).

ESAU, K.: Plant anatomy, 2nd ed. New York: John Wiley and Sons 1965.

ESAU, K.: The phloem. In: ZIMMERMANN, W., OZENDA, P., WULFF, H.D., Encyclopedia of plant anatomy. Vol. V/2. Berlin-Stuttgart: Gebrüder Borntraeger 1969.

ESAU, K.: Development of P-protein in sieve elements of *Mimosa pudica*. Protoplasma **73**, 225–238 (1971).

ESAU, K., CHEADLE, V.I.: An evaluation of studies on ultrastructure of sieve plates. Proc. Natl. Acad. Sci. U.S. **47**, 1716–1726 (1961).

ESAU, K., CHEADLE, V.I., RISLEY, E.B.: Development of sieve-plate pores. Botan. Gaz. **123**, 233–243 (1962).

ESAU, K., CRONSHAW, J.: Tubular components in cells of healthy and tobacco mosaic virus-infected *Nicotiana*. Virology **33**, 26–35 (1967).

ESAU, K., CRONSHAW, J., HOEFERT, L.L.: Relation of beet yellows virus to the phloem and to movement in the sieve tube. J. Cell Biol. **32**, 71–87 (1967).

ESAU, K., HOEFERT, L.L.: Composition and fine structure of minor veins in *Tetragonia* leaf. Protoplasma **72**, 237–253 (1971).

ESCHRICH, W.: Callose. Ein kritischer Sammelbericht. Protoplasma **47**, 487–530 (1956).

ESCHRICH, W.: Callosebildung in plasmolysierten *Allium cepa*-Epidermen. Planta **48**, 578–586 (1957).

ESCHRICH, W.: Untersuchungen über den Ab- und Aufbau der Callose. Z. Botan. **49**, 153–218 (1961).

ESCHRICH, W.: Cytoplasmabrücken zwischen den Pollenmutterzellen von *Cucurbita ficifolia* im Elektronenmikroskop. Protoplasma **56**, 718–722 (1963a).

ESCHRICH, W.: Beziehungen zwischen dem Auftreten von Callose und der Feinstruktur des primären Phloems bei *Cucurbita ficifolia*. Planta **59**, 243–261 (1963b).

ESCHRICH, W.: Der Phloemsaft von *Cucurbita ficifolia*. Planta **60**, 216–224 (1963c).

ESCHRICH, W.: Physiologie der Siebröhrencallose. Planta **65**, 280–300 (1965).

ESCHRICH, W., CURRIER, H.B.: Identification of callose by its diachrome and fluorochrome reactions. Stain Technol. **39**, 303–307 (1964).

ESCHRICH, W., CURRIER, H.B., YAMAGUCHI, S., MCNAIRN, R.B.: Der Einfluß verstärkter Callosebildung auf den Stofftransport in Siebröhren. Planta **65**, 49–64 (1965).

ESCHRICH, W., ESCHRICH, B.: Das Verhalten isolierter Callose gegenüber wäßriger Lösungen. Ber. Deut. Botan. Ges. **77**, 329–331 (1964).

ESCHRICH, W., EVERT, R.F., HEYSER, W.: Proteins of the sieve-tube exudate of *Cucurbita maxima*. Planta **100**, 208–221 (1971).

ESCHRICH, W., HÜTTERMANN, A., HEYSER, W., TAMMES, P.M.L., VAN DIE, J.: Evidence for the synthesis of "callose" in sieve-tube exudate of *Yucca flaccida*. Z. Pflanzenphysiol. **67**, 468–470 (1972).

ESCHRICH, W., STEINER, M.: Die Struktur des Leitgewebesystems von *Polytrichum commune*. Planta **82**, 33–49 (1968).

ESSER, K.: Bildung und Abbau von Callose in den Samenanlagen der Petunia hybrida. Z. Botan. **51**, 32–51 (1963).

EVERT, R.F., BORNMAN, C.H., BUTLER, V., GILLILAND, M.G.: Structure and development of sieve areas in leaf veins of *Welwitschia*. Protoplasma **76**, 23–34 (1973).

EVERT, R.F., DERR, W.F.: Callose substance in sieve elements. Am. J. Bot. **51**, 552–559 (1964).

EVERT, R.F., DESHPANDE, B.P.: Electron microscope investigation of sieve-element ontogeny and structure in *Ulmus americana*. Protoplasma **68**, 403–432 (1969).

EVERT, R.F., DESHPANDE, B.P.: Nuclear P-protein in sieve elements of *Tilia americana*. J. Cell Biol. **44**, 462–466 (1970).

EVERT, R.F., ESCHRICH, W., EICHHORN, S.E.: Sieve-plate pores in leaf veins of *Hordeum vulgare*. Planta **100**, 262–267 (1971).

EVERT, R.F., ESCHRICH, W., EICHHORN, S.E.: P-protein distribution in mature sieve elements of *Cucurbita maxima*. Planta **109**, 193–210 (1973).

EVERT, R.F., TUCKER, C.M., DAVIS, J.D., DESHPANDE, B.P.: Light microscope investigation of sieve-element ontogeny and structure in *Ulmus americana*. Am. J. Bot. **56**, 999–1017 (1969).

FALK, H.: Zur Herkunft des Siebröhrenschleims bei *Tetragonia expansa* Murr. Planta **60**, 558–567 (1964).

FREY-WYSSLING, A., EPPRECHT, W., KESSLER, G.: Zur Charakterisierung der Siebröhren-Kallose. Experientia **13**, 22 (1957).

FU, Y.L., GUTMANN, P.J., TIMELL, T.E.: Polysaccharides in the secondary phloem of scots pine (*Pinus sylvestris* L.). I. Isolation and characterization of callose. Cellulose Chem. Technol. **6**, 507–512 (1972).

GIAQUINTA, R.T., GEIGER, D.R.: Mechanism of inhibition of translocation by localized chilling. Plant Physiol. **51**, 372–377 (1973).

GORSKA-BRYLASS, A.: Temporary callose wall in the generative cell of pollen grains. Z. Naturwiss. **9**, 230–231 (1967).

GORSKA-BRYLASS, A.: Callose in the cell walls of the developing male gametophyte in Gymnospermae. Acta Soc. Botan. Polon. **37**, 119–124 (1968).

GORSKA-BRYLASS, A.: Callose in gametogenesis in liverworts. Bull. Acad. Polon. Sci. Cl. II **17**, 549–554 (1969).

GORSKA-BRYLASS, A.: The "callose stage" of the generative calls in pollen grains. Grana Palynologica **10**, 21–30 (1970).

HARTIG, T.: Über die Querscheidewände zwischen den einzelnen Gliedern der Siebröhren in *Cucurbita pepo*. Botan. Z. **12**, 51–54 (1854).

HÉBANT, CH.: A new look at the conducting tissues of mosses (Bryopsida): Their structure, distribution, and significance. Phytomorphology **20**, 390–410 (1970).

HEPTON, C.E.L., PRESTON, R.D., RIPLEY, G.W.: Electron microscopic observations on the structure of the sieve plates in *Cucurbita*. Nature **176**, 868–870 (1955).

HESLOP-HARRISON, J.: Cytoplasmic continuities during spore formation in flowering plants. Endeavour **25**, 65–72 (1966).

HESLOP-HARRISON, J.: Sexuality of Angiosperms. In: Plant physiology—a treatise (ed. F.C. STEWARD), vol. VIc, p. 133–271. New York-London: Academic Press 1972.

HOFFMANN, G.C., SIMSON, B.W., TIMELL, T.E.: Structure and molecular size of pachyman. Carbohyd. Res. **20**, 185–188 (1971).

HOFFMANN, G.C., TIMELL, T.E.: Isolation of a β-1,3-glucan (Laricinan) from compression wood of *Larix laricina*. Wood Science and Technol. **4**, 159–162 (1970).

JALOUZOT, M.F.: Mise en évidence de parois callosiques au cours de la mégasporogenèse et de l'oogenèse d'Oenothera biennis. Compt. Rend. **270**, Ser.D, 317–319 (1970).

JARVIS, P., THAINE, R., LEONARD, J.W.: Structures in sieve elements cut with a cryostat following different rates of freezing. J. Exptl. Bot. **24**, 905–919 (1973).

KESSLER, G.: Zur Charakterisierung der Siebröhrencallose. Ber. Schweiz. Botan. Ges. **68**, 5–43 (1958).

KNOX, R.B., HESLOP-HARRISON, J.: Direct demonstration of the low permeability of the angiosperm meiotic tetrad using a fluorogenic ester. Z. Pflanzenphysiol. **62**, 451–459 (1970).

KOLLMANN, R., DÖRR, I., KLEINIG, H.: Protein filaments-structural components of the phloem exudate. Planta **95**, 86–94 (1970).

KOLLMANN, R., SCHUMACHER, W.: Über die Feinstruktur des Phloems von *Metasequoia glyptostroboides* und seine jahreszeitlichen Veränderungen. II. Vergleichende Untersuchungen der plasmatischen Verbindungsbrücken in Phloemparenchymzellen und Siebzellen. Planta **58**, 366–386 (1962).

KRULL, R.: Untersuchungen über den Bau und die Entwicklung der Plasmodesmen im Rindenparenchym von *Viscum album*. Planta **55**, 598–629 (1960).

LAFLÈCHE, D.: Ultrastructure et cytochimie des inclusions flagellées des cellules criblées de *Phaseolus vulgaris*. J. Microscopie **5**, 493–510 (1966).

LEHMANN, J.: Zur Lokalisation von Dehydrogenasen des Energiestoffwechsels im Phloem von *Cucurbita pepo* L. Planta **111**, 187–198 (1973).

LIBERMANN-MAXE, M.: Étude cytologique de la différenciation des cellules criblées de *Polypodium vulgare* (Polypodiaceae). J. Microscopie **12**, 271–288 (1971).

MCNAIRN, R.B.: Phloem translocation and heat-induced callose formation in field-grown *Gossypium hirsutum* L. Plant Physiol. **50**, 366–370 (1972).

MCNAIRN, R.B., CURRIER, H.B.: The influence of boron on callose formation in primary leaves of *Phaseolus vulgaris* L. Phyton **22**, 153–158 (1965).

MCNAIRN, R.B., CURRIER, H.B.: Translocation blockage by sieve plate callose. Planta **82**, 369–380 (1968).

MILBURN, J.A.: Phloem transport in *Ricinus*. Pestic. Sci. **3**, 653–665 (1972).

MÜLLER-STOLL, W.R., LERCH, G.: Über Nachweis, Entstehung und Eigenschaften der Kallosebildungen in Pollenschläuchen. Flora **144**, 297–334 (1957).

NÄGELI, C.W.: Über die Siebröhren von Cucurbita. Sitzber. Königl. Bayer. Akad. Wiss. **1**, 212–238 (1861).

NEUBERGER, D.S., EVERT, R.F.: Structure and development of the sieve-element protoplast in the hypocotyl of *Pinus resinosa*. Am. J. Bot. **61**, 360–374 (1974).

NORTHCOTE, D.H., WOODING, F.B.P.: Development of sieve tubes in *Acer pseudoplatanus*. Proc. Roy. Soc. (London), Ser. B **163**, 524–537 (1966).

PALEVITZ, B.A., NEWCOMB, E.H.: The ultrastructure and development of tubular and crystalline P-protein in the sieve elements of certain papilionaceous legumes. Protoplasma **72**, 399–426 (1971).

RODKIEWICZ, B., GORSKA-BRYLASS, A.: Callose in the walls of the developing megasporocyte and megaspores in the orchid ovule. Acta Soc. Botan. Polon. **37**, 19–28 (1968).

SATHYANARAYANA, B.K., RAO, V.S.R.: Conformational studies of β-glucans. Biopolymers **10**, 1605–1615 (1971).

SCHUMACHER, W.: Die Fernleitung der Stoffe im Pflanzenkörper. In: Encyclopedia of plant physiology (ed. W. RUHLAND), vol. XIII, p. 60–177. Berlin-Heidelberg-New York: Springer 1967.

SHIH, C.Y., CURRIER, H.B.: Fine structure of phloem cells in relation to translocation in the cotton seedling. Am. J. Bot. **56**, 464–472 (1969).

Siddiqui, A.W., Spanner, D.C.: The state of the pores in functioning sieve plates. Planta **91**, 181–189 (1970).

Sitte, P.: Zur Kenntnis der Zwischenschichte im Sporoderm von *Pinus mugo*. Grana Palynologica **4**, 41–52 (1963).

Steinbiss, H.H., Schmitz, K.: CO_2-Fixierung und Stofftransport in benthischen marinen Algen. V. Zur autoradiographischen Lokalisation der Assimilattransportbahnen im Thallus von *Laminaria hyperborea*. Planta **112**, 253–263 (1973).

Tammes, P.M.L.: Observations on the bleeding of palm trees. Rec. Trav. Bot. Neerl. **30**, 514–536 (1933).

Tamulevich, S.R., Evert, R.F.: Aspects of sieve-element ultrastructure in *Primula obconica*. Planta **69**, 319–337 (1966).

Ullrich, W.: Über die Bildung von Kallose bei einer Hemmung des Transportes in den Siebröhren durch Cyanid. Planta **59**, 387–390 (1963).

Van Went, J.L., Tammes, P.M.L.: Trumpet filaments in *Laminaria digitata* as an artefact. Acta Botan. Neerl. **22**, 112–119 (1973).

Van Went, J.L., van Aelst, A.C., Tammes, P.M.L.: Open plasmodesmata in sieve plates of *Laminaria digitata*. Acta Botan. Neerl. **22**, 120–123 (1973).

Walker, T.S., Thaine, R.: Proteins and fine structural components in exudate from sieve tubes in *Cucurbita pepo* stems. Ann. Botany (London) **35**, 773–790 (1971).

Webster, D.B., Currier, H.B.: Callose: Lateral movement of assimilates from Phloem. Science **150**, 1610–1611 (1965).

Webster, D.H., Currier, H.B.: Heat-induced callose and lateral movement of assimilates from phloem. Can. J. Botany **46**, 1215–1220 (1968).

Weiling, F.: Licht- und elektronenmikroskopische Beobachtungen zum Problem der Cytomixis sowie ihrer möglichen Beziehungen zur Potocytose. Untersuchungen bei *Cucurbita*-Arten und *Lycopersicum esculentum*. Planta **67**, 182–212 (1965).

Wergin, W.P., Newcomb, E.H.: Formation and dispersal of crystalline P-protein in sieve elements of soybean (*Glycine max* L.). Protoplasma **71**, 365–388 (1970).

Ziegler, H.: Untersuchungen über die Leitung und Sekretion der Assimilate. Planta **47**, 447–500 (1956).

Ziegler, H., Ruck, I.: Untersuchungen über die Feinstruktur des Phloems. III. Die Trompetenzellen von *Laminaria*-Arten. Planta **73**, 62–73 (1967).

Zimmermann, M.H.: Absorption and translocation: transport in the phloem. Ann. Rev. Plant Physiol. **11**, 167–190 (1960).

II. Nature of Substances in Phloem

3. Nature of Transported Substances

H. ZIEGLER

A. Introduction

A detailed knowledge of the chemical nature of the substances transported in the sieve tubes of angiosperms or their analogs in other groups of the plant kingdom is of special interest in several respects:

1. These transport-substances are the bulk of the organic material which is available for all non-autotrophic cells and tissues in a plant. (A very restricted additional source is the transpiration stream, which usually carries organic compounds in very low concentrations.) The transport substances in the phloem, therefore, can be considered as the skeletons, from which all necessary substances in tissues like cambium, meristems, developing fruits and storage tissues, must be synthesized.

2. A knowledge of the transport substances may also give some indications of the transport mechanism. A simultaneous transport of several substances of very different molecular architecture, would, for example, make the assumption of a carrier transport very improbable, as would the translocation of substances of very different hydrophilic and lipophilic properties for the migration on phase surfaces (VAN DEN HONERT, 1932; Chapter 15, p. 356). For a streaming solution the transport of water is of course an inevitable prerequisite.

3. A clear idea about the question of what can move in the phloem and what can not is necessary for the pertinent use of applied substances, e.g. herbicides or fertilizers.

4. The content of the assimilate-conducting cells is the food source for a great number of animal species, mainly aphids and coccids. A detailed knowledge of the composition of this diet allows an understanding of the nutrition of these organisms. It is impressive how far the synthetic diet for phloem-sucking aphids (cf. MITTLER, 1970) resembles the "standard composition" of the sieve-tube sap, as outlined below.

B. Methods for the Analysis of the Transported Substances

It is surprisingly difficult to obtain a complete and unequivocal picture of the substances transported in the sieve elements. Most of the commonly used methods for these analyses have some disadvantages.

1. One of the oldest methods for determining transport substances is the analysis of the sieve-tube sap. It can be obtained from a number of plants, especially many angiosperm trees, by a simple incision in the bark, which opens the turgescent, functioning sieve tubes (HARTIG, 1960; MÜNCH, 1930; for further literature cf.

CRAFTS and CRISP, 1971). This method does not work in most of the herbaceous plant species (exception e.g. Cucurbitaceae species) and in plants with sieve cells (e.g. pteridophytes, gymnosperms), but it is useful for some of the larger algae (some Laminariales, which contain sieve elements as assimilate-conducting channels). An interesting new achievement is the enhancement of phloem exudation in leaf petioles by chelating agents (KING and ZEEVART, 1974), which may be applicable to several herbaceous species.

This tapping method has the following disadvantages: a) it is not applicable to all plants; b) it delivers only part of the content of the sieve tubes (mainly the content of the lumen, but not the ectoplasm); c) the original composition of the sieve-tube sap may be changed by dilution (by sudden water inflow into the opened sieve tube from the surrounding cells) or by "contamination" with substances from the wounded cells which are passed by the exuding fluid. Since the obtained sap is not sterile in general, there is also some danger of metabolic changes, which can also be brought about by enzymes of the sap itself.

2. Some of these disadvantages of the tapping method are avoided by using aphid stylets as tools for obtaining sieve-tube sap (cf. Chapters 6 and 7). This method can also be applied to a large number of herbaceous plants (cf. VON DEHN, 1961) and to gymnosperms (cf. ZIEGLER and MITTLER, 1959) and it delivers uncontaminated, "pure" sieve-tube sap. There are, however, two main problems in applying this method: one is to find a suitable (not too small and not too nervous) phloem-sucking insect and the other, to obtain amounts of exudate which are sufficient for the relevant analyses.

3. The analysis of the whole conducting bundle or of the phloem part of it, as well as of the phloem region or even the whole bark in plants with secondary thickening, which is now mostly done following photosynthesis in the leaves of $^{14}CO_2$ or after feeding the plant with labeled substances, is even more problematic, since it is difficult to decide whether a substance identified in the tissue was really part of the conducting channels themselves, i.e. of the sieve tubes. Hexoses, which—so far as we know—are never constituents of the sieve tubes are readily formed in other living cells of the phloem by hydrolysis of sucrose or oligosaccharides, which are the migrating substances (see below).

4. Microautoradiographic demonstration of labeled substances in the sieve elements is another way of checking the migrating substances. As far as labeling is specific for one substance or an isotope can be attributed to a distinct compound, this method can at least indicate the ability of a substance to be translocated in the phloem.

5. Specific substances which are needed by non-autotrophic tissues in the plant (e.g. apical meristems or the cambium) and cannot be formed from simple transport compounds by these tissues, are likely to be translocated in the phloem.

The most unequivocal proof for a transport substance in the phloem could be obtained by a combination of the different methods mentioned above. If a compound is found in the sieve-tube sap, and if it accumulates above a girdle in the bark and is part of the moving front of labeled assimilates after synthesis or feeding of labeled substances, then there is no doubt that this compound is translocated in the phloem. Only a few substances mentioned below are proved to be transported in such correct detail. There is, therefore, some uncertainty in our knowledge about the nature of the migrating compounds.

C. Different Groups of Transported Substances

1. Water

One of the most fundamental questions for the understanding of phloem transport is whether water moves together with the other transport substances in the sieve elements. It is characteristic of the present state of phloem research that even this seemingly simple question is controversial.

The following points indicate mass flow of water in the sieve elements:

a) From a theoretical point of view it is difficult to see how large amounts of osmotically active substances could move in a semipermeable system, connected with water-containing cells, without carrying with them osmotically attracted water. (This assumption is indeed the basis of the solution-flow theory of MÜNCH, 1930.) The only way to avoid such simultaneous streaming of water would be a transport of the assimilates, mineral elements and so on in a bound, osmotically inactive form (e.g. bound to carriers). It is extremely improbable that this is the case.

b) MÜNCH (1930) "demonstrated" the secretion of water from bark flaps, still connected with the source leaves, which received assimilates *via* the phloem and used them for thickening growth. These flaps had no other source of water than the phloem (but see Chapter 14, p. 333).

c) The exudation after incising the phloem or by cutting off the stylets of phloem-feeding insects shows unequivocally that a solution can move in the sieve elements (a seemingly controversial result will be discussed below).

d) According to the experiments of HAGEMANN (1964), sprouting tubers of *Solanum tuberosum* show initially a decrease in dry-matter constituents, phosphorus, and potassium, and an increase in calcium and water content, while the magnesium content remains almost constant. Assuming that the tuber was importing *via* the root xylem (mainly water and calcium) and exporting *via* phloem (*no* calcium—see below, p. 88, but potassium, phosphorus and water) WIERSUM (1967) calculated the influx and efflux of the different substances in the tuber (Table 1). These assumptions—including the transport of water in the phloem—lead to reasonable values for the concentration of calcium in the influx and for the concentration of phosphorus and potassium in the phloem efflux.

Table 1. Derived data, in italics, and estimated amounts of influx and efflux of substances in the sprouting potato tuber (WIERSUM, 1967)

Weeks from planting	Water balance of the tuber in ml					Increase of CaO in mg	Concentration of CaO in influx in mg/ml
	Net H_2O increase	Total influx	Phloem efflux	Loss of P_2O_5 (efflux)	Loss of K_2O (efflux)		
0	—	—	—	—			
3	15.5	*37.5*	*22*	25.0	100	21.8	*0.58*
4	18.7	*60.9*	*42.2*	48.0	179	35.4	*0.58*
5	19.9	*78.0*	*59.0*	66.9	231	48.9	*0.63*
6	19.1	*85.1*	*66.0*	75.8	266	54.9	*0.64*
7	22.0	*94.2*	*72.2*	81.9	279	57.8	*0.61*
8	15.4	*91.1*	*75.7*	85.9	297	60.3	*0.66*

e) A further indication of a streaming solution and, therefore, of water transport in the sieve elements is the lack of simultaneous bidirectional transport in one and the same part of the transport channel; all seemingly contradictory results are not convincing (cf. p. 337 and Chapter 10).

f) ZIEGLER and VIEWEG (1961) using a thermoelectric method on isolated, but still intact phloem strands of *Heracleum mantegazzianum*, demonstrated a heat transfer with a velocity of 35–70 cm per h. This can only be explained by streaming of an aqueous solution carrying the heat pulse with it.

g) The easiest way to demonstrate water transport seems the use of labeled water. This has been done repeatedly, but with controversial results. BIDDULPH and CORY (1957) applied THO and ^{14}C-sucrose to kidney beans in the light by spraying the lower surface while maintaining the leaflet and the stem at pressures of 2 mm and 4 mm H_2O respectively, below ambient conditions. They observed a "flow" of tritiated water but the apparent velocities of translocation of THO and ^{14}C-sucrose varied. GAGE and ARONOFF (1960) supplied THO to soybean or cucumber plants in the dark by enclosing a leaf for 1 h in a chamber containing THO-vapor, followed by a 15- or 30 min-period in the light. They reported little or no movement of THO from the supply leaf to the petiole and stem. In other experiments with soybeans in which THO was introduced in the same way THO and T-labeled photosynthates moved from the source leaf to the petiole and stem (CHOI and ARONOFF, 1966); the transport was greatly reduced by steam girdling and it is therefore probable that it proceeded in the phloem. The movement of THO did not parallel that of T-photosynthates. It was 2 to 3 times greater in the dark (80 min) than in the dark (60 min) followed by light (20 min). The authors interpreted their results as indicating that mass flow is not a dominant process in phloem translocation.

Considering the fact that THO, introduced in intact leaves, either as liquid or vapor, must move against the natural water potential gradient in the leaf to reach the sieve elements, TRIP and GORHAM (1968) introduced ^{14}C-sugar and THO simultaneously through a cut side vein or flap of a squash leaf. They observed a concurrent translocation of ^{14}C-sugars, T-photosynthates and THO with parallel, almost flat, gradients in the petiole for periods of 1 to 3 h. Since steam girdling blocked the movement of ^{14}C and T, it is probable that water and sugar moved together in the phloem.

The most spectacular experiments which seemed to speak strongly against a linear flow of an aqueous solution in the sieve elements were performed by PEEL et al. (1969) and PEEL (1970) (cf. Chapter 7). PEEL and coworkers supplied a bark strip of *Salix viminalis* locally with a solution of THO, ^{14}C-sucrose and/or $^{32}PO_4^{3-}$ and followed the appearance of the different isotopes in the exudate of an aphid stylet situated in a sieve tube of the bark at some distance from the feeding site. Although activity from both ^{14}C and ^{32}P was detected in the stylet exudate usually 1 h from isotope application, tritium activity was not detected, even after a period of 8 h in most experiments, though in certain cases, low activities were detected after 4 h. Subsequent experiments in which stylets were sited immediately under the point of isotope application showed that tritium activity entered the punctured sieve element even more rapidly than either ^{14}C or ^{32}P. The authors conclude that water is not transported in the sieve tubes, at least not with a velocity comparable with that of the photosynthates. The water in the stylet exudate would then not come from the sieve tubes but from surrounding cells; this would mean that all other cells would be more penetrable for water than the sieve tubes.

It seems much more probable that the THO is lost during the transport by lateral exchange with unlabeled water, while ^{14}C-sugars and ^{32}phosphate are not lost, or not lost to the same extent (cf. Chapter 7, p. 181 and Appendix II). This explanation also holds true for the difference in apparent velocity of THO and ^{14}C-sugars in the experiments of BIDDULPH and CORY and of sucrose and potassium after injection in a sieve tube of *Heracleum* (FENSOM and DAVIDSON, 1970). There is little doubt that the selectively permeable ectoplasm of the sieve elements is a greater barrier for the lateral loss of sugars or ions than for water. Comparable results were obtained, when DHO was supplied to plants *via* the xylem: it took several hours for the appearance of deuterium in the transpired water vapor (HÜBNER, 1960). Nobody doubts that water is translocated in the xylem!

In an other set of experiments, PEEL (1970) established gradients of tritiated water, ^{35}S-sulphate and ^{32}P-phosphate in isolated segments of willow stems. Sieve tube exudate was collected as honeydew from the high activity end of the segment. After girdling the stem a few centimeters from the site of sieve tube puncture (towards the low activity end) the specific activity of ^{35}S and ^{32}P in the honeydew rose, whilst the specific activity of tritium remained constant. The authors concluded that prior to girdling, unlabeled sulphates and phosphates contributed to the honeydew, whilst there had been no detectable contribution by unlabeled water from the low activity end of the segment; water should, therefore, be relatively immobile in sieve tubes of willow as compared to solutes. Again, another explanation is much more obvious. Girdling causes an accumulation of the sugars and the phosphate but not of the water which can easily pass the ectoplast of the sieve tubes.

In conclusion, the bulk of evidence is in favor of a movement of water in the translocating sieve elements. Water seems to be quantitatively the most important translocation substance.

2. Carbohydrates

In most plant species sugars or sugar alcohols form the bulk of the transport substances (besides water) in the phloem. (Exceptions are species of Cucurbitaceae, where nitrogenous substances are quantitatively the most important fraction, see p. 67.) To date about 500 species have been analyzed for the sugar composition of the sieve-tube sap, belonging to 43 orders of the magnoliophyta (angiosperms) (Fig. 1). 145 species from 70 genera and 35 families were studied by HELGA KLUGE (1967), while most of the other species were examined by ZIMMERMANN (1957, 1961); cf. Appendix III.

On the basis of the composition of the sugars in the sieve-tube sap three main types can be distinguished (cf. reviews of SCHUMACHER, 1967; ZIEGLER, 1968; CRAFTS and CRISP, 1971; ZIMMERMANN and BROWN, 1971):

a) Species with *sucrose* as the predominant sugar. Small amounts of the oligosaccharides of the raffinose type may also be present. Most of the analyzed species belong to this group, as do the only fern species studied up to date (*Pteridium* spec.; HAMILTON and CANNY, 1960), and all the species pinophyta (gymnosperms) (*Picea abies;* ZIEGLER and MITTLER, 1959; *Pinus strobus* and *P. resinosa;* HILL

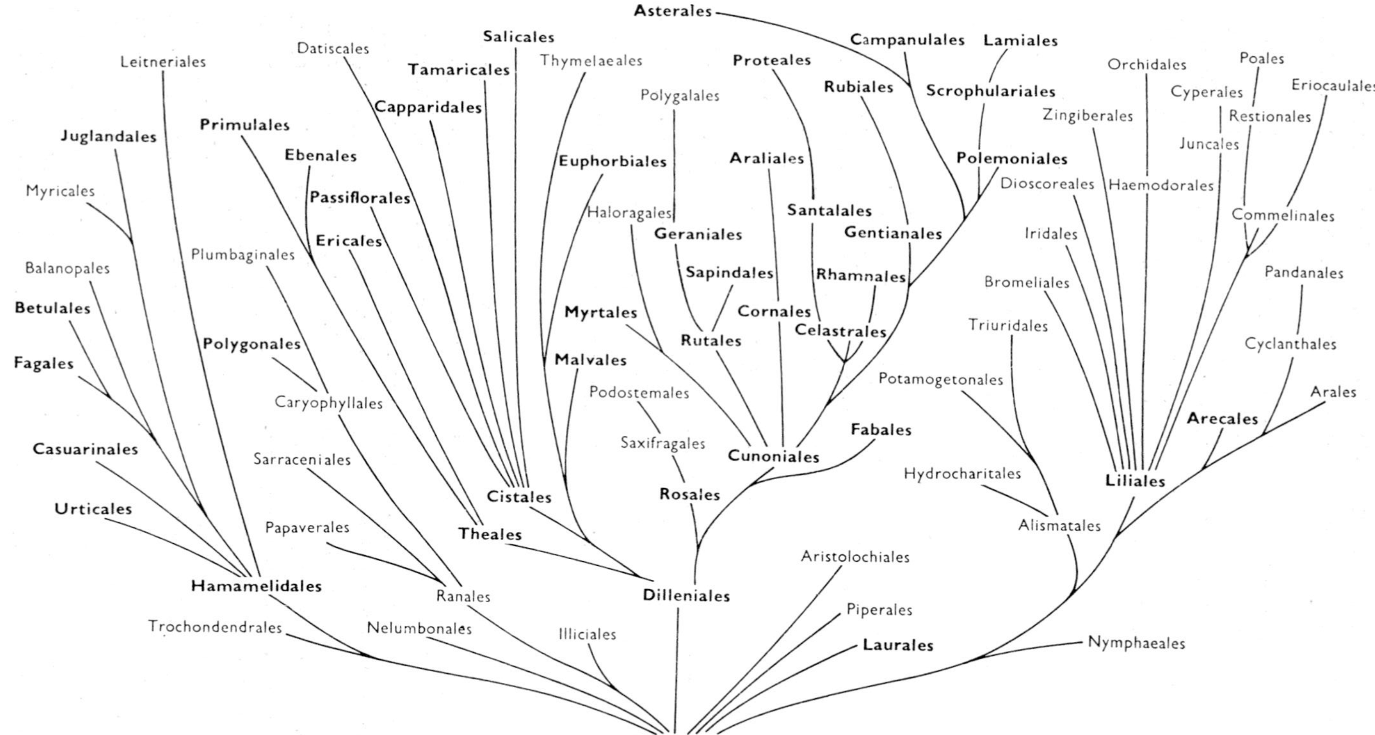

Fig. 1. System of the Magnoliophyta (Angiosperms) according to TAKHTAJAN (1959). Species from the orders in bold type have been analyzed for the sugar composition of their sieve-tube sap (ZIEGLER, 1974)

unpublished) and liliopsida (monocotyledons) (cf. Chapter 8) so far examined. In a number of families, sucrose is the only sugar so far detected in the sieve-tube sap, e.g. in the Fabaceae.

b) Species which have considerable amounts of oligosaccharides as well as sucrose. These oligosaccharides belong to the *raffinose family* (Fig. 2) which is characterized by the attachment of one or more galactose residues to the sucrose. These raffinose-type sugars were first demonstrated in sieve-tube sap by ZIMMERMANN (1957). According to this author (cf. ZIMMERMANN and BROWN, 1971) they occur in species belonging

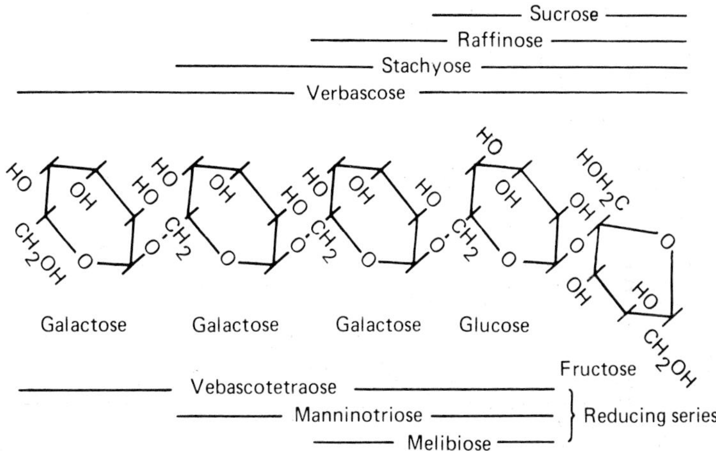

Fig. 2. The raffinose family of oligosaccharides. (From ZIMMERMANN and BROWN, 1971)

to Bignoniaceae, Celastraceae, Combretaceae, Lamiaceae, Myrtaceae, Oleaceae, Onagraceae, and Verbenaceae. In addition H. KLUGE (1967) found these oligosaccharides in considerable concentrations also in members of Anacardiaceae, Buxaceae, Clethraceae, Corylaceae, Rutaceae, Tiliaceae, and Ulmaceae. In some species also ajugose, the compound with 4 galactose-residues bound to sucrose, was detected in low concentration *(Fraxinus ornus, Buddleia davidii, Buxus sempervirens, Escallonia* spec., *Syringa vulgaris, Paulownia tomentosa, Catalpa bignonioides, Carya laciniosa)*. Verbascose and ajugose occur only in those species which also contain higher amounts of raffinose and stachyose in the phloem exudate.

c) Species which contain considerable quantities of *sugar alcohols* (Fig. 3) in addition to the sugars mentioned above. To this group belong species of the Oleaceae (e.g. *Fraxinus, Syringa*) which contain D-*mannitol* in the sieve-tube sap (ZIMMERMANN, 1961). The "ash-manna" of the trade is obtained from the phloem exudate of *Fraxinus ornus* (HUBER, 1953). In *Prunus serotina* (ZIMMERMANN, 1961) and *Malus domestica* (WEBB and BURLEY, 1962) *sorbitol* was found beside sucrose. A detailed study of a large number of rosaceous species (H. KLUGE, 1967) revealed that all species analyzed of the subfamilies Spiroideae, Pomoideae, and Prunoideae contained sorbitol in the sieve-tube sap, but not the species of the Rosoideae. This occurrence in the sieve-tube sap corresponds with the storage of sorbitol in the leaves and fruits: this sugar alcohol occurs in leaves and fruits of the first three subfamilies but only in traces if at all in the leaves of the Rosoideae (cf. HEGNAUER, 1973). Exceptions are the Kerrieae *(Kerria japonica, Neviusa alabamensis, Rhodotypos kerrioides)*; their leaves contain sorbitol (PLOUVIER, 1955). It would be interesting to analyze the sieve-tube sap of these species which are perhaps more related to the Spiroideae than to the Rosoideae.

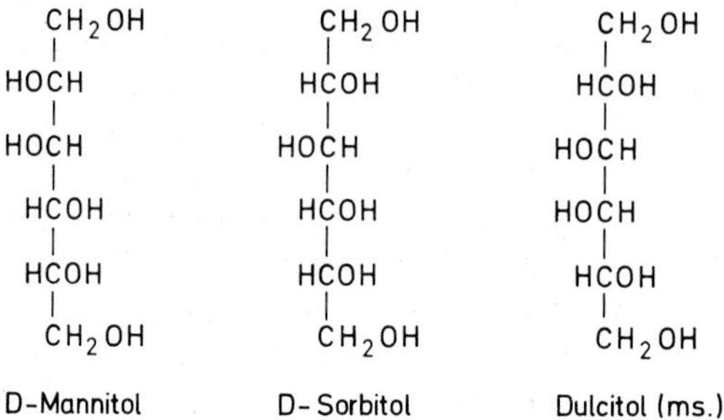

Fig. 3. Sugar alcohols

Dulcitol was found in the sieve-tube sap of those species of Celastraceae so far analyzed (H. KLUGE, 1967). Free hexoses are found in the phloem exudates—if at all—in very low concentrations (cf. references in SCHUMACHER, 1967; CRAFTS and CRISP, 1971). Larger amounts of free hexoses, as reported by MEYER-MEVIUS (1959) do not presumably originate from the sieve tubes or they are formed by hydrolysis of the original di- or oligosaccharides.

Sugar-phosphates are described later (p. 84). It is striking that all transport sugars are nonreducing. In *Fraxinus americana* and *Syringa vulgaris* the sugars of the raffinose family and mannitol—all nonreducing compounds—were phloem-mobile whereas the reducing sugars, melibiose (which could be formed by incomplete hydrolysis of raffinose), galactose, glucose, fructose and pentoses, were immobile (TRIP et al., 1965).

It is probable, that reducing sugars are excluded at the sites of loading the sieve elements. Perhaps this reflects a specifity of a carrier system. In maize seedlings, however, the loading system cannot distinguish between sucrose and 2-deoxy-D-glucose-β-fructoside which is synthesized from supplied 2-deoxy-D-glucose in analogy to the synthesis of sucrose from glucose (SAMMLER et al., 1974).

The nature of sugars transported in the phloem is very often different from the predominant carbohydrates in the source or sink tissues. This is also true if the predominant sugar outside the transport channels is not sucrose: In *Buddleia davidii*, e.g., sucrose is the predominant sugar in the leaves, but stachyose is the main transport sugar and the one which shows the most pronounced seasonal changes in the sieve-tube sap (H. KLUGE, 1970).

The predominance of sucrose and its derivatives and of sugar alcohols as transport carbohydrates in the phloem is probably significant for several reasons. An ideal transport-carbohydrate should be highly water-soluble, easily synthesized without large energy investment from the first stable products of photosynthesis or from compounds produced by mobilization of storage substances, and easily handled by the metabolism of the receiving cells. It should be protected against breakdown in the (living!) transport channels, and it should also be suitable for active transport through membranes.

All the transport sugars and sugar alcohols mentioned above are easily synthesized from the early products of photosynthesis (Fig. 4). If we assume that a major part of the transport sucrose and oligosaccharides is formed from phosphorylated sugars—derived from photosynthesis or starch metabolism—instead of free hexoses, then the glycosidic bond preserves energy (cf. ZIEGLER, 1956). The di- or oligosaccharides are energetically more economic than free hexoses because all monoses bound to the terminal fructose (Fig. 2), can be transglycosylated and have, therefore, no need for ATP-dependent activation to join the metabolic pathways. ARNOLD (1968) argues against this idea of "metabolic advantage" to sucrose, that two molecules of glucose (or fructose) catabolized yield potentially 76 molecules of ATP, while the two hexoses from sucrose yield 77. This would indicate an "advantage" of only $^1/_2$ ATP molecule per glucose equivalent in the sucrose solution, an increment of only 1.3%. This argument is, however, not convincing: most of the photosynthates are not catabolized in the receiving cells, but used to build up storage products like starch, or structural compounds, like cell-wall material. If only every second glucose needed activation before being transferred to a starch or cellulose molecule, there would be a considerable saving of energy.

Sucrose, the raffinose sugars, and the sugar alcohols also fulfill the other conditions mentioned above. It is striking, for example, that invertase is absent from sieve tubes (cf. Chapter 4, p. 120). It is probable that the same is true for the enzymes attacking the raffinose-sugars and the sugar alcohols.

Some phloem exudates show a completely different composition from the "normal" ones: in the Cucurbitaceae analyzed so far for example, the carbohydrates are quantitatively only a minor constituent and reach no more than 1% of the fresh weight, while nitrogen compounds are predominant (COOIL, 1941; CRAFTS and LORENZ, 1944; CRAFTS, 1961; ESCHRICH, 1963). It is not clear whether the Cucurbitaceae indeed prefer nitrogen compounds as transport substances or whether the nitrogen belongs mainly to structures which are fixed in the intact sieve tubes and only broken down after wounding. In the latter (less probable) case, the effective concentration of the transport photosynthates would be unusually low in the Cucurbitaceae.

In the exudate of the sieve elements of the brown alga *Macrocystis* there is no sugar at all. In 14.9% dry matter the main substance was D-mannitol (3.6%). When the phylloid was photosynthesizing in $^{14}CO_2$, mannitol was the only labeled compound in the exudate (PARKER, 1966).

Diurnal, seasonal and local changes in the carbohydrate composition and concentration are described in Chapter 14.

3. Nitrogenous Substances

As mentioned above, in most species nitrogenous substances are much less concentrated in sieve-tube sap than carbohydrates. In the stylet exudate from an aphid feeding on the phloem of *Salix* spec. MITTLER (1958) found a total N-content of 2 mg/ml during the bud swelling, of 1.2 mg/ml during the development of the leaves, of 0.3 mg/ml during the summer, and of 1.3 mg/ml during the mobilization and export of the nitrogen from the leaves in the autumn. MOOSE (1938) found in summer

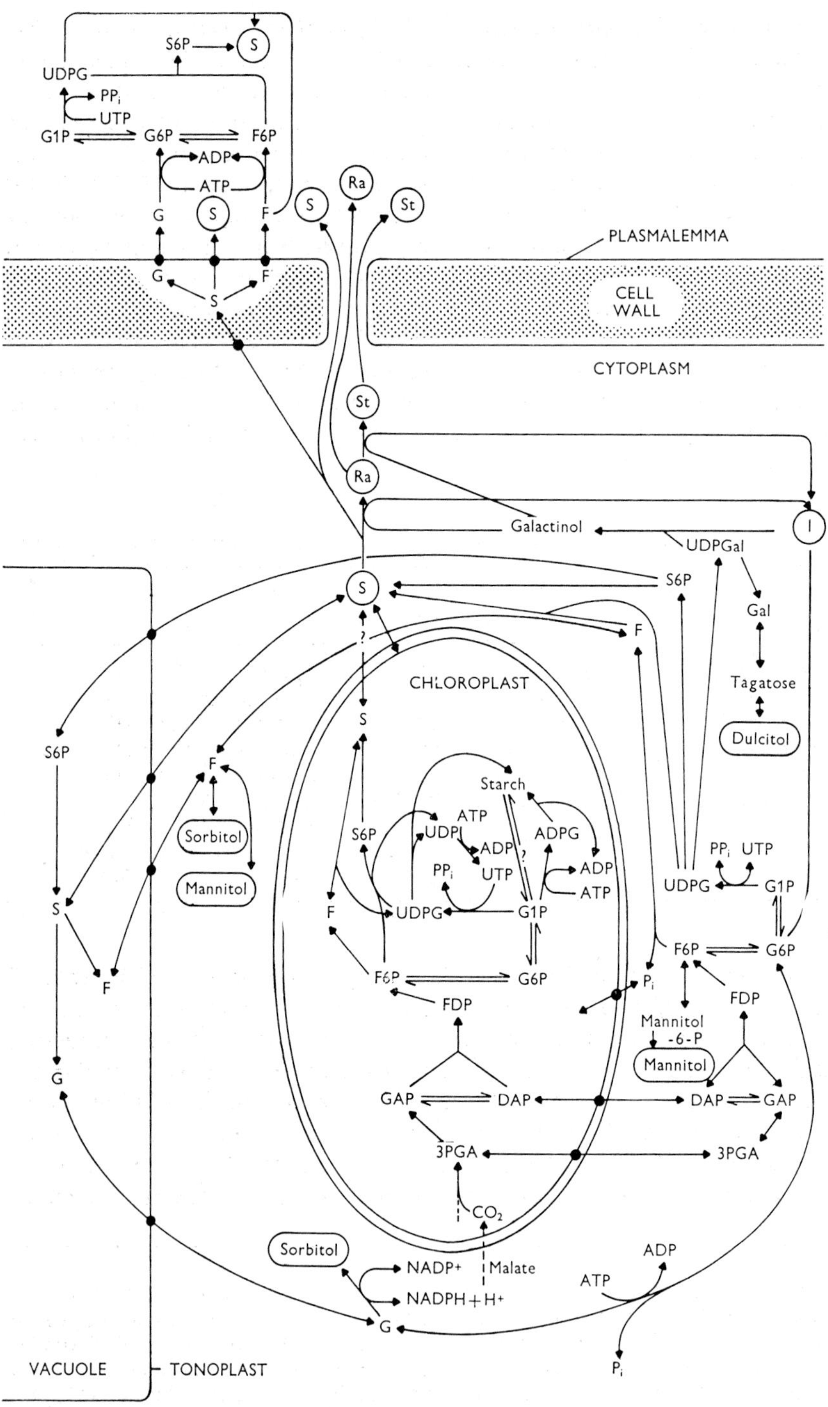

Fig. 4. Legend see page 69

phloem exudate from *Fraxinus pennsylvanica* 0.49, *Robinia pseudoacacia* 0.56, *Platanus occidentalis* 0.2, and *Fraxinus americana* 2.4–3.6 mg/ml. The percentage of the protein-N and of the trichloracetic-soluble nitrogen changes even in the same species according to the nutritional status and to the season. In general, the protein content is in the order of 1 mg/ml (cf. Table 2, and Chapter 8, p. 203). It is exceptionally high in the sieve-tube exudate of *Cucurbita* species (COOIL, 1941; CRAFTS and LORENZ, 1944; KOLLMANN et al., 1970; ESCHRICH et al., 1971; cf. Table 2). It is noteworthy that v. DEHN (1961) could not find protein (an oligopeptide only in one case) in the stylet exudate of aphids feeding on herbaceous plants. This can be explained in two different ways. It could be that the method of determination was not sensitive enough to detect the protein in the very small amount of exudate obtainable *via* the stylets. It is also possible that in contrast to the method of incising the phloem the less drastic stylet method retains the structural proteins inside the sieve tubes and delivers only the "pure" content of the lumen. The question is unanswered at the moment.

Table 2. Protein concentrations in phloem exudates of some species (further values in the text)

Species	Time of exudation	Protein-content	Reference
Tilia platyphyllos SCOP.	Oct.	0.31	KENNECKE et al. (1971)
Carpinus betulus L.	Oct.	0.60	KENNECKE et al. (1971)
Fraxinus americana L.	Oct.	1.12	KENNECKE et al. (1971)
Quercus borealis MICHX.	Oct.	1.06	KENNECKE et al. (1971)
Salix viminalis L.	Oct.	1.30	KENNECKE et al. (1971)
Robinia pseudoacacia L.	Sept.	1.95–2.10	ZIEGLER (1956)
Ricinus communis L.		1.45–2.20	HALL and BAKER (1972)
Yucca flaccida HAW.		0.5–0.8	TAMMES and VAN DIE (1964)
Cucurbita maxima DUCH.		9.8	KOLLMANN et al. (1970)

The protein in the exudate of incised phloem largely consists of the "P-protein". These filamentous and/or tubular structures have been of much interest recently, because there were some indications that this protein could have actin-like properties. The protein from *Cucurbita maxima* sieve-tube exudate is precipitated by vinblastine or Ca^{++} and reversibly aggregated into filamentous structures in solutions of low ionic strength (KLEINIG et al., 1971). However, the same authors could find neither binding capacity for ATP, GTP, and colchicine by isolated P-protein, nor detect ATPase activity in the presence of divalent cations. Also the ATPases in the phloem

◀

Fig. 4. Biochemical processes involved with production and transfer of transport sugars and sugar derivatives in a chlorenchymatous cell. ● Supposed carriers in the membranes. S, sucrose; S6P, sucrose-6-phosphate; G, glucose; F, fructose; 3PGA, 3-phosphoglycerate; GAP, glyceraldehyde-3-phosphate; DAP, dihydroxyacetone phosphate; F6P, fructose-6-phosphate; G6P, glucose-6-phosphate; G1P, glucose-1-phosphate; UDPG, uridinediphosphate-glucose; UTP, uridinetriphosphate; UDP, uridinediphosphate; ADPG, adenosinediphosphate-glucose; FDP, fructose-1,6-diphosphate; UDPGal, uridinediphosphate-galactose; M6P, mannitol-6-phosphate; I, myo-inositol; Ra, raffinose; St, stachyose. Main transport substances encircled (ZIEGLER, 1974)

extract of *Heracleum mantegazzianum* do not possess any of the characteristics of ATPase associated with contractile systems (SABNIS and HART, 1974). Further, none of the P-protein filaments in phloem exudate of *Cucurbita pepo* and *Ricinus communis* showed any ability to bind heavy meromyosin subfragment one, a reaction typical for actin-like proteins (WILLIAMSON, 1972).

There are, in conclusion, no indications that P-protein is a contractile protein which could contribute to the "activation" of mass flow. It is, therefore, not surprising that cytochalasine B, which inhibits many processes dependent on contractile filaments, does not influence the movement of ^{14}C-assimilates in the phloem of *Lepidium sativum* (WILLIAMSON, 1972).

A second important aspect of the proteins in the sieve-tube exudate and in the sieve tubes themselves is their enzymatic activity (described in Chapter 4). While it is not clear whether the protein compounds found in the sieve-tube exudate are transported in the intact phloem, there is no doubt that the low-molecular weight nitrogenous substances are transport compounds; their concentration in the sieve tubes of trees decreases as do the sugars (ZIEGLER, 1956). The main substances in this fraction are *amino acids* and *amides*. The different plant species show great qualitative and quantitative differences in these compounds, and even in the same species or an individual plant there are changes in the composition

Table 3. Concentration of free amino acids in the sieve-tube sap of several tree species, measured

	Asp	Thr	Ser	Glu	Pro	Ala
Quercus bicolor WILLD., Fagaceae	17.7	2.1	13.8	9.8	tr	0.9
Q. palustris MÜNCHH., Fagaceae	0.1	tr	0.1	0.1	—	0.0
Q. imbricaria L., Fagaceae	4.4	0.6	6.0	3.9	—	0.2
Q. borealis MICHX., Fagaceae	1.2	0.2	7.3	4.0	—	0.2
Q. cerris L., Fagaceae	3.0	tr	8.0	7.6	—	0.3
Fagus engleriana SEEM., Fagaceae	5.0	3.5	10.0	10.0	—	1.0
Tilia × euchlora KOCH, Tiliaceae	2.3	4.01	10.0	6.8	12.5	1.03
T. petiolaris DC, Tiliaceae	0.8	1.1	6.6	1.2	—	1.2
T. vulgaris HAYNE, Tiliaceae	15.9	4.9	17.3	10.9	—	1.5
Tilia × blechiana DIECK, Tiliaceae	20.0	3.6	10.0	10.0	tr	0.9
T. oliveri SZYSZ., Tiliaceae	10.7	0.9	3.3	9.7	tr	0.2
Fraxinus americana var. *acuminata* WESM., Oleaceae	tr	0.8	21.5	0.5	—	0.1
F. oregona NUTT., Oleaceae	0.8	2.1	28.1	4.7	—	0.3
Betula ermani CHAM., Betulacea	7.8	2.9	30.0	3.6	—	0.6
Magnolia kobus DC, Magnoliaceae	0.2	1.1	20.9	3.7	—	5.0
Robinia neomexicana M., Fabaceae	5.5	3.5	30.9	4.7	68.2	3.0
Salix rubens Schrank, Salicaceae	0.1	1.1	10.0	0.5	—	0.1
S. pendulifolia SPÄTH, Salicaceae	0.9	9.8	20.0	13.3	—	1.0
Liquidambar stryraciflua L., Hamamelidaceae	0.5	0.8	20.0	0.7	—	—
Acer heldreichii ORPH., Aceraceae	1.0	2.8	20.0	44.5	6.8	3.9
A. platanoides L., Aceraceae	8.5	6.1	10.0	10.3	—	1.7
Buddleia davidii FRANCH., Loganiaceae	0.2	0.2	0.6	5.0	—	0.3
Maclura pomifera SCHN., Moraceae	1.1	0.7	10.1	1.7	tr	0.4

tr = traces.

of the phloem exudate during the season. Normally, *glutamine/glutamate* and *asparagine/aspartate* are the quantitatively predominant nitrogenous compounds (Table 3; cf. also Chapter 8, p. 202, and HALL and BAKER, 1972). Many species also have a relatively high concentration of *serine*. This may be due to the fact that this amino acid is formed readily from 3-phosphoglycerate, which is one of the photosynthetic products leaving the chloroplast (Fig. 4). Serine is, therefore, a suitable transport carrier for nitrogen which is to be translocated in the phloem.

In *Robinia*, which as a member of the Fabaceae is relatively rich in nitrogen, *proline* is quantitatively the most predominant amino acid in the sieve-tube sap, especially at the end of the season, when the nitrogen is transported out of the leaves after mobilization of the leaf protein (cf. ZIEGLER, 1956). Proline is synthesized from glutamate and carries additional reduction equivalents (in comparison to glutamate) which can be used at the sink sites as such or as a source of energy (ZIEGLER, 1974). It is also possible that the appearance of high proline concentrations at the end of the growing season is caused by the effect of accumulating abscisic acid in the leaves; it is known that abscisic acid has such an effect (STEWART, 1972). In the exudate of the sieve elements in the brown alga *Macrocystis pyrifera* alanine (9,830 µg/ml), aspartic acid (2,630 µg/0Gg/ml) and glutamic acid (1,450 µg/ml) are the most important amino acids (PARKER, 1966).

by an amino-acid analyzer (BECKER, 1973)

Val	Ileu	Leu	Phen	Lys	NH_3	Hist	Arg	Gly	Tyr	Whole µmol ml^{-1}
6.6	3.6	1.7	2.5	0.3	2.9	0.8	0.1	—	0.5	58.4
0.1	0.1	tr	0.1	0.1	—	0.0	tr	tr	tr	0.8
1.3	0.7	tr	0.6	tr	1.9	0.3	tr	0.1	0.3	20.3
0.4	0.3	—	0.4	0.3	1.1	tr	tr	—	—	15.5
1.6	3.2	1.6	1.4	—	6.7	0.4	tr	—	0.5	34.1
4.2	3.2	1.8	1.9	2.7	10.0	1.5	2.9	—	0.8	58.4
6.7	5.7	4.4	2.9	—	1.0	0.4	—	—	—	57.7
1.0	1.1	0.8	0.7	0.8	1.2	0.4	—	—	—	17.0
5.0	4.1	3.2	3.7	1.8	3.7	1.2	0.4	—	0.6	74.3
3.8	2.6	2.5	2.2	0.6	4.3	0.6	tr	—	—	61.3
0.8	0.8	0.4	0.6	—	1.6	—	tr	—	—	29.0
3.4	2.9	3.3	—	0.5	1.4	0.1	0 tr	—	0.5	88.6
3.0	2.0	0.7	1.1	—	3.2	0.1	tr	0.3	0.8	47.2
6.4	5.8	2.2	2.2	1.1	1.5	1.4	tr	—	—	65.6
2.2	2.0	2.2	0.6	tr	1.7	0.6	—	—	0.2	40.4
6.9	4.3	5.9	2.1	—	1.5	1.2	tr	—	—	137.8
0.4	0.2	0.1	0.3	—	0.9	0.2	tr	—	tr	14.1
10.6	6.5	7.4	6.5	0.5	19.5	2.2	tr	—	1.9	100.2
1.1	0.9	2.3	0.7	0.5	2.1	—	tr	—	—	29.6
4.9	3.9	9.0	3.1	0.6	2.7	0.8	tr	—	—	64.0
2.0	5.6	4.7	1.3	—	6.9	1.4	1.2	—	—	59.8
0.4	0.5	0.1	0.1	0.1	0.6	tr	tr	—	0.1	8.5
0.7	0.5	0.1	0.5	tr	4.6	0.2	tr	0.2	0.3	20.4

It is interesting that the non-physiological isomer D-phenylalanine, supplied exogenously, cannot move in the phloem, but is held in the parenchyma as N-malonyl-D-phenylalanine (ESCHRICH and HARTMANN, 1969).

Some plant species show special nitrogenous substances in their sieve-tube sap. *Putrescine* (Fig. 5), which can be formed by decarboxylation of *ornithine* (which was detected in the sieve-tube sap of *Yucca flaccida*, cf. Chapter 8, p. 202), was demonstrated in low concentrations (15–70 μg/ml) in *Quercus borealis, Qu. robur, Qu. petraea, Robinia pseudoacacia, Tilia europaea,* and *Salix alba* (G. ZIMMERMANN, 1961). *Canavanine* (a derivative of guanidine, Fig. 5) is an important nitrogen storage compound in many legumes; it is found in considerable concentration (300–400 μg/ml) in the sieve-tube sap of *Robinia pseudoacacia* (ZIEGLER and SCHNABL, 1961). In species of the genera *Acer, Platanus,* and *Aesculus* the sieve-tube sap contains the urea-derivatives *allantoin* and *allantoic acid* (Fig. 5) in a concentration of 0.3–1 mg/ml; this is about 15% of the total nitrogen. Low concentrations of these substances are perhaps also present in the phloem exudate of *Yucca flaccida* (Chapter 8, p. 201).

Species of the genera *Betula, Carpinus, Alnus,* and *Juglans* (ZIEGLER and SCHNABL, 1961), but also *Cucurbita* (ESCHRICH, 1963; KATING and ESCHRICH, 1964) and the brown alga *Macrocystis pyrifera* (PARKER, 1966) show considerable concentrations of *citrulline* (Fig. 5), again an ureide, in their phloem exudate.

In general, low molecular nitrogen substances seem readily mobile in the phloem, and there is to date no clear-cut demonstration that any of these nitrogen substances

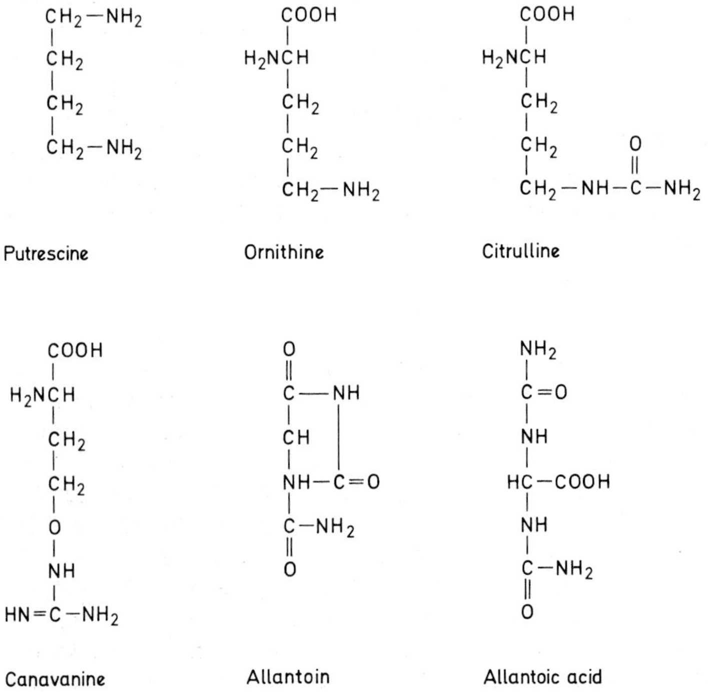

```
CH2—NH2            COOH               COOH
|                  |                  |
CH2             H2NCH              H2NCH
|                  |                  |
CH2                CH2                CH2
|                  |                  |
CH2—NH2            CH2                CH2        O
                   |                  |          ||
                   CH2—NH2            CH2—NH—C—NH2

Putrescine         Ornithine          Citrulline
```

```
  COOH             O                  NH2
  |                ||                 |
H2NCH              C——NH              C=O
  |                |    |             |
  CH2              CH   |             NH
  |                |    |             |
  CH2              NH—C=O            HC—COOH
  |                |                  |
  O                C—NH2              NH
  |                ||                 |
  NH               O                  C—NH2
  |                                   ||
HN=C—NH2                              O

Canavanine         Allantoin          Allantoic acid
```

Fig. 5

is excluded from the sieve tubes, in sharp contrast to the situation described for the sugar transport.

Considering the activity of the enzymes of nitrogen metabolism in the sieve tube sap (cf. Chapter 4, Table 1), we have to assume that the nitrogen compounds are biochemically transformed during the transport in the sieve tubes. It is possible that at least a part of the NH_4^+ found in the phloem exudate (Table 3) is produced during these processes (some may also be formed after exudation before or during the analysis).

4. Lipids

There are very few analyses, none of which is systematic, of the lipid content of the sieve tubes. In the sieve-tube exudate of *Robinia pseudoacacia* the ether-soluble fraction amounts to 0.13% of the dry weight, in that of *Tilia platyphyllos* to 0.54%. Free fatty acids are a minor component: 5.2% of the ether-soluble fraction in *Robinia*, 1.2% in *Tilia* (KLUGE, 1964). KOLLMANN et al. (1970) could not find phospholipids or galactolipids in the sieve-tube exudate of *Cucurbita maxima*; this finding is interpreted as indicating absence of membraneous material.

According to ROUSCHAL (1941) scarcity of lipids should be characteristic for the sieve-tube cytoplasm. In contrast to this opinion, ESCHRICH (1963) considers the content of the sieve tubes of *Cucurbita* as a "lipoprotein network". Experimental data are too sparse to date to answer the question of the role of lipids in the structure and function of the sieve tubes, and whether lipids belong to the transport material in the phloem. It is highly improbable that extremely lipophilic substances are phloem-mobile, but polar substances (e.g. fatty acids) may be mobile.

According to BIDDULPH and CORY (1965) young leaves of *Glycine max* export substances besides sucrose which appear to be steroids, while older leaves export only sucrose. This interesting report should be proved in more detail since the steroids are often physiologically highly active compounds which could function not only as transport assimilates (as sources of organic material for the heterotrophic cells in the plant), but also as effectors which could specifically influence metabolic and developmental processes.

5. Organic Acids

Considering the great importance of the organic acids in the intracellular (e.g. in photosynthetic active cells of CAM-plants) and transcellular transport (e.g. in the C_4-plants) our knowledge on the role of organic acids in phloem transport is surprisingly poor. PEEL and WEATHERLEY (1959) detected *citric, tartaric* and possibly *oxalic acid* in the stylet exudate of aphids feeding on the phloem of *Salix viminalis*. KURSANOV (1963) assumed that most of the keto acids found in the leaf tissue of rhubarb were excluded from the phloem and demonstrated a selective transport of small quantities of *malic* and *citric acid* only. KLUGE (1964) found in the sieve-tube sap of *Robinia pseudoacacia α-ketoglutaric, pyruvic, oxalacetic, fumaric, succinic, malonic, oxalic, malic, citric, tartaric, shikimic, quinic,* and *gluconic acid*. In the sieve-tube sap of *Tilia platyphyllos α-ketoglutaric, pyruvic, fumaric, malic, citric, tartaric, shikimic,* and *quinic acid* could be detected. All these acids reach only μg/ml concentrations. The organic acids in the exudate of *Ricinus com-*

munis phloem totalled 30–47 meq/l and only *malate* was observed on the chromatograms of exudate samples (HALL and BAKER, 1972). In *Yucca flaccida* exudate *malate* and *oxalate* could be identified (TAMMES and VAN DIE, 1964; cf. Chapter 8, p. 201). In the phloem exudate of *Cucurbita ficifolia succinate, malate, α-ketoglutarate,* and *citrate* are present (KATING and ESCHRICH, 1964). *Quinic acid* seems also to be phloem-mobile in *Larix decidua* (FRANZ and MEIER, 1969), as is *oleanolic acid* in *Calendula* (KASPRZYK et al., 1968).

These few reports suggest that organic acids are quantitatively a minor constituent of sieve-tube content. Syntheses in the sink tissues which need large amounts of organic acids as building material (e.g. shikimic acid in the formation of phenylpropane derivatives) apparently use transported sugars as basic skeletons, as they do for the most other substances.

6. Nucleic Acids and Their Constituents, Including ATP

The knowledge of the nucleic acids and their constituents in the sieve tubes is especially interesting for several reasons: a) functioning sieve elements are cells, which have lost their nucleus. b) there are indications that at least in some cases nucleic acids or their constituents are transported in the phloem. This holds true for the transport of some viruses (cf. p. 91). It seems also possible that the flowering-inducing stimulus, which is known to move in the phloem, belongs to this group of substances (or to the steroids?).

BUVAT (1963) demonstrated the presence of RNA in the "slime bodies" of the *Cucurbita pepo* sieve tubes by histochemical means. After feeding *Cucurbita* plants with $^{32}PO_4^{3-}$, labeled RNA could also be detected in the phloem exudate (BIELESKI, 1969). In young nucleated sieve tubes of *Vicia faba* ^{3}H-uridine is incorporated primarily into the nuclear RNA and later into the cytoplasmic RNA (NEUMANN and WOLLGIEHN, 1964). In sieve tubes with degenerated nuclei no incorporation of uridine in RNA takes place, whilst ^{3}H-phenylalanine is still incorporated into the proteins of old sieve tubes without RNA-synthesis.

A quantitative analysis of DNA and RNA in the sieve-tube sap of *Robinia pseudoacacia* revealed an average concentration of 4.7 μg DNA/ml and 1.65 μg RNA/ml (ZIEGLER and KLUGE, 1962).

Of the compounds which are structurally related to the nucleic acids or to their constituents, *ATP* is of special interest. Any one of the mechanisms discussed for the phloem transport at present is energy-dependent (even the osmotically driven solution flow according to MÜNCH needs at least an intact, selectively permeable ectoplast in the sieve tubes), and especially in the sieve tubes with their scarce mitochondria it is to be supposed that energy is supplied in the form of ATP by the companion cells or their analogs which are very rich in mitochondria.

PAVLINOVA and AFANASJEVA (1962) found ATP, ADP and AMP in the complete bundles of sugar beet. KLUGE and ZIEGLER (1964) analyzed the phloem exudate of a number of tree species and found varying but always considerable concentrations of ATP. Similar results were obtained with stylet exudate of aphids feeding on willow (GARDNER and PEEL, 1969, 1972), and with phloem exudate from *Ricinus communis* (HALL and BAKER, 1972) and *Yucca flaccida* (KLUGE et al., 1970); even the "sieve-element" exudate of the brown alga *Macrocystis* shows a high concentration of ATP (SCHMITZ and SRIVASTAVA, 1974) (see Table 4).

Table 4. ATP content in phloem exudate of several species

Species	Time of exudation	ATP (μg/ml)	Reference
Prunus padus L.	Sept.	227.3	KLUGE and ZIEGLER (1964)
Cladrastis lutea KOCH	Sept.	161.6	KLUGE and ZIEGLER (1964)
Robinia pseudoacacia L.	Sept.	96.3	KLUGE and ZIEGLER (1964)
Hippophaë salicifolia DON.	Sept.	186.8	KLUGE and ZIEGLER (1964)
Koelreuteria paniculata LAXM.	Sept.	112.6	KLUGE and ZIEGLER (1964)
Tilia platyphyllos SCOP.	Sept.	225.3	KLUGE and ZIEGLER (1964)
Acer opalus MIL.	Sept.	126.8	KLUGE and ZIEGLER (1964)
Evodia rutaecarpa HOOK. F. et THOMPS.	Sept.	181.9	KLUGE and ZIEGLER (1964)
Salix alba L.	Sept.	186.8	KLUGE and ZIEGLER (1964)
Salix daphnoides VILL.	Sept.	131.2	KLUGE and ZIEGLER (1964)
Salix viminalis L.	Sept.	250–1,335	GARDNER and PEEL (1969, 1972)
Ulmus glabra HUDS.	Sept.	157.4	KLUGE and ZIEGLER (1964)
Fraxinus excelsior L.	Sept.	139.9	KLUGE and ZIEGLER (1964)
Fraxinus americana L.	Sept.	299.3	KLUGE and ZIEGLER (1964)
Fagus sylvatica L.	Sept.	132.2	KLUGE and ZIEGLER (1964)
Carpinus betulus L.	Sept.	186.8	KLUGE and ZIEGLER (1964)
Quercus petraea LIEBL.	Sept.	34.9	KLUGE and ZIEGLER (1964)
Quercus phellos L.	Sept.	48.1	KLUGE and ZIEGLER (1964)
Quercus borealis MICHX.	July	100	KLUGE et al. (1970)
	Oct.	250–575	KLUGE et al. (1970)
Yucca flaccida HAW.		300–976	KLUGE et al. (1970)
Ricinus communis L.		240–360	HALL and BAKER (1972)

Besides ATP other members of the adenylic acid family are present in sieve-tube exudate. ATP is usually the predominant member. In stylet exudate of willow the ratio ATP:ADP varied between 2.0 and 5.3 (GARDNER and PEEL, 1972), in the phloem exudate of *Robinia pseudoacacia* the ratio was 8.5 and in that of *Tilia platyphyllos* 5.0 (KLUGE and ZIEGLER, 1964).

For the last two species also the concentration of AMP was determined (KLUGE and ZIEGLER). It is, therefore, possible to calculate the "energy charge":

$$\frac{1}{2}\,\frac{[ADP]+2[ATP]}{[AMP]+[ADP]+[ATP]}\,.$$

This value is an expression of the energy status of a cell or a compartment (ATKINSON, 1969). It can vary between 1.0 (all the adenine nucleotide present as ATP) or 0 (all present as AMP). For the *Robinia* phloem exudate the energy charge is 0.88, for *Tilia* 0.77; this is fairly high in both cases. This means that ATP-requiring processes will show a relatively high rate, while the ATP generating processes are at a relatively low level.

In *Robinia* phloem exudate there is also a relatively high concentration of free adenine (KLUGE and ZIEGLER, 1964); this may be due to the activity of an enzyme which decomposes ATP to adenine. It is present in the sap of *Robinia* but not in that of *Tilia* (ZIEGLER and KLUGE, 1962; KLUGE and ZIEGLER, 1964).

The ATP concentration in the phloem exudate of *Robinia* and *Tilia* shows seasonal fluctuations (Fig. 6) very similar in both species. The highest concentration coincides with the highest transport rate (in the autumn during the export of the substances from the wilting leaves). This may be considered as an indication for the influence of ATP on assimilate transport.

It is not clear how far the ATP in the sieve tubes functions as a transport substance, moving together with the other assimilates. The lack of a concentration gradient at the different stem-heights (Table 5) indicates that ATP does not show the typical pattern of the main transport compounds which decrease in their concentration in the direction of translocation (Chapter 14, p. 344).

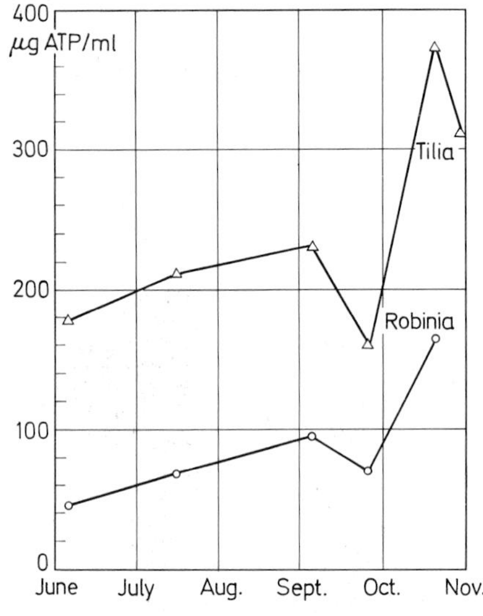

◀ Fig. 6. Seasonal changes in the ATP concentrations of phloem exudate of *Robinia pseudoacacia* and *Tilia platyphyllos*. Values are the average of three parallel determinations (KLUGE and ZIEGLER, 1964)

Table 5. ATP concentration in phloem exudate of *Tilia euchlora* in different heights of the stem (KLUGE and ZIEGLER, 1964)

Height (m)	Concentration (μg/ml)
10	179.3
8	196.7
2	174.8
0	179.3

GARDNER and PEEL (1969) showed that the ATP concentration of stylet exudate from willow did not decrease during a long period of exudation. The same is true for the phloem exudate of *Yucca* inflorescences (Fig. 7). It is improbable that such continuous production of a relatively high ATP-concentration proceeds in the sieve tubes themselves. In the thin ectoplasmic layer in the opened sieve tubes neither the enzymatic apparatus nor the building material for such an ample ATP-production can be present. It is assumed that the neighboring cells, especially companion cells, are involved in these processes.

An important question in connection with the role of ATP in the sieve-tube function is whether the ATP in the sieve tubes is a static compound or whether it shows a high turnover of its phosphate groups. BIELESKI (1969) supplied *Cucurbita maxima* with $^{32}PO_4^{3-}$ and found a fast labeling of ATP and other phosphorous compounds in the phloem exudate of these plants. Surprisingly, the cell-free phloem exudate of *Yucca flaccida* inflorescences and stylet exudate of aphids feeding on *Salix triandra* phloem incorporated $^{32}PO_4^{3-}$ very rapidly into most of the phosphorylated compounds present (BECKER et al., 1971). Labeled ATP can be detected chromatographically very soon (Fig. 8), and the specific activity of ATP increases very

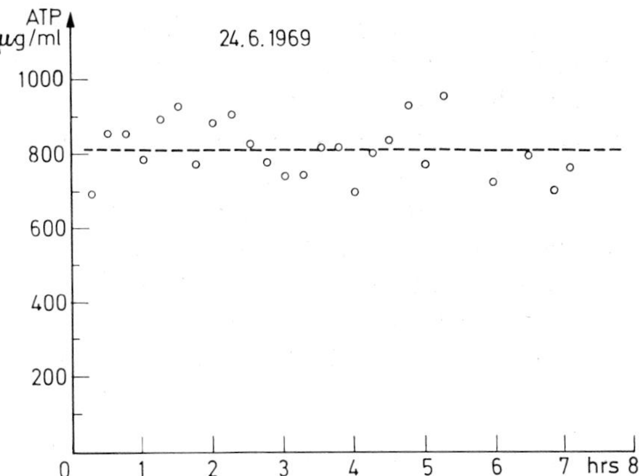

Fig. 7. Concentration of ATP in the phloem exudate of *Yucca flaccida* during continuous secretion (KLUGE et al., 1970)

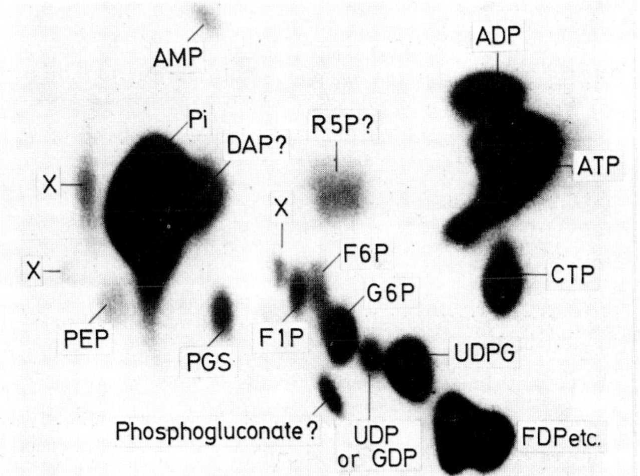

Fig. 8. Autoradiography of a thin-layer chromatogram, showing the ^{32}P-labeled compounds in the phloem exudate of *Tilia platyphyllos* after 3 h incubation of the sap with $^{32}PO_4^{3-}$. Pi inorganic phosphate; ATP adenosinetriphosphate; ADP adenosinediphosphate; AMP adenosinemonophosphate; CTP cytidinetriphosphate; DAP dihydroxyacetone phosphate; F1P fructose-1-phosphate; F6P fructose-6-phosphate; FDP fructose-1,6-diphosphate; GDP guanosinediphosphate; G6P glucose-6-phosphate; PEP phosphoenolpyruvate; PGS 3-phosphoglyceric acid; R5P ribose-5-phosphate; UDPG uridinediphosphateglucose; UDP uridinediphosphate; unidentified substances (BECKER et al., 1971)

rapidly (half-life about 15 min). Similar results were also obtained with the exudate from the sieve elements of the brown alga *Macrocystis integrifolia* (SCHMITZ and SRIVASTAVA, 1974).

In conclusion, we can assume that the ATP in the sieve tubes is in a state of intensive turnover while the concentration is held ± constant.

Besides the members of the adenylic family several other constituents or derivatives of nucleotides could be detected either in the whole phloem or whole conducting bundles or in the sieve-tube sap itself. In the first two cases, it is of course not decided whether these compounds belong to the sieve tubes or to other cells of the complex tissue (or to both). Uracil-derivatives are of special interest, because some of them (e.g. UDPG) are very probably involved in the biosynthesis of the transport sugars. Uracil itself was found in low concentration in the phloem exudate of *Robinia pseudoacacia*. Formation by breakdown of uracil derivatives during the analysis was not excluded. UMP, UDP, and UTP are reported to be present in the bundles of sugar beet (PAVLINOVA and AFANASJEVA, 1962) and of *Heracleum sosnowskyi* (PAVLINOVA, 1965). UTP appeared also as a labeled substance in the phloem exudate of *Cucurbita maxima* if the plant was fed with $^{32}PO_4^{3-}$ (BIELESKI, 1969). UDP (or GDP?) was one of the substances which were labeled after incubation of sieve-tube sap of *Tilia platyphyllos* and of *Yucca flaccida* with $^{32}PO_4^{3-}$ (BECKER et al., 1971; Fig. 8). UDPG and UDP incorporated the isotope after incubation of the sieve-element exudate of *Macrocystis* with $^{32}PO_4^{3-}$ (SCHMITZ and SRIVASTAVA, 1974).

UDPG was detected in the isolated phloem of *Heracleum mantegazzianum* (ZIEGLER, 1960), in the bundles of sugar beet and *Heracleum sosnowskyi* (see above) and also as a labeled substance in the phloem exudate of *Cucurbita* after supplying the plant, and of *Tilia* and *Yucca* after supplying the exudate itself with $^{32}PO_4^{3-}$ (see above).

UDPGal and UDP-pentose have been reported from the bundles of *Heracleum sosnowskyi* (PAVLINOVA, 1965).

CDP and CTP were found in the same bundles. Labeled CTP appeared also after incubation of the phloem exudate of *Tilia* and *Yucca* (BECKER et al., 1971), or of the sieve-element exudate of *Macrocystis* (SCHMITZ and SRIVASTAVA, 1974) with $^{32}PO_4^{3-}$.

Guanosine-phosphates have been found in the conducting bundles of sugar beet (PAVLINOVA and AFANASJEVA, 1962), but not as yet in the phloem exudate.

It is assumed that the fraction of nucleic acids and their derivatives in the sieve tubes is drastically changed when the plant is infected with a phloem-mobile virus (see p. 91).

It is not yet clear whether these other nucleosides and nucleotides besides ATP are real transport substances in the phloem.

7. Growth Substances and Inhibitors

It is of profound importance for the role of growth regulators in the correlative regulation of the growth processes that they can be transported in the "long-distance channels" of a plant. In connection with IAA transport in the plant, for example, it is often overlooked that a strictly polar transport is possible only in parenchyma, not in the sieve tubes, where the direction of transport can be reversed if the relative positions of sources and sinks change.

IAA. There is very strong evidence that IAA can move in the sieve tubes. In this case it follows, like all other compounds, the direction of the bulk assimilates. The first evidence for the presence of IAA-like substances was the demonstration of compound(s) active in the *Avena*-curvature-test in the sieve-tube sap of *Robinia*,

Fagus, and *Aesculus* (HUBER et al., 1937). Later it was shown that exogenously applied ^{14}C-IAA can move as such in the phloem (ESCHRICH, 1968; LEPP and PEEL, 1970, 1971a; GOLDSMITH et al., 1974). N-(indolyl-3-acetyl) aspartate, on the contrary, is not phloem-mobile, apparently because it cannot enter the sieve tubes (ESCHRICH, 1968).

In the phloem exudate of *Ricinus communis* the average concentration of IAA was estimated to be 0.0105 mg/l or 0.6×10^{-7} M (HALL and BAKER, 1972).

Auxin could also be detected in the honeydew of several aphids (MAXWELL and PAINTER, 1962). Substance(s) active in the *Avena*-mesocotyl-assay were also found in the honeydew collected from aphids feeding on willow phloem (HOAD et al., 1971).

There are indications that auxins transported in the phloem not only affect the activation of the sieve tubes and initiate cambial activity in trees after winter dormancy (cf. HILL, 1962; WAREING et al., 1964; ZIMMERMANN, 1968), but also exert a considerable influence over the translocation of sugar in both a tangential (sugar loading from the storage parenchyma into the sieve elements) and longitudinal direction (LEPP and PEEL, 1971b).

Table 6. Gibberellin activity in phloem exudate of several species (in GA_3 equivalents)

Species	Method	Concentration (μg/ml)	Reference
Robinia pseudoacacia L.	dwarf *Zea* test	6×10^{-4}	KLUGE et al. (1964)
Tilia cordata	dwarf *Zea* test	45×10^{-4}	KLUGE et al. (1964)
Quercus robur L.	dwarf *Zea* test	17×10^{-4}	KLUGE et al. (1964)
Fagus sylvatica L.	dwarf *Zea* test	11×10^{-4}	KLUGE et al. (1964)
Ricinus communis L.	barley endosperm test	230×10^{-4}	HALL and BAKER (1972)

Gibberellins. Gibberellin-like activity in phloem exudate was first reported for *Robinia pseudoacacia, Tilia cordata, Fagus sylvatica* and *Quercus robur* (KLUGE et al., 1964) with the dwarf maize (d_5) assay (Table 6). The concentration in the sieve tube sap of *Ricinus communis* is of the same order of magnitude (HALL and BAKER, 1972). Especially with substances which occur in such low concentrations, there is always the danger that they could be washed out from the cells around the sieve tubes by the exuded sap. It is therefore important to know that gibberellin activity was also detected in the honeydew of aphids feeding on *Taraxacum officinale, Vicia faba,* and *Salix viminalis* (HOAD and BOWEN, 1968). Results obtained with *Salix* showed that the concentration of gibberellin-like substances in the sieve-tube sap is day-length dependent; high levels being present in plants having long days, but low levels in plants with short days. It is not clear whether the gibberellin-like substances in the phloem are exported from mature leaves or whether they are synthesized in the root and arrive in the phloem sap as a result of lateral transfer (cf. HOAD and BOWEN, 1968).

Cytokinins. Soybean-callus assay indicated that honeydew from aphids feeding on the sieve tubes of *Xanthium strumarium* contained a substance with cytokinin activity (PHILLIPS and CLELAND, 1972). The concentration of this active compound(s) seems to be higher in the honeydew from flowering plants than from vegetative plants. The absence of cytokinin in the honeydew of aphids feeding on a chemically defined diet indicates that the insects themselves do not produce a cytokinin.

With the barley leaf chlorophyll preservation test three chromatographically distinct, cytokinin-active principles could be demonstrated in the phloem exudate of *Ricinus communis* (HALL and BAKER, 1972). One coincides with the Rf's of kinetin and zeatin, and the estimated level of kinetin-like activity in this peak was 0.004 mg/l or 2.0×10^{-8} M. The activity of the two other peaks was supposed to represent Factor I described by KENDE (1965) for kinetin-like factors in the root exudate of sunflowers. KENDE supposed that Factor I is a bound form of the other cytokinin found in the root exudate (Factor II). The estimated levels of activity in these two peaks in the phloem exudate were 0.0032 mg/l or 1.5×10^{-8} M and 0.0036 mg/l or 1.7×10^{-8} M respectively.

A-3′:5′-MP. Cyclic adenosine-3′:5′-monophosphate is a well known secondary messenger in animals, bacteria and cellular slime moulds. Its role in higher plants is not yet clear (cf. WELLBURN et al., 1973). There are even doubts whether it occurs at all in higher plants (AMRHEIN, 1974). The radio-isotope dilution test for identification of A-3′:5′-MP gave positive results with sieve-tube exudate of *Robinia pseudoacacia* and exudate from the trumpet hyphae in the cauloids of the brown alga *Laminaria saccharina* (BECKER and ZIEGLER, 1973). The concentration was about 0.1 μM in *Laminaria* exudate and 9.0 nM in the *Robinia exudate*. Pretreatment of the saps with phosphodiesterase removed the activity. This is an indication that A-3′:5′-MP may occur in the translocation tissues of plants. Sieve-tube exudates of *Cucurbita maxima* and of *Yucca flaccida*, on the other hand, contain practically no A-3:5-MP (cf. HEYSER et al., 1974), when tested with the bioassay using the sensitive Amoeba *Dictyostelium discoideum* (KONIJN, 1970). A phosphodiesterase, occurring in the sieve-tube exudate of *Cucurbita*, hydrolyzed neither A-3′:5′-MP nor other nucleoside-3′:5′-(cyclic) monophosphates (HEYSER et al., 1974).

In conclusion: the occurrence of A-3′:5′-MP in the sieve tubes as in higher plants in general has to be proved in further experiments. The present state of knowledge does not allow us to discuss a possible role of this substance in the phloem transport.

Abscisic Acid. HOAD (1967) found abscisic acid in the honeydew of the aphid *Tuberolachnus salignus* feeding on *Salix viminalis*. The level of this inhibitor was found to be higher with short days than with long days (BOWEN and HOAD, 1968); i.e. in this respect abscisic acid and the gibberellins behave conversely (see p. 79).

Non-identified Hormonal Factors. Several additional factors with hormone-like activity are reported to be translocated in the phloem (cf. review ESCHRICH, 1970). The floral stimulus; a cold-hardiness factor; a factor which is synthesized in leaves and is necessary for successful graft union; a controlling factor for assimilation of certain substances by roots. Since none of these factors are chemically identified as yet, it cannot be excluded that some of these active principles may be distinct new substances or it may reflect the effect of different concentration ratios of the known growth regulators. There is no doubt that the identification of the phloem-mobile floral stimulus is one of the most fascinating problems not only in phloem transport but also in the physiology of development.

Table 7. Relations between mobility in the phloem P and xylem X and some physical and chemical characteristics of herbicides (JACOB et al., 1973). Brackets (P) and (X) indicate mobility is probable but not proved.

Herbicide	Mobility P	Mobility X	Solubility in H_2O, g/l	Katabolism in plants	Cl, Br, I	—NH_2	—NH—	—N—	—NO_2	—NH—C(=O)—O—	—NH—C(=O)—S—	—NH—C(=O)—NH—	—COOH	—CH_3	—OCH_3
2,4-D	P		0.4	+	+								+		
MCPA	P		0.5	+	+								+	+	
2,4,5-T	P		0.3	+	+								+		
2,4-DB	(P)		0.04		+								+		
Dicamba	P	X	8.0	+	+								+		+
2-I-3-nitrobenzoic acid	P	X			I				+				+		
Amiben	P	(X)	0.7	+			+						+		
2,3,6-TBA	P	X	8.0	+									+		
2,3,5-TIBA	P				I								+		
2,6-Dichlobenil	(P)	(X)	0.02	+ +	+										
TCA	P	X	1200	+ +	+								+		
Dalapon	P	X	570	+ +	+								+		
Propham		(X)	0.25	+ +						+					
Chlorpropham		(X)	0.1	+ +	+					+					
Eptan (EPTC)	(P)	(X)									+				
Diallat	(P)	(X)	0.01	+ + +	+						+				
Fenuron		X	3.85	+								+		+	
Monuron		X	0.23	+	+							+		+	
Diuron (DCHU)		X	0.04	+	+							+		+	
Linuron		X	0.07	+	+							+		+	+
Metabromuron		X	0.33	+	Br							+		+	+
Diquat		(X)	670	+ +	Br			+							
Paraquat				+				+				+			
Maleic acid hydrazide	P	(X)	0.4	+ +			+								
Atrazine		X	0.03	+ +	+		+	+							
Ipazine		X			+		+	+							
Prometone		X	0.75	+			+	+							+
Prometryne		X	0.05	+			+	+						+	
Propazine		X	0.008	+	+		+	+							
Pyrazon		X	0.4	+	+	+		+							
Simazine		X	0.005	+	+		+	+							
Amitrole	P	X	280	+ +		+	+	+							
Picloram	P	X	0.4	+	+	+		+					+		
DNOC		(X)	0.12	+ +					+						

Synthetic Growth Regulators and Herbicides. It is a question of great practical importance as to whether or not a growth regulator or a herbicide is mobile in the phloem. It is not intended to give a complete list of the mobility of the great number of synthetic growth regulators, herbicides, fungicides, and insecticides. The reader is referred to the reviews of CRAFTS and CRISP (1971), and ASHTON and CRAFTS (1973).

A general question seems important to us in this connection: what structural prerequisites in the molecule determine the mobility of an exogenously applied compound in the phloem and in the xylem respectively?

JACOB et al. (1973) tried to answer this question, using published research and their own experiments. As can be seen from Table 7, no relationship exists between the water solubility of herbicides or the velocity of their metabolic degradation and their phloem mobility. Also the chlorine substitution which is so important for the herbicidal effect of many substances plays no decisive role with regard to the mode of mobility of herbicides. There exists, however, a striking correlation between the occurrence of carboxyl groups and the translocation in the phloem of very different compounds. For example, 2,4-D[(2,4-dichlorophenoxy) acetic acid] loses its phloem mobility if the acetyl group is replaced by a methyl group (Fig. 9).

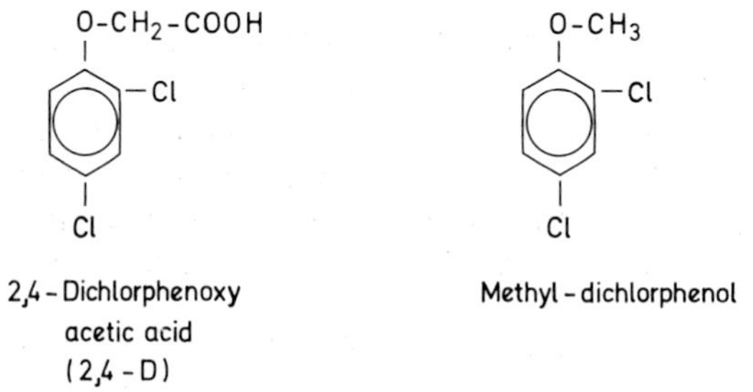

$O-CH_2-COOH$ / $-Cl$ / Cl

2,4-Dichlorphenoxy acetic acid (2,4-D)

$O-CH_3$ / $-Cl$ / Cl

Methyl-dichlorphenol

Fig. 9

There seem to be some exceptions from the rule that the occurrence of carboxyl groups is correlated with phloem mobility. This concerns maleic hydrazide and amitrole (Table 7), which move in the phloem as well as in the xylem. Maleic acid however, which is generally formulated in the anhydride form, can act like a monovalent acid (BAILEY and WHITE, 1964). Amitrole is known to be metabolized to a certain degree in the plant. Among the most important products of degradation are the amino-triazolyl compounds of alanine, glycine and serine (MILLER and HALL, 1961). Such metabolites could be responsible for the translocation of amitrole in the phloem. A similar explanation is also discussed for the (limited) phloem mobility of EPTC and diallat, which do not have carboxyl groups in their molecules.

In the group of synthetic growth regulators alar (B-995) and chlorflurenol (morphactin) have carboxyl groups (Fig. 10) and are able to move in the phloem (and more or less in the xylem), while the translocation patterns of AMO 1618 and CCC, which do not have carboxyl groups (Fig. 10), are not studied in detail (cf. JACOB et al., 1973).

Among the very many substances which act as fungicides, few are considered to be systemic. The present data on the relationship between chemical structure and phloem mobility in this group of substances do not yet allow general conclusions. The same is also true for insecticides. In general, insecticides with good phloem mobility have not yet been found.

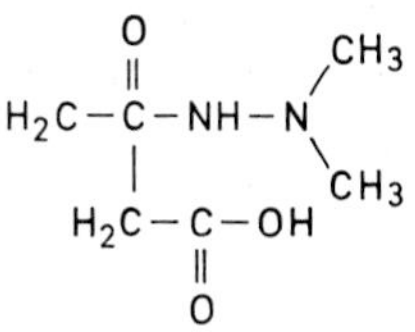

$$H_2C-\overset{\overset{O}{\|}}{C}-NH-N(CH_3)_2$$
$$H_2C-\underset{\underset{O}{\|}}{C}-OH$$

Alar (B 995)

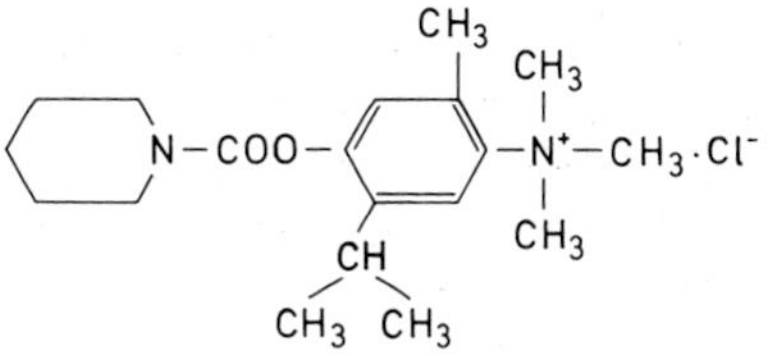

Amo 1618

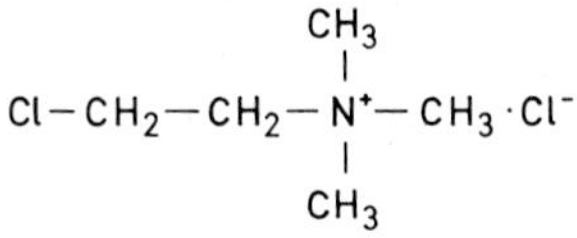

$$Cl-CH_2-CH_2-N^+(CH_3)_3\cdot Cl^-$$

CCC

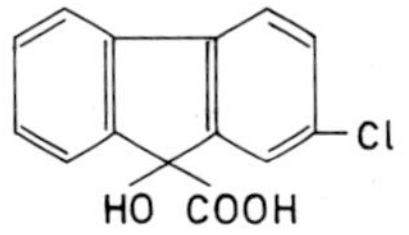

Chlorflurenol (Morphaktin)

Fig. 10

8. Vitamins

The occurrence and transport of vitamins in the sieve tubes is of interest for two reasons. First, phloem transport has to carry all those organic compounds which cannot be synthesized from the transport assimilates by non-autotrophic cells and tissues of a plant (e.g. meristems or roots). Secondly, a knowledge of the vitamin content of the sieve tubes is of great importance for the understanding of the nutrition of the numerous phloem-feeding animals (mainly insects). As yet, only water-soluble vitamins have been analyzed.

Thiamine is known as a substance which cannot be synthesized by heterotrophic tissues of a higher plant. It has to be supplied, for example, to isolated roots *in vitro*. This vitamin accumulated above a girdle and it was therefore presumed to be translocated in the phloem (cf. review in ZIEGLER and ZIEGLER, 1962). BUCHBERGER (1952) detected thiamine in the phloem exudate of *Cucurbita pepo, Tilia platyphyllos,* and *Quercus rubra,* SCHWARZ (cf. FINK, 1952) in that of *Quercus borealis.* ZIEGLER and ZIEGLER found this vitamin in the phloem exudate of all 21 tree species analyzed (14 genera of 10 families) in varying amounts. Almost all of the thiamine occurs in free form.

Niacin is another vitamin which is needed by isolated roots (e.g. in *Robinia;* SEELIGER, 1956). SCHWARZ found higher concentrations of this substance in the sieve-tube sap of *Quercus borealis.* In the phloem exudate of 17 tree species analyzed by ZIEGLER and ZIEGLER, niacin was always present in considerable amounts, part of it apparently in bound form.

Pantothenic acid is also needed by tissue cultures *in vitro* and accumulates above a girdle (BONNER and DORLAND, 1943). It was found in varying amounts in the phloem exudate of 25 species analyzed for this vitamin (ZIEGLER and ZIEGLER). Part of the pantothenic acid in the sap was present in bound form, possibly as coenzyme A.

Other vitamins which are supposed to be phloem-mobile on the basis of tissue culture and girdling experiments, are those of the *B_6-complex,* including *pyridoxine,* *pyridoxale, pyridoxamine* and the 5-phosphate derivatives of the last two substances. The vitamin B_6-complex was detectable in the phloem exudate of 18 tree species, always in free form (ZIEGLER and ZIEGLER). Only the sieve-tube sap of *Robinia pseudoacacia* and possibly *Populus nigra* lacked these pyridoxin compounds. This is surprising, because isolated *Robinia* roots need this vitamin (SEELIGER, 1956). If the vitamin is indeed absent in the sieve tubes (and not only because the method of determination is inadequate), the roots have to be supplied from other sources besides the phloem, perhaps by the symbiontic bacteria. *Riboflavin, biotin, folic acid, vitamin* B_{12}, and *"Crithidiafactor"* occur in phloem exudates, if at all, only in very low concentrations (ZIEGLER and ZIEGLER).

Two other substances, *myo-inositol* and *vitamin C*, are present in all phloem exudates analyzed in such high concentrations (mostly $\gg 100$ μg/ml) that they should perhaps not be considered as true vitamins. The inositol concentration shows a seasonal variation in the phloem exudate of *Tilia petiolaris* and *Buddleia davidii* with relatively low concentrations in the summer and high concentrations in the autumn; these are in reverse to concentration changes of the sugars in the exudates (H. KLUGE, 1970).

Inositol plays an important role in the biosynthesis of the galactose-containing oligosaccharides (Fig. 4; TANNER and KANDLER, 1966) which are predominant transport sugars in many species (see above). Besides this function they also seem to be precursors for pectins and related carbohydrates (cf. LOEWUS, 1971). It is therefore assumed that myo-inositol is one of the transport substances which are used in substrate quantities in the receiving cells.

Ascorbic acid belongs to the same category, but its exact role in the plant cells is less well known than that of inositol. There is no doubt that it can be transported in the phloem. In two species a differentiation of the vitamin C-compounds was apparent: while the phloem exudate of *Robinia pseudoacacia* contained predominantly ascorbic acid and only minor amounts of dehydroascorbic acid and diketogulonic acid, that of *Quercus robur* showed also considerable amounts of the latter two substances (ZIEGLER and ZIEGLER).

9. Other Organic Substances

It is almost certain that a systematic search for other organic substances, not mentioned in the foregoing chapters, in the sieve tubes or their exudates would reveal a great number of additional compounds. It is more interesting to ask what and why organic substances can *not* be translocated in the phloem, than what *can*.

A group of substances present in the phloem exudate of all analyzed species in several compounds, but in low concentrations, are the *organic phosphate-compounds*. We described previously the derivatives or constituents of nucleotides. Besides these compounds a number of other substances were found in the phloem exudate, especially after labeling with $^{32}PO_4^{3-}$. In the sieve-tube exudate of *Cucurbita maxima* glucose-6-phosphate, fructose-6-phosphate, mannose-6-phosphate, glucose-1-phosphate, hexose diphosphates, phosphoglycerate, phosphoryl ethanolamine, phosphoryl choline and (tentatively) triose-phosphate were detected (BIELESKI, 1969). In the phloem exudate of *Yucca flaccida* and *Salix triandra* glucose-6-phosphate, fructose-6-phosphate, fructose-1,6-diphosphate, phosphoglycerate, phosphoenol pyruvate, and phosphoryl choline were reported (KLUGE et al.,

1970; BECKER et al., 1971; Fig. 8). A similar picture was also obtained with the exudate of *Tilia platyphyllos* which also contained ribose-5-phosphate, dihydroxyacetone phosphate and phosphogluconate (BECKER et al., 1971). FORD and PEEL (1967) found glucose-6-phosphate, glucose-1-phosphate and fructose-1,6-diphosphate in the phloem exudate of *Salix viminalis*, ESCHRICH (1961) glucose-1-phosphate in that of *Tilia tomentosa*. "Sugar-monophosphates" become labeled after incubation of the sieve-element exudate of *Macrocystis* with $^{32}PO_4^{3-}$ (SCHMITZ and SRIVASTAVA, 1974).

It seems probable that these organic phosphorus compounds are not substrates for the metabolism of the phloem-supplied tissues, but mirror the metabolic activity of the sieve tubes themselves. The enzymatic constitution of the sieve tubes (cf. Chapter 4, Table 1) readily accounts for the appearance of most of the compounds mentioned above.

There are indications that also *anthrachinone* derivatives (in *Rhamnus*; MALICKY-SCHLATTE, 1966) and phenolic substances (in *Salix* and *Vicia*; MACLEOD and PRIDHAM, 1966) can move in the phloem. HATHWAY (1959) found phenolic compounds in the phloem exudate of *Quercus robur*, between them the pyrogalloyl-precursors of the oak-bark tannins(+)-gallocatechine and leucodelphinidine (cf. also ZIEGLER, 1956). Flavonoids, on the other hand, are apparently not phloem-mobile in *Trifolium* (SCHULTZ, 1969).

It is of course possible that such substances, found in low concentration in phloem exudate, are washed from bark cells by the sieve-tube sap during efflux. But since the tannin precursors accumulate above a girdle, it is at least probable that these substances really move in the sieve tubes.

10. Inorganic Substances

The phloem is usually considered to be the pathway for the assimilate transport. This is certainly its most important and obvious function. However, it should not be forgotten that the phloem also transport water and inorganic ions in a way comparable to, but by no means identical with xylem.

If we assume that phloem transport takes place as a flowing solution, then all the substances including inorganic ions which enter the sieve tubes should be translocated in the phloem. Substances which are not phloem mobile would then be excluded from the loading reaction (see Chapter 17).

It has been clear since the investigations of MASON and MASKELL (1953) that there are differences in the phloem mobility of different inorganic substances. Phosphorus and potassium accumulated in cotton plants above a girdle and were depleted below it, while the distribution of calcium was not affected by girdling. They concluded that phosphorus and potassium were transported in the phloem while calcium was not. MASON and PHILLIS (1937) also found that sulfur, magnesium, and chlorine were phloem mobile.

With the help of radioisotopes, BUKOVAC and WITTWER (1957) systematically studied the mobility of mineral elements in the phloem of bean plants. They found groups of mobile, relatively mobile, and immobile elements (Table 8). This different phloem mobility of the inorganic elements is also reflected in the mineral content of the phloem exudates (see Table 9 and Chapter 8, p. 201). Furthermore, in the case of mineral deficiency, withholding a phloem-mobile element from the rooting

Table 8. Mobility of mineral elements in the phloem. (From EPSTEIN, 1972, enlarged)

Mobile	Intermediate	Immobile
Potassium (a)	Iron (a)	Lithium (a)
Rubidium (a)	Manganese (a)	Calcium (a)
Caesium (b)	Zinc (a)	Strontium (a)
Sodium (a)	Copper (a)	Barium (a)
Magnesium (a)	Molybdenum (a)	Boron (a)
Phosphorus (a)		Lead (c)
Sulfur (a)		Polonium (d)
Chlorine (a)		

(a) BUKOVAC and WITTWER (1957). (b) WITHERSPOON and BROWN (1965). (c) KLOCKE et al. (1966). (d) TSO and FISENNE (1968).

medium causes deficiency symptoms in *old* leaves which supply the young developing parts of the plant with mineral elements *via* phloem. On the other hand withholding a phloem immobile element affects the *young* leaves first which have a low transpiration rate and, therefore, a lower xylem supply.

Mobile Elements. In all the investigated cases the predominant cation in sieve-tube sap was *potassium*. The concentration in the phloem exudate varied in the different species (possibly also affected by the different methods of determination), but it is always high (Table 9). There is little doubt that potassium not only functions as an element which is readily redistributed in the plant, but also has some function in phloem transport itself (see Chapters 13 and 17).

Like potassium, other alkali metals (*sodium, rubidium,* and *caesium*) are also phloem mobile (cf. Table 9). It is interesting that *lithium* does not show the same behavior: It is phloem-immobile like calcium (KENT, 1941), which is understandable, because lithium chemically resembles calcium in many respects more than alkali metals (cf. EPSTEIN, 1960, 1972).

On the other hand, *magnesium* is readily mobile in the phloem, while the heavier alkaline earths cations (calcium, strontium, barium) are not (see below).

The predominant anion in phloem exudates is usually *phosphate* (Table 10). In *Ricinus communis* exudate, *chloride* is of about the same concentration, but this seems to be an exception. This high concentration of free inorganic phosphate has important consequences: one is the fact that all the cations which form phosphates of low solubility (e.g. calcium, barium, lead) can only be present in the sieve tubes (and be transported there) in the extremely low concentration determined by the solubility product of the phosphate salt. The second consequence is the influence on the pH of sieve-tube sap: the predominance of potassium as a cation and of phosphate as an anion seems to be the main reason for the mostly alkaline pH of phloem exudate (see below). *Sulphate* does not seem to play a major role in phloem transport of sulfur; this element moves mostly in organic form.

The same is true for *nitrate* which is reported to be absent in most phloem exudates so far analyzed (cf. Table 10). However, in the older literature nitrate has been reported in considerable amounts in phloem exudate of *Fraxinus americana,*

Table 9. Concentration (µg/ml) of the most important inorganic cations in sieve-tube exudate of some species

	Potassium	Sodium	Calcium	Magnesium		Reference
Ricinus communis	2,300–4,400	46–276	20–92	109–122	(29 Ammonium)	HALL and BAKER (1972)
Yucca flaccida	1,650	1.2	12	95		TAMMES and VAN DIE (1964)
Arenga saccharifera	1,200		10	96		TAMMES (1958)
Salix viminalis	up to 20,000	tr	0			PEEL and WEATHERLEY (1959)
Fraxinus americana	450–1,200		340–1,180 (?)	180–530		MOOSE (1938)
	2,430	6.5	46	260		KIMMEL (1962)
Fraxinus pennsylvanica var. *lanceolata*	370–580		1,040–1,330 (?)	210–610		
Platanus occidentalis	800–960		760–1,260 (?)	190–660		MOOSE (1938)
Robinia pseudoacacia	900–1,140		440–900 (?)	150–390		MOOSE (1938)
	2,650	1.5	32	330		KIMMEL (1962)
Acer platanoides[a]	1,330		156	2,240		KIMMEL (1962)
Acer pseudoplatanus	2,080		99	3,900 (?)		KIMMEL (1962)
Fagus sylvatica	960	1.4	38			KIMMEL (1962)
Juglans regia	1,180	5.4	165	190		KIMMEL (1962)
Populus nigra	2,020		114			KIMMEL (1962)
Quercus petraea	1,150		72			KIMMEL (1962)
Quercus borealis			39	50		KIMMEL (1962)
Salix babylonica	2,030		73			KIMMEL (1962)
Tilia platyphyllos	2,550	6.7	66	250		KIMMEL (1962)
Cucurbita maxima	200–240		70–180	60–100		MOOSE (1938)
Macrocystis pyrifera	9,200	920			(210 Iodine)	PARKER (1966)

[a] In this species phloem exudate is partly mixed with exudate from laticifers.

Table 10. Concentration of the most important inorganic anions in phloem exudate of *Yucca flaccida* (VAN DIE et al., 1974) and *Ricinus communis* (HALL and BAKER, 1972) in μeq/ml

	Yucca flaccida	*Ricinus communis*
Phosphate	4.2	7.4–11.4
Sulphate	0.7	0.5–1.0
Chloride	ca. 1.0	10–19
Nitrate		absent
Bicarbonate		1.7

F. pennsylvanica, Robinia pseudoacacia, and *Platanus occidentalis* (MOOSE, 1938) and in *Cucurbita pepo* (ZACHARIAS, 1884; KRAUS, 1885). It is not clear whether the method was inadequate in these analyses, or whether the presence or absence of nitrate in the sieve tubes depends on the nitrogen supply to the plant and on the capacity of nitrate reduction in the cells loading the sieve tubes.

Relatively Mobile Elements. Most of the heavy-metal nutrients seem to belong to this group, as suggested by the composition of phloem exudate and by experiments on redistribution and export from leaves. In *Yucca flaccida, zinc* (2 μg/ml), *iron* (1.4 μg/ml), *manganese* (0.5 μg/ml), *copper* (0.4 μg/ml), and *molybdenum* (0.01 μg/ml) were found (TAMMES and VAN DIE, 1964). Additional elements which could be detected in sieve-tube exudates include *cobalt* in *Arenga saccharifera* (TAMMES, 1958), *aluminum* and *titanium* in *Robinia pseudoacacia* (KIMMEL, 1962).

The degree of mobility of these elements as measured by export from the leaves varies from species to species: BROWN et al., 1965, EDDINGS and BROWN, 1967, on iron; URIU and KOCH, 1964, VOSE, 1963, on manganese; LEVI, 1968, SUDIA and LINCK, 1963, and WALLIHAN and HEYMANN-HERSCHBERG, 1956, on zinc (cf. EPSTEIN, 1972).

Immobile Elements. Of these elements, *calcium, boron,* and *lead* are especially interesting biologically.

Calcium. The immobility of calcium in the phloem has been confirmed by many research workers since the early report of MASON and MASKELL (1931), particularly with the help of ^{45}Ca (cf. BLEDSOE et al., 1949; WIERSUM, 1951; BIDDULPH, 1951, 1954, 1959; SWANSON and WHITNEY, 1953; ZIEGLER, 1956, 1963a; BUKOVAC et al., 1956; BUKOVAC and WITTWER, 1957; BIDDULPH et al., 1958; ANSIAUX, 1958, 1959; PEEL and WEATHERLEY, 1959; KIMMEL, 1962; WELLS and METZ, 1963; OLAND, 1963; LEVI, 1967, 1968; BAKER, 1969). The calcium content of the sieve-tube exudate, therefore, is in general very low (Table 9); the high concentrations reported by MOOSE are presumably due to inadequate methods. Under certain circumstances, e.g. high Ca^{2+} concentration in the surroundings of the sieve tubes, Ca^{2+} can enter the sieve tubes (MILLIKAN and HANGER, 1969; RINGOET et al., 1967, 1968) and is then translocated like the other constituents in the lumen of the sieve tubes (WIERSUM et al., 1971). The immobility of calcium under normal conditions is therefore not caused by the inability of the sieve tubes to transport the ion, but by the inability of this element to enter into the sieve tubes. It would be interesting to check the phosphate content of the Ca^{2+}-transporting sieve tubes. It is not clear, whether Ca^{2+} transport in the phloem takes place at any time under natural conditions; it seems quite improbable (but see also Chapters 6, 7, 8).

The exclusion of calcium from the sieve elements has a lot of very interesting consequences. Some of them are outlined briefly.

EPSTEIN (1973) points out that the exclusion of calcium may be the reason for the special cytological differentiation of the sieve tube members with the disintegration of the cell content and especially of various membranous structures, structural changes, which may be a prerequisite for the longitudinal conduction of a solution flow. The only membrane which is fully functional in the sieve tubes, and the function of which is essential for the phloem transport, the plasmalemma, is exposed to the calcium present in the cell wall and could satisfy its need from there. As a matter of fact, absence of calcium inhibits assimilate translocation in bean plants to a large degree (GEY, 1972).

A striking consequence of the immobility of calcium in the phloem and its mobility in the xylem is the fact that the Ca/K-ratio of an organ is lower the more the phloem supply predominates over the xylem supply. Examples include the fruits or storage organs growing in the soil, such as the fruits of the peanut, *Arachis hypogaea,* or the potato tuber. There is, on the average, no difference in the water potential between the roots and these organs, because they grow in the same soil. The fruits or storage organs can therefore not be supplied by the transpiration stream and must depend on import of inorganic nutrients *via* phloem, or on absorption from the soil. When calcium was supplied to the roots but not to the gynophores (fruit-stalk-like structures) of *Arachis,* only few peanuts developed (HARRIS, 1949). This is to be expected if the developing fruit depends on calcium of the environment and cannot be supplied *via* phloem. These results were confirmed in experiments with $^{45}Ca^{2+}$ (BLEDSOE et al., 1949). WIERSUM (1951) showed that the developing peanut fruit needs only calcium and no other mineral from outside for normal development.

In potato tuber, the calcium content is low (due to the supply *via* phloem), and the sprouting tuber needs calcium to develop normal shoots (KATHAREY, 1966). Other aspects of calcium nutrition of the potato tuber are mentioned above (p. 61).

Fruits grown in the normal fashion on shoots may also have a relatively low transpiration and may therefore be supplied with mineral elements mainly *via* phloem. These fruits typically contain very little calcium (WIERSUM, 1966). It can even be shown with the help of the phloem-immobile $^{45}Ca^{2+}$ that such fruits (like *Cucurbita*) retransport water back to the mother plant *via* the xylem (ZIEGLER, 1963a).

The green parts of variegated leaves normally show a higher transpiration than the white areas. In 25 species the calcium-content (per unit dry weight) was higher in the green areas than in the white. The only exception (*Chlorophytum comosum* Bak., *variegatum* hort.) which had a higher calcium-content in the white parts also had a higher transpiration rate here (PALAZY, 1969).

Sun leaves of a tree have a higher transpiration rate than shade leaves and therefore also a higher Ca/K ratio (HAAS and KAUSCH, 1966).

Leaf galls have a lower Ca/K ratio than the surrounding leaf, because they are sinks for phloem translocation and have a relatively low transpiration (KIRST, 1974).

All parasites which feed on the phloem have a low calcium and a high potassium content in their bodies and excretions. This is true for plants (Table 11) as well as for animals (cf. ZIEGLER, 1963b). By determination of the Ca/K ratio it is therefore possible to distinguish between phloem-feeding and xylem-feeding parasites.

Table 11. Content of the most important inorganic cations in phloem and xylem parasites and in their non-parasitic relatives (ANSIAUX, 1958)

Species	% of the sum of the cations		
	K	Ca	Mg
Orobanche ramosa (a)	80	3	17
Veronica arvensis (b)	30	48	22
Cuscuta europaea (a)	87	5	8
Convolvulus arvensis (b)	32	49	20
Monotropa hypopitys (a)	79	12	9
Vaccinium myrtillus (b)	27	45	28
Viscum album (c) on *Populus*	17	59	24
branch of the host	5	81	14
Viscum album (c) on *Pinus*	30	51	19
branch of the host	3	77	20

(a) Phloem parasite. (b) Non-parasitic species. (c) Xylem parasite.

Boron. The immobility of boron in the phloem was first indicated by the lack of boron in phloem exudate (ZIEGLER, 1956) and confirmed in later experiments. GARIN and THELLIER (1958) supplied leaves of *Raphanus sativus* with ^{10}B, bombarded the leaves with neutrons and photographed the emitted α-particles. They found the boron only in the vicinity of the feeding region and no indication of phloem transport. If an isolated tobacco leaf which has been split at the base and has developed roots on both parts of the split petiole, is supplied with boron *via* one root system but not *via* the other, the boron could not be transported from the one half of the leaf to the other (SCHOLZ, 1960), and the non-supplied part showed only poor growth (Fig. 11). In a tobacco plant grown in a very humid atmosphere, newly developing leaves did not grow normally, and suffered boron deficiency. Minimized transpiration stops xylem transport and the supply of xylem-mobile elements (MICHAEL et al., 1969).

Exclusion of boron from the sieve tubes might prevent callose formation (EPSTEIN, 1973), which normally restricts the opening of sieve pores. On the other hand, ESCHRICH et al. (1965) reported increased assimilate export from leaves whose hollow petioles had been injected with borate solution.

OERTLI and RICHARDSON (1970) discussed the possibility of boron entering the phloem in the leaves, but passing so fast into the xylem that no effective transport can proceed. It is not clear in their case how the deleterious effect of boron on the sieve-tube structure can be avoided.

Lead. This element is one of the most important air-polluting substances in regions with high automobile traffic. It cannot be transported in the phloem for the same reasons as calcium: lead phosphates are very insoluble in water. As a consequence, plant parts above the soil surface show lead accumulation, while the subterraneous parts do not (KLOCKE et al., 1966).

Fig. 11. Split leaf of *Nicotiana rustica* with two root systems. The right one supplied with boron, the left one not (SCHOLZ, 1960)

11. Viruses and Flagellates

There are a number of excellent and comprehensive reviews concerning virus transport in the plant beginning with the first report of BENNETT in 1927 (see literature in CRAFTS and CRISP, 1971). Since viruses are not "normal" phloem constituents, this topic is only briefly touched upon here.

Viruses can move from cell to cell *via* plasmodesmata; this transcellular movement is relatively slow. Some of them can move in the phloem. The velocity and direction of transport is then identical with that of the assimilates. The curlytop virus, for example is limited to the phloem. Other viruses (the one of Pierce's disease, for example) are restricted to the xylem and move with the transpiration stream. Others again may infect most of the living cells of a plant, also those of phloem and xylem (the mosaic viruses belong to this group). ESAU et al. (1967) found particles of beet-yellows virus in the plasmodesmata and in the sieve-plate pores of *Beta vulgaris*. Since the particles are about 5–10 nm in diameter, the plasmodesmata 50–100 nm and the sieve pores 250 nm, it is not difficult for the particles to move through these connections.

Much more astonishing is the movement of the trypanosome-like *Phytomonas leptovasarum* which causes a phloem necrosis in the coffee tree (STAHEL, 1933). This organism has a length of 6–10 μm and a diameter of 0.4–0.6 μm and moves in the sieve tubes with a velocity of 2–2 $^1/_2$ mm per h. Thus it must pass 8–10 sieve plates per h. It is probable that this flagellate squeezes actively through the sieve pores.

12. Note on Some Physical Properties of Sieve-Tube Exudate

A striking characteristic of phloem exudate is the *pH*, which is usually slightly or moderately alkaline, about 7.2–8.5 (see Table 12). The reasons were discussed before: the predominant cation (potassium) is strong, while the predominant anion (normally phosphate) is weak. Since the pH of cell sap in the other plant cells is mostly slightly acid, it is probably that there is a proton gradient between the sieve tubes and the surrounding cells. It seems possible that this gradient is used for ATP production (plasmalemma-bound ATPase in the sieve-tube plasmalemma?). The driving force for this process would perhaps be an active secretion of potassium into the sieve tubes (see Chapters 13 and 17). The *conductivity* of the phloem exudate was measured only in few cases and it seems to vary widely in different species. In *Yucca* it was 1.03 micromhos/cm at 20° C (TAMMES and VAN DIE, 1964), in *Beta vulgaris* 10.79 micromhos/cm at 20° C (FIFE et al., 1962), in *Ricinus* 13.2 micromhos/cm at 18° C (HALL and BAKER, 1972). HALL and BAKER suppose that in *Yucca* a large proportion of the ions is bound: at the level reported (1.680 mg/ml or 43 meg/l) potassium alone would give a conductance of 2.78 micromhos/cm at 18° C if all the ions would be in the free state.

Table 12. pH values in sieve-element exudates

Species	pH	Reference
Fraxinus americana L.	7.05–7.49	MOOSE (1938)
Fraxinus pennsylvanica MARSH.	7.2–7.58	MOOSE (1938)
Platanus occidentalis L.	7.28–7.35	MOOSE (1938)
Robinia pseudoacacia L.	7.25–7.40	MOOSE (1938)
	7.0–7.3	WANNER (1953)
	7.95–8.66	ZIEGLER (1956)
Quercus borealis MICHX.	7.45–8.4	ZIEGLER (1950)
Quercus robur L.	7.8–8.55	ZIEGLER (1956)
Tilia tomentosa MOENCH	7.8–8.0	ESCHRICH (1961)
Acer platanoides L.	4.0–7.8[a]	ESCHRICH (1961)
Beta vulgaris L.	8.02	FIFE et al. (1962)
Ricinus communis L.	8.0–8.2	HALL and BAKER (1972)
Yucca flaccida HAW.	8.0–8.2	TAMMES and VAN DIE (1964)
Cucurbita maxima DUCH.	8.0–8.1	MOOSE (1938)
Cucurbita pepo L.	6.8–7.4	COOIL (1941)
Cucurbita pepo L. (different strains)	5.6–7.4	MEYER-MEVIUS (1959)
Macrocystis pyrifera (L.) AG.	7.8	PARKER (1966)

[a] In this species sieve-tube exudate is mixed to a variable degree with exudate from laticifers.

The *solute potential* of the phloem exudate of *Ricinus* was −14.2 to −15.2 bars (HALL and BAKER), that of *Beta vulgaris* 18.3 bars (FIFE et al., 1962). Older reports give values of 20–40 bars (MÜNCH, 1930; FIFE et al., 1962). These values are consistent with the large concentrations of organic and inorganic solutes in the sap. This solute potential in all cases analyzed decreased in the direction of assimilate transport (PFEIFFER, 1937; HUBER et al., 1937; ZIEGLER, 1956; ZIMMERMANN, 1957). This is important in connection with the discussion of the driving forces for the assimilate transport (see Chapters 12–16).

The *viscosity* of the sieve-tube content is an important value for the calculation of the flow characteristics in the case of a solution streaming in the sieve tubes on the one hand and on the other, of the suction forces needed by the phloem-feeding animals to extract food. The viscosity is determined mainly by the concentration of the sugars (in species, where sugars are the predominant component in the sap) (ZIEGLER, 1956). Since the sugar concentration varies in response to ecological and physiological conditions and also in the different parts of the phloem, the viscosity of the phloem exudate is not a constant value. In the sieve-tube exudate of *Ricinus communis* it was found to be 1.34 cP at 20° C, which is very similar to the viscosity of a 10% sucrose solution; the sucrose concentration was 8–10.6% (HALL and BAKER, 1972). For *Beta vulgaris* exudate a value of 1.58 relative to water (at 20° C) was reported for the viscosity (FIFE et al., 1962).

The *density* of the phloem exudate of *Beta vulgaris* was 1.059 at 20° C, the *surface tension* at the same temperature 50.3 dyne/cm (FIFE et al., 1962).

D. Concluding Remarks

All those substances, or suitable precursors, which cannot be synthesized in the non-green receiving tissues of the plant, have to be transported in the phloem. It is not surprising that carbohydrates, precursors for a wide variety of substances, are quantitatively the most important fraction (next to water, which can be considered mainly as a transport vehicle and not so much as a substance to satisfy the need of the sink tissues). However, in addition to the carbohydrates, a surprisingly large number of other substances is reported to move in the phloem. In most cases it is an open question whether these compounds are transport substances *sensu stricto* (i.e. needed as such by the sink tissues), substances needed or produced by the sieve tubes themselves, or merely substances that cannot be excluded. One of these sieve-tube components, namely ATP, may be of particular interest in the function of the sieve tubes, especially because it shows a high turnover of its phosphate groups. The actual role of ATP in sieve tubes is still obscure.

Since transport substances of very different molecular weight, shape, charge and surface activity all move together in bulk with water along a gradient of osmotic potential, it is very probable that the transport mechanism in the phloem is an osmotically driven solution flow.

References

AMRHEIN, N.: Evidence against the occurrence of adenosine-3′:5′-cyclic monophosphate in higher plants. Planta **118**, 241–258 (1974).

ANSIAUX, J.R.: Sur l'alimentation minérale des phanérogames parasites. Bull. Acad. Roy. Belg., Cl. Sci. **44**, 787–793 (1958).

ANSIAUX, J.R.: La composition minérale des fruits et la voie de transport des ions alimentaires vers ceux-ci. Ann. Physiol. Végétale Univ. Bruxelles **4**, 53–88 (1959).

ARNOLD, W.N.: The selection of sucrose as the translocate of higher plants. J. Theoret. Biol. **21**, 13–20 (1968).

ASHTON, F.M., CRAFTS, A.S.: Mode of action of herbicides. New York-London-Sydney-Toronto: Wiley and Sons 1973.

ATKINSON, D.E.: Enzyme modulation and metabolic regulation. XI. Internat. Bot. Congr., Seattle 1969.

BAILEY, G.W., WHITE, J.L.: Review of adsorption and desorption of organic pesticides by soil colloids, with implications concerning pesticide bioactivity. J. Agr. Food Chem. **12**, 324–332 (1964).

BAKER, D.A.: Transport pathways in sprouting tubers of potato. J. Exptl. Botany **20**, 336–340 (1969).

BECKER, D.: Beiträge zur Kenntnis der biochemischen Leistung pflanzlicher Assimilatleitbahnen. Diss. Techn. Univ. München, 1973.

BECKER, D., KLUGE, M., ZIEGLER, H.: Der Einbau von $^{32}PO_4^{---}$ in organische Verbindungen durch Siebröhrensaft. Planta **99**, 154–162 (1971).

BECKER, D., ZIEGLER, H.: Cyclisches Adenosin-3′:5′-monophosphat in pflanzlichen Leitbahnen? Planta **110**, 85–89 (1973).

BENNETT, C.W.: Virus diseases of raspberries. Mich. Agr. Exptl. Sta. Tech. Bull. **80** (1927).

BIDDULPH, O.: The translocation of minerals in plants. In: Mineral nutrition of plants (ed. E. TNUOG), p. 261–275. Madison, Wisc.: Univ. of Wisconsin Press 1951.

BIDDULPH, O.: The distribution of P, S, Ca and Fe in bean plants as revealed by use of radioactive isotopes. Plant analysis and fertilizer problems, p. 7–17. 8. Internat. Bot. Congr., Paris 1954.

BIDDULPH, O.: Translocation of inorganic solutes. In: Plant physiology (ed. F.C. STEWARD), vol. II, p. 553–603. New York-London: Academic Press 1959.

BIDDULPH, O., BIDDULPH, S.F., CORY, R., KOONTZ, H.: Circulation patterns for P^{32}, S^{35} and Ca^{45} in the bean plant. Plant Physiol. **33**, 293–300 (1958).

BIDDULPH, O., CORY, R.: An analysis of translocation in the phloem of the bean plant using THO, P^{32} and C^{14}. Plant Physiol. **32**, 608–619 (1957).

BIDDULPH, O., CORY, R.: Translocation of C^{14}-metabolites in the phloem of the bean plant. Plant Physiol. **40**, 119–129 (1965).

BIELESKI, R.L.: Phosphorus compounds in translocating phloem. Plant Physiol. **44**, 497–502 (1969).

BLEDSOE, R.W., COMAR, C.L., HARRIS, H.C.: Absorption of radioactive calcium by the peanut fruit. Science **109**, 329–330 (1949).

BONNER, J., DORLAND, R.: Some observations concerning riboflavin and pantothenic acid in tomato plants. Am. J. Botany **30**, 414–418 (1943).

BOWEN, M.D., HOAD, G.V.: Inhibitor content of phloem and xylem sap obtained from willow *(Salix viminalis)* entering dormancy. Planta **81**, 64–70 (1968).

BROWN, A.L., YAMAGUCHI, S., LEAL-DIAZ, J.: Evidence for translocation of iron in plants. Plant Physiol. **40**, 35–38 (1965).

BUCHBERGER, W.: Aneurin im auf- und absteigenden Pflanzensaft. Phyton (Horn) **4**, 101 (1952).

BUKOVAC, M.J., WITTWER, S.H.: Absorption and mobility of foliar applied nutrients. Plant Physiol. **32**, 428–435 (1957).

BUKOVAC, M.J., WITTWER, S.H., TUKEY, H.B.: Anesthetization by diethylether and the transport of foliar-applied radiocalcium. Plant Physiol. **31**, 254–255 (1956).

BUVAT, R.: Sur la présence d'acide ribonucléique dans les »corpuscule muqueux« des cellules criblées de *Cucurbita pepo*. Compt. Rend. **257**, 733–735 (1963).

CHOI, I.C., ARONOFF, S.: Photosynthate transport using tritiated water. Plant Physiol. **41**, 1119–1129 (1966).

COOIL, B.J.: Significance of phloem exudate of *Cucurbita pepo* with reference to translocation of organic materials. Plant Physiol. **16**, 61–84 (1941).

CRAFTS, A.S.: Translocation in plants. New York: Holt, Rinehart and Winston 1961.

CRAFTS, A.S., CRISP, C.E.: Phloem transport in plants. San Francisco: Freeman and Co. 1971.

CRAFTS, A.S., LORENZ, O.A.: Composition of fruits and phloem exudate of cucurbits. Plant Physiol. **19**, 326–337 (1944).

DEHN, M.: Untersuchungen zur Ernährungsphysiologie der Aphiden. Die Aminosäuren und Zucker im Siebröhrensaft einiger Krautgewächsarten und im Honigtau ihrer Schmarotzer. Z. Vergleich. Physiol. **45**, 88–108 (1961).

EDDINGS, J.L., BROWN, A.L.: Absorption and translocation of foliar-applied iron. Plant Physiol. **42**, 15–19 (1967).

EPSTEIN, E.: Calcium-lithium competition in absorption by plant roots. Nature **185**, 705–706 (1960).

EPSTEIN, E.: Mineral nutrition of plants: Principles and perspectives. New York-London-Sydney-Toronto: Wiley and Sons 1972.

EPSTEIN, E.: Flow in the phloem and the immobility of calcium and boron: A new hypothesis in support of an old one. Experientia **29**, 133–134 (1973).

ESAU, K., CRONSHAW, J., HOEFERT, L.L.: Relation of beet yellows to the phloem and to movement in the sieve tube. J. Cell. Biol. **32**, 71–87 (1967).

ESCHRICH, W.: Untersuchungen über den Ab- und Aufbau der Callose. Z. Botan. **49**, 153–218 (1961).

ESCHRICH, W.: Der Phloemsaft von *Cucurbita ficifolia*. Planta **60**, 216–224 (1963).

ESCHRICH, W.: Translokation radioaktivmarkierter Indolyl-3-Essigsäure in Siebröhren von *Vicia faba* L. Planta **78**, 144–157 (1968).

ESCHRICH, W.: Biochemistry and fine structure of phloem in relation to transport. Ann. Rev. Plant Physiol. **21**, 193–214 (1970).

ESCHRICH, W., CURRIER, H.B., YAMAGUCHI, S., MCNAIRN, R.B.: Der Einfluß verstärkter Callosebildung auf den Stofftransport in Siebröhren. Planta **65**, 49–64 (1965).

ESCHRICH, W., EVERT, R.F., HEYSER, W.: Proteins of the sieve-tube exudate of *Cucurbita maxima*. Planta **100**, 208–221 (1971).

ESCHRICH, W., HARTMANN, T.: Translocation and biochemical behavior of D- and L-phenylalanine in *Vicia faba*. Planta **85**, 213–227 (1969).

FENSOM, D.S., DAVIDSON, H.R.: Micro-injection of ^{14}C-sucrose into single living sieve tubes of *Heracleum*. Nature **227**, 857–858 (1970).

FIFE, J.M., PRICE, C., FIFE, D.C.: Some properties of phloem exudate collected from root of sugar beet. Plant Physiol. **37**, 791–792 (1962).

FINK, R.: Morphologische und physiologische Untersuchungen an den intrazellularen Symbionten von *Pseudococcus citri* Risso. Z. Morphol. Ökol. Tiere **41**, 78 (1952).

FORD, J., PEEL, A.J.: The movement of sugars into the sieve elements of bark stripes of willow. Metabolism during transport. J. Exptl. Botany **18**, 607–619 (1967).

FRANZ, M., MEIER, H.: Die organischen Säuren im Cambialsaft von *Larix decidua* Mill. Planta **85**, 202–208 (1969).

GAGE, R.S., ARONOFF, S.: Translocation, III. Experiments with carbon 14, chlorine 36, and hydrogen 3. Plant Physiol. **35**, 53–64 (1960).

GARDNER, D.C., PEEL, A.J.: ATP in sieve-tube sap from willow. Nature **222**, 774 (1969).

GARDNER, D.C., PEEL, A.J.: Some observations on the role of ATP in sieve-tube translocation. Planta **107**, 217–226 (1972).

GARIN, A., THELLIER, M.: Méthode de microdétermination et de microdosage de bore dans une solution ou un tissue végétal par activation aux neutrons et examen microscopique des autoradiographies. Bull. Microscop. Appl. **2**, 129–148 (1958).

GEY, B.: The leaf uptake of $^{14}CO_2$ and translocation of ^{14}C-assimilates in bean plants grown under conditions of P-, Ca- or K-deficiency. Bull. Acad. Polon Sci., Sér. Sci. Biol. **2**, 803–808 (1972).

GOLDSMITH, M.H., CATALDO, D.A., KARN, J., BRENNEMAN, T., TRIP, P.: The rapid non-polar transport of auxin in the phloem of intact *Coleus* plants. Planta **116**, 301–317 (1974).

HAAS, W., KAUSCH, W.: Die Quotienten Calcium/Kalium und Rohlignin/Holocellulose bei Sonnen- und Schattenblättern der Blutbuche. Naturwissenschaften **53**, 112 (1966).

HAGEMANN, O.: Mineralstoffernährung und Mineralstoffumsatz der Kartoffel. Kühn-Arch. **78**, 225–258 (1964).

HALL, S.M., BAKER, D.A.: The chemical composition of *Ricinus* phloem exudate. Planta **106**, 131–140 (1972).

HAMILTON, S., CANNY, M.J.: The transport of carbohydrates in Australian bracken. Australian J. Biol. Sci. **13**, 479–485 (1960).

HARRIS, H.C.: The effect on the growth of peanuts of nutrient deficiencies in the root and the pegging zone. Plant Physiol. **24**, 150–161 (1949).

HARTIG, TH.: Beiträge zur physiologischen Forstbotanik. Allg. Forst- u. Jagdztg. **36**, 257–261 (1860).

HATHWAY, D.E.: Experiments on the origin of oak-bark tannin. Biochem. J. **71**, 533–537 (1959).

HEGNAUER, R.: Chemotaxonomie der Pflanzen. Vol VI, p. 94. Basel-Stuttgart: Birkhäuser 1973.

HEYSER, W., ESCHRICH, W., HÜTTERMANN, A., EVERT, R.F., BURCHARDT, R., FRITZ, E., HEYSER, R.: Phosphodiesterase in sieve-tube exudate of *Cucurbita maxima*. Z. Pflanzenphysiol. **71**, 413–423 (1974).

HILL, G.P.: Exudation from aphid stylets during the period from dormancy to bud break in *Tilia americana* (L.). J. Exptl. Botany **13**, 144–151 (1962).

HOAD, G.V.: (+) Abscisin II [(+)-dormin] in phloem exudate of willow. Life Sci. **6**, 1113–1118 (1967).

HOAD, G.V., BOWEN, M.R.: Evidence for gibberellin-like substances in phloem exudate of higher plants. Planta **82**, 22–32 (1968).

HOAD, G.V., HILLMAN, S.K., WAREING, P.F.: Studies on the movement of indole auxins in willow (*Salix viminalis* L.). Planta **99**, 73–88 (1971).

HONERT, TH. VAN DEN: On the mechanism of the transport of organic materials in plants. Proc. Koninkl. Ned. Acad. Wetenschap. **35**, 1104–1111 (1932).

HUBER, B.: Die Gewinnung von Eschenmanna – eine Nutzung von Siebröhrensaft. Ber. Deut. Botan. Ges. **66**, 341–346 (1953).

HUBER, B., SCHMIDT, E., JAHNEL, H.: Untersuchungen über den Assimilatstrom. I. Tharandter Forstl. Jahrb. **88**, 1017–1050 (1937).

HÜBNER, G.: Zum Wassertransport in *Vicia faba*. Flora (Jena) **148**, 550–594 (1960).

JACOB, F., NEUMANN, ST., STROBEL, U.: Studies on mobility of exogen-applied substances in plants. Transactions 3rd Symp. on Accumulation and Translocation of Nutrients and Regulators in Plant organisms, p. 315–330. Warszawa, Jablonna, Skierniewice, Brzezna, Kraków, 1973.

KASPRAZYK, Z., WOJCIECHOWSKI, Z., CZERNIAKIWSKA, K.: The transport of oleanolic acid in *Calendula officinalis*. Physiol. Plantarium **21**, 966–970 (1968).

KATHAREY, H.: Zur Physiologie keimender Kartoffelknollen. Staatsexamensarbeit, Techn. Univ. Darmstadt 1966.

KATING, H., ESCHRICH, W.: Uptake, incorporation, and transport of ^{14}C in *Cucurbita ficifolia*, II. Application of bicarbonate ^{14}C to the roots. Planta **60**, 598–611 (1964).

KENDE, H.: Kinetin-like factors in the root exudate of sunflower. Proc. Natl. Acad. Sci. U.S. **53**, 1302–1307 (1965).

KENNECKE, K., ZIEGLER, H., DE FEKETE, M.A.R.: Enzymaktivitäten im Siebröhrensaft von *Robinia pseudoacacia* L. und anderer Baumarten. Planta **98**, 330–356 (1971).

KENT, M.A.: Absorption, translocation, and ultimate fate of lithium in the wheat plant. New Phytologist **40**, 291–298 (1941).

KIMMEL, CH.: Über das Vorkommen anorganischer Ionen in Siebröhrensäften und den Transport von Salzen im Phloem. Diss., Techn. Univ. Darmstadt 1962.

KING, R.W., ZEEVART, J.A.D.: Enhancement of phloem exudation from cut petioles by chelating agents. Plant Physiol. **53**, 96–103 (1974).

KLEINIG, H., DÖRR, I., WEBER, C., KOLLMANN, R.: Filamentous proteins from plant sieve tubes. Nature New Biol. **229**, 152–153 (1971).

KLOCKE, A., RIEBARTSCH, LEH, H.-O.: Verunreinigungen von Kulturpflanzen mit Blei aus Kraftfahrzeugen. Landwirtsch. Forsch. **13**, Sonderheft 20, 119–123 (1966).

KLUGE, H.: Untersuchungen über Kohlenhydrate und myo-Inosit in Siebröhrensäften von Holzgewächsen. Diss. Techn. Univ. Darmstadt 1967.

KLUGE, H.: Jahreszeitliche Schwankungen des Kohlenhydratgehaltes in Siebröhrensäften, Blättern und Wurzeln einiger Holzgewächse. Biochemie Physiol. Pflanz. **161**, 142–165 (1970).

KLUGE, M.: Untersuchungen über die Zusammensetzung von Siebröhrensäften. Diss. Techn. Univ. Darmstadt 1964.

KLUGE, M., BECKER, D., ZIEGLER, H.: Untersuchungen über ATP und andere organische Phosphorverbindungen im Siebröhrensaft von *Yucca flaccida* und *Salix triandra*. Planta **91**, 68–79 (1970).

KLUGE, M., REINHARD, E., ZIEGLER, H.: Gibberellin-Aktivität von Siebröhrensäften. Naturwissenschaften **6**, 145–146 (1964).

KLUGE, M., ZIEGLER, H.: Der ATP-Gehalt der Siebröhrensäfte von Laubbäumen. Planta **61**, 167–177 (1964).

KOLLMANN, R., DÖRR, I., KLEINIG, H.: Protein filaments-structural components of the phloem exudate. I. Observations with *Cucurbita* and *Nicotiana*. Planta **95**, 86–96 (1970).

KONIJN, TH.M.: Microbiological assay of cyclic 3′,5′-AMP. Experientia **26**, 367–369 (1970).

KRAUS, G.: Botanische Mitteilungen. III. Zur Chemie des Siebröhrensaftes und alkalischer Pflanzensäfte überhaupt. Abhandl. Naturforsch. Ges. Halle **16**, 16–27 (1885).

KURSANOV, A.L.: Metabolism and the transport of organic substances in the phloem. Advan. Botan. Res. **1**, 209–274 (1963).

LEPP, N.W., PEEL, A.J.: Some effect of IAA and kinetin upon the movement of sugars in the phloem of willow. Planta **90**, 230–235 (1970).

LEPP, N.W., PEEL, A.J.: Patterns of translocation and metabolism of ^{14}C-labeled IAA in the phloem of willow. Planta **96**, 62–73 (1971 a).

LEPP, N.W., PEEL, A.J.: Influence of IAA upon the longitudinal and tangential movement of labeled sugars in the phloem of willow. Planta **97**, 50–61 (1971 b).

LEVI, E.: Distribution du calcium absorbé par les racines ou par les feuilles d'une jeune plant de haricot (*Phaseolus vulgaris* var. Beka), manifestée par la localisation de l'isotope radioactif. Compt. Rend. **264**, 1977–1988 (1967).

LEVI, E.: The distribution of mineral elements following leaf and root uptake. Physiol. Plantarum **21**, 213–226 (1968).

LOEWUS, F.: Carbohydrate interconversions. Ann. Rev. Plant Physiol. **22**, 337–364 (1971).

MACLEOD, N.J., PRIDHAM, J.B.: Observations on the translocation of phenolic compounds. Phytochemistry **5**, 777–781 (1966).

MALICKY-SCHLATTE, G.: Antrachinonderivate in der Mine von *Bucculatrix frangulella* Goeze. Z. Pflanzenkrankh. **73**, 450–452 (1966).

MASON, T.G., MASKELL, E.J.: Further studies on transport in the cotton plant. I. Preliminary observations on the transport of phosphorus, potassium and calcium. Ann. Botany (London) **45**, 125–173 (1931).

MASON, T.G., PHILLIS, E.: The migration of solutes. Botan. Rev. **3**, 47–71 (1937).

MAXWELL, F.G., PAINTER, R.H.: Auxins in honeydew of *Toxoptera graminum*, *Therioaphis maculata* and *Macrosiphum pisi*, and their relation to degree of tolerance in host plants. Ann. Entomol. Soc. Am. **55**, 229–233 (1962).

MEYER-MEVIUS, U.: Vorkommen und Transport von Kohlenhydraten und Stickstoffverbindungen in den pflanzlichen Leitungsbahnen. Flora (Jena) **147**, 553–594 (1959).

MICHAEL, G., WILBERG, E., KOUHSIAHI-TORK, K.: Durch hohe Luftfeuchtigkeit induzierter Bormangel. Z. Pflanzenernähr. Bodenk. **122**, 1–3 (1969).

MILLER, C.S., HALL, W.C.: Absorption and metabolism of aminotriazole in cotton. J. Agric. Food Chem. **9**, 210–212 (1961).

MILLIKAN, C.R., HANGER, B.C.: Redistribution of ^{45}Ca in *Trifolium subterraneum* L. and *Antirrhinum majus* L. Australian. J. Biol. Sci. **20**, 1119–1130 (1967).

MITTLER, T.C.: Studies on the feeding and nutrition of *Tuberolachnus salignus* (Gmelin), II. The nitrogen and sugar composition of ingested phloem sap and excreted honeydew. J. Exptl. Biol. **35**, 74–84 (1958).

MITTLER, T.C.: Uptake rates of plant sap and synthetic diet by the aphid *Myzus persicae*. Ann. Entomol. Soc. Am. **63**, 1701–1705 (1970).

MOOSE, C.A.: Chemical and spectroscopic analysis of plants. Plant Physiol. **13**, 365–380 (1938).

MÜNCH, G.: Die Stoffbewegungen in der Pflanze. Jena: G. Fischer 1930.

NEUMANN, ST., WOLLGIEHN, R.: Über die Beziehungen der RNS- und Proteinsynthese zum Zellkern in Siebzellen von *Vicia faba*. Z. Naturforsch. **19**b, 1066–1071 (1964).

OERTLI, J.J., RICHARDSON, W.F.: The mechanism of boron immobility in plants. Physiol. Plantarum **23**, 108–116 (1970).

OLAND, K.: Changes in the content of dry matter and major nutrient elements of apple foliage during senescence and abscission. Physiol. Plantarum **16**, 682–694 (1963).

PALAZY, W.: Cytologische und physiologische Untersuchungen an panaschierten Pflanzen. Diss. Techn. Univ. Darmstadt 1969.

PARKER, B.C.: Translocation in Macrocystis. III. Composition of sieve-tube exudate and identification of the major C^{14}-labeled products. J. Physiol. (London) **2**, 38–41 (1966).

PAVLINOVA, O.A.: A comparative investigation of acid-soluble nucleotides in the phloem and xylem of the conducting bundles of the cow parsnip *(Heracleum Sosnowskyi)* [Russ.] Fiz. Rast. **12**, 606–617 (1965).

PAVLINOVA, O.A., AFANASJEVA, T.P.: Acid-soluble nucleotides and phosphorylated sugars in the conducting tissues of the sugar beet [Russ.] Fiz. Rast. **9**, ·133–141 (1962).

PEEL, A.J.: Further evidence for the relative immobility of water in sieve tubes of willow. Physiol. Plantarum **23**, 667–672 (1970).

PEEL, A.J., FIELD, R.J., COULSON, C.L., GARDNER, D.C.J.: Movement of water and solutes in sieve tubes of willow in response to puncture by aphid stylets. Evidence against a mass flow of solution. Physiol. Plantarum **22**, 768–775 (1969).

PEEL, A.J., WEATHERLEY, P.E.: Composition of sieve-tube sap. Nature **184**, 1955–1956 (1959).

PFEIFFER, M.: Die Verteilung der osmotischen Werte im Baum im Hinblick auf die Münchsche Druckstromtheorie. Flora (Jena) **132**, 1–47 (1937).

PHILLIPS, D.A., CLELAND, C.F.: Cytokinin activity from the phloem sap of *Xanthium strumarium* L. Planta **102**, 173–178 (1972).

PLOUVIER, V.: Sur le sorbitol des Rosacées. Compt. Rend. **241**, 1220–1222 (1955).

RAPP, H., KIRST, G.O.: Zur Physiologie der Galle von *Mikiola fagi* Htg. auf Blättern von *Fagus silvatica* L. 1. Vergleichende Untersuchungen einiger Inhaltsstoffe der Galle und des Blattes. Biochem. Physiolog. Pflanz. **165**, 437–444 (1974).

RINGOET, A., RECHENMANN, R.V., VEEN, H.: Calcium movement in oat leaves measured by semi-conductor detectors. Radiation Botany **7**, 81–90 (1967).

RINGOET, A., SAUER, G., GIELINK, A.J.: Phloem transport of calcium in oat leaves. Planta **801**, 15–20 (1968).

ROUSCHAL, E.: Untersuchungen über die Protoplasmatik und Funktion der Siebröhren. Flora (Jena) **35**, 135–200 (1941).

SABNIS, D.D., HART, J.W.: Studies on the possible occurrence of actomyosin-like proteins in phloem. Planta **118**, 271–282 (1974).

SAMMLER, P., EHWALD, R., GÖRING, H.: 2-Deoxy-D-Glukose-β-Fructosid als „marker" des Kohlenhydrat-Ferntransportes bei höheren Pflanzen. Biochem. Physiol. Pflanz. **165**, 291–302 (1974).

SCHMITZ, K., SRIVASTAVA, L.M.: The enzymatic incorporation of ^{32}P into ATP and other organic compounds by sieve-tube sap of *Macrocystis integrifolia* Bory. Planta **116**, 85–89 (1974).

SCHOLZ, G.: Über die Translokation des Bors in Tabak-Blattstecklingen mit geteilten Wurzelsystemen. Flora (Jena) **148**, 484–488 (1960).

SCHULTZ, G.: Zur Frage des Transports von Flavonoiden in oberirdischen Organen von *Trifolium.* Z. Pflanzenphysiol. **61**, 29–40 (1969).

SCHUHMACHER, W.: Die Fernleitung der Stoffe im Pflanzenkörper. In: Encyclopedia of plant physiology (ed. W. RUHLAND), vol. XIII "Translocation in plants". Berlin-Heidelberg-New York: Springer 1967.

SEELIGER, I.: Über die Kultur isolierter Wurzeln der Robinie (*Robinia pseudoacacia* L.). Flora (Jena) **144**, 47–83 (1956).

STAHEL, G.: Zur Kenntnis der Siebröhrenkrankheit (Phloemnekrose) des Kaffeebaumes in Surinam. III. Phytopathol. Z. **6**, 335–357 (1933).

STEWART, C.R.: Proline content and metabolism during rehydration of wilted excised leaves in the dark. Plant Physiol. **50**, 679–681 (1972).

SUDIA, T.W., LINCK, A.W.: The absorption and translocation of zinc-65 in *Pisum sativum* in relation to fruit development. Plant Soil **19**, 249–254 (1963).

SWANSON, C.A., WHITNEY, J.B., JR.: Studies on the translocation of foliar-applied P^{32} and other radioisotopes in bean plants. Am. J. Botany. **40**, 816–823 (1953).

TAMMES, P.M.L.: Micro- and macro-nutrients in sieve-tube sap of palms. Acta Botan. Neerl. **7**, 233–234 (1958).

TAMMES, P.M.L., VAN DIE, J.: Studies on phloem exudation from *Yucca flaccida* Haw. I. Some observations on the phenomenon of bleeding and the composition of the exudate. Acta Botan. Neerl. **13**, 76–83 (1964).

TANNER, W., KANDLER, O.: Biosynthesis of stachyose in *Phaseolus vulgaris*. Plant Physiol. **41**, 1540–1542 (1966).

TRIP, P., GORHAM, P.R.: Translocation of sugar and tritiated water in squash plants. Plant Physiol. **43**, 1845–1849 (1968).

TRIP, P., NELSON, C.D., KROTKOV, G.: Selective and preferential translocation of ^{14}C-labeled sugars in white ash and lilac. Plant Physiol. **40**, 740–747 (1965).

TSO, T.C., FISENNE, I.: Translocation and distribution of lead-210 and polonium-210 supplied to tobacco plants. Radiation Botany **8**, 457–462 (1968).

URIU, K., KOCH, E.C.: Response of Yellow Newton apple leaves to foliar applications of manganese and zinc. Proc. Am. Soc. Hort. Sci. **84**, 25–31 (1964).

VAN DIE, J., VAN DE RUIT, J.M., TAMMES, P.M.L.: Studies on phloem exudation from *Yucca flaccida* Haw. XIII. Balance-sheet of the cations and anions present in the exudate. Acta Botan. Neerl. **23**, (1974).

VOSE, P.B.: The translocation and redistribution of manganese in Avena. J. Exptl. Botany. **14**, 448–457 (1963).

WALLIHAN, E.F., HEYMANN-HERSCHBERG, L.: Some factors affecting absorption and translocation of zinc in *Citrus* plants. Plant Physiol. **31**, 294–299 (1956).

WANNER, H.: Enzyme der Glykolyse im Phloemsaft. Ber. Schweiz. Botan. Ges. **63**, 201–212 (1953).

WAREING, P.F., HANNEY, C.E.A., DIGBY, J.: The role of endogenous hormones in cambial activity and xylem differentiation. In: The Formation of wood in forest trees (ed. M.H. ZIMMERMANN). New York: Academic Press 1964.

WEBB, K.L., BURLEY, J.W.A.: Sorbitol translocation in apple. Science **137**, 766 (1962).

WELLBURN, A.R., ASHBY, J.P., WELLBURN, F.A.M.: Occurrence and biosynthesis of adenosine-3′,5′-cyclic monophosphate in isolated *Avena* etioplasts. Biochim. Biophys. Acta **320**, 363–371 (1973).

WELLS, C.G., METZ, L.J.: Variation in nutrient content of Loblolly pine needles with season, age, soil and position on the crown. Proc. Soil Sci. Soc. Am. **27**, 90–93 (1963).

WIERSUM, L.K.: Water transport in the xylem as related to calcium uptake by groundnuts (*Arachis hypogaea* L.). Plant Soil **3**, 160–169 (1951).

WIERSUM, L.K.: Calcium content of fruits and storage tissues in relation to the mode of water supply. Acta Botan. Neerl. **15**, 406–418 (1966).

WIERSUM, L.K.: The mass-flow theory of phloem transport: a supporting calculation. J. Exptl. Botany **18**, 160–162 (1967).

WIERSUM, L.K., VONK, C.A., TAMMES, P.M.L.: Movement of ^{45}Ca in the phloem of *Yucca*. Naturwissenschaften **58**, 59 (1971).

WILLIAMSON, R.E.: An investigation of the contractile protein hypothesis of phloem translocation. Planta **106**, 149–157 (1972).

WITHERSPOON, J.P., BROWN, G.N.: Translocation of cesium-137 from parent trees to seedlings of *Liriodendron tulipifera*. Botan. Gaz. **126**, 181–185 (1965).

ZACHARIAS, E.: Über den Inhalt der Siebröhren von *Cucurbita pepo*. Z. Botan. **42**, 65–73 (1884).

ZIEGLER, H.: Untersuchungen über die Leitung und Sekretion der Assimilate. Planta **47**, 447–500 (1956).

ZIEGLER, H.: Über den Nachweis von Uridindiphosphatglukose (UDPG) im Phloem von *Heracleum Mantegazzianum* Somm. et Lev. Naturwissenschaften **47**, 140 (1960).

ZIEGLER, H.: Verwendung von ^{45}Calcium zur Analyse der Stoffversorgung wachsender Früchte. Planta **60**, 41–45 (1963a).

ZIEGLER, H.: Der Ferntransport organischer Stoffe in den Pflanzen. Naturwissenschaften **50**, 177–186 (1963b).

ZIEGLER, H.: La sève des tubes criblés. In: Traité de biologie de l'abeille (ed. R. CHAUVIN), vol. 3, p. 205–217. Paris: Masson 1968.

ZIEGLER, H.: Biochemical aspects of phloem transport. In: Symp. Soc. Exp. Biol.: Transport at the cellular level, p. 43–62. London: Cambridge University Press 1974.

ZIEGLER, H., KLUGE, M.: Die Nucleinsäuren und ihre Bausteine im Siebröhrensaft von *Robinia pseudoacacia* L. Planta **58**, 144–153 (1962).

ZIEGLER, H., MITTLER, T.C.: Über den Zuckergehalt der Siebröhren- bzw. Siebzellensäfte von *Heracleum Mantegazzianum* und *Picea abies* (L.) Karst. Z. Naturforsch. **14**b, 278–281 (1959).

ZIEGLER, H., SCHNABEL, M.: Über Harnstoffderivate im Siebröhrensaft. Flora (Jena) **150**, 306–317 (1961).

ZIEGLER, H., VIEWEG, G.H.: Der experimentelle Nachweis einer Massenströmung im Phloem von *Heracleum Mantegazzianum*. Somm. et Lev. Planta **56**, 402–408 (1961).
ZIEGLER, H., ZIEGLER, I.: Die wasserlöslichen Vitamine in den Siebröhrensäften einiger Bäume. Flora (Jena) **152**, 257–278 (1962).
ZIMMERMANN, G.: Der Nachweis von Aminosäuren im Siebröhren- und Blutungssaft einiger Bäume. Staatsexamensarbeit, Techn. Univ. Darmstadt 1961.
ZIMMERMANN, M.H.: Translocation of organic substances in trees, I. The nature of the sugars in the sieve-tube exudate of trees. Plant Physiol. **32**, 288–291 (1957).
ZIMMERMANN, M.H.: Translocation of nutrients. In: Physiology of plant growth and development (ed. M.B. WILKINS), p. 383–417. London: MacGraw-Hill 1968.
ZIMMERMANN, M.H.: Movement of organic substances in trees. Science **133**, 73–79 (1969).
ZIMMERMANN, M.H., BROWN, C.L.: Trees structure and function. Berlin-Heidelberg-New York: Springer 1971.

4. Biochemistry of Phloem Constituents

W. ESCHRICH and W. HEYSER

A. Introduction

This contribution surveys the available data on catalytic abilities and biochemical reactions of phloem constituents. Since data from lower vascular plants are scarce, mainly the phloem of angiosperms will be considered. This tissue is composed of 3 to 4 types of living cells. Phloem parenchyma, sometimes transfer cells, and companion cells are nucleate members of the phloem. They are equipped with organelles and cytoplasmic structures commonly found in parenchymatic cells, although certain signs of specialization can be recognized. It can be assumed that these cells do not differ in metabolism from other parenchymatous elements.

Sieve elements can be regarded as members of a "functional unit" which is highly branched and interconnected, and which extends into numerous juvenile endings, but is enucleate in its functional state. It is this system which attracts attention by its function and its uniqueness.

At first sight, it might seem desirable to consider the dynamic biochemistry of the nucleate phloem cells apart from that of the sieve tubes. However, it has been sufficiently documented that sieve element and companion cell(s) constitute not only an ontogenetic, but also a functional unit. For example, tracers of assimilate transport such as K-fluorescein (SCHUMACHER, 1933) and ^{14}C-labeled compounds (FRITZ and ESCHRICH, 1970) occur in both sieve tubes and companion cells. The exchange of solutes of low molecular weight may be facilitated by identical osmotic concentrations in both companion cells and sieve tubes (GEIGER et al., 1973).

The passage of macromolecules from the companion cell through the great number of special connections into the sieve element is indicated by histochemical assays for dehydrogenases (LEHMANN, 1973a): high concentrations of such enzymes occurred in companion cells of bundles which were frozen prior to cutting. When the bundles were cut prior to freezing, most of the enzymes had left the companion cells, obviously by exuding into the sieve elements.

It is not known whether an exchange of macromolecules between companion cell and sieve element takes place in undisturbed phloem. The investigation of catalytic abilities of the sieve tubes, however, depends primarily on the analyses of sieve-tube exudates. Thus, contamination of the exudate with constituents of the companion cells or other parenchymatous elements cannot be excluded. Unfortunately, histochemical assays are often relatively unspecific and cannot cover all enzymes.

Data reported in this chapter must be evaluated carefully and the source of the material investigated must be given careful consideration.

B. Enzymic Activities in Sieve Tubes

I. Comparison of Sources of Sieve-Tube Exudates

As in the preceding Chapter 3, determination of phloem constituents depends on productive sources of phloem sap, mainly exudates. However, species which deliver phloem exudate from cut bundles are rare. There are some trees, for example *Robinia pseudoacacia*, which exude droplets of phloem sap when an incision is made into the bark. By repeated cutting, phloem exudate can be collected in ml-amounts during certain months of the season. It has been shown by KENNECKE et al. (1971), that phloem exudate of *Robinia* contains mitochondria and other membranous structures. Thus, surging by turgor release in a severed sieve tube of *Robinia* may be so strong that parts of the parietal layer of cytoplasm are swept through the hole in the pierced bark; or it is possible that the phloem exudate is contaminated with mitochondria and other cytoplasmatic material derived from severed parenchyma cells of the bark.

Another source of phloem constituents for biochemical investigations is the sieve-tube exudate of Cucurbitaceae, mainly *Cucurbita maxima, C. pepo* and *C. ficifolia*. Since exudate is limited in these species, it seems logical to use seedlings rather than large plants, for collection of sufficient amounts. It was shown with the electronmicroscope (ESCHRICH et al., 1971) that cut *Cucurbita* sieve elements do not exude mitochondria and other parts of the parietal layer of cytoplasm. Only filamentous structures can be recognized in the exudate (ESCHRICH, 1963). Contamination with material from cut parenchyma is very slight.

In the electronmicroscope the exudate droplet appears delimited from the environment by a membrane-like structure. Sometimes it appears covered with a thin layer of callose (ESCHRICH et al., 1964).

Another species which delivers phloem exudate is *Ricinus communis var. gibsonii* (MILBURN, 1971). Diagonal incisions of the bark of a young plant deliver over 1 ml of exudate. This material contains coiled filaments presumed to be P-protein (WILLIAMSON, 1972). Whether this exudate is contaminated with components of cut parenchyma cells or laticifers is not yet known.

The most productive sources of sieve-tube exudate are certain monocotyledons. A variety of palms exude liters of sieve-tube sap (TAMMES, 1933), but exudate of inflorescence stalks of *Yucca flaccida* has been investigated most extensively (see Chapter 8). Unfortunately, *Yucca* exudate can be obtained only during a few weeks in summer. Two procedures have been followed to obtain *Yucca* exudate. 1. The inflorescence stalk is decapitated and sap is collected as it exudes from the stump, which is attached to the root system. This "sieve-tube exudate" also contains various amounts of xylem sap, depending on the water supply. 2. A part of the inflorescence stalk, about 30 cm long, is excised and one end is put into a beaker of water. Sap exuding from the upper end is regarded as sieve-tube exudate, which may be diluted by water ascending through the xylem vessels. In both cases, exudation can proceed for hours or even days when thin slices of the cut surface are removed from time to time. The amount of exudate obtained can be many times that which originally had filled the sieve tubes (TAMMES and VAN DIE, 1964).

A few other plant species can deliver low yields of sieve-tube exudate. The method of massaging the stem prior to cutting, which was introduced by MILBURN (1970), proved helpful in obtaining exudate (KOLLMANN et al., 1970). Honeydew of aphids and exudate from cut stylet bundles of aphids constitute the purest sieve-tube sap obtainable. However, enzymes undoubtedly are denatured in honeydew, and enzyme activity of stylet-bundle exudate is low (BECKER et al., 1971).

Sieve-tube exudates from different sources are of different quality. Contamination of sieve-tube exudate with xylem sap and material from cut parenchyma cells or laticifers varies widely. Particulate material normally attached to the parietal layer of cytoplasm may or may not occur in exudate. In addition, surging of sieve-tube content induced by cutting of bundles may promote secretion of substances out of companion cells (LEHMANN, 1973a). It is not surprising that enzymes described for one source of sieve-tube exudate were lacking in another.

Since exudates of *Yucca* and *Robinia* are not available at all times, continous work depends on exudates from *Cucurbita* or *Ricinus*. When *Yucca* exudate is collected according to Procedure 2, it can be assumed that surging evoked by sudden turgor release has declined and therefore has no influence on exudation. Proteins occurring in such exudate (Fig. 1a) probably constitute material normally secreted

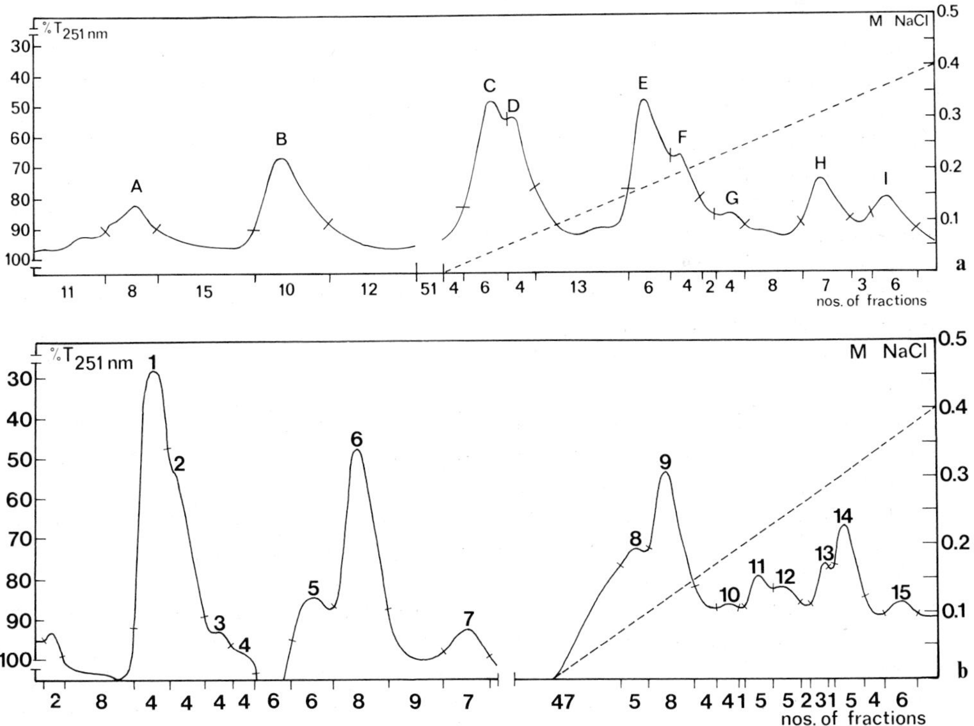

Fig. 1a and b. Fractionation of sieve-tube exudates on DEAE cellulose columns by elution with 0.05 M tris buffer, pH 7.8, containing 0.01 M mercaptoethanol and 0.5 mM Cleland's reagent, followed by an additional gradient of NaCl (broken line). Fractions of approximately 1.6 ml of elute. Lettered (a) and numbered (b) peaks cover one to several proteins, as was shown by disc electrophoresis. (a) Exudate of *Yucca flaccida* collected after decline of initial surging. 50 ml of exudate were concentrated to 3.7 ml. (b) Exudate of *Cucurbita maxima*, collected from 60 seedlings. 0.65 ml of exudate were diluted to 3.7 ml. (By HEYSER et al., 1974)

into the sieve tubes. During collection of *Cucurbita* sieve-tube exudate, many plants must be cut to obtain sufficient amounts of exudate.

Thus, the surging effect cannot be eliminated. When comparing elution profiles of DEAE cellulose columns (Serva, Type SS) of exudates from *Yucca* (Fig. 1a) and *Cucurbita* (Fig. 1b), it seems obvious that the number of peaks is of the same magnitude. Although both curves differ in many details and each peak may or may not contain two to several proteins, the impression remains that both types of exudate—that of *Yucca* obtained without surging and that of *Cucurbita* obtained by surging—are equipped with a similar set of proteins. This suggests that surging evoked by the cutting of sieve tubes influences mainly the quantity of macromolecules, the composition of the exudate being less affected.

II. Compilation of Enzymes Described for Sieve Tubes

In this section data are compiled which give evidence for the occurrence or non-occurrence of enzymes in sieve tubes. Data obtained from extracts of phloem tissue are omitted. Fig. 2 shows pathways of possible enzyme reactions, which are numbered and refer to numbers given in Table 1.

C. Maintenance of the Living State of Sieve Tubes

I. Respiration

General agreement exists that mature sieve elements are living and bounded by a plasmalemma so long as they are functional. It can be assumed that the minimum energy necessary for the maintenance of turgor is provided by respiration. Although conducting cells contain small mitochondria, the generation of energy by respiration may be mainly accomplished by companion cells. Since it is not possible to obtain isolated sieve tubes for measurements of respiration, translocation has been investigated in relation to blocked and unblocked respiration of the phloem.

Results obtained by local application of cyanide (WILLENBRINK, 1966) and oxygen deficiency (ULLRICH, 1961) to isolated parts of a bundle of the petiole of a *Pelargonium* leaf have shown that translocation out of the leaf blade is not affected by oxygen deficiency. Transport was stopped, however, in front of the cyanide barrier. It has been concluded that the respiratory chain is incomplete in sieve elements. Anaerobic fermentation or respiration with the aid of a peroxidase-H_2O_2 system could substitute for aerobic respiration (ULLRICH, 1961). SIJ and SWANSON (1973) observed a temporary decline of transport when a 15-cm portion of petiole of a *Cucurbita* leaf was kept under nitrogen. Recovery was complete after 60 to 90 min. GEIGER and CHRISTY (1971) have shown that anaerobiosis inhibits phloem unloading in a sink region. This indicates that oxygen deficiency seems to act primarily in cells *other* than sieve elements.

The localized blockage of transport by cyanide provides evidence that translocation in sieve tubes is dependent on metabolic processes generated by respiration.

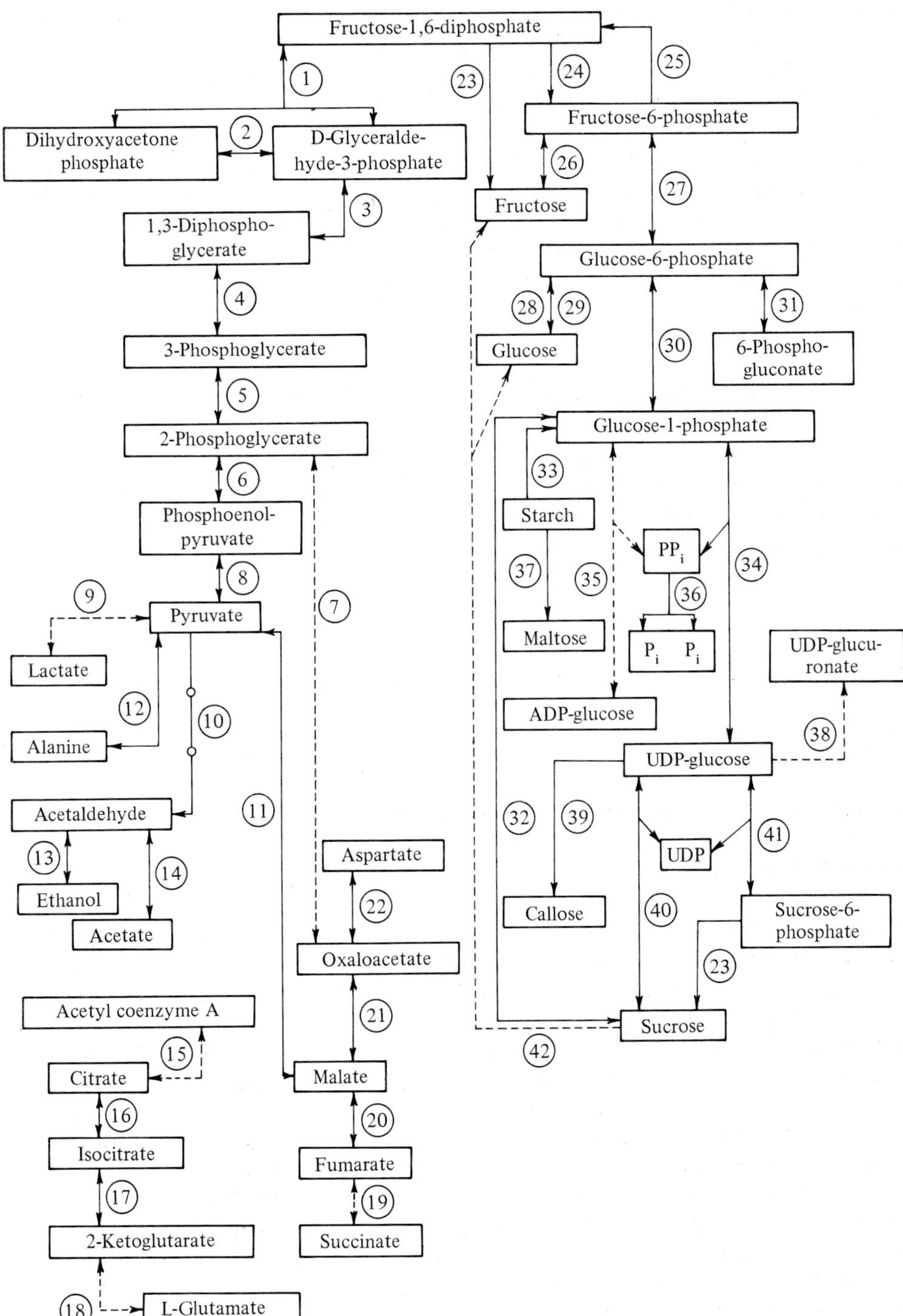

Fig. 2. Metabolic pathways for which enzymic activities found in sieve tubes give evidence. Stippled arrows indicate that no activity was found by all authors. The numbers beside the arrows refer to those enzymes listed in Table 1

Table 1. Compilation of enzymes and enzymic activities described for sieve tubes. Numbers exudate precipitated by 0–80% $(NH_4)_2SO_4$ and centrifuged

No.	Name of enzyme	E.C.No.	Plant	Source	Purity
1	aldolase	4.1.2.13	*Robinia*	exudate	crude
			Cucurbita maxima	exudate	dialyzed
			Cucurbita pepo	exudate	crude
2	triose phosphate isomerase	5.3.1.1	*Robinia*	exudate	crude
			Cucurbita pepo	exudate	crude
3	glyceraldehyde 3-phosphate dehydrogenase	1.2.1.12	*Robinia*	exudate	crude
			Cucurbita pepo	exudate	crude
			Cucurbita pepo	histo-chemically	
4	phosphoglycerate kinase	2.7.2.3	*Cucurbita pepo*	exudate	crude
5	phosphoglycero-mutase	2.7.5.3	*Robinia*	exudate	crude
			Cucurbita pepo	exudate	crude
6	enolase	4.2.1.11	*Robinia*	exudate	crude
			Cucurbita pepo	exudate	crude
7	phosphopyruvate-carboxylase	4.1.1.32	*Cucurbita pepo*	exudate	crude
8	pyruvate kinase	2.7.1.40	*Robinia*	exudate	crude
			Cucurbita pepo	exudate	crude
9	lactate dehydro-genase	1.1.1.27	*Cucurbita pepo*	exudate	crude
10	pyruvate decarboxylase	4.1.1.1	*Cucurbita pepo*	exudate	crude
11	malic enzyme	1.1.1.40	*Cucurbita pepo*	exudate	crude
12	alanine ketoglu-tarate transaminase	2.6.1.2	*Robinia*	exudate	crude
13	alcohol dehydro-genase	1.1.1.1	*Robinia*	exudate	crude
			Cucurbita pepo	exudate	crude
			Cucurbita pepo	histo-chemically	
14	aldehyde dehydro-genase	1.2.1.4	*Cucurbita pepo*	exudate	crude
15	citrate synthase	4.1.3.7	*Robinia*	exudate	amm-SO_4 precip.
16	aconitase	4.2.1.3	*Cucurbita pepo*	exudate	crude

relate to those in Fig. 2. Activities in U or mU refer to 1 ml exudate. Amm-SO_4-precip. means

pH	Assay	Activity	References
7.5	TC-O-test (Boehringer)	33 nM/ml/min	KENNECKE et al. (1971)
8.0	disc electrophoresis	2 isoenzymes	ESCHRICH et al. (1971)
7.2	optical test	112 mU	LEHMANN (1973b)
7.6	glyceraldehyde-P/ glycerol-1-P	1.7 μM/ml/min (NADH)	KENNECKE et al. (1971)
7.2	optical test	30 U	LEHMANN (1973b)
7.4	glyceraldehyde-3-P/ 1,3-diphosphoglycerate	90 nM/ml/min (NADH)	KENNECKE et al. (1971)
7.6	optical test	960 mU	LEHMANN (1973b)
7.6	NAD^+, tetrazolium (NBT)	in all phloem cells, mainly companion cells	LEHMANN (1973b)
7.2	optical test	4.2 U	LEHMANN (1973b)
7.5	glycerate-2-P/ glycerate-3-P	21 nM/ml/min (NADH)	KENNECKE et al. (1971)
7.2	optical test	640 mU	LEHMANN (1973b)
7.5	glycerate-2-P/phosphoenol pyruvate/lactate	59 nM/ml/min	KENNECKE et al. (1971)
7.2	optical test	270 mU	LEHMANN (1973b)
7.6	oxaloacetate + GTP/ determination of phosphoenolpyruvate	no activity	LEHMANN (1973c)
7.5	phosphoenol pyruvate + ADP/lactate	120 nM/ml/min (NADH)	KENNECKE et al. (1971)
7.2	optical test	28 mU	LEHMANN (1973b)
9.5	pyruvate/lactate	no activity	LEHMANN (1973b)
6.5	pyruvate, NADH	68 mU	LEHMANN (1973b)
7.6	optical test	241 mU	LEHMANN (1973c)
	UV-test TC-H (Boehringer)	21 nM/ml/min (NADH)	KENNECKE et al. (1971)
	optical test	9 nM/ml/min (NAD^+)	KENNECKE et al. (1971)
		58 mU	LEHMANN (1973b)
8.7	tetrazolium-red. + NAD^+	in all phloem cells, mainly companion cells	LEHMANN (1973a)
7.6	$NADP^+$/NADPH + 10 mM K^+	0.1 mU	LEHMANN (1973b)
8.0	malate + NAD^+ + acetyl-CoA	no activity	KENNECKE et al. (1971)
7.6	$NADP^+$/NADPH	0.4 mU	LEHMANN (1973b)

Table 1 (continued)

No.	Name of enzyme	E.C.No.	Plant	Source	Purity
17	isocitrate dehydrogenase	1.1.1.42	*Robinia*	exudate	crude
			Cucurbita pepo	exudate	crude
			Cucurbita pepo	histo-chemically	
			Cucurbita pepo	histo-chemically	
18	glutamate dehydrogenase	1.4.1.2	*Robinia*	exudate	crude
			Cucurbita maxima	exudate	dialyzed
19	succinate dehydrogenase	1.3.99.1	*Cucurbita pepo*	exudate	crude
			Cucurbita pepo	histo-chemically	
20	fumarase	4.2.1.2	*Robinia*	exudate	crude
			Cucurbita pepo	exudate	crude
21	malate dehydrogenase	1.1.1.37	*Robinia*	exudate	crude
			Cucurbita pepo	exudate	crude
			Cucurbita pepo	histo-chemically	
22	aspartate transaminase	2.6.1.1	*Robinia*	exudate	crude
23	"phosphatases"		*Robinia*	exudate	crude
			Cucurbita pepo	exudate	crude
			Cucurbita maxima	exudate	dialyzed
			Cucurbita maxima	exudate	dialyzed
24	diphosphofructose phosphatase	3.1.3.11	*Cucurbita pepo*	exudate	crude
25	phosphofructo-kinase	2.7.1.11	*Robinia*	exudate	amm-SO_4-precip.
			Cucurbita pepo	exudate	crude
26	fructokinase	2.7.1.4	*Robinia*	exudate	amm-SO_4-precip.
			Cucurbita maxima	exudate	dialyzed

pH	Assay	Activity	References
	UV-test TC-ID (Boehringer)	25 nM/ml/min ($NADP^+$)	KENNECKE et al. (1971)
		10 mU	LEHMANN (1973b)
7.6	tetrazolium-red. + $NADP^+$	in all phloem cells, mainly companion cells	LEHMANN (1973a)
7.6	tetrazolium-red. + NAD^+	only on particular structures	LEHMANN (1973a)
7.3	UV-test TC-Y (Boehringer)	9 nM/ml/min	KENNECKE et al. (1971)
7.0	disc electrophoresis	no activity	ESCHRICH et al. (1971)
7.2	succinate + $K_3[Fe(CN)_6]$ at 405 nm	no activity	LEHMANN (1973b)
7.2	tetrazolium-red.	only in nucleate cells	LEHMANN (1973a)
7.5	L-malate/fumarate	23 nM/ml/min	KENNECKE et al. (1971)
7.6	L-malate at 240 nm	0.4 mU	LEHMANN (1973b)
	UV-test TC-L (Boehringer)	1.1 μM/ml/min (NADH)	KENNECKE et al. (1971)
7.6	tetrazolium-red. NAD^+	3.8 U	LEHMANN (1973b)
7.6	tetrazolium-red. + NAD^+	in all phloem cells, mainly companion cells	LEHMANN (1973a)
	2-ketoglutarate + aspartate/oxaloacetate – malate (340 nm)	26 nM/ml/min (NADH)	KENNECKE et al. (1971)
7.0–7.3	fructose-1,6-diphosphate	paper chromatogram showed fructose	WANNER (1953)
	incubation of glucose-6-phosphate yielding glucose and of fructose-6-phosphate yielding fructose shows the presence of unspecific phosphomonoesterases		LEHMANN (1973c)
5.5	disc electrophoresis and incubation with α-naphthyl phosphate yielded 4 red bands, showing the presence of multiple acid phosphatases		ESCHRICH et al. (1971)
9.5	incubation at pH 9.5 yielded no phosphatase bands, alkaline phosphatases were lacking (phosphatases also have been shown histochemically, (see page 116, 117)		ESCHRICH et al. (1971)
7.6	$NADP^+$/NADPH	183 mU	LEHMANN (1973c)
7.4	fructose-6-P/fructose-1,6-diphosphate	no activity	KENNECKE et al. (1971)
7.4	same, with ^{14}C-labeled fructose-6-phosphate, paper chromatography	activity recorded 20.5 mU	LEHMANN (1973c)
7.6	incubated with ^{14}C-fructose, paper chromatography	activity recorded	KENNECKE et al. (1971)
8.0	$NADP^+$-red. disc electrophoresis	no activity	ESCHRICH et al. (1971)

Table 1 (continued)

No.	Name of enzyme	E.C.No.	Plant	Source	Purity
[fructokinase continued]			*Cucurbita maxima*	exudate	dialyzed
27	phosphogluco-isomerase	5.3.1.9	*Robinia*	exudate	amm-SO_4-precip.
			Cucurbita pepo	exudate	crude
28	glucose-6-phosphatase		*Robinia*	exudate	crude
29	glucokinase	2.7.1.2	*Robinia*	exudate	amm-SO_4-precip.
			Cucurbita maxima	exudate	dialyzed
30	phosphogluco-mutase	2.7.5.1	*Robinia*	exudate	amm-SO_4-precip.
			Robinia	exudate	crude
			Cucurbita maxima	exudate	dialyzed
			Cucurbita pepo	exudate	crude
31	glucose-6-phosphate dehydrogenase	1.1.1.49	*Robinia*	exudate	amm-SO_4-precip.
			Cucurbita maxima	exudate	dialyzed
			Cucurbita pepo	histo-chemically	
32	sucrose phosphorylase	2.4.1.7	*Cucurbita pepo*	exudate	crude
33	$\alpha(1\rightarrow4)$-glucan phosphorylase	2.4.1.1	*Robinia*	exudate	amm-SO_4-precip.
			Robinia	exudate	crude
			Cucurbita pepo	exudate	crude
34	UDPG pyrophospho-rylase	2.7.7.9	*Robinia*	exudate	amm-SO_4-precip.
			Cucurbita pepo	exudate	crude
			Robinia	exudate	amm-SO_4-precip.

pH	Assay	Activity	References
7.6	hexokinase assay (Boehringer) with and without 0.1 M KCl	no activity	ESCHRICH et al. (1971)
	by hexokinase assays always fructose-6-P as well as glucose-6-P were found, indicating activity of phosphoglucoisomerase		KENNECKE et al. (1971)
		activity recorded	LEHMANN (1973c)
7.0–7.3	fructose-6-phosphate, paper chromatography (comp. 23. probably an unspecific phosphomonoesterase)	fructose present	WANNER (1953)
7.6	^{14}C-glucose, paper chromatography	activity recorded	KENNECKE et al. (1971)
8.0	NADP$^+$-red. disc electrophoresis	no activity	ESCHRICH et al. (1971)
7.8	glucose-1-P/ glucose-6-phosphate, paper chromatography	no activity recorded	KENNECKE et al. (1971)
7.0–7.3	glucose-1-P/ glucose-6-P, paper chromatography	with high activity	WANNER (1953)
7.5	NADP$^+$-red. disc electrophoresis	no activity	ESCHRICH et al. (1971)
7.2	optical test	3.2 U	LEHMANN (1973c)
7.8	^{14}C-labeled reactants paper chromatography	weak activity	KENNECKE et al. (1971)
7.0	NAD$^+$-red. disc electrophoresis	no activity	ESCHRICH et al. (1971)
7.6	tetrazolium-red. +NADP$^+$	in all phloem cells, mainly companion cells	LEHMANN (1973a)
7.2	glucose-1,6-diphosphate, inorganic phosphate, sucrose	0.65 mU	LEHMANN (1973c)
6.1	with ^{14}C-glucose-1-P incubated	radioactivity in insoluble precipitate	KENNECKE et al. (1971)
	glucose-1-P/PO_4+Mo at 720 nm	10.7 nM PO_4/ml/min	KENNECKE et al. (1971)
7.0	UDPG with soluble starch or glycogen as primer	starch: 30 mU glycogen: 76 mU	LEHMANN (1973c)
7.5	^{14}C-glucose-1-P, UTP, ^{14}C-UDPG, paper chromatography	activity recorded	KENNECKE et al. (1971)
7.6	UDPG, Na-pyrophosphate, NADP$^+$	5.2 U	LEHMANN (1973c)
7.5	UDP-^{14}C-glucose paper chromatography	high. activity, ^{14}C-glucose-1-P present although phosphatases active	KENNECKE et al. (1971)

Table 1 (continued)

No.	Name of enzyme	E.C.No.	Plant	Source	Purity
35	ADPG pyrophosphorylase	2.7.7.b	*Robinia*	exudate	amm-SO_4-precip.
36	pyrophosphatase (inorganic)	3.6.1.1	*Robinia*	exudate	crude
37	β-amylase	3.2.1.2	*Robinia*	exudate	crude
38	UDPG dehydrogenase	1.1.1.22	*Robinia*	exudate	amm-SO_4-precip.
			Cucurbita maxima	exudate	dialyzed
39	$\beta(1\rightarrow3)$-glucan synthetase		*Yucca flaccida*	exudate	dialyzed
40	sucrose synthetase	2.4.1.13	*Robinia*	exudate	amm-SO_4-precip.
			Cucurbita maxima	exudate	dialyzed
			Cucurbita pepo	exudate	crude
41	sucrose-6-phosphate synthetase	2.4.1.14	*Robinia*	exudate	amm-SO_4-precip.
			Cucurbita pepo	exudate	crude
42	invertase	3.2.1.26	*Robinia*	exudate	crude
			Cucurbita pepo	exudate	crude
Enzymes not numbered in Fig. 2:					
	acetyl esterase	3.1.1.6	*Cucurbita maxima*	exudate	dialyzed
	catalase	1.11.1.6	*Cucurbita maxima*	exudate	dialyzed
	peroxidase	1.11.1.7	many species	histochemically	
			Cucurbita maxima	exudate	dialyzed
			Acer pseudoplatanus	EM-histochemically	
	ATP-ase	3.6.1.3	*Robinia*	exudate	crude
			Cucurbita maxima	exudate	dialyzed
			Cucurbita maxima	EM-histochemically	
	phosphodiesterase	3.1.4.1	*Cucurbita maxima*	exudate	dialyzed and purified

pH	Assay	Activity	References
7.5	^{14}C-glucose-1-P + ATP paper chromatography	no labeled ADPG recorded	KENNECKE et al. (1971)
7.6	Na-pyrophosphate/ inorganic phosphate	1.25 μM/ml/min (P_i)	KENNECKE et al. (1971)
6.1	starch/I_2KI at 620 nm	4.56 mg starch/ml/min	KENNECKE et al. (1971)
7.8	^{14}C-UDPG, NAD^+ paper chromatography	no labeled UDP-glucu-ronate recorded	KENNECKE et al. (1971)
7.5	UDPG, NAD^+ disc electrophoresis	no activity	ESCHRICH et al. (1971)
	UDP-^{14}C-glucose and pachyman as primer	radioactivity in insoluble precipitate	ESCHRICH et al. (1972)
7.5	^{14}C-UDPG + fructose	labeled sucrose indicates activity	KENNECKE et al. (1971)
	UDPG + fructose	no activity	ESCHRICH et al. (1971)
7.2	UDPG + fructose	6.3 mU	LEHMANN (1973c)
	^{14}C-UDPG + fructose-6-P paper chromatography	no labeled sucrose-phosphate recorded	KENNECKE et al. (1971)
7.2	optical test	0.72 mU	LEHMANN (1973c)
7.8	^{14}C-sucrose paper chromatography	no activity	KENNECKE et al. (1971)
5.4	colorimetrically at 340 nm	no activity	LEHMANN (1973c)
7.4	α-naphthyl acetate disc electrophoresis	no activity	ESCHRICH et al. (1971)
6.8	disc electrophoresis H_2O_2/K-iodide	no activity	ESCHRICH et al. (1971)
	guajacol/H_2O_2	activity in phloem, mainly companion cells	RACIBORSKI (1898a)
5.5	disc electrophoresis, Benzidine/H_2O_2	high activity, 3 isoenzymes	ESCHRICH et al. (1971)
9.0	diamino benzidine	activity only in companion cells	CZANINSKI and CATESSON (1970)
7.0–7.3	paper chromatography	no activity	WANNER (1953)
	colorimetrically	no activity	ESCHRICH et al. (1971)
7.2		activity in ectoplasm of sieve elements	GILDER and CRONSHAW (1973)
5.5	colorimetrically with several substrates	variable activities	HEYSER et al. (1974)

Table 1 (continued)

No.	Name of enzyme	E.C.No.	Plant	Source	Purity
	β-(1→3)-glucanase		*Cucurbita* spec. div. *Tilia tomentosa*	exudates	crude and dialyzed
	ribonuclease		*Cucurbita maxima*	exudate	dialyzed
	aminopeptidase		*Cucurbita maxima*	exudate	dialyzed and purified

WILLENBRINK (1966) observed complete blockage when a 4 cm length of the isolated bundle was treated for 2 to 3 h with cyanide. In his experiments demonstrating reversibility of cyanide blockage, lengths of 1.2 to 1.5 cm of the bundle were treated. This is reminiscent of the blockage of transport by heat (WEBSTER and CURRIER, 1968; MCNAIRN and CURRIER, 1968). There, a 4-cm portion of heated hypocotyl stopped transport, whereas a 1-cm portion did not. Although ULLRICH (1963) assumed that increase in sieve-pore callose after cyanide treatment should have no influence on transport, side effects other than inhibition of respiration, like plugging of sieve pores (QURESHI and SPANNER, 1973) or changes in permeability (GINSBURG and GINZBURG, 1970), may occur by cyanide poisoning. In addition, HO and MORTIMER (1971) found evidence that cyanide is translocatable, and may influence phloem loading.

Although WILLENBRINK'S (1966) experiments are methodologically of high performance, and his results confirm his former findings of blockage by cyanide of K-fluorescein transport (WILLENBRINK, 1957), actions other than inhibition of respiratory energy generation are possible.

II. Enzymes of Glycolysis and Gluconeogenesis

Glycolytic phosphorylations are not bound to mitochondria. According to the variety of phosphorus compounds occurring in sieve-tube exudates (see Chapter 3), enzymes catalyzing phosphorylations can be expected in phloem exudates. Several authors have shown that phloem exudates of different sources contain a more or less complete set of enzymes involved in glycolysis and subsequent reactions (WANNER, 1953; KENNECKE et al., 1971; LEHMANN, 1973b, c; ESCHRICH et al., 1971). These reactions are shown on the left in Fig. 2. The corresponding enzymes are listed in Table 1.

The enzyme assays used have been quite variable. KENNECKE et al. (1971) used, in part, enzymes purified by precipitation with ammonium sulfate. ESCHRICH et al. (1971) carried out assays on gels after disc electrophoresis. WANNER (1953) incubated crude exudate and determined the products by paper chromatography. Crude exudate

pH	Assay	Activity	References
	sieve-tube callose as substrate, staining with resorcin blue	variable activities	ESCHRICH (1961)
	disc electrophoresis, soluble RNA as substrate	5 isoenzymes active	HEYSER et al. (1974)
	optical tests	2 enzymes active	J. NUSKE (personal communication)

was also used by LEHMANN (1973b, c). The yields of products were measured photometrically. Since micro-amounts of reactants were incubated, concurrent substrates already present in the exudate may have lead to errors (certainly when calculating enzyme units).

The data listed in Table 1 demonstrate adequately that sieve-tube exudates carry most enzymes of the glycolytic pathway and the citric acid cycle. Their origin, however, has to be considered in a separate section.

Since sucrose is assumed to be the main solute translocated in sieve tubes, enzymic reactions of gluconeogenesis and carbohydrate metabolism are of central interest.

In two sources of sieve-tube exudate, i.e. *Robinia* (KENNECKE et al., 1971) and *Cucurbita pepo* (LEHMANN, 1973c), a variety of transferases, phosphorylases and phosphatases were found. This suggests that besides glycolytic reactions, reactions of gluconeogenesis can also be catalyzed in the phloem. Because of the high amount of ATP, the activity of phosphofructokinase (F6PK) is problematical. Only negligible activity of this enzyme has been found by LEHMANN (1973c). However, KENNECKE et al. (1971) were able to demonstrate F6PK-activity with partly purified enzyme. Since this enzyme is inhibited by high concentrations of ATP, the authors guessed that ATP controls synthesis of fructose diphosphate in sieve tubes. Diphosphofructose phosphatase, which is activated by high concentrations of ATP, has been found in *Cucurbita* exudate (LEHMANN, 1973c).

Fig. 2 surveys, on the right, the enzymic reactions recorded in sieve-tube exudates, which catalyze ultimate steps in gluconeogenesis and sugar metabolism.

The data presented thus far focus attention on the role of organic phosphorus compounds, especially ATP, in sieve tubes. This has been taken into account by experiments with $^{32}PO_4$ (BIELESKI, 1969; KLUGE et al., 1970; BECKER et al., 1971; GARDNER and PEEL, 1972; SCHMITZ and SRIVASTAVA, 1974). These experiments certainly should be discussed in this context. However, the uncertainty of whether or not a particular enzyme is active in any sieve tube is sufficiently demonstrated in Table 1. It seems therefore reasonable to elucidate first the possible origins of enzymes occurring in sieve-tube exudates.

D. Origin of Enzymes in Sieve Tubes

In the previous sections it was shown that a great variety of enzymes occurs in sieve-tube exudates.

Electronmicroscopy has revealed that few, if any, ribosomes occur in mature sieve elements. It cannot be expected that protein synthesis occurs in enucleate sieve elements. In addition, the functional period of mRNA usually does not exceed two days.

A first set of enzymes will certainly be provided by the differentiating sieve element and, in dicotyledons, enzymes occurring in sieve-tube exudate could come from the younger sieve tubes of the secondary phloem. However, monocotyledons like *Yucca flaccida* have only primary phloem in the inflorescence stalk. It could be that intercalary growth provides enzymes which are transported to the mature sieve elements of the stalk. However, prolonged exudation of sieve-tube content of isolated pieces of the stalk was not accompanied by a decrease in enzyme content. This has been demonstrated by tracing enzyme activity with $^{32}PO_4$ (KLUGE et al., 1970; BECKER et al., 1971). Enzymes must have been secreted continuously from cells surrounding the sieve tubes, so long as exudation took place. In addition, the histochemical studies of LEHMANN (1973a) suggest that in *Cucurbita*, enzymes are secreted from companion cells into the sieve tubes when the latter are cut. Thus it can be concluded that the surging of sieve-tube contents, caused by turgor release upon cutting the bundles, induces the companion cells to secrete proteinaceous material into the sieve tubes. After the initial surge, secretion can proceed for hours, as in *Yucca*. The term "secretion" implies active processes, which provide energy for emptying and replenishing pools of solutes, for the synthesis of nucleic acids and proteins, for active passage of membranes, and for surmounting concentration gradients.

Companion cells seem to fulfill such conditions, since they are nucleate and rich in mitochondria and ribosomes. The abundance of connections between sieve elements and companion cells supports the idea that the latter are concerned with phloem loading.

It is commonly agreed that phloem loading (see Chapter 17) is a secretory process i.e. solutes of lower molecular weight are secreted actively into the sieve tubes. Whether phloem loading extends to macromolecules has not as yet been demonstrated.

Careful histochemical assays should give the best information as to which enzymes are normally present in sieve elements. Most reports of this type have recorded acid phosphatase activity in sieve elements at both light-microscopic (ZIEGLER and HUBER, 1960; KUO, 1964/65; LESTER and EVERT, 1965; BRAUN and SAUTER, 1964a, b; DAUWALDER et al., 1969) and electronmicroscopic levels (FIGIER, 1968; CATESSON, 1973). Acid phosphatase also has been found in sieve-tube exudate of *Cucurbita maxima* (ESCHRICH et al., 1971), where 4 bands with activity have been recorded after disc-electrophoresis.

Peroxidase activity in sieve elements of many species has been reported by RACIBORSKI (1898a, b) and VAN FLEET (1959). However, CZANINSKI and CATESSON (1969, 1970) and CATESSON (1973), who investigated peroxidase activity at the electronmicroscopic level, found this enzyme only on the plasmalemma of sieve elements of

Robinia and *Acer pseudoplatanus,* although it was abundant in companion cells. Peroxidase occurs in relatively great amounts in sieve-tube exudate of *Cucurbita maxima* (ESCHRICH et al., 1971).

Phosphatase activity at neutral pH, with ATP added as substrate, was found histochemically in sieve elements of both *Cucurbita maxima* (GILDER and CRONSHAW, 1973) and *Acer pseudoplatanus* (CATESSON, 1973), however, no ATPase was found in sieve-tube exudates of either *Robinia* (WANNER, 1953) or *Cucurbita maxima* (ESCHRICH et al., 1971).

From the differing data reported for the three enzymes mentioned above the following can be deduced:

A. Acid phosphatases are normally present in sieve elements. Histochemically, they occur in the ectoplasm as well as in connection with P-protein. Acid phosphatases are abundant in sieve-tube exudates from different sources.

B. Peroxidases, if normally present in sieve elements, seem to be located only in the ectoplasm. They are abundant in companion cells. Since peroxidases occur in sieve-tube exudate, it seems that they are easily secreted into the sieve elements when surging occurs.

C. ATPase, as judged from histochemical assays, seems to be located in the ectoplasm of both sieve element and companion cell. Since exudate of different sources failed to give positive ATPase reactions, it seems that surging neither removes structures containing ATPase, nor causes secretion of this enzyme into the sieve elements.

These are three examples showing where enzymes may be localized in sieve elements and companion cells.

Considering the unequal sensitivity and specificity of enzyme assays, the instability of some enzymes and the stability of others, the turnover, especially of phosphate esters, the necessity of cofactors for certain enzymes, the occurrence of soluble, particulate and absorbed enzymes, and the differing kinetics of enzymes with different substrates mainly used in standard assays, it seems questionable whether a discussion of all enzymes reported for sieve-tube exudates will lead to a better understanding of phloem physiology. A considerable number of enzymes occurring in sieve-tube exudates, may have nothing to do with metabolism of the sieve elements, with phloem loading and unloading, or with the transport process itself. In addition, the strength of surging may vary according to the osmotic concentration of the contents of the sieve-tubes and may influence the amount and quality of material secreted.

It can be summarized that enzymes occurring in mature sieve-tube members probably have their origin in the companion cells. Certain enzymes, of which acid phosphatase is probably an example, are normally present in the sieve elements. Others, for example peroxidase and ATPase, occur normally associated with the ectoplasm of the sieve elements. Many other enzymes found in sieve-tube exudates may be secreted into sieve elements only when surging occurs. Thus, sieve elements are metabolically dependent on companion cells and the two must be regarded as a functional unit.

E. Biochemical Reactions in Sieve Tubes in Relation to Function

I. Enzymes Normally Present in Sieve Elements

In the previous section, it was pointed out that companion cells might provide enzymes to mature sieve elements. To differentiate between enzymes forced out by surging and those secreted normally, it would be necessary to evaluate histochemical assays carried out on sieve tubes frozen prior to sectioning. In addition, preparations must be washed free of solutes, which could serve as substrates and obscure histochemical assays. Unfortunately, only a few enzymes can be assayed in this way (Table 1).

It would seem worth-while to consider sieve-tube exudates obtained after prolonged bleeding as sources for enzymes either naturally present or secreted into sieve elements. Exudate of inflorescence stalks of *Yucca flaccida* constitutes the principal source of information of this kind. When a *Yucca* stalk is cut, exudation proceeds for hours. It can be assumed that the stimulus of initial surging levels out after a few minutes. Thus, enzymes secreted into the bleeding sieve tubes after surging probably represent material which companion cells normally provide to sieve elements. Exudation undoubtedly differs from the transport process. Consequently, it is possible that exuding sieve tubes are provided with a different set of enzymes than transporting sieve tubes. This uncertainty must be kept in mind.

During the investigation of BECKER et al. (1971), in which $^{32}PO_4$ was incubated with *Yucca*-exudate, it was shown that the pattern of labeling did not change significantly in exudate taken several times within 7 h after the cut was made. The following compounds were labeled with ^{32}P: Phosphoglyceric acid, fructose-6-phosphate, glucose-6-phosphate, UDPglucose, hexose-diphosphates, ATP, CTP, phosphatidyl choline.

In addition, sieve-tube exudate of *Yucca*, collected by prolonged bleeding, incubated with UDP-^{14}C-glucose yielded a labeled insoluble product, obviously callose (ESCHRICH et al., 1972).

Furthermore, stylet exudate of severed aphids which fed in bark sieve tubes of *Salix viminalis* was incubated with $^{32}PO_4$ by GARDNER and PEEL (1972). ATP, UTP, nucleoside diphosphates and traces of fructose-1,6-diphosphate were labeled. An aphid constitutes only a minor sink and its piercing apparently does not cause surging. Therefore, it can be neglected that the suction of the aphid prior to its amputation could have stimulated secretion of enzymes out of the companion cells.

Although it could be argued that phosphate was simply exchanged, incubation with heated exudates gave no labeled organic esters. However, some of the precursors to be phosphorylated, especially ADP, are unstable. They may have been decomposed by heating and may not have been available in the control for the exchange of phosphate.

It is certainly not possible to reconstruct the complete sequence of enzyme reactions leading to all labeled products. It can be assumed that $^{32}PO_4$ could have been incorporated in organic matter by two ways:

1. The reaction: D-glyceraldehyde-3-phosphate + NAD^+ + $P_i \rightarrow$ 1,3-diphosphoglycerate + NADH + H^+ is catalyzed by glyceraldehyde-3-phosphate dehydrogenase and requires NAD^+. Since 1,3-diphosphoglycerate was not found labeled, it can be assumed that the labeled phosphate group of the C_1-atom is transferred to ADP

yielding labeled ATP and 3-phosphoglycerate. Thus, phosphoglycerate kinase is a second enzyme necessary for introducing the inorganic $^{32}PO_4$ into ATP.

2. Sucrose phosphorylase, which catalyzes the reversible reaction: sucrose $+ P_i \rightarrow$ glucose-1-phosphate + fructose, has been found in sieve-tube exudate of *Cucurbita pepo* by LEHMANN (1973c), although with low activity. Since glucose-1-phosphate did not appear labeled, it may have been converted to glucose-6-phosphate by phosphoglucomutase. This enzyme has been found by LEHMANN (1973c) for *Cucurbita pepo*, and by WANNER (1953) for *Robinia*. It seems more reasonable that G-1-P and UTP deliver UDPG and inorganic pyrophosphate. This reaction is catalyzed by UDPG pyrophosphorylase, an enzyme found highly active. Since the inorganic pyrophosphate is delivered by the two terminal phosphates of UTP, $^{32}PO_4$ of G-1-P would be incorporated into UDPG.

Having labeled ATP, it remains a question of stability, as to which of the phosphate esters of glycolytic and gluconeogenetic pathways can be detected labeled after the incubation period.

3. The occurrence of labeled phosphatidylcholine in the incubation mixture is somewhat contradictory to BIELESKI's (1969) report that ^{32}P-labeled phosphocholine (and phosphoethanolamine) appeared in *Cucurbita* exudate. However, KLUGE et al. (1970) also found labeled phosphatidylcholine in *Yucca* exudate.

Irrespective of possible errors in the interpretations of the chromatograms, incorporation of labeled phosphate into both compounds in principle depends on a single reaction: choline + ATP $\rightarrow$ phosphocholine + ADP. However, synthesis of phosphatidylcholine includes several intermediate reactions, because 1,2-diacylglycerol reacts with CDP-choline or CDP-ethanolamine but not with phosphocholine.

Since CDP-choline is synthesized from CTP + phosphocholine, the labeled phosphate of the latter should keep its position because inorganic pyrophosphate, the second product of this reaction, derives from CTP. The lack of labeled inorganic pyrophosphate may be due to an active pyrophosphatase. It does not exclude participation of labeled CTP.

Data presented so far indicate that catabolic and anabolic reactions take place in sieve-tube exudate of *Yucca*, in which ATP, CoA and NAD^+ can participate.

II. Metabolism of Sucrose and Its Derivatives

Non-reducing sugars like sucrose and its galactosides (especially raffinose, stachyose and verbascose) are commonly regarded as the principal transport forms of photosynthates. However, in some investigations free hexoses were also found in sieve-tube exudate of *Cucurbita pepo* (COOIL, 1941) and phloem exudate of *Platanus occidentalis* (MOOSE, 1938). Free fructose and glucose also were found in sieve-tube exudate of *Cucurbita ficifolia* (ESCHRICH, 1963), but neither ever appeared ^{14}C-labeled when the plant was treated with $H^{14}CO_3$ either over a leaf (ESCHRICH and KATING, 1964) or *via* the roots (KATING and ESCHRICH, 1964).

In the first case, sucrose and raffinose were the only labeled sugars. In the latter case, no labeled sugars appeared in the sieve-tube exudate.

Since most investigations of exudate obtained by piercing or cutting the bark of perennial dicotyledons indicate that reducing sugars are absent (ZIMMERMANN, 1957; HALL and BAKER, 1972; c.f. Chapter 3), it might be argued that glucose and fructose found in sieve-tube exudate of other types of plants are products of invertase activity. However, invertase activity has never been found in sieve-tube exudates (WANNER, 1953; KENNECKE et al., 1971; LEHMANN, 1973c), although this enzyme is abundant in other cells of the phloem (TURKINA and DUBININA, 1954; FEKETE et al., 1967; KENNECKE et al. 1971). In addition, when labeled sucrose occurs in exudate, it is difficult to understand why only unlabeled fructose and glucose appear, when invertase should be active.

Regarding the galactosides of sucrose occurring in sieve-tube exudates, it seems remarkable that the galactose moieties can be labeled prior to the sucrose moiety *via* myo-inositol and galactinol (TANNER and KANDLER, 1966; SENSER and KANDLER, 1967). This may explain the observed preferential transport of labeled stachyose after photosynthesis in $^{14}CO_2$ (HENDRIX, 1968). Free galactose, whether labeled or not, has never been found in sieve-tube exudates, not even when ^{14}C-galactose was supplied to the base of a detached inflorescence stalk of *Yucca* (TAMMES et al., 1973).

One might ask whether sucrose and its galactosides are metabolized at all in sieve tubes. Some contributions to this problem were made by introducing sucrose specifically labeled in one of the hexose moieties into the sieve tubes.

HATCH and GLASZIOU (1964) supplied fructosyl-(U)-^{14}C sucrose to the cut end of a midrib of a sugar cane leaf. After 8 h a part of the internode subtending the leaf was squeezed to obtain parenchyma sap and the fibrous residue, including the bundles, was extracted separately. It was found that parenchyma-sap sucrose had a ratio of 0.12 for ^{14}C-activity in the glycosyl to fructosyl moieties, and a ratio of 0.03 was recorded in the sucrose of the bundle tissue. It was concluded that sucrose passes the sieve tubes unaffected, but is split and reorganized when leaving the conducting tissue. However, this result should be regarded a little more physiologically. Solutes supplied to the cut end of a leaf will be more or less sucked up by the vessels, depending on the water tension. This can be demonstrated with any dye solution. Thus, the asymmetrically labeled sucrose is provided to both the conducting and non-conducting tissues *via* the xylem. In monocotyledons, as in *Saccharum*, vessels are in close contact with the phloem (some in physical contact with sieve tubes). Non-conducting tissue situated outside a sclerenchyma sheath may be reached by solutes only over bundle anastomoses. An extract of the vascular tissue will surely show a less metabolized sucrose than an extract of the parenchyma of the non-conducting tissue. A certain amount of the supplied sucrose may probably have been extracted unchanged from the vessels, even when the fibrous tissue was washed prior to extraction.

It seems clear that such experiments do not contribute to the question whether sucrose is metabolized inside the sieve tubes but rather to the problem of phloem loading, which is discussed in Chapter 17 of this volume.

Investigations pertaining to this problem (BROVCHENKO, 1967; TAMMES et al., 1967; YAMAMOTO et al., 1970; GARDNER and PEEL, 1971; TAMMES et al., 1973) agree that sucrose applied to the plant in any way is metabolized prior to its deposition in the sieve tubes. Although the "free space", i.e. the cell wall, has been considered as a possible pathway for sucrose-entry into the sieve tubes (KURSANOV and BROVCHENKO, 1970; cf. also Chapter 17), occurrence of an acid invertase in cell walls (SACHER et al., 1963; HATCH, 1964; HAWKER and HATCH, 1965) suggests that sucrose uptake is under control. SACHER (1966) has observed that the acid invertase of the cell wall has inconstant activities, and GAYLER and GLASZIOU (1972) give a reasonable explanation for the existence of different invertases. Although growing and storing tissues of sugar cane have been investigated by GAYLER and GLASZIOU, their definitions seem also of interest for phloem physiology: acid invertase (pH optimum 5), whether soluble or insoluble is bound to the "outer space", which includes the cell wall, but appears in its soluble form also in the vacuoles of storage parenchyma cells in a growing internode. The outer-space enzyme obviously controls the dry matter input accompanying cell extension growth. Its activity declines with maturation of the internode. A neutral invertase (pH optimum 7), active in mature tissues, is a vacuolar component and appears to be concerned with regulation of both turgor pressure and internal sugar pool.

If these data can be generalized, it may be assumed that free hexoses occurring in sieve-tube exudates are products of outer space-invertase activity. Their secretion into the sieve tubes should be restricted to growing parts of a plant. Since exudate-delivering parts of *Yucca* plants are still growing, and exudate of dicotyledons comes from parts where the cambium is producing new phloem elements, acid invertase of the outer space should be available everywhere. Accordingly, free hexoses can be expected in any source of sieve-tube exudate. It seems, however, that unlimited uptake of free hexoses in the sieve tubes is avoided. Data provided by TAMMES et al. (1973) give evidence that none of the ^{14}C-labeled hexoses, glucose, fructose or galactose, supplied to the base of an excised *Yucca* stalk appeared in the exudate except incorporated in sucrose. In addition, supplied uniformly-labeled sucrose appeared in the exudate with asymmetric label (^{14}C-glucose/^{14}C-fructose = ca. 3:1). Since other uniformly labeled compounds such as maltose, lactose, sorbitol, UDPG, F-1,6-diP, and glyceric acid also occurred incorporated in sucrose, it seems that any substance which can be utilized for sucrose synthesis, including sucrose itself, is metabolized prior to its secretion into the sucrose pool of the sieve tube.

One might argue that sieve tubes simply tend to exclude any reducing sugar. However, sorbose, which also was tested by TAMMES et al. (1973), appeared in the exudate unchanged.

This leads, consequently, to a general statement. Sieve tubes will transport any substance which has the opportunity to enter this pathway. This includes not only the impressive, 11-page list of "assimilates" in CRAFTS and CRISP (1971, Table 6.1), but also K-fluorescein (SCHUMACHER, 1933), D-phenylalanine (ESCHRICH and HARTMANN, 1969), β-alanine (HASHEM and ESCHRICH, 1972) and some herbicides (PEEL, 1972). Certainly, translocation of such exotic compounds cannot be part of the normal function of sieve tubes. It seems that selectivity of uptake into the sieve tubes is limited. Since it is highly unlikely that uptake of solutes into a cut sieve tube can occur, all must be secreted *via* companion cells or some similar system. The capacity of such secretory cells will also be limited. It seems obvious that overloading with a substance by prolonged application, high concentrations or covering great areas will eventually lead to uncontrolled phloem loading. Since sieve elements have no vacuole for deposition of "waste", all solutes once taken up must be translocated.

One might conclude that such "illegally" imported substances would show a long half-life by circulating inside the sieve-tube system. However, the contrary has been found for D-phenylalanine (ESCHRICH and HARTMANN, 1969). This "unnatural" amino acid was quickly removed and deposited in parenchyma cells as N-malonyl D-phenylalanine. It is not known whether such self-cleansing processes also extend to natural substances such as free hexoses.

When sucrose synthesis occurs in sieve tubes, it should be catalyzed either by sucrose synthetase (UDP-glucose: D-fructose 2-glucosyltransferase) or by sucrose-P synthetase (UDP-glucose: D-fructose-6-phosphate 2-glucosyltransferase). The latter enzyme can be excluded, since it was not found by KENNECKE et al. (1971), and LEHMANN (1973c) recorded it only at extremely low activity. Sucrose synthetase, on the other hand, was found to be active in sieve-tube exudates of *Robinia* (KENNECKE et al., 1971) and *Cucurbita pepo* (LEHMANN, 1973c). The negative results obtained by ESCHRICH et al. (1971) with dialyzed exudate of *Cucurbita maxima* may have been due to the—as the authors say—tricky assay utilized.

Labeled sucrose was found when sieve-tube exudate of *Robinia* was incubated with UDP-^{14}C-glucose (KENNECKE et al., 1971), and it also appeared in sieve-tube exudate of *Yucca,* when the base of the inflorescence stalk was provided with UDP-^{14}C-glucose (TAMMES et al., 1973).

The absence of invertase (and probably also of galactosidase) in sieve tubes raises the question whether sucrose and its galactosides can be hydrolyzed another way. KENNECKE et al. (1971) proposed the possibility that sucrose can be hydrolyzed by the reversal of the sucrose synthetase (UDPG-D-fructose-2-glucosyltransferase) reaction. This is supported by studies of DELMER and ALBERSHEIM (1970), who found that both sucrose synthetase and UDPG pyrophosphorylase show high activities in extracts of non-photosynthetic tissues. They propose that the synthesis of UDPG and other nucleotide diphosphate glucoses may be catalyzed by the back reaction of sucrose synthetase coupled with the nucleotide diphosphate glucose pyrophosphorylase. In addition, MURATA (1971, 1972) has shown that sucrose synthetase of storage organs (potato, sweet potato, rice grains) is mainly engaged in the cleavage of sucrose, but not in its synthesis.

If this reaction occurs in sieve tubes, it may be responsible for the production of sufficient amounts of UDPG for the synthesis of callose. The occurrence of labeled UDP after incubation of *Yucca* exudate with $^{32}PO_4$ (BECKER et al., 1971) supports this idea.

Finally, the possibility that sucrose could be split by the action of sucrose phosphorylase should be considered. In the previous section (E I) it was assumed that inorganic phosphate might be introduced into G-1-P by this reaction.

III. Nucleic Acids

A first report on the occurrence of nucleic acids in sieve-tube exudate of *Robinia* was given by ZIEGLER and KLUGE (1962). From the total of 6.35 µg/ml, 4.7 µg/ml were considered as DNA and 1.65 µg/ml as RNA. The presence of DNA was indicated by a violet coloration occurring with the Feulgen reaction. For its quantitative estimation a microbiological growth test with a strain of *Streptococcus faecalis* was used. This organism needs folic acid for the synthesis of thymine from uracil. By omitting the vitamin, the amount of added thymine (present in DNA) can be estimated by the growth response of that organism.

KOLLMANN et al. (1970) tested the trichloro-acetic-acid precipitate of sieve-tube exudate of *Cucurbita maxima* with the orcinol and the diphenylamine reactions for RNA and DNA, respectively. They estimated amounts of less than 0.02 mg of DNA and less than 0.01 mg RNA per ml of sieve-tube exudate.

Further evidence for the occurrence of RNA in sieve-tube exudates is given by labeling experiments with $^{32}PO_4$. BIELESKI (1969) found an increase of labeled RNA from 0.6% (of total organic ^{32}P) 10 min after application of $^{32}PO_4$ to a leaf blade of *Cucurbita maxima* to 12.4% when the exudate was collected after 22 h. Traces of labeled nucleic acids also were obtained by KLUGE et al. (1970) from severed aphid stylets tapping 5 cm below an area of the bark of *Salix triandra* where $^{32}PO_4$ was applied. In an elaborate study HEYSER et al. (unpublished data) analyzed the nucleic acids of sieve-tube exudate of *Cucurbita maxima* seedlings, and compared them with extracts of hypocotyls of the same species.

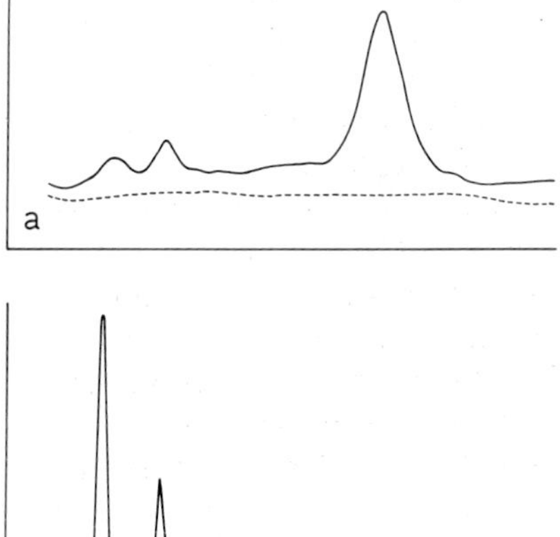

Fig. 3a and b. RNA of sieve-tube exudate (a) and of hypocotyl extract (b) of *Cucurbita maxima* seedlings. Separation on polyacrylamide by disc electrophoresis. Recorded by photometric scanning at 260 nm. Top of gels left, front of moving bands right. Length of gels approx. 8 cm. Solid lines represent peaks of nucleic acids of 25 S, 18 S and 4 S from left to right. Stippled lines represent extinction curves after treatment with RNAase. (From HEYSER et al., in preparation)

Special care was taken to inactivate nucleases. The material was deproteinized on DEAE-Sephadex A 25 and separated on polyacrylamide gel by electrophoresis. Fig. 3 shows the scanned nucleic-acid bands of the hypocotyl extract (b) and of the sieve-tube exudate (a). Pretreatment of the purified extracts with DNAase gave only negligible changes of the curves, whereas pretreatment with RNAase resulted in curves represented by the dotted lines. All peaks occurring in Fig. 3 therefore are RNA's. By analysis on sucrose density gradients it was shown that the first two peaks, especially prominent in the hypocotyl extract (Fig. 3b) are ribosomal RNA's with 25 S and 18 S. The third peak represents 4 S RNA. The quantitative determination of its bases after enzymatic digestion with snake venom phosphodiesterase and alkaline phosphatase resulted in the relation

$$\frac{C+G}{A+U} = \frac{6}{4}.$$

Thus, a considerable amount of double-stranded RNA must be present. The very small amounts of ribosomal RNA's in the sieve-tube exudate may be contaminations from cut parenchyma cells, because 100 to 250 plants were necessary to collect 1 ml of sieve-tube exudate, in which only 0.45 mg RNA were found, but 18.3 mg protein.

From these data it seems obvious that sieve-tube exudate of *Cucurbita maxima* contains one well-defined RNA. Therefore it seems unlikely that nucleic acids described for sieve-tube exudates constitute a mixture of broken-down material derived from formerly active nucleic acids.

Although several RNAases seem to be present in the *Cucurbita* sieve-tube exudate, and a phosphodiesterase was found (HEYSER et al., 1974) which exhibited a slight activity against soluble RNA, uncertainty still exists about the possible functions of both 4 S RNA and nucleases.

When t-RNA is normally secreted from companion cells and not merely forced out by surging, it could be speculated that the pool of amino acids present in sieve tubes of *Cucurbita* is used for protein synthesis in the companion cells. However, secreting t-RNA into the pool to bring back an amino acid seems to be less economical than movement of the free amino acid into the companion cell.

IV. Synthesis and Breakdown of Callose

Callose, its abundance in sieve tubes, and its changes in amount during differentiation and during the functional life of sieve elements is treated specially in Chapter 2. However, the biochemical aspects were omitted in that chapter. Since functions of β-(1→3)-glucans are not yet understood, discussion of this type of polysaccharide is extended to other sources in addition to sieve tubes. Doubtless the very rapid deposition of callose evoked by different stimulations is the main manifestation of "life-reactions" occurring in sieve tubes. The physical properties of sieve-tube callose are described in Chapter 2.

Biochemically, it seems of particular interest, that the samples of more or less purified callose examined thus far were of surprising insolubility. However, this substance is easily degraded by β-(1→3)-glucanases, which are widespread in nature and which occur in many types of plants and plant organs (ESCHRICH, 1961). The same richness extends to β-(1→3)-glucans, predominantly synthesized by bacteria (dextrans), algae (paramylon, chrysolaminarin, laminaran) and fungi (pachyman). However, most β-(1→3)-glucans occurring in lower plants are branched, i.e. mixed with β-(1→6)- and β-(1→4)-glucan chains.

A survey on the bacterial dextrans is given by JEANES et al. (1954). The literature on algal and fungal β-(1→3)-glucans is scattered. Main objects of investigations are glucans of *Euglena* (DWYER and SMILLIE, 1971; DWYER et al., 1970); *Ochromonas* (ALBRECHT and KAUSS, 1971); *Phytophthora* (ZEVENHUIZEN and BARTNICKI-GARCIA, 1969); the pachyman of *Poria cocos* (HOFFMANN et al., 1971); glucans of yeast (MANNERS et al., 1973) and *Achlya* (FARO, 1972), to cite only some of the more recent publications.

A wide variety of β-(1→3)-glucan decomposing enzymes has been isolated from lower plants. Both endo- and exo-β-(1→3)-D-glucanases were found, the latter yielding D-glucose as end product. Endo-β-(1→3)-D-glucanases in general deliver laminaribiose and its polymer homologs besides glucose.

The synthesis of β-(1→3)-D-glucans seems to follow mainly the reaction first described by FEINGOLD et al. (1958), by which glucosyl is transferred from UDPG to a β-(1→3)-linked primer, for instance laminaribiose. However, another system has been described for *Astasia* (Euglenales) (MANNERS and TAYLOR, 1967) and *Phytophthora* (ESCHRICH, 1961), by which α-D-glucose-1-phosphate and glucose are combined to laminaribiose by liberation of orthophosphate. This synthesis is enhanced by divalent cations, probably mainly Ca^{++}.

Since UDPG is present in any source of sieve-tube exudate, but G-1-P seems to occur only temporarily (ESCHRICH, 1961), it can be concluded that sieve-tube callose is synthesized by the action of a UDPG: β-(1→3)-glucan glucosyltransferase. This "callose synthetase" seems to be already present in sieve tubes, for it was observed by ESCHRICH et al. (1964) that the first droplets of sieve-tube exudate of *Cucurbita maxima* were covered with a thin layer of callose.

Callose synthetase also seems to be very stable. Sieve-tube exudate of *Yucca flaccida* which had been stored frozen for over two years, when incubated with UDP-^{14}C-glucose and pachyman as a primer, yielded a labeled insoluble polysaccharide. This product obviously was callose (ESCHRICH et al., 1972).

β-(1→3)-glucan synthetase extracted from various tissues and organisms is particulate, although it can be dissolved by addition of digitonin (FLOWERS et al., 1968; CHAMBERS and ELBEIN, 1970). Callose synthetase of *Yucca*-exudate, however, seems to be soluble and the enzyme of *Cucurbita*-exudate can be kept dissolved when sufficient amounts of dithioerythritol are present.

Since callose can be deposited very quickly [plasmolysis callose has been found substantially visible within 30 sec (ESCHRICH, 1961, 1965)], and in sieve tubes in relatively great amounts (which can be seen microscopically even under low magnification) it seems unlikely that its synthesis should proceed step by step, adding one glucosyl residue after the other to form a chain of the β-(1→3)-glucan.

Although our imagination is incapable of perceiving the velocities of biochemical reactions, the existence of precursors for callose formation would seem to be more suitable for such a rapid synthesis. Nevertheless, no substance which could be regarded as a precursor of callose (except UDPG) has been found in sieve-tube exudates.

In addition, year-round investigations of the sugar components of the sieve-tube exudate of *Tilia tomentosa* (ESCHRICH, 1961) have shown that even at times when pH is low (4.8) and β-(1→3)-glucanase is active (1 March to 26 March), no reducing sugars occurred which could be regarded as hydrolysis products of callose. Only sucrose, raffinose and stachyose were recorded.

The complete lack of breakdown products of callose in sieve-tube exudate collected during reactivation in early spring is in contrast with results obtained using male flowers of *Cucurbita ficifolĭa*. The synandria exhibited a significant change in sugar compositon before, during and after the occurrence of pollen mother-cell callose (ESCHRICH, 1961; Table 12): before callose occurred, sucrose was the main constituent. When callose started to disappear, laminaritetraose was the main constituent besides glucose (which was probably formed by the action of an additional glucosidase). Laminaritriose and -biose were present too, but sucrose was lacking. The latter occurred again when no trace of callose remained.

This comparison suggests that sucrose may be a potential source for callose formation. Sucrose phosphorylase (formation of G-1-P), glucose phosphorylase (formation of UDPG) and UDPG: β-(1→3)-glucan glucosyltransferase would be necessary. All three enzymes have been found in sieve-tube exudates, although sucrose phosphorylase was of low activity (LEHMANN, 1973c). However, a certain level of UDPG seems to be present in sieve tubes at all times.

Since deposition of callose occurs concomitantly with slime plugging of sieve pores, it was concluded that the callose-forming agents are squeezed out of the plasmalemma. This conclusion also was based on results obtained with centrifuged *Allium cepa* bulb scales (ESCHRICH, 1965). When a bulb scale is centrifuged prior to plasmolysis, a layer of callose is formed, covering the plasmolyzed protoplast completely. However, when a bulb scale is plasmolyzed before centrifugation, plasmolysis callose is deposited only on the centrifugal ends of the cells.

The lack of break-down products of callose such as laminaribiose and its polymer homologs in sieve-tube exudate can be interpreted variously. Sieve-tube callose may be hydrolyzed very slowly, and its soluble products converted to sucrose. Since callose is deposited outside the plasmalemma, its products of hydrolysis may be transported through the wall into other cells, and they may not appear in the sieve-tube exudate.

Callose deposits can also be regarded as a storage of glycosyl residues. Since glucanase activity of sieve-tube exudate of three *Cucurbita* species and of *Tilia* was very low (ESCHRICH, 1961), it might be speculated that sieve-tube callose is decomposed by a β-(1→3)-glucan phosphorylase, which was found in some algae MANNERS and TAYLOR, 1967; ALBRECHT and KAUSS, 1971). However, no data are available on the occurrence of this enzyme in sieve-tube exudates.

In contrast to the low activities of β-(1→3)-glucanase in sieve-tube exudates, callose is hydrolyzed by extracts of practically any kind of plant tissue, provided incubation is carried out in the range of pH 4.5 to 6.0 (ESCHRICH, 1961; CLARKE and STONE, 1962; MOORE and STONE, 1972b; BIELY et al., 1972; SOVA and ELYAKOVA, 1972). Especially high activities appeared in the fresh latex of the fruit of *Carica papaya,* as well as in commercially available papain. Comparable high activities were found in extracts of bulb scales of Allium cepa and in the secretion of the pitcher of *Nepenthes* (ESCHRICH, 1961). MOORE and STONE (1972a) found an increase up to 200-fold of β-(1→3)-glucanase [β-(1→3)-glucan hydrolase] activity in lesion areas of TMV-infected *Nicotiana glutinosa* leaves. The same enzyme also increased in activity up to 14-fold during the course of senescence in *Nicotiana* leaves (MOORE and STONE, 1972b). It was shown that β-(1→3)-glucanase activity of leaf disks of *Nicotiana* floating on water increased sharply to the fourth day. This increase was followed by a similar sharp decrease during the next two days. Indole acetic acid and gibberellic acid added to the water had no influence, but kinetin caused a slight, but steady increase, which was not followed by a decrease of β-(1→3)-glucanase activity. Interestingly, abscisic acid had a similar influence.

ABELES and FORRENCE (1970) also reported that excision of plant tissue (*Phaseolus vulgaris*) increases its β-(1→3)-glucanase activity. However, this increase was prevented by IAA, gibberellic acid and kinetin. On the other hand, ethylene and 10% CO_2 promoted the synthesis of β-(1→3)-glucanase. Similarly, DATKO and MACLACHLAN (1968) found that decapitated *Pisum* stems treated with IAA showed an increase in the activity of several enzymes including β-(1→3)-glucanase. It can be speculated that activation of β-(1→3)-glucanase by IAA is part of the process of reactivation of the secondary phloem in spring.

These data, although fragmentarily surveyed, show that phytohormones seem to influence the level of β-(1→3)-glucanase activity in plant tissue. The sudden rise in enzyme activity following excision of a leaf shows relations to senescence i.e. protein decomposition. Since senescing leaves export most of the organic matter which can be mobilized, it can be speculated that the increase of β-(1→3)-glucanase activity is due to the removal of pit callose. Whether such activities also extend to sieve-tube callose is scarcely investigated yet (ABELES and FORRENCE, 1970).

V. P-Protein and Plastids

The term P-protein replaces the "slime" of early phloem investigators, because slimes are normally polysaccharides, not proteins. P-protein has not yet been precisely defined. Since it occurs in electronmicrographs in several different forms, it should be expected that P-protein is at least a mixture of different proteins, if not a mixture of proteins and other constituents of the sieve elements.

As nebulous as its nature is its origin. Initially, it must be synthesized during stages of cell differentiation, where ribosomes are present. Concomitantly, certain compartments for storage of protein are set up. Those compartments are typical of the species. Many dicotyledons form several slime bodies (P-protein bodies), others one only (Fabaceae) and still others develop one large and several small slime bodies (*Ulmus*).

There are also protein crystals (WERGIN and NEWCOMB, 1970). Even the "extruded nucleoli" may, in part, be spherical protein crystals (DESHPANDE and EVERT, 1970). The Caryophyllales and the monocotyledons develop plastids in their sieve elements, which originally are amyloplasts but later are used to store protein.

Apart from those protein-storing plastids, typical amyloplasts occur in sieve elements of dicotyledons (Solanaceae, Apiaceae and many others). It was shown by PALEVITZ and NEWCOMB (1970) that the "transitory" starch of sieve-element plastids, staining reddish-brown with I_2KI, is similar to amylopectin.

Typical filaments of P-protein still attached to ribosomes have been observed in differentiating sieve elements of *Tradescantia albiflora* (HEYSER, 1971). It can be expected that the first P-protein filaments are set up the same way in other plants, at least in Caryophyllales and monocotyledons.

When a sieve element matures, some or all of the protein-storage compartments disperse to contribute its contents to the P-protein. It is remarkable that short-lived sieve elements (dicotyledons) disperse their storage protein at once, whereas long-lived sieve elements (perennial monocotyledons without secondary growth) keep the protein plastids for long periods (PARTHASARATHY, 1974). A clear relation between protein bodies and P-protein filaments is still missing.

Observations on cortical sieve tubes of *Cucurbita maxima* revealed undispersed slime bodies in mature sieve elements (CRONSHAW and ESAU, 1968b). Obviously, sieve elements located in vascular bundles need (or consume?) more P-protein than those of isolated phloem strands. Whether this is related to a greater functional stress to which bundle sieve tubes are exposed has not yet been investigated.

It seems pertinent to note that proteolytic enzymes, at least two aminopeptidases, have recently been found in sieve-tube exudate of *Cucurbita maxima* (Thesis by Joachim NUSKE, in preparation). A certain turnover of P-protein during the life of a sieve element seems quite reasonable inasmuch as P-protein may be involved in temporary processes (cf. Chapter 2).

Upon examination of Fig. 1b, it seems obvious that sieve-tube exudates carry a considerable number of proteins. Disc electrophoresis has shown that each of the peaks represent more than one protein. Since the proteinaceous fraction of sieve-tube exudate is mixed with enzymes secreted from companion cells, it is not possible to determine whether P-protein is a single protein or whether there are several proteins constituting the P-protein.

The classification of CRONSHAW and ESAU (1968a, b), distinguishing between P1, P2 ... P-proteins, is based entirely on structural aspects. Since P-protein occurs in electron micrographs in many different shapes (branched or unbranched, fibrillar and solid or tubular, helical, beaded, striated) and has diameters ranging from 4.5–23 nm, it is difficult to imagine that a single protein can change its conformation so often. However, PARTHASARATHY and MÜHLETHALER (1972) have shown that filamentous units of 50 to 60 Å in diameter occur in a variety of elongating cells. This supports their theory that the different forms of P-protein could be derived from such filamentous units. One or two of these units can be twisted more or less tightly into cork-screw-like forms. Each filament is composed of globular subunits, which probably occur in two sizes (PARTHASARATHY and MÜHLETHALER, 1969). A model similar to those designed by PARTHASARATHY and MÜHLETHALER has been proposed, based on observations of negatively stained sieve-tube exudate of *Ricinus communis* (WILLIAMSON, 1972). Structures depicted by STONE and CRONSHAW (1973) are in accordance with those of WILLIAMSON (1972), and were also obtained by negative staining of sieve-tube exudate of *Ricinus*. However, these helical structures are different from those in P-protein of other plants.

Few attempts have been made to isolate the filament-forming P-protein from sieve-tube exudates. WALKER and THAINE (1971) centrifuged and filtered sieve-tube exudate of *Cucurbita pepo* diluted with buffer containing 2-mercaptoethanol. The pellet, dissolved partly in 2 M KCl, yielded 6 protein bands by disc electrophoresis. Electron-micrographs of the pellet material showed membrane-like structures, but no filaments.

KLEINIG et al. (1971a) dissolved sieve-tube exudate of *Cucurbita maxima* in buffer containing 0.01% dithioerythritol to a concentration of 1–3 mg protein/ml. Vinblastine, (one of the alkaloids which prevent formation of mitotic-spindle microtubules) was added to a final concentration of 2×10^{-3} M. By warming up to room temperature, a whitish substance precipitated, which was centrifuged.

Negatively stained preparations of the precipitate appeared somewhat striated in the electronmicroscope. However, sections of the embedded pellet showed membrane-like lamellae, sometimes coated with fluffy material. There was no difference in appearance in electronmicrographs when Sephadex G-200 fractions of the precipitate were investigated. According to WEBER and KLEINIG (1971), proteins of the exudate precipitated by 42% ammonium sulfate saturation were separated on a Sephadex G-200 columm into two fractions. Further separation by sodium dodecyl sulfate-polyacrylamide electrophoresis yielded bands with molecular weights of approximately 116,000 and 220,000 (high molecular weight-fraction) and 15,000,

28,000 and 59,000 (low molecular weight-fraction). Since these values are nearly doubled from protein to protein, formation of oligomers seems to occur.

In a further publication, KLEINIG et al. (1971b) reported that filamentous structures were completely absent in the purified protein solutions. When $CaCl_2$ was added to a final concentration of 20 mM, a precipitate appeared which could not be reversibly dissolved. However, solubilized proteins were reaggregated into filamentous structures, when dialyzed against 0.1 M KCl. Thus, certain similarities to the G-F transition of actin can be recognized, but tests for ATP-binding and ATPase activity gave negative results.

In a preliminary study, YAPA and SPANNER (1972) tried to separate P-protein of phloem exudate and phloem tissue of *Heracleum mantegazzianum* by isoelectric focusing on gel. Except with phloem exudate collected in 8 M urea, only denatured protein was obtained, and even the phloem exudate dissolved in urea showed a considerable amount of denatured protein. Using an LKB column for electrofocusing, phloem tissue extract in 8 M urea gave a peak at pI 4.95 delivering a filamentous fraction.

Investigations concerned with isolation of P-protein reported so far agree that it is a single protein (although it may polymerize to oligomers), which constitutes the filaments in the sieve tubes. However, methods used in these investigations are insufficient to obtain purified P-protein. For instance, KLEINIG et al. (1971b) investigated the protein which precipitated at 42% ammonium sulfate saturation, and WEBER and KLEINIG (1971) separated from this fraction 5 proteins with defined molecular weights. Our own investigations carried out with sieve-tube exudate of the same species (*Cucurbita maxima*) have shown that 10% ammonium sulfate saturation precipitated 7 proteins, as shown by disc electrophoresis. Between 10 and 20% ammonium sulfate saturation, 6 proteins precipitated. Between 20 and 30% ammonium sulfate, more than 7 proteins were found in the precipitate. Between 30 and 40% ammonium sulfate saturation also more than 7 proteins were recorded, and between 40 and 50% ammonium sulfate saturation, 10 proteins appeared when the precipitate was dissolved and subjected to disc electrophoresis. Additional 9 protein bands appeared between 50 and 60%, and a further 10 bands were found in the 60 to 70% ammonium sulfate precipitate. Naturally, several protein bands in subsequent fractions should be identical. However, any fraction of this sequence alone contains more than 5 proteins. In addition, between 30 and 50% ammonium sulfate saturation, the bulk of the basic gelling protein appeared which has been characterized by WALKER (1972). This protein does not band sharply by disc electrophoresis, and traces of it also appeared in all fractions between 20 and 70% ammonium sulfate saturation. WALKER and THAINE (1971) have shown that this gelling factor does not form P-protein filaments when observed negatively stained in the electron microscope. Obviously, it is this material which by oxidation usually causes exudate droplets of cucurbits to become rigid after a while. To keep this protein dissolved, relatively great amounts of dithioerythritol or 2-mercaptoethanol must be added. The occurrence of membrane-like structures in electron-micrographs after vinblastine treatment (KLEINIG et al., 1971a) may be due to precipitation of the gelling protein. This happens easily when the concentration of SH-group protecting thiols is reduced either by dilution or by dialysis. This gelling protein can be removed from the other proteins of the sieve-tube exudate by chromatography on DEAE cellulose columns (HEYSER et al., 1974). By this procedure, it elutes first, appearing as peak 1 and 2 (Fig. 1b). Our attempts to obtain a reaggregation to filaments in one or more of the fractions following the gelling component have been unsuccessful thus far.

Although biochemical data have not revealed the nature of the P-protein, its existence as a real structure can be accepted. The possibility of a fixation artifact has been questioned by JOHNSON's (1968, 1973) pictures of filamentous sieve-pore contents obtained by the freeze-etching technique. Speculations on the contractility of P-protein filaments are premature since evidence is given only for its reaggregation from the soluble state by increasing ionic strength.

Thus, increasing ion concentration in sieve tubes might cause aggregation of a dissolved protein to filaments. When this happens after stimulations, influx of ions might be preferably at sites where filaments occur in abundance i.e. in sieve pores. This would suggest that callose may participate as a mediator between symplast and apoplast, the source of ions. That permeation of solutes and ions through callose is greatly enhanced by Ca ions has been shown by ESCHRICH and ESCHRICH (1964). This assumption implies that P-protein which has accumulated in sieve pores must have been dislocated by surging prior to its precipitation.

Another point of view is the apparent fragility of the P-protein structures. Obviously, light-grown plants have the P-protein distributed over the lumen of the sieve elements either as a network or as strands, which may depend on the developmental stage of the sieve element. *Cucurbita* seedlings, whose epicotyls were darkened for 2 days with the cotyledons removed showed the P-protein displaced to the parietal layer of cytoplasm of the sieve elements (EVERT et al., 1973). In recent studies, we were able to show (ESCHRICH et al., in preparation) that darkened seedlings of *Cucurbita maxima* drastically reduce the turgor of the sieve tubes. This can be seen either by the reduction of exudation or by cryoscopic determinations of the osmotic concentration of the exudate. 5 days' dark treatment were sufficient to prevent any exudation.

F. Conclusions

The lack of compartments in mature sieve elements, and the surging preceding exudation make it difficult, if not impossible, to discriminate between biochemical reactions occurring in the lumina of the sieve elements, in the parietal cytoplasm of the sieve elements and in the companion cells. Since ribosomes are lacking in mature sieve elements, enzymes must be provided to sieve tubes either by companion cells or by comparable cells. Disregarding the proteins of mitochondria, plastids and some other parts of the ectoplasm, the only protein native to sieve elements seems to be the P-protein. The fluid surrounding it is especially set up to preserve it in undenatured form (low Ca^{++} content, high concentrations of K^+ and sucrose).

Since a great variety of enzymes found in sieve-tube exudates scarcely contributes to the function of sieve tubes, those enzymes lacking in sieve-tube exudates probably elucidate the biochemistry of sieve tubes better. Invertase and galactosidase, for instance, do not occur in sieve-tube exudates, although invertase is abundant in companion cells. It seems therefore that secretion into sieve elements, even when induced by surging, is under control. If invertase and galactosidase were present in sieve tubes, concentrations of sucrose and its galactosides would be reduced and the content of reducing hexoses would be increased.

Sieve tubes tend to keep a certain level of nonreducing di- and oligosaccharides for as yet unknown purposes.

Since osmotic concentration in sieve tubes is quickly adapted to changes of water potential (HALL and MILBURN, 1973, and literature cited therein), it can be surmised that sucrose is not only the main solute transported, but that it also regulates the osmotic potential of sieve tubes. In this way, the sucrose pool in sieve tubes functions like the vacuole of sucrose-storing cells. In addition, sucrose may be utilized for the generation of UDPG, which must be available for callose synthesis.

The role of ATP in sieve tubes will remain obscure as long as kinetic data are missing. The same is the case for the role of hexose diphosphates. Since both substances appeared labeled first when sieve-tube exudate of *Yucca* was incubated with $^{32}PO_4$ (BECKER et al., 1971), it would be reasonable to think of a balance between phosphofructo-kinase and fructose diphosphatase, the catalysts of the "futile cycle", which is regulated by ATP and AMP concentrations, and can be regarded as the main switch between glycolysis and gluconeogenesis.

The question whether phosphorylations normally occur in sieve tubes must be reconsidered since SCHMITZ and SRIVASTAVA (1974) have recently shown that sieve-tube exudate of the giant kelp *Macrocystis* catalyzed the incorporation of $^{32}PO_4$ into ATP, ADP, CTP, UDP, UDPG and hexose monophosphates. Sieve tubes of *Macrocystis* are not equipped with companion cells, but it is still uncertain whether they also lack nuclei.

The uncertainty about the real catalytic abilities of the sieve tubes also extends to products of enzyme action. With regard to the sugars in sieve tubes, some analyses have shown that only sucrose and its galactosides occur. However, others recorded hexoses besides the nonreducing sugars. PEEL and FORD (1968) gave a reasonable explanation for this discrepancy.

When ^{14}C-labeled sugars (^{14}C-sucrose, ^{14}C-glucose, ^{14}C-fructose) were applied to the cambial surface of a strip of willow bark, the exudate of severed aphid stylets contained ^{14}C-labeled hexoses besides ^{14}C-sucrose. However, when a leaf attached to a willow branch was supplied with $^{14}CO_2$, only labeled sucrose appeared in the stylet exudate, although extracts of the bark contained labeled hexoses as well as sucrose in either case. PEEL and FORD (1968) postulated two pathways for the entry of sugars into the sieve tubes: one leading from the external milieu directly through the cytoplasm of the companion cell into the sieve tube, the other leading from the external milieu first into vacuoles of storage cells, and then through the cytoplasm of the companion cell into the sieve tube. The first pathway would be open to sucrose and hexoses, the latter only to sucrose. This implies that sugars provided from the vacuole of a parenchyma cell can pass only as sucrose. It is true that the direct pathway mentioned first included only one barrier, the plasmalemma. The indirect pathway is controlled by at least three barriers (plasmalemma, and entry and exit through the tonoplast).

This interpretation of why sometimes only sucrose appears in sieve-tube exudate, and at other times hexoses in addition, leads to the conclusion that solutes administered directly to phloem tissue may enter the sieve tubes uncontrolled. This would explain why practically any substance administered in this way is transported in sieve tubes. Without consideration of the less valuable interpretations of biochemical reactions based on such experiments, it seems that all parts of the complex phloem tissue must be regarded as an integrated physiological unit.

References

Abeles, F.B., Forrence, L.E.: Temporal and hormonal control of β-1,3-glucanase in *Phaseolus vulgaris* L. Plant Physiol. **45**, 395–400 (1970).

Albrecht, G.J., Kauss, H.: Purification, crystallization and properties of a β-(1,3)-glucan phosphorylase from *Ochromonas malhamensis*. Phytochemistry **10**, 1293–1298 (1971).

Becker, D., Kluge, M., Ziegler, H.: Der Einbau von $^{32}PO_4^{---}$ in organische Verbindungen durch Siebröhrensaft. Planta **99**, 154–162 (1971).

Bieleski, R.L.: Phosphorus compounds in translocating phloem. Plant Physiol. **44**, 497–502 (1969).

Biely, P., Farkas, V., Bauer, S.: Secretion of β-glucanase by *Saccharomyces cerevisiae* protoplasts. FEBS letters **23**, 153–156 (1972).

Braun, H.J., Sauter, J.J.: Phosphatase-Aktivität in den Siebzellen der Koniferennadeln. Naturwissenschaften **51**, 170 (1964a).

Braun, H.J., Sauter, J.J.: Phosphatase-Lokalisation in Phloembeckenzellen und Siebröhren der Dioscoreaceae und ihre mögliche Bedeutung für den aktiven Assimilattransport. Planta **60**, 543–557 (1964b).

Brovchenko, M.I.: Some proofs of splitting of sucrose during its translocation from the mesophyll to the thin bundles of sugar beet leaves. Fiziol. Rast. **14**, 415–424 (1967).

Catesson, A.M.: Observations cytochimique sur les tubes criblés de quelques angiospermes. J. de Microscopie **16**, 95–104 (1973).

Chambers, J., Elbein, A.D.: Biosynthesis of glucans in mung bean seedlings. Formation of β-(1-4)-glucans from GDP-glucose and β-(1-3)-glucans from UDP-glucose. Arch. Biochem. Biophys. **138**, 620–631 (1970).

Clarke, A.E., Stone, B.A.: β-1,3-glucan hydrolases from the grape vine (*Vitis vinifera*) and other plants. Phytochemistry **1**, 175–188 (1962).

Cooil, B.: Significance of phloem exudate of *Cucurbita pepo* with reference to translocation of organic materials. Plant Physiol. **16**, 61–84 (1941).

Crafts, A.S., Crisp, C.E.: Phloem transport in plants. San Francisco: W.H. Freeman and Company 1971.

Cronshaw, J., Esau, K.: P-protein in the phloem of *Cucurbita*. I. The development of P-protein bodies. J. Cell Biol. **38**, 25–39 (1968a).

Cronshaw, J., Esau, K.: P-protein in the phloem of *Cucurbita*. II. The P-protein of mature sieve elements. J. Cell Biol. **38**, 292–303 (1968b).

Czaninski, Y., Catesson, A.M.: Localisation ultrastructurale d'activités peroxydasiques dans les tissus conducteurs végétaux au cours du cycle annuel. J. de Microscopie **8**, 875–888 (1969).

Czaninski, Y., Catesson, A.M.: Activités peroxydasiques d'origines diverses dans les cellules d'*Acer pseudoplatanus* (tissus conducteurs et cellules en culture) J. de Microscopie **9**, 1089–1102 (1970).

Datko, A.H., Maclachlan, G.A.: Indoleacetic acid and the synthesis of glucanase and pectic enzymes. Plant Physiol. **43**, 735–742 (1968).

Dauwalder, M., Whaley, W.G., Kephart, J.E.: Phosphatases and differentiation of the Golgi apparatus. J. Cell Sci. **4**, 455–497 (1969).

Delmer, D.P., Albersheim, P.: The biosynthesis of sucrose and nucleoside diphosphate glucose in *Phaseolus aureus*. Plant Physiol. **45**, 782–786 (1970).

Deshpande, B.P., Evert, R.F.: A re-evaluation of extruded nucleoli in sieve elements. J. Ultrastruct. Res. **33**, 483–494 (1970).

Dwyer, M.R., Smillie, R.M.: β-1,3-glucan: A source of carbon and energy for chloroplast development in *Euglena gracilis*. Australian J. Biol. Sci. **24**, 15–22 (1971).

DWYER, M.R., SMYDZUK, J., SMILLIE, R.M.: Synthesis and breakdown of β-1,3-glucan in *Euglena gracilis* during growth and carbon depletion. Australian J. Biol. Sci. **23**, 1005–1013 (1970).

ESCHRICH, W.: Untersuchungen über den Ab- und Aufbau der Callose. Z. Botan. **49**, 153–218 (1961).

ESCHRICH, W.: Der Phloemsaft von *Cucurbita ficifolia*. Planta **60**, 216–224 (1963).

ESCHRICH, W.: Physiologie der Siebröhrencallose. Planta **65**, 280–300 (1965).

ESCHRICH, W., ESCHRICH, B.: Das Verhalten isolierter Callose gegenüber wäßrigen Lösungen. Ber. Deut. Botan. Ges. **77**, 329–331 (1964).

ESCHRICH, W., ESCHRICH, B., CURRIER, H.B.: Historadiographischer Nachweis von Calcium-45 im Phloem von *Cucurbita maxima*. Planta **63**, 146–154 (1964).

ESCHRICH, W., EVERT, R.F., HEYSER, W.: Proteins of the sieve-tube exudate of *Cucurbita maxima*. Planta **100**, 208–221 (1971).

ESCHRICH, W., HARTMANN, T.: Translokation und biochemisches Verhalten von D- und L-Phenylalanin bei *Vicia faba*. Planta **85**, 213–227 (1969).

ESCHRICH, W., HÜTTERMANN, A., HEYSER, W., TAMMES, P.M.L., VAN DIE, J.: Evidence for the synthesis of callose in sieve tube exudate of *Yucca flaccida*. Z. Pflanzenphysiol. **67**, 468–470 (1972).

ESCHRICH, W., KATING, H.: Aufnahme, Einbau und Transport von ^{14}C in *Cucurbita ficifolia*. I. Applikation von Bicarbonat-^{14}C an oberirdische Pflanzenorgane. Planta **60**, 523–539 (1964).

EVERT, R.F., ESCHRICH, W., EICHHORN, S.E.: P-protein distribution in mature sieve elements of *Cucurbita maxima*. Planta **109**, 193–210 (1973).

FARO, S.: The role of a cytoplasmic glucan during morphogenesis of sex organs in *Achlya*. Am. J. Botany **59**, 919–923 (1972).

FEINGOLD, D.S., NEUFELD, E.F., HASSID, W.Z.: Synthesis of a β-1,3-linked glucan by extracts of *Phaseolus aureus* seedlings. J. Biol. Chem. **233**, 783–788 (1958).

FEKETE, M.A.R. DE, ZIEGLER, H., WOLF, R.: Enzyme des Kohlenhydratstoffwechsels in Nektarien. Planta **75**, 125–138 (1967).

FIGIER, J.: Localisation infrastructurale de la phosphomonoestérase acide dans la stipule de *Vicia faba* L. au niveau du nectaire. Planta **83**, 60–79 (1968).

FLEET, D.S., VAN: Analysis of the histochemical localization of peroxidase related to the differentiation of plant tissues. Can. J. Botany **37**, 449–458 (1959).

FLOWERS, H.M., BATRA, K.K., KEMP, J., HASSID, W.Z.: Biosynthesis of insoluble glucans from uridine-diphosphate D-glucose with enzyme preparations from *Phaseolus aureus* and *Lupinus albus*. Plant Physiol. **43**, 1703–1709 (1968).

FRITZ, E., ESCHRICH, W.: ^{14}C-Mikroautoradiographie wasserlöslicher Substanzen im Phloem. Planta **92**, 267–281 (1970).

GARDNER, D.C.J., PEEL, A.J.: Transport of sugars into the sieve elements of willow. Phytochemistry **10**, 2621–2625 (1971).

GARDNER, D.C.J., PEEL, A.J.: Some observations on the role of ATP in sieve tube translocation. Planta **107**, 217–226 (1972).

GAYLER, K.R., GLASZIOU, K.T.: Physiological functions of acid and neutral invertase in growth and sugar storage in sugar cane. Physiol. Plantarum **27**, 25–31 (1972).

GEIGER, D.R., CHRISTY, A.L.: Effect of sink region anoxia on translocation rate. Plant Physiol. **47**, 172–174 (1971).

GEIGER, D.R., GIAQUINTA, R.T., SOVONICK, S.A., FELLOWS, R.J.: Solute distribution in sugar beet leaves in relation to phloem loading and translocation. Plant Physiol. **52**, 585–589 (1973).

GILDER, J., CRONSHAW, J.: Adenosine triphosphatase in the phloem of *Cucurbita*. Planta **110**, 189–204 (1973).

GINSBURG, H., GINZBURG, B.Z.: Radial water and solute flows in roots of *Zea mays*. I. Water flow. J. Exptl. Botany **21**, 580–592 (1970).

HALL, S.M., BAKER, D.A.: The chemical composition of *Ricinus* phloem exudate. Planta **106**, 131–140 (1972).

HALL, S.M., MILBURN, J.A.: Phloem transport in *Ricinus*: Its dependence on the water balance of the tissues. Planta **109**, 1–10 (1973).

HASHEM, M., ESCHRICH, W.: Transport and utilization of β-alanine by *Vicia faba*. Biochem. Physiol. Pflanzen **163**, 225–228 (1972).

Hatch, M.D.: Sugar accumulation by sugar cane storage tissue: the role of sucrose phosphate. Biochem. J. **93**, 521–526 (1964).

Hatch, M.D., Glasziou, K.T.: Direct evidence for translocation of sucrose in sugarcane leaves and stems. Plant Physiol. **39**, 180–184 (1964).

Hawker, J.S., Hatch, M.D.: Mechanism of sugar storage by mature stem tissue of sugar cane. Physiol. Plantarum **18**, 444–453 (1965).

Hendrix, J.E.: Labeling pattern of translocated stachyose in squash. Plant Physiol. **43**, 1631–1636 (1968).

Heyser, W.: Phloemdifferenzierung bei *Tradescantia albiflora*. Cytobiology **4**, 186–197 (1971).

Heyser, W., Eschrich, W., Hüttermann, A., Evert, R.F., Burchardt, R., Fritz, E., Heyser, R.: Phosphodiesterase in sieve-tube exudate of *Cucurbita maxima*. Z. Pflanzenphysiol. **71**, 413–423 (1974).

Ho, L.C., Mortimer, D.C.: The site of cyanide inhibition of sugar translocation in sugar beet leaf. Can. J. Botany **49**, 1769–1775 (1971).

Hoffmann, G.C., Simson, B.W., Timell, T.E.: Structure and molecular size of pachyman. Carbohyd. Res. **20**, 185–188 (1971).

Jeanes, A., Haynes, W.C., Wilham, C.A., Rankin, J.C., Melvin, E.H., Austin, M.J., Cluskey, J.E., Fisher, B.E., Tsuchiya, H.M., Rist, C.E.: Characterization and classification of dextrans from ninety-six strains of bacteria. J. Am. Chem. Soc. **76**, 5041–5052 (1954).

Johnson, R.P.C.: Microfilaments in pores between frozen-etched sieve elements. Planta **81**, 314–332 (1968).

Johnson, R.P.C.: Filaments but no membranous transcellular strands in sieve pores in freeze-etched, translocating phloem. Nature **244**, 464–466 (1973).

Kating, H., Eschrich, W.: Aufnahme, Einbau und Transport von ^{14}C in *Cucurbita ficifolia*. II. Applikation von Bicarbonat-^{14}C über die Wurzel. Planta **60**, 598–611 (1964).

Kennecke, M., Ziegler, H., de Fekete, M.A.R.: Enzymaktivitäten im Siebröhrensaft von *Robinia pseudoacacia* L. und anderen Baumarten. Planta **98**, 330–356 (1971).

Kleinig, H., Dörr, I., Kollmann, R.: Vinblastine-induced precipitation of phloem proteins *in vitro*. Protoplasma **73**, 293–302 (1971 a).

Kleinig, H., Dörr, I., Weber, C., Kollmann, R.: Filamentous proteins from plant sieve tubes. Nature New Biol. **229**, 152–153 (1971 b).

Kluge, M., Becker, D., Ziegler, H.: Untersuchungen über ATP und andere organische Phosphorverbindungen im Siebröhrensaft von *Yucca flaccida* und *Salix triandra*. Planta **91**, 68–79 (1970).

Kollmann, R., Dörr, I., Kleinig, H.: Protein filaments-structural components of the phloem exudate. Planta **95**, 86–94 (1970).

Kuo, Chi-Fang: Histochemical localization of various enzymes in plant vascular bundles, with special reference to their significance in transportation of organic substance. Acta Botan. Sinica **12/13**, 105–106 (1964/65).

Kursanov, A.L., Brovchenco, M.I.: Sugars in the free space of leaf plates: their origin and possible involvement in transport. Can. J. Botany **48**, 1243–1250 (1970).

Lehmann, J.: Zur Lokalisation von Dehydrogenasen des Energiestoffwechsels im Phloem von *Cucurbita pepo* L. Planta **111**, 187–198 (1973 a).

Lehmann, J.: Untersuchungen am Phloemexsudat von *Cucurbita pepo* L. I. Enzymaktivitäten von Glykolyse, Gärung und Citrat-Cyclus. Planta **114**, 41–50 (1973 b).

Lehmann, J.: Untersuchungen am Phloemexsudat von *Cucurbita pepo* L. II. Enzymaktivitäten der Gluconeogenese und des Auf- und Abbaus von Di- und Polysacchariden. Planta **114**, 51–61 (1973 c).

Lester, H.H., Evert, R.F.: Acid-phosphatase activity in sieve-tube members of *Tilia americana*. Planta **65**, 180–185 (1965).

Manners, D.J., Masson, A.J., Patterson, J.: The structure of a β-(1-3)-D-glucan from yeast cell walls. Biochem. J. **135**, 19–30 (1973).

Manners, D.J., Taylor, D.C.: Studies on carbohydrate metabolizing enzymes. XVI. Specificity of laminaribiose phosphorylase from *Astasia ocellata*. Arch. Biochem. Biophys. **121**, 443–451 (1967).

McNairn, R.B., Currier, H.B.: Translocation blockage by sieve plate callose. Planta **82**, 369–380 (1968).

Milburn, J.A.: Phloem exudate from castor bean: induction by massage. Planta **95**, 272–276 (1970).

MILBURN, J.A.: An analysis of the response in phloem exudation on application of massage to *Ricinus*. Planta **100**, 143–154 (1971).

MOORE, A.E., STONE, B.A.: Effect of infection with TMV and other viruses on the level of a β-1,3-glucan hydrolase in leaves of *Nicotiana glutinosa*. Virology **50**, 791–798 (1972a).

MOORE, A.E., STONE, B.A.: Effect of senescence and hormone treatment on the activity of a β-1,3-glucan hydrolase in *Nicotiana glutinosa* leaves. Planta **104**, 93–109 (1972b).

MOOSE, C.A.: Chemical and spectroscopic analysis of phloem exudate and parenchyma sap from several species of plants. Plant Physiol. **13**, 365–380 (1938).

MURATA, T.: Sucrose synthetase of sweet potato roots. Part II. A kinetic study. Agr. Biol. Chem. (Tokyo) **35**, 1441–1448 (1971).

MURATA, T.: Sucrose synthetase of rice grains and potato tubers. Agr. Biol. Chem. (Tokyo) **36**, 1815–1818 (1972).

PALEVITZ, B.A., NEWCOMB, E.H.: A study of sieve-element starch using sequential enzymatic digestion and electron microscopy. J. Cell Biol. **45**, 383–398 (1970).

PARTHASARATHY, M.V.: Ultrastructure of phloem in palms. III. Mature phloem. Protoplasma **79**, 265–315 (1974).

PARTHASARATHY, M.V., MÜHLETHALER, K.: Ultrastructure of protein tubules in differentiating sieve elements. Cytobiologie **1**, 17–36 (1969).

PARTHASARATHY, M.V., MÜHLETHALER, K.: Cytoplasmic microfilaments in plant cells. J. Ultrastruct. Res. **38**, 46–62 (1972)

PEEL, A.J.: The control of solute movement into sieve elements. Pestic. Sci. **3**, 631–641 (1972).

PEEL, A.J., FORD, J.: The movement of sugars into the sieve elements of bark strips of willow. J. Exptl. Botany **19**, 370–380 (1968).

QUERESHI, F.A., SPANNER, D.C.: Cyanide inhibition of phloem transport along the stolon of *Saxifraga sarmentosa* L. J. Exptl. Botany **24**, 751–762 (1973).

RACIBORSKI, M.: Ein Inhaltskörper des Leptoms. Ber. Deut. Bot. Ges. **16**, 52–63 (1898a).

RACIBORSKI, M.: Weitere Mitteilungen über das Leptomin. Ber. Deut. Bot. Ges. **16**, 119–123 (1898b).

SACHER, J.A.: The regulation of sugar uptake and accumulation in bean pod tissue. Plant Physiol. **41**, 181–189 (1966).

SACHER, J.A., HATCH, M.D., GLASZIOU, K.T.: Sugar accumulation cycle in sugar cane. III. Physical and metabolic aspects of cycle in immature storage tissues. Plant Physiol. **38**, 348–354 (1963).

SCHMITZ, K., SRIVASTAVA, L.M.: The enzymatic incorporation of ^{32}P into ATP and other organic compounds by sieve-tube sap of *Macrocystis integrifolia* Bory. Planta **116**, 85–89 (1974).

SCHUMACHER, W.: Untersuchungen über die Wanderung des Fluoreszeins in den Siebröhren. Jahrb. Wiss. Bot. **77**, 685–732 (1933).

SENSER, M., KANDLER, O.: Galactinol, ein Galactosyldonor für die Biosynthese der Zucker der Raffinosefamilie in Blättern. Z. Pflanzenphysiol. **57**, 376–388 (1967).

SIJ, J.W., SWANSON, C.A.: Effect of petiole anoxia on the phloem transport in squash. Plant Physiol. **51**, 368–371 (1973).

SOVA, V.V., ELYAKOVA, L.A.: Some aspects of specificity and action pattern of β-1,3-glucan glucanohydrolase from *Spisula sachalinensis*. Biochim. Biophys. Acta **258**, 219–227 (1972).

STONE, D.L., CRONSHAW, J.: Fine structure of P-protein filaments from *Ricinus communis*. Planta **113**, 193–206 (1973).

TAMMES, P.M.L.: Observations on the bleeding of palm trees. Rec. Trav. bot. Néer. **30**, 514–536 (1933).

TAMMES, P.M.L., VAN DIE, J.: Studies on phloem exudation from *Yucca flaccida* Haw. I. Some observations on the phenomenon of bleeding and the composition of the exudate. Acta Botan. Neerl. **13**, 76–83 (1964).

TAMMES, P.M.L., VONK, C.R., VAN DIE, J.: Studies on phloem exudation from *Yucca flaccida* Haw. VI. The formation of exudate-sucrose from supplied hexoses in excised inflorescence parts. Acta Botan. Neerl. **16**, 244–246 (1967).

TAMMES, P.M.L., VONK, C.R., VAN DIE, J.: Studies on phloem exudation from *Yucca flaccida* Haw. XI. Xylem feeding of ^{14}C-sugars and some other compounds, their conversion and recovery from the phloem exudate. Acta Botan. Neerl. **22**, 233–237 (1973).

TANNER, W., KANDLER, O.: Biosynthesis of stachyose in *Phaseolus vulgaris*. Plant Physiol. **41**, 1540–1542 (1966).

Turkina, M.W., Dubinina, I.M.: Einige Besonderheiten des Atmungssystems der Leitbündel. Dokl. Akad. Nauk. SSSR **95**, 199–202 (1954).

Ullrich, W.: Zur Sauerstoffabhängigkeit des Transportes in den Siebröhren. Planta **57**, 402–429 (1961).

Ullrich, W.: Über die Bildung von Callose bei einer Hemmung des Transportes in den Siebröhren durch Cyanid. Planta **59**, 387–390 (1963).

Walker, T.S.: The purification and some properties of a protein causing gelling in phloem sieve tube exudate from *Cucurbita pepo*. Biochim. Biophys. Acta **257**, 433–444 (1972).

Walker, T.S., Thaine, R.: Proteins and fine structural components in exudate from sieve tubes in *Cucurbita pepo* stems. Ann. Botany (London) **35**, 773–790 (1971).

Wanner, H.: Enzyme der Glykolyse im Phloemsaft. Ber. Schweiz. Botan. Ges. **63**, 201–212 (1953).

Weber, C., Kleinig, H.: Molecular weights of *Cucurbita* sieve tube proteins. Planta **99**, 179–182 (1971).

Webster, D.H., Currier, H.B.: Heat-induced callose and lateral movement of assimilates from phloem. Can. J. Botany **46**, 1215–1220 (1968).

Wergin, W.P., Newcomb, E.H.: Formation and dispersal of crystalline P-protein in sieve elements of soybean (*Glycine max* L.). Protoplasma **71**, 365–388 (1970).

Willenbrink, J.: Über die Hemmung des Stofftransportes in den Siebröhren durch lokale Inaktivierung verschiedener Atmungsenzyme. Planta **48**, 269–342 (1957).

Willenbrink, J.: Zur lokalen Hemmung des Assimilattransports durch Blausäure. Z. Pflanzenphysiol. **55**, 119–130 (1966).

Williamson, R.E.: An investigation of the contractile protein hypothesis of phloem translocation. Planta **106**, 149–157 (1972).

Yamamoto, T., Sekiguchi, S., Noguchi, M.: The translocation of photosynthetic products from mesophyll into midrib in tobacco plant. III. The transformation of translocated ^{14}C-sugars in the veins. Plant Cell Physiol. (Tokyo) **11**, 367–375 (1970).

Yapa, P.A.J., Spanner, D.C.: Isoelectric focusing of sieve-tube protein. Planta **106**, 369–373 (1972).

Zevenhuizen, L.P.T.M., Bartnicki-Garcia, S.: Chemical structure of the insoluble hyphal wall glucan of *Phytophthora cinnamomi*. Biochemistry **8**, 1496–1502 (1969).

Ziegler, H., Huber, F.: Phosphataseaktivität in den „Strasburger-Zellen" der Koniferennadeln. Naturwissenschaften **47**, 305 (1960).

Ziegler, H., Kluge, M.: Die Nucleinsäuren und ihre Bausteine im Siebröhrensaft von *Robinia pseudoacacia* L. Planta **58**, 144–153 (1962).

Zimmermann, M.H.: Translocation of organic substances in trees. I. The nature of the sugars in the sieve-tube exudate of trees. Plant Physiol. **32**, 288–291 (1957).

III. Phloem Transport: Assessment of Evidence

5. Mass Transfer

M.J. CANNY

A. Introduction

Translocation can be defined as the transport of dry weight. Leaves of higher plants are organised to produce an increase in dry weight by assimilation and are necessarily ill-adapted to carry out the other functions of the body: mechanical support, storage of reserves, invasion of air and soil space, and reproduction. So the functioning of the differentiated body requires the existence of a transport system to carry material between places of manufacture and places of storage and growth. This gross transfer of material in amounts sufficient to account for the swelling gourd, the exploring root network or the thrusting bamboo shoot, is the easily-grasped fact that translocation physiologists attempt to explain. Though the fact is simple, their diverse explanations have not met with wide acceptance. It is the purpose of this chapter to consider how this transport may be measured, what results have been obtained in different plant parts, the magnitude of the traffic that needs explanation, and what relation the transport may have to other properties of the plant. A more complete account may be sought in CANNY (1973a).

The places of manufacture of new organic substance, or the places where it has been stored and is being remobilized, are called *sources;* mature leaves, cotyledons or endosperms of germinating seeds, storage tissues of stem, leaf or root when they are sprouting. The places of disposal of the body substance for the formation of new organs or the laying down of reserves, are called *sinks*: meristems, very young leaves, cotyledons or endosperms of seeds being formed, storage tissues of stem, leaf or root when they are accumulating. The plant functions throughout its life by transferring material from sources to sinks by translocation: switching on dormant meristems to being active sinks, as when buds grow into axillary branches, or the cambium makes its annual ring, or the ovary forms the fruit; switching on dormant sources, as when the wood parenchyma feeds the bursting buds on bare branches, or the endosperm the growing embryo, or when the synthetic power of the unfolding leaf exceeds its own growth requirements. All the time the translocation machinery must carry material away from whichever are the active sources, and, by-passing the dormant sources, feed it to the active sinks. The problems of control, switching, and pattern alteration can be seen to be complex and important, but form no central part of this review, which concerns itself with the magnitude of the traffic.

B. Methods of Measuring Mass Transfer

In assessing magnitude of translocation it is convenient and sufficient to neglect the water content of the depleting source or growing sink, and concentrate on the transfer of dry weight between them. The justification for this is that it works better, in the sense of giving more reproducible and consistent results, than assessing movement of fresh weight (since the water content of plant tissue varies rapidly and widely), or changes of volume, or area. This must not be taken to imply that the water accompanying the moving material is not an important component of the transport process, only that it is too variable to be part of a useful primary measurement. The disadvantage of using changing dry weight as a measure is that it can be assessed only by destructive sampling, leading at once to the need for sufficient replicates to reduce the variability to an acceptable level, and to a cumbersome and laborious experimental routine.

Dry weight transfer per unit time, then, provides a simple estimate of the process, and the quotient obtained by dividing this by the cross-sectional area of the channel of transport has been widely used as a comparative measure under the name Specific Mass Transfer (SMT). The size of this channel is presumably the average total area of functioning sieve tubes connecting source and sink. It is however, in most organs, a matter of great difficulty to identify with certainty which cells of the phloem are sieve tubes, even by the most refined techniques of light and electronmicroscopy. It is always easier, and as a first step sufficient, to identify the phloem and use its area as the denominator in the value of SMT_{ph}. Then at the stage that a value is required in terms of sieve-tube area, a laborious investigation by serial sectioning may be required to find the proportion of sieve tubes in the phloem, and arrive at a value of SMT_{st}. The initial survey of the rates will be made in the simpler form, since most workers have measured phloem area only.

I. Gain by Fruit Sinks

Most fruits contribute little to their own growth by the assimilatory activity of their green tissues, so gain in dry weight over a period gives a measure of translocation into the fruit. Moreover measurement of fruit dimensions or volume may be carried on continuously during growth, and related to the dry weight of other fruit samples harvested at intervals. The correction for loss by respiration can be made, but is usually neglected because it is so small. This method gives a long-period integration of the transport, since appreciable growth in fruit volume or dry weight takes several days. The growth curve of a fruit against time is typically sigmoid, so the stage of growth of the fruit at which the measurements are made influences the result. Commonly, experimenters have either taken the maximum rate of change of dry weight from the slope of the steepest part of the sigmoid curve, or the average rate over the whole period of fruit growth from pollination to maturity. The former may be expected to be more than twice the latter, and, though more laborious to collect, is clearly a much more useful measure.

The method and its properties may be illustrated by the measurement of transport into the yam (*Dioscorea alata*) by MASON and LEWIN (1926). By using an underground organ, complications of fruit assimilation were avoided.

"The tubers from 43 individual plants were dug and weighed every week, the dry weight being determined on only 6 tubers. As an individual plant may have more than one stem supplying its tuber (or tubers), the results have been expressed as the weight of dry material per single stem. For example, on the 17th of September

(35 weeks after the date of planting) the average tuber-weight per plant amounted to 2,363 g, while the average percentage of moisture in the tuber was 78.6, so that the average tuber dry weight was 505.7 g per plant. As the average number of stems per plant at this time was 1.72, the dry weight per stem was evidently just 294 g."

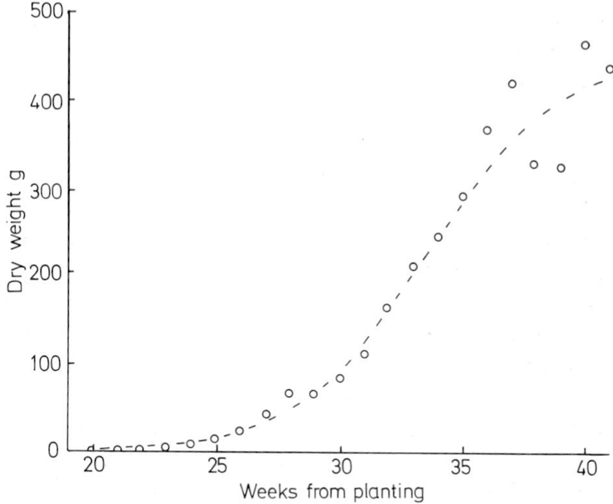

Fig. 1. The growth of the tubers of *Dioscorea alata* plotted as changing dry weight against time from planting. The curve is an auto-catalytic function $\log\frac{x}{a-x}=J(t-t_1)$ with $a=450$ g, $J=0.165$ week^{-1}, $t_1=33.5$ weeks. The maximum slope of the curve leads to the SMT value in Table 1. Re-drawn from MASON and LEWIN (1926)

Their graph of dry weight against time is given in Fig. 1, with the autocatalytic curve they fitted. The variability increases towards the end of the experiment because of the few individuals left. "The stem," they state, "had attained its maximum cross-section before the tuber began development", so the curve gives the changing SMT into the tubers during growth. The average sieve-tube area of 9 stems at the time of maximum growth was 0.0115 cm^2 per stem, giving an average rate of increase (the straight line joining the beginning and end of the curve) of 11 g week^{-1}, and a value for SMT_{st} of $11/(7\times24\times0.0115)=5.7$ g h^{-1} cm$_{st}^{-2}$; while the maximum (the slope at the inflection) gives $40/(7\times24\times0.0115)=20.7$ g h^{-1}cm$_{st}^{-2}$.

To convert this back to SMT_{ph} for comparison with other methods of measurement one needs a value for the proportion of sieve tubes in the phloem, which the authors do not provide. They record only total cross-sectional area of sieve tubes plus vessels, and that the sieve tubes occupied less than 20% of this. Clearly they neglected the parenchyma and companion cells of the vascular tissues. The proportion of sieve tubes in the phloem has been variously estimated between 20% and 70% (CANNY, 1973a, Chapter 11) giving a range of possible values from 4 to 13 g h^{-1}cm$_{ph}^{-2}$. If we take the lower value it is not widely different from many others assembled in Part I of Table 1.

Table 1. Measured values of specific mass transfer

Plant	SMT $g\ h^{-1} cm^{-2}_{ph}$	Reference
I. Gain by fruit sinks		
Solanum	4.5	DIXON and BALL (1922)
Dioscorea	4.2 [a]	MASON and LEWIN (1926)
Pyrus	0.6	MÜNCH (1930)
Prunus	0.6	MÜNCH (1930)
Fagus	0.6	MÜNCH (1930)
Quercus	0.6	MÜNCH (1930)
Solanum	2.1 [a]	CRAFTS (1933)
Kigelia	2.6 [a]	CLEMENTS (1940)
Cucurbita	3.3 [a]	CRAFTS and LORENZ (1944)
Cucurbita	4.8 [a]	COLWELL, quoted in last
Triticum	4.4 [a]	EVANS et al. (1970)
Kigelia	0.2 to 1.3 [a]	CANNY (1973b)
II. Loss by leaf sources		
Phaseolus	0.6	BIRCH-HIRSCHFELD (1920)
Tropaeolum	1.4	DIXON (1923)
Tropaeolum	0.5 light 0.16 dark	CRAFTS (1931)
Helianthus	4.6	SACHS (1884), CANNY (1973a)
Beta	1.7±0.5	GEIGER et al. (1969)
Beta	0.4 to 0.6 light 0.12 to 0.15 dark	TERRY and MORTIMER (1972)
III. Transfer through tree trunks		
Pinus	1.1	MÜNCH (1930)
Acer	6.3	MÜNCH (1930)
Tilia	2.9	MÜNCH (1930)
Carpinus	6.2	MÜNCH (1930)
Quercus	4.5	MÜNCH (1930)
Pyrus	0.9	CRAFTS (1931)
IV. Special systems		
Arenga inflorescence stalk	99	TAMMES (1933, 1952)
Salix aphid stylet	1.9 to 6.3	WEATHERLEY et al. (1959), CANNY (1961, 1973a)

[a] Maximum rates in the sense explained in the text.

Some of these are maximum rates (distinguished by [a] in Table 1), others averages over the growth period. The value for *Triticum* is more sophisticated than the rest. It is derived from a range of hybrid wheats having different amounts of phloem in the inflorescence axis, and calculated from a regression line of mass transfer on phloem area (CANNY, 1973a, Fig. 1a). The congruence of the values for different fruits is striking.

II. Loss from Leaf Sources

The gain in dry weight of unit area of a leaf in the light is the result of the positive contribution of photosynthesis and the two negative contributions of respiration and translocation. By comparison of intact leaves with those whose translocation function has been stopped by detachment, or, better, by steaming the petiole, the size of the negative translocation contribution may be assessed. A similar experiment in the dark provides the same information. Simple as the measurement is in concept, the practical pitfalls are many, and anyone intending to work with this system would be well advised to study the account by THODAY (1910a, b) of the errors encountered and the precautions needed to circumvent them. Changes of leaf area during the experiment due to changes of water content are one serious source of error, but can be eliminated by THODAY's "stamping" method. The residual error of "asymmetry", the inherent variability in dry weight per unit area, remains, and is of such a size that the physiological changes become distinguishable from it only over periods of about 10 h in samples of practical size. This method typically then integrates the measure of translocation over about a day or a night, and will not readily give measures over shorter or longer times. A modification that may be useful for shorter periods is discussed below.

A simple example of this kind of measure is that of CRAFTS (1931). Forty *Phaseolus* leaves were used. Dry weights were determined by THODAY's stamping method employing a 4-cm^2 stamp on each side of the midrib of the centre leaflet of the compound leaves. Each sample of leaf taken consisted of 40 cm^2 (ten 4-cm^2 pieces). Their dry weights and treatments were:

	Dry wt g
a) 16 h in dark	0.0773
b) 16 h in dark + 10 h light detached	0.0912
c) 16 h in dark + 10 h light attached	0.0832
d) 16 h in dark + 10 h light attached + 14 h dark detached	0.0798
e) 16 h in dark + 10 h light attached + 14 h dark attached	0.0773

Whence translocation in the light period was (b–c) = 0.008 g; and in the dark (d–e) = 0.0025 g. The phloem areas in the petioles of each leaf were measured, and on averaging gave 0.00123 cm^2. So the SMT_{ph} is, in the light 0.0008/0.00123 = 0.65; and in the dark, $0.0025/(14 \times 0.00123) = 0.15$ g $h^{-1} cm_{ph}^{-2}$. This is the most complete set of this kind of data among the first four in this section of Table 1. The other three are rather estimates based on one or more assumed values of the quantities that CRAFTS measured. Three of the four estimates are closely similar, but that for the sunflower leaf is much larger—in the same bracket as the fast fruit systems of the last section. The sunflower is famous for the spectacular scale of its life style, which is often matched by measurements of its physiological processes. It is likely that the translocation rates typical of small leaves may rise to this level in large and vigorous leaves.

A useful extension of this method that should give integrations of SMT over shorter time intervals has been made by TERRY and MORTIMER (1972). This is to measure simultaneously (in a leaf chamber) the uptake of CO_2 and the accumulation of dry weight by the leaf, and calculate the translocation rate as the difference between them. By choosing the large lamina of sugar beet these workers attempted to avoid the laborious statistical comparisons of many leaves involved in destructive sampling, and, by removing punched samples at intervals, gauge the changing dry weight of the single leaf with time. This technique has obvious dangers if the area density of the leaf is not very uniform, and their paper provides no account of the variation found over a single leaf at one time. This would be the equivalent of the error called "asymmetry" for half-leaf samples by THODAY. The method is not free either from the danger of shrinkage errors, but TERRY and MORTIMER give some estimate of this. They record (but do not give the data) that they passed CO_2-free air through the leaf chamber in the light, and took punched samples at intervals. "On six occasions there was no change in the dry weight: leaf area ratio in leaves which remained fully turgid either with change in illumination or after repeated punching". One might expect a slow downward drift in area density from respiration. In two experiments there was serious shrinkage of up to six percent in 2 h accompanied by wilting. On this basis they are probably justified in neglecting the shrinkage error, after discounting the first 2- or 4-hour period of changed conditions.

They did not record areas of phloem in the petiole, so that accurate figures for the SMT cannot be derived. Nevertheless it has seemed worth-while to estimate the probable phloem areas, and obtain approximate values for SMT. GEIGER et al. (1969) give several measurements of phloem in the petioles of their standard beet leaf, which was 0.5 cm^2 in area. Using these, and assuming that the phloem area of the petiole is proportional to the area of the lamina, I have calculated possible phloem areas for TERRY and MORTIMER'S leaves, and applied them to their measures of translocation. The values so obtained are closely similar to those of CRAFTS, and the less reliable petiole estimates, namely 0.4 to 0.6 g $h^{-1}cm_{ph}^{-2}$ in the light and 0.12 to 0.15 in the dark.

The method that GEIGER et al. were using in the paper just cited (1969) to measure loss from the beet leaves involved labeling the assimilate stream with ^{14}C, and following the transport of the label. The carbohydrate pools of the leaf were equilibrated with radioactive carbon by steady-state feeding of $^{14}CO_2$ to the leaf in a chamber. Then, after various translocation times, they analyzed the sinks of the pruned and simplified plant for ^{14}C, and "multiplying the amount of radioactivity present by the specific activity and an isotope effect factor of 1/0.85", found a value for the total carbon moved out of the leaf. Measurements of petiole phloem then allowed them to calculate values for SMT. The average derived from their thirteen measurements is 1.7 ± 0.5 g $h^{-1}cm_{ph}^{-2}$ (not, as they state, 1.4).

III. Transfer through Tree Trunks

Two attempts have been made to measure or estimate the translocation rate through the secondary phloem of tree trunks downwards from the crown of leaves. MÜNCH (1930) uses measurements of the volume increment in annual rings of large tree trunks, together with estimates of the mass of roots and bark based on foresters' rule-of-thumb, to assess the dry matter moved through the top of the trunk. This, divided by a measured area of secondary phloem and the length of the growing season, gave him the values listed in Table 1, which are fully consistent with the rates already discussed.

CRAFTS (1931), using two-year-old pear trees whose complete material could be harvested and measured, obtained a value of about 6 g day^{-1} dry weight increment in trunk and roots during August and December, and a phloem area at the top of the trunk of 0.30 cm^2. This gave a SMT value of 0.8, lower than any of MÜNCH's estimates for the larger trees. Whether this discrepancy is due to a greater vigor of the large trees, or some overestimate in MÜNCH's assumptions will require further experiments to decide. The problems of making the actual measurements on large trees are formidable.

IV. Special Systems

1. The Bleeding Palm Inflorescence Stalk

TAMMES (1933, 1952, and Chapter 8 of this volume) has devoted much study to the sugary sap that bleeds copiously from the cut inflorescence stalk of many palms and large Liliaceous plants, and is used as a major source of sugar and beverages in some regions. His measurements of the volume flow and sugar concentration of the sap, and the assumption that all the sugar is brought by the phloem in the translocation system, lead to values of SMT much higher than any so far noted (Table 1. IV). Until there is clear evidence that rates of this magnitude are a widespread capacity of intact translocation systems, it seems correct to place them in a group by themselves as perhaps requiring a special explanation.

2. The Exuding Aphid Stylet

The use of the cut stylet of a feeding aphid as a tool for studying translocation (e.g. WEATHERLEY et al., 1959, and Chapters 6 and 7 in this volume) has provided some data on the sugar coming from a single sieve tube. The SMT figure into which such data is translated depends upon the assumptions made about the source of this sugar and the fraction of the phloem occupied by sieve tubes (see CANNY, 1973a, p. 112, 250). The sugar output from a single stylet of the willow aphid is recorded during $5^1/_2$ h by CANNY (1961), and is fairly steady at about 80 μg h^{-1}. The cross section of a sieve tube of willow is taken by WEATHERLEY et al. to be 414 $\mu m^2 = 4.14 \times 10^{-6}$ cm^2. If the sugar arrives at the stylet from only one direction in the stem, this implies a SMT of 19 g $h^{-1} cm_{st}^{-2}$. Or if, as I have argued is more likely, the stylet constitutes an emergency leak in the translocation system to which sugar comes from both directions along the sieve tube, 9.5 g $h^{-1} cm_{st}^{-2}$. To compare this with the others of Table 1 it is necessary to assume a figure for the proportion of sieve tubes in the phloem. The most popular figure is one fifth, which would give a value of 1.9 g $h^{-1} cm_{ph}^{-2}$; I have advanced reasons for preferring (often) a fraction nearer to two thirds, which would give 6.33 g $h^{-1} cm_{ph}^{-2}$. Either of these might be deemed to compare with the general set of rates found in intact systems.

V. Results of the Measurements

It is clear that, expressed in this simple way, the rate of translocation in a wide variety of plant parts falls within quite narrow limits: that fast translocating systems have SMT values of about 4.5 g $h^{-1} cm_{ph}^{-2}$, and that slow rates may be a tenth of this or a little less. The uniformity of the results suggests that the measure is a useful one, and would be worth standardizing. From the discussion above it will be plain that there has been too little uniformity in the parameters measured, and too much assumption is necessary to make them comparable. From what is now known about translocation it is surely the sieve-tube area which must form the sensible denominator of the SMT fraction. The ease of measurement of the phloem area should not blind us to its lesser relevance and likely variable proportion of sieve tubes. It is plain that, when an SMT is measured, the extra effort should be put into measuring sieve-tube cross section even if this is difficult. In my experience the only practical way of identifying most sieve tubes is to cut a number of serial resin sections (say 200–400 at 2 μ), stain with aniline blue and photograph in far blue light to show up the fluorescence of the callose, tracing each cell through the phloem and looking for the occurrence of sieve plates. Even with these precautions it has proved extremely difficult in certain phloems to arrive at estimates of the sieve tubes.

The published information conspicuously lacks any data on translocation in roots, which for completeness and comparison would be most desirable. Our knowledge of root transport is very much based upon extrapolation from measurements on shoots rather than real investigations. (*Note added in proof*: The announcement of SMT values of 180 g $h^{-1} cm_{st}^{-2}$ by PASSIOURA and ASHFORD [Aust. J. Plant. Physiol. I, 521, 1974] for translocation into the root of wheat emphasizes the danger of such extrapolation.)

C. Factors Related to Mass Transfer

Setting aside environmental influences such as temperature and light, there is only one property of the plant that has been experimentally related to the SMT with any degree of certainty, and this is the concentration of sucrose in the phloem. A number of other properties *may* be related to SMT, and will be briefly discussed.

I. Concentration Gradient

In the course of their detailed study of translocation in cotton in which they established the phloem tissue as the channel of transport, MASON and MASKELL (1928a, b) made a number of measurements of the SMT. They measured the changing concentrations of sugar in samples of phloem at frequent intervals in the course of the day, using a large number of replicates, and the pathways of movement of the sugar were defined and limited by incisions and rings in the bark. Their results are expressed on the same basis as those of Table 1, and are fairly low on the scale, ranging from 0.1 to 0.7 g $h^{-1} cm_{ph}^{-2}$. They consistently noted that the direction of movement, whether within stems, from leaf to stem, or from stem to boll, was from tissues whose sieve tubes had a high concentration of sucrose to tissues where the sucrose concentration was less, and further, that the rate of movement (SMT) was proportional to the magnitude of this gradient. They summed up their observations on this relation by the plot (Fig. 2) of SMT against gradient of sucrose in the sieve tubes, and state: "The odds that correlation coefficients of this high order, even in the small number of cases (nine) available for calculation, arise by chance are of the order of 1 in 1,000." Though this correlation has never been further investigated, similar gradients of concentration in the direction of transport have been found in trees (HUBER et al., 1937; ZIEGLER, 1956; ZIMMERMANN, 1957). The data were so carefully collected that the relation cannot be discarded, and the gradient remains the single known internal factor that is linked with SMT.

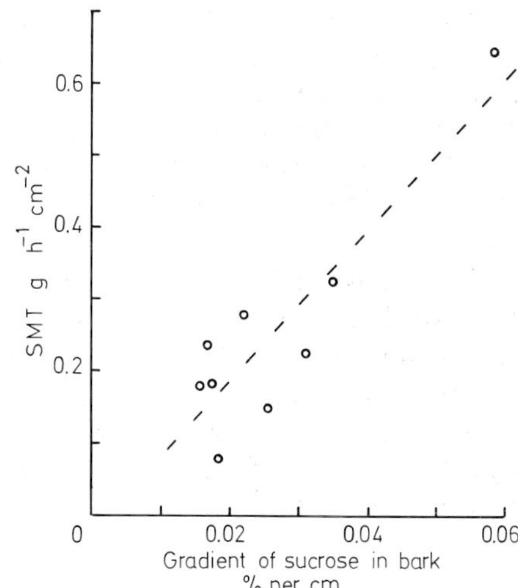

Fig. 2. The relation between SMT and gradient of sucrose in the phloem for translocation in *Gossypium* with the fitted regression line. Redrawn from MASON and MASKELL 1928b, Fig. 14B

This study also identified the chemical nature of the substance making up most of the traffic in dry weight as sucrose. This result has been amply confirmed by later work using ^{14}C-labeled assimilates. While particular plants may as exceptions transport a few other related sugars, in the great majority of experiments it is sucrose primarily, and often exclusively, that moves (see Chapter 3 and Appendix III).

The interpretation that MASON and MASKELL placed upon the straight line of Fig. 2 was that the translocation process was working in a way analogous to diffusion; that because the SMT could be expressed as a relation of the form of Fick's Law:

$$\text{SMT} = \text{constant } x \text{ gradient of sucrose concentration} \tag{1}$$

it was likely that the process shared other similarities with diffusion. Translocation was about four to five orders of magnitude faster than diffusion, and this was brought out by the size of the constant (the slope of the line in Fig. 2) which they measured as $7 \times 10^{-2} \text{cm}^2 \text{sec}^{-1}$, and compared with the coefficient of diffusion of sucrose in water, $2 \times 10^{-6} \text{cm}^2 \text{sec}^{-1}$. This large constant of the Equation (1) I have called the translocation coefficient. It can be estimated by an independent method using tracers, and the published records of 28 experiments by various workers yield values in the range 2×10^{-4} to 6×10^{-2}, with a mean of 1.4 ± 10^{-2} (see CANNY, 1973a, Table 16.13). The agreement of these independent estimates with MASON and MASKELL's value strengthens the analogy with diffusion, since the tracer method depends upon using the non-steady-state form of Fick's Law.

II. Path Distance

Were the translocation process indeed to show the close analogies with diffusion suggested, a consequence of Eq. (1) would be that the SMT would depend critically upon the distance between source and sink, since this distance appears in the denominator of the gradient. Put simply, rapid translocation would be possible only over short distances, and beyond distances of half a meter or so, would necessarily be slow. The plot of SMT against distance between source and sink would be a hyperbola (CANNY, 1973a, Fig. 16.1). Such a serious limitation in the capacity of sources to feed sinks might be deemed worthy of close attention. Surprisingly, very little study has been given to the question and only one set of experiments carried out to test it. The rate of transport into fruits of *Kigelia* on different lengths of stalk (CANNY, 1973b) yielded results that were consistent with this limitation, though the variability was large (Fig. 3). The size of the inflorescences of this tree is such that fruits do not grow at less than about 25 cm from the source leaves, so the variation with distance cannot be tested in the critical range 0–20 cm where the hyperbola would be falling most steeply. Certainly over very long distances (about 2 m), the SMT values are low, around 0.5 g $h^{-1}cm^{-2}_{ph}$.

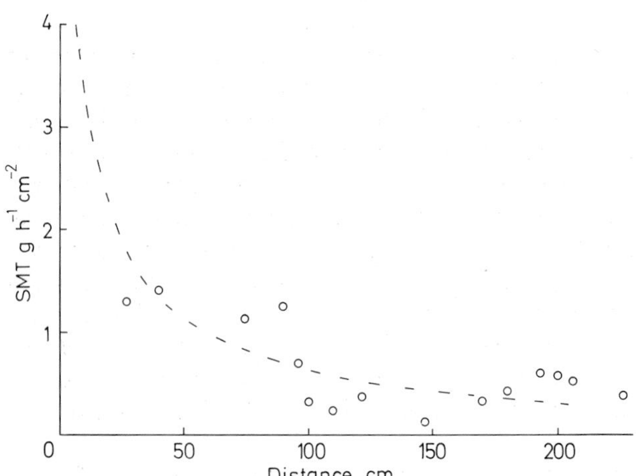

Fig. 3. The variation of translocation with distance in fruit stalks of *Kigelia*. The points are measured values of SMT into fruits growing on different lengths of stalk from the sources in the tree. The curve is the predicted relation if the SMT is governed by Eq. (1) in the text, and the constant K is interpreted according to the model of CANNY and PHILLIPS (1963) with a strand diffusion time of 200 sec. Redrawn from CANNY (1973b) Fig. 8

Nor is the relationship to distance interesting solely from the point of view of the analogy with diffusion. The pressure-flow mechanism to explain translocation has an equation for its mass-carrying capacity (Poiseuille) which has distance in the denominator. For it also the plot of SMT against distance would be expected to be a hyperbola, and long distances would impose drastic restrictions on the possible rate of transport.

III. Morphology and Patterns of Movement

If the quantitative measurements have not been made that might relate variation of transport with distance, nevertheless a study of the shapes of plant bodies supports the notion that they are laboring under some such constraint as that just mentioned. Vigorous sinks do not occur except in close proximity to abundant sources: fruits on short stalks subtended and sheathed by substantial bracts and leaves; tubers branching from stems rich in stored reserves (INCOLL and NEALES, 1970); the corn cob, the hazel nut, the apple or pear on its short shoot. Where the SMT is high the plant appears to keep the transport distance to a minimum, seldom as much as 15 cm. Where the distance between source and sink is large, what evidence is available suggests that the SMT is small.

A strengthening of this morphological impression comes from experiments on the pattern of distribution of labeled assimilates (CRAFTS and CRISP, 1971; CANNY, 1973a, Chapter 5). The major traffic of label from particular source leaves is always to the nearest active sink, the stem apex from an apical leaf, the root system from a basal leaf (THROWER, 1962), the growing apple from the leaves of its short shoot, or the lemon from the two or three leaves nearest to it (KRIEDEMANN, 1970). Moreover, when the main supply source is removed and the supply interrupted, the patterns of transport are altered so that the next nearest source takes on the task of supply, and the sink then commonly grows more slowly.

This limitation would clearly impose very special conditions upon transport within a tall tree. With the source leaves separated from the root-tip sinks by distances in excess of 100 m, translocation must be very slow if it works by either the diffusion-analog or flow mechanism. The gradient for the one is very flat, and the resistance for the other very high. I have argued that such a limitation may not matter in a tree, since there is abundant storage parenchyma all along the path, and which may be filled with reserves very slowly along gradual gradients, but which is available as a local source for fast, short-distance translocation when needed. Our view derived from pot-grown herbs, that carbon fed to a leaf appears within a few hours at the root tips, may not apply, and has never been shown to apply in a long plant. The few existing measurements of sugar gradients in tree phloem reveal small gradients (references cited above, C.I.). The problem calls for attention by forest physiologists.

There is an interesting correspondence between these measurements of sugar concentration gradient in trees, and the only data known to me on the turgor pressure gradient in tree phloem. HAMMEL (1968) measured the latter by means of a needle probe and manometer, and gives a table of values measured at two heights around the bark of a tree of *Quercus rubra* on eight days in October and November. The values range from 10 to 20 atmospheres, but the mean of all values at the higher station (6.3 m) differs from the mean of all values at the lower station (1.5 m) by 1.47 atmospheres and the difference is significant at the 0.1% level. (see Chapter 14). The pooling of all values at each height is probably permissible, since the largest divergence of the mean of the readings on a particular occasion from the pooled mean is significant only at the 5% level, and most of the nine means are not significantly different from the pooled mean. As he says, 0.5 atmospheres of the difference is due to gravity, leaving 0.97 atmospheres gradient of turgor pressure in 4.8 m.

The gradient is 0.20 atm m^{-1}, which corresponds to a gradient of sucrose concentration of 0.008 M m^{-1}. This compares closely with measured sugar concentration gradients in trees: 0.009 to 0.014 M sucrose m^{-1} in *Q. rubra* (HUBER et al., 1937); 0.026 M sucrose m^{-1} in *Acer platanoides* and 0.01 M sucrose m^{-1} in *Q. rubra* (PFEIFFER, 1937); 0.013 M sucrose m^{-1} in *Fraxinus americana* (ZIMMERMANN, 1957). The slight gradient, which seems thus well substantiated, is a faint force to drive either pressure flow (0.2 at m^{-1}) or diffusion-analog (0.01 M m^{-1}) transport over many meters.

IV. Flow Models

While experiment suggests that the SMT may be expressed as the product of Eq. (1), theoretical speculation has concentrated attention on a more common transport equation, that expressing the flow of a sugar solution through a tube. Then,

$$\text{SMT} = \text{concentration of solution } x \text{ speed} \quad (2)$$

To assume this relation is to assume a knowledge of the mechanism of movement, and the existence of a flow of solution in the sieve tubes. It leads to a consistent set of figures, since high values selected from Table 1 may be expressed as the product of a concentration of a solution that may be obtained from sieve tubes, and a speed which, though large, is believable. For example:

$$5 \text{ g h}^{-1}\text{cm}_{\text{ph}}^{-2} = 25 \text{ g h}^{-1}\text{cm}_{\text{st}}^{-2} \text{ (on a one-fifth proportion)}$$

and can be set equal to the flow of a 25% solution:

$$= 0.25 \text{ g cm}^{-3} \times 100 \text{ cm h}^{-1},$$

and for lower values and higher proportions of sieve tubes the concentration and/or the speed may be reduced. Many experimenters who have measured SMT have preferred to express their results in these terms, though commonly neither the speed nor the concentration are measured along with the SMT.

In the data already referred to on the sugar solution exuding from an aphid stylet implanted in a willow sieve tube, the concentration of exuded solution was indeed measured, and its mean value (23 samples) was 0.048 ± 0.003 g cm^{-3}. I have advanced reasons (CANNY, 1973a, Chapter 8) for believing that the concentration of sugar in stylet exudate is probably lower than in the sap of the intact sieve tube, but if this is not so we could calculate that the flow of sugar to the stylet from two directions would necessitate a speed of

$$\frac{\text{SMT}}{\text{concentration}} = \frac{9.5}{0.048} = 198\,\text{cm h}^{-1}.$$

These data were obtained in the course of an attempt to measure the speed of translocation by another means which yielded values in the neighborhood of 2 to 14 cm h^{-1}. There is thus a wide discrepancy somewhere either in the measurements or in the assumptions.

ZIMMERMANN (1969) has measured simultaneously the concentration of sap (0.2 to 0.25 g cm^{-3}) exuding from cuts in the phloem of *Fraxinus americana*, and a speed derived from the progress of a wave of concentration ratios of different sugars in the sap (30 to 70 cm h^{-1}). He points out that the product of these may be taken to agree with the values of SMT that MÜNCH estimated in other trees (Table 1). The range is generous according to the assumptions. The SMT value would lie between the extremes $0.2 \times 30 \times \frac{1}{5} = 1.2\,\text{g h}^{-1}\,\text{cm}_{\text{ph}}^{-2}$ for a one-fifth proportion of sieve tubes, and $0.25 \times 70 \times \frac{2}{3} = 11.7\,\text{g h}^{-1}\,\text{cm}_{\text{ph}}^{-2}$ for a two-thirds proportion. Nevertheless the agreement with Eq. (2) is clearly better than in the case of the exuding stylet.

V. Speed Components

The SMT is the quantity component of translocation, and Eq. (2) expresses a way in which it might be related to a speed component of the process. Other relations are possible, and it will be seen that Eq. (1) contains no overt speed component. Indeed, the diffusion process to which it is analogous has a speed component detached from its quantity component in the same sense that mass transfer by diffusion may be positive, zero or negative across a particular space with no change in the speed component (molecular motion). The gradient of concentration determines the transfer. At the same time, changing the speed component (by changing the temperature) greatly affects the quantity component for a fixed gradient. The relationship between the SMT and speed components is therefore highly interesting. It has not, however, been investigated.

Since radio-tracers became available it has been apparently very easy to measure speed of translocation, and many such measures are on record. The very ease of experimentation has encouraged neglect of the more laborious assessment of SMT, and the new has become a substitute for the old. No one has bothered to check the relation between the two, and to show either that the SMT is directly proportional to measured speeds as in Eq. (2), or that, following Eq. (1), the SMT may be large or small (or even negative) for the same measured value of the speed component. As an experimental assessment of translocation the speed component has proved surprisingly awkward to measure by a variety of methods and very variable in the range 0.3 to 300 cm h^{-1} (CANNY, 1973a, Table 14.1). The size of this range and the lack of any clear correlation between the speed in a particular organ and its SMT-capacity incline me to the suspicion that we are not dealing with a simple linear relation like Eq. (2).

D. Summary

I. The translocation process may be conveniently measured as the transfer of dry weight per unit area of path. The path may be easily measured in terms of phloem, and, more usefully but with much greater difficulty, as sieve-tube area. The resulting quantity is called the Specific Mass Transfer (SMT_{ph} or SMT_{st}).

II. This quantity has been measured in a variety of plant organ systems, and the results of such measurements have yielded values in the range 0.2 to 6 g $h^{-1} cm^{-2}_{ph}$ for intact fruits stalks, leaf petioles and tree trunks. The highest values are found generally during only a short period of growth.

III. At least one special system has yielded a value of nearly 100 g $h^{-1} cm^{-2}_{ph}$. Data are lacking on root translocation.

IV. The proportion of sieve elements in the phloem required to convert SMT_{ph} to SMT_{st} is variable and difficult to measure. Values between 20% and 70% have been reported.

V. The sole property of the plant that has been experimentally related to SMT is the gradient of concentration of sucrose in the sieve tubes.

VI. The dependence of translocation upon gradient of sucrose (or also the mechanism of flow of sugar solution) implies a drastic limitation of rate of translocation by the distance between source and sink. Some evidence for such a limitation exists.

VII. The speed of translocation is a very variable quantity, and there is no certainty about the relation it bears to SMT.

References

BIRCH-HIRSCHFELD, L.: Untersuchungen über die Ausbreitungsgeschwindigkeit gelöster Stoffe in der Pflanze. Jahrb. Wiss. Bot. **59**, 171–262 (1920).

CANNY, M.J.: Measurements of the velocity of translocation. Ann. Botany N.S. **25**, 152–167 (1961).

CANNY, M.J.: Phloem translocation. London: Cambridge University Press 1973a.

CANNY, M.J.: Translocation and distance. I. The growth of the fruit of the sausage tree, *Kigelia pinnata*. New Phytol. **72**, 1269–1280 (1973b).

CANNY, M.J., PHILLIPS, O.M.: Quantitative aspects of a theory of translocation. Ann. Botany N.S. **27**, 379–402 (1963).

CLEMENTS, H.F.: Movement of organic solutes in the sausage tree, *Kigelia africana*. Plant Physiol. **15**, 689–700 (1940).

CRAFTS, A.S.: Movement of organic material in plants. Plant Physiol. **6**, 1–41 (1931).

CRAFTS, A.S.: Sieve-tube structure and translocation in the potato. Plant Physiol. **8**, 81–104 (1933).

CRAFTS, A.S., CRISP, C.E.: Phloem transport in plants. San Francisco: Freeman 1971.

CRAFTS, A.S., LORENZ, O.A.: Fruit growth and food transport in cucurbits. Plant Physiol. **19**, 131–138 (1944).

DIXON, H.H.: Transport of organic substances in plants. Nature **110**, 547–551 (1923).

DIXON, H.H., BALL, N.G.: Transport of organic substances in plants. Nature **109**, 236–237 (1922).

EVANS, L.T., DUNSTONE, R.L., RAWSON, H.M., WILLIAMS, R.F.: The phloem of the wheat stem in relation to requirements for assimilate by the ear. Australian J. Biol. Sci. **23**, 743–752 (1970).

GEIGER, D.R., SAUNDERS, M.A., CATALDO, D.A.: Translocation and accumulation of translocate in the sugar beet petiole. Plant Physiol. **44**, 1657–1665 (1969).

HAMMEL, H.T.: Measurement of turgor pressure and its gradient in the phloem of oak. Plant Physiol. **43**, 1042–1048 (1968).

HUBER, B., SCHMIDT, E., JAHNEL, H.: Untersuchungen über die Assimilatstrom. I. Tharandt. Forstl. Jb. **88**, 1017–1050 (1937).

INCOLL, L.D., NEALES, T.F.: The stem as a temporary sink before tuberization in *Helianthus tuberosus* L. J. Exptl. Botany **21**, 469–476 (1970).

KRIEDEMANN, P.E.: The distribution of ^{14}C-labeled assimilates in mature lemon trees. Australian J. Agri. Res. **21**, 623–632 (1970).

MASON, T.G., LEWIN, C.T.: On the rate of carbohydrate transport in the greater yam, *Dioscorea alata*. Roy. Dublin Soc. Sci. Proc. **18**, 203–205 (1926).

MASON, T.G., MASKELL, E.J.: Studies on the transport of carbohydrates in the cotton plant. I. A study of diurnal variation in the carbohydrates of leaf, bark and wood, and of the effects of ringing. Ann. Botany **42**, 189–253 (1928a).

MASON, T.G., MASKELL, E.J.: Studies on the transport of carbohydrates in the cotton plant. II. The factors determining the rate and the direction of movement of sugars. Ann. Botany **42**, 571–636 (1928b).

MÜNCH, E.: Die Stoffbewegungen in der Pflanze. Jena: Fischer 1930.

PFEIFFER, M.: Die Verteilung der osmotischen Werte im Baum im Hinblick auf die Münchsche Druckstromtheorie. Flora (Jena) **132**, 1–17 (1937).

SACHS, J.: Ein Beitrag zur Kenntnis der Ernährungstätigkeit der Blätter. Arb. bot. Inst. Würzburg **3**, 1–33 (1884).

TAMMES, P.M.L.: Observations on the bleeding of palm trees. Rec. Trav. bot. neerl. **30**, 514–536 (1933).

TAMMES, P.M.L.: On the rate of translocation of bleeding-sap in the fruitstalk of *Arenga*. Proc. Sect. Sci. Koninkl. Ned. Acad. Wetenschap., C **55**, 141–143 (1952).

TERRY, N., MORTIMER, D.C.: Estimation of the rates of mass carbon transfer by leaves of sugar beet. Can. J. Botany **50**, 1049–1054 (1972).

THODAY, D.: Experimental researches on vegetable assimilation. V. A critical examination of SACHS' method for using increase of dry weight as a measure of carbon dioxide assimilation in leaves. Proc. Roy Soc. (London), Ser. B **82**, 1–55 (1910a).

THODAY, D.: Experimental researches on vegetable assimilation. VI. Some experiments on assimilation in the open air. Proc. Roy. Soc. (London), Ser. B **82**, 421–450 (1910b).

THROWER, S.L.: Translocation of labeled assimilates in the soybean. Australian J. Biol. Sci. **15**, 629–649 (1962).

WEATHERLEY, P.E., PEEL, A.J., HILL, G.P.: The physiology of the sieve tube. Preliminary experiments using aphid mouth-parts. J. Exptl. Bot. **10**, 1–16 (1959).

ZIEGLER, H.: Untersuchungen über die Leitung und Sekretion der Assimilate. Planta **47**, 447–500 (1956).

ZIMMERMANN, M.H.: Translocation of organic substances in trees. II. On the translocation mechanism in the phloem of white ash (*Fraxinus americana* L.). Plant Physiol. **32**, 399–404 (1957).

ZIMMERMANN, M.H.: Translocation velocity and specific mass transfer in the sieve tubes of *Fraxinus americana* L. Planta **84**, 272–278 (1969).

6. Aphids and Translocation

A.F.G. DIXON

A. Introduction

Aphids are small insects which feed by inserting their very fine mouthparts (stylets) into plant tissue, where they feed on cell sap (Fig. 1A+B). As an aphid inserts its stylets into plant tissue it secretes a stylet sheath around the stylets (Fig. 2A+B). When the stylets are withdrawn the stylet sheath remains in the tissues of the plant and indicates the exact passage taken by the stylets. The point where the sheath ends indicates the tissue on which the aphid has fed, and this proves to be the sieve tubes (AUCLAIR, 1963; EVERT et al., 1968).

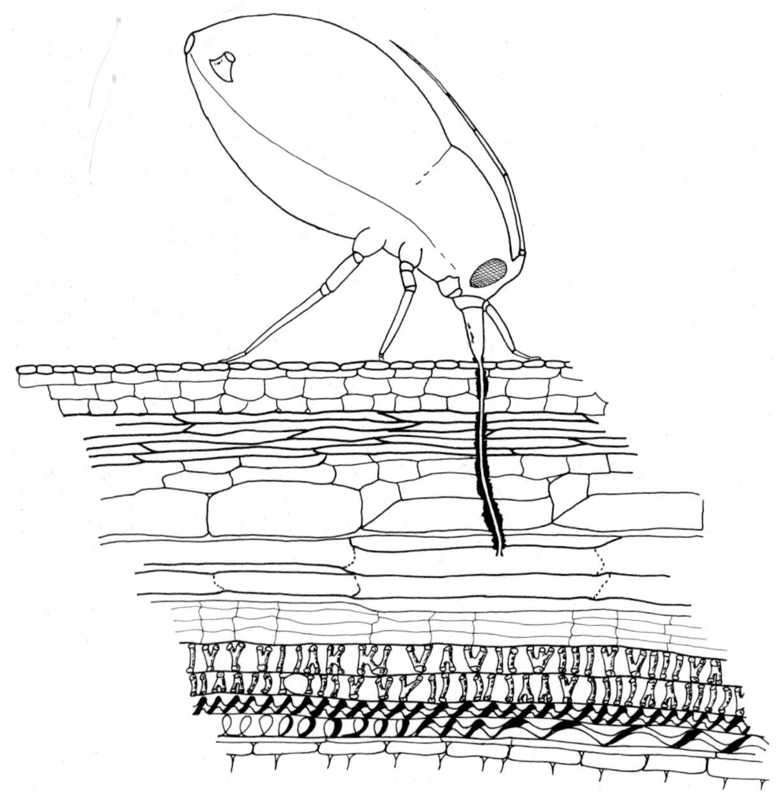

Fig. 1A. Diagram of an aphid in feeding position with its stylets inserted into a sieve element. The stylets in the plant tissue are enclosed in a stylet sheath produced by the aphid

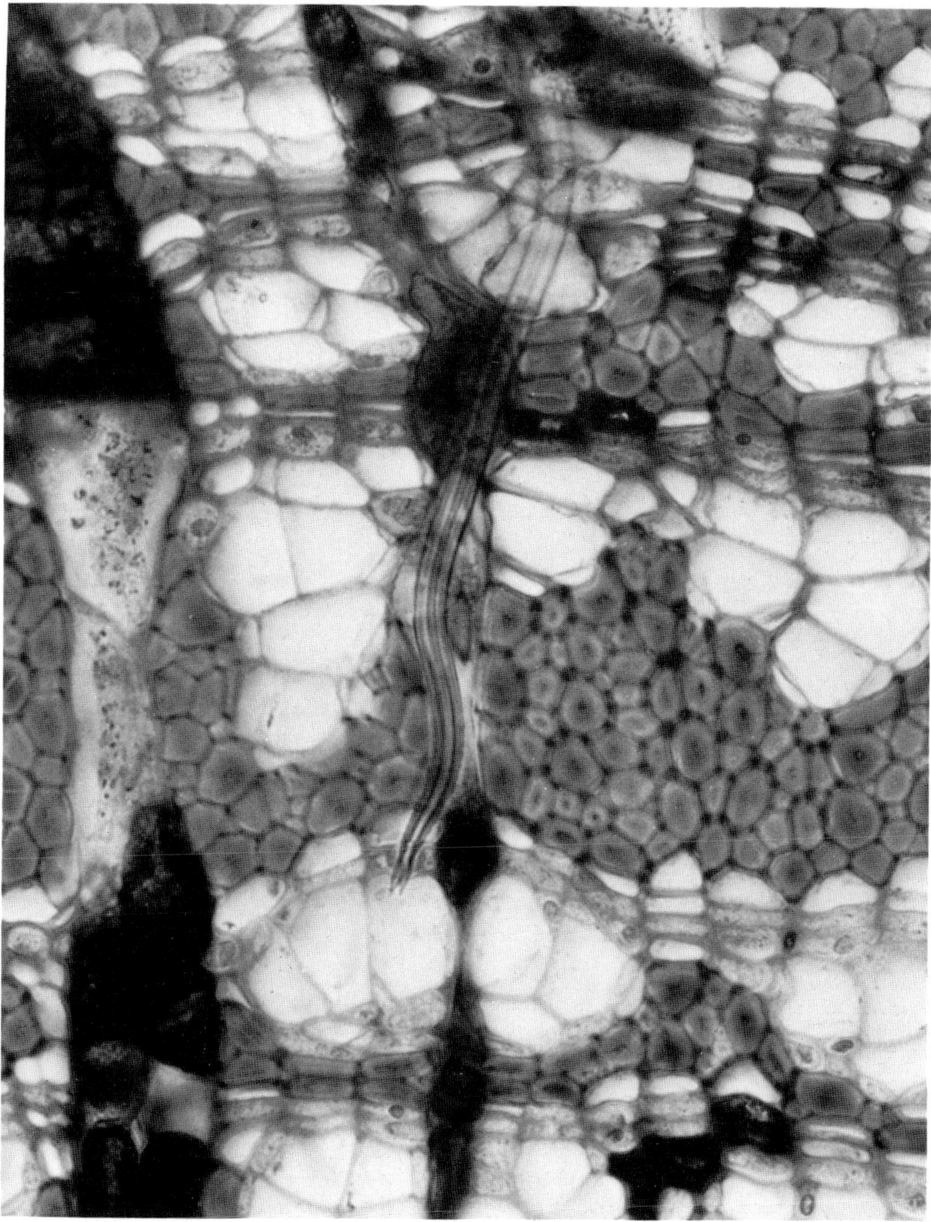

Fig. 1B. Photomicrograph of (a previously exuding) stylet bundle of the aphid *Longistigma caryae* Harris in the phloem of a linden branch (*Tilia americana* L.) showing the tip inside a sieve element. (Photograph M.H. ZIMMERMANN)

The tip of each of the four stylets tapers to a very fine point of 0.04 μ or less in diameter. Because of their shape any pressure applied to the relatively broad base of the stylets is transformed into a very much greater pressure at the tip, so that the stylets are well adapted to penetrate plant tissue. In penetrating the

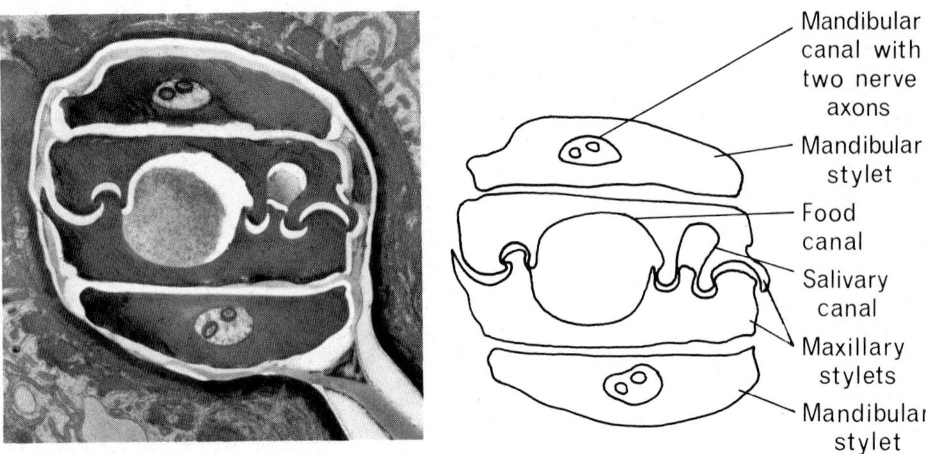

Fig. 2A. Electronmicrograph and diagram of the stylet bundle of the pea aphid *Acyrthosiphon pisum* (Harris) (× 19,750) (Electronmicrograph supplied by Dr. A.R. Forbes)

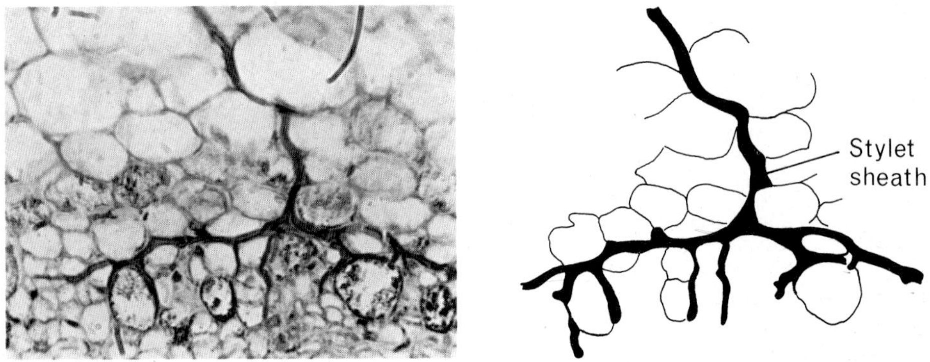

Fig. 2B. Photograph and diagram of a transverse section of the stem of an apple seedling illustrating a stylet sheath which indicates the tortuous path taken by the stylets of the aphid *Dysaphis devecta* (Walk.) in probing phloem elements

tissues of a plant the stylets of large aphids tend to pass directly through the cells, but the stylets of small aphids travel tortuously between cells and rarely pierce any until they reach the phloem elements (Evert et al., 1968; Pollard, 1973). Penetration between cells may be assisted by the secretion of saliva which passes down the salivary duct enclosed by the stylets and is exuded from the tip of the stylet bundle; a pectinase present in the saliva of some species of aphid breaks down the bonding between the cells (McAllan and Adams, 1961). Large species of aphid tend to feed on stems, rather than the leaves preferred by small species of aphid. As the cells in stems are more tightly packed and bonded together than they are in the leaves, probably this and possibly the absence of pectinase in saliva of large aphids, rather than their greater strength (Evert et al., 1968), accounts for the mainly intracellular course of the stylets of large aphids.

Aphids which feed on leaves do not need to probe very deeply to find phloem elements and in these shallow-feeding aphids the stylets are relatively short (240–570 μ, Gibson, 1972; Dixon and Logan, 1973). However, the stylets in stem-feeding aphids, such as *Stomaphis quercus* L. are long, up to as much as 1.25 cm in length. *S. quercus* settles in the fissures in the bark of an oak tree from where its remarkably long stylets can reach the phloem elements in the tree trunk. Small aphids can withdraw their short stylets quickly from plant tissue and move off when threatened by predators or parasites. On the other hand, aphids like *Stomaphis quercus* take up to an hour to withdraw their stylets and during this time are extremely vulnerable. However, such aphids are usually attended and protected by ants, with the larger species, such as *Stomaphis* spp., always found associated with particular species of attendant ant, e.g. *S. quercus* with *Lasius fuliginosus*.

Aphids remove large quantities of sap from plants. An adult sycamore aphid ingests an average of 2.06 μl of sap per day, which is equivalent to the contents of approximately 5,150 sieve elements, and even a first instar aphid ingests 0.78 μl per day or the contents of approximately 1,950 sieve tubes (Dixon and Logan, 1973). Sieve-tube sap will exude from a severed stylet bundle of the large willow aphid, *Tuberolachnus salignus* Gmel., at the rate of 1 μl/h, a volume of sap 2,500 times that of the capacity of a single pierced sieve element (Weatherley et al., 1959). Much of this sap is excreted by aphids as honeydew. Trees often support extremely large numbers of aphids. A 14 m lime tree can carry over a million aphids at one time, and in one year the population on such a tree can produce 42 l of honeydew with a dry weight of 8.5 kg, mainly accounted for as sucrose (Llewellyn, 1972).

Phloem sap is under 15–30 atm, sufficient to force the sap through the extremely fine food canal in an aphid's stylets. This has led to the suggestion that aphids are passively fed. However, anesthetized aphids cease to excrete but nevertheless do not leak or swell up (Mittler, 1957). It is likely that aphids control the flow of sap by means of their cibarial pump (Banks, 1965; Dixon, 1973). The rate of intake of sap by aphids feeding on plants is determined by the concentration of amino acids in the sap. It is slow when the amino acid concentration is high, and fast when it is low (Mittler, 1958; Dixon, 1963). Phloem sap ingested by an aphid can contain as much as 20% sucrose with an osmotic potential of 17 atm, but nevertheless aphids do not dehydrate. By converting some of the sucrose into trisaccharides like melezitose (Auclair, 1963) aphids can reduce the osmotic potential of their gut contents and impede the absorption of sugars which are present in excess of their requirements (Kennedy and Stroyan, 1959; Kennedy and Fosbrooke, 1973). Aphids lack Malpighian tubules which in other insects regulate the balance of water and ions in the body fluids and also remove nitrogenous waste. Aphids excrete ammonia into the gut instead of uric acid and exploit the large volume of water in their diet to dilute and flush out the ammonia (Lamb, 1959). The continuous secretion of saliva into plants (Lamb et al., 1967) may also have an excretory function (Kennedy and Fosbrooke, 1973).

The host plants of most species of aphid are angiosperms, although some live on gymnosperms and a few species attack ferns and mosses. With the notable exception of the study by Kollmann and Dörr (1966) on a gymnosperm, aphids have been used for studying phloem transport mainly in angiosperms.

The dependence of aphids on phloem sap as a source of food has recently been exploited by an increasing number of people in the attempt to solve problems of phloem transport. A popular technique is to sever the stylets of feeding aphids and collect the sap that exudes from the cut ends of the stylet bundle left embedded in the host plant. This "stylet sap" is assumed to be chemically identical with sieve-tube sap. The technique was first used by entomologists trying to determine the composition of the food ingested by aphids (KENNEDY and MITTLER, 1953) and by virologists investigating the transport of virus in the phloem of plants (VAN SOEST and DE MEESTER-MANGER, CATS, 1956). The technique was then used extensively by botanists interested in phloem transport and Dr. PEEL has given an account of this work in Chapter 7. A study of where aphids feed on a plant, the chemical composition of their excreta, and the damage they do to plants are also relevant to understanding phloem transport and supplement the information obtained from cutting aphid stylets.

B. Distribution of Aphids on Plants and Its Bearing on Translocation

Aphids aggregate on parts of a plant where food is of a high quality (KENNEDY and BOOTH, 1951). Therefore, changes in the distribution of an aphid with time could indicate changes in concentration gradients within the phloem system. For example, when leaves of sycamore are unfurling in spring, sycamore aphids are frequently to be found on petioles and stems rather than on leaves which, however, are the preferred feeding site later in the year. That is, while leaves are growing and importing food materials, aphids feed as close to the source as the length of their stylets permit. Mature leaves, on the other hand, export sugars and amino acids to the rest of the plant and with the cessation of leaf growth sycamore aphids in fact move out onto the leaves, away from the stem and petioles. The minor leaf veins of mature leaves which are closest to the site of both sugar and protein synthesis (FISCHER, 1885; ESAU, 1967) are likely to contain the highest concentration of these substances. Away from these sites of synthesis osmotic dilution of the sap is likely (MÜNCH, 1930; MILBURN, 1972). By feeding on the minor, rather than the major veins of a leaf, a sycamore aphid has the advantage of a shorter pathway to the sieve tubes, less sclerenchyma to impede the passage of its stylets and also a food supply richer in both sugars and proteins. However, only immature sycamore aphids feed on the minor veins, and the adult aphids which are larger prefer to feed on the larger leaf veins (DIXON and LOGAN, 1973).

The preponderance of adult aphids feeding on the larger veins may be explained by the physiology of sieve tubes. There is considerable evidence from the study of exudation from wounded phloem that sieve tubes can transport sap at rates up to a given threshold, but when this threshold is exceeded, a blockage of the conducting system is rapidly induced at the sieve plates (e.g. MILBURN, 1972). Rapid removal of relatively large volumes of sap by adult aphids, through their wider stylet tubes, could cause the rate of sap conduction to exceed the critical threshold and induce the blockage of the sieve tubes in minor veins. Conceivably the demand could be met without blockage if tapped by stylets of young aphids. EVERT et al. (1968) showed that sieve plates of sieve tubes that had been punctured by aphids were blocked by tylosoids. However, they were not able to determine if the blockage had caused the cessation of feeding, but suggested that initially the large wide phloem elements are less likely to be affected than the narrower elements. It seems, therefore, that an aphid selects a feeding site according to the quality and quantity of food it will yield. Some sieve tubes are beyond the reach of smaller aphids. Shallower sieve tubes can be reached by most aphids, but will promptly seal if tapped by the stylets of a large aphid. However, extremely little information has been collected about the factors determining the feeding sites of aphids. The problem is an interesting one and pertinent to understanding translocation in plants as well as the feeding biology of aphids.

C. Aphid Honeydew as a Source of Information on Substances Translocated in Phloem Elements

It is a very difficult operation to cut the stylets of an aphid, leaving them in position and intact, especially those of the smaller species which feed on the softer parts of plants. Aphids which feed on leaves do not have to probe very deeply to find sieve tubes and consequently the stylets are easily dislodged when cut.

The chemical composition of phloem sap ingested by aphids is altered as it passes through the gut of an aphid. Amino acids are selectively removed (BRAGDON and MITTLER, 1963) and some of the simple sugars are changed to oligosaccharides (DUSPIVA, 1953). Many substances, however, pass through an aphid's gut unchanged. Therefore, the identification of substances present in aphid excreta (honeydew) can provide a useful indication of the substances present in phloem sap, especially as honeydew is very easy to collect and can be obtained in large quantities.

1. Sterols

Insects are unable to synthesise sterols which are nevertheless essential for their growth. As aphids have been reared over several generations on sterol-free artificial diets (DADD and MITTLER, 1966; DADD and KRIEGER, 1967; EHRHARDT, 1968a, b; AKEY and BECK, 1971; SRIVASTAVA and AUCLAIR, 1971), it has been assumed that aphids obtain sterols from their symbionts. Although cholesterol and other sterols are known to be important constituents of many plants, until recently it was not known that these substances are transported in phloem sap. Honeydew of *Myzus persicae* Salz. feeding on radish seedlings contains 150–210 μg of sterol per g dry weight. The relative proportion of sterols in radish seedlings, and sap, and the honeydew of the aphid are given in Table 1.

The sterols which occur in radish plants are also present in honeydew collected from *M. persicae* feeding on radish. Likewise, cholesterol, campesterol, β-sitosterol and lophenol occur in wallflower, *Cheiranthus cleiri* L. and in the honeydew of *M. persicae* feeding on wallflower (FORREST and KNIGHT, 1972). This is strong evidence in favor of sterols being transported in phloem sap.

Table 1. Percentage of seven sterols in tops and sap of radish plants and in honeydew of *Myzus persicae* Sulz. fed on radish. From FORREST and KNIGHT (1972)

	Plant		Aphid honeydew
	Tops	Sap	
Cholesterol	5.0	18.1	38.4
Brassicasterol	12.8	18.4	1.4
Campesterol	25.0	17.3	0.5
Stigmasterol	Trace	5.3	3.2
β-Sitosterol	57.2	40.9	48.3
Δ^5-Avenasterol	Trace	Trace	8.2

Table 2. Phenolic acids in radish plants and in honeydew of *Myzus persicae* Sulz. fed on radish. From HUSSAIN et al. (1974)

Phenolic acid	Present in	
	Plant	Honeydew
3,4 dihydroxy benzoic	+	−
ortho hydroxy hippuric	+	−
4 hydroxy 3 methoxy cinnamic	+	−
3,4 dihydroxy cinnamic	+	+
para hydroxy cinnamic	+	+
para hydroxy phenyl lactic	+	+
2,5 dihydroxy phenyl acetic	+	+
ortho hydroxy phenyl propionic	+	+
2,6 dihydroxy benzoic	−	+
2,5 dihydroxy benzoic	−	+
3,5 dimethoxy 4 hydroxy benzoic	−	+
2,5 dihydroxy cinnamic	−	+
ortho hydroxy phenyl acetic	−	+
meta hydroxy benzoic	−	+
meta hydroxy phenyl propionic	−	+
para hydroxy benzoic	−	+
para hydroxy mandellic	−	+
para hydroxy phenyl acetic	−	+

2. Phenols

There is evidence from the examination of the gut contents of *Macrosiphum pisi* that phenols are translocated in plants and are taken up by aphids feeding on these plants (PRIDHAM, 1966). The honeydew of *M. persicae* contained 15 phenolic substances five of which were also present in radish seedlings on which the aphids fed (Table 2). It is likely that the phenols present in both radish seedlings and aphid honeydew are translocated in the phloem of radish seedlings. The phenols present only in aphid honeydew are either derived from the breakdown of the ingested plant phenols or else they are products of aphid metabolism (HUSSAIN et al., 1974).

3. Minerals

Several minerals have been recorded in the honeydew of aphids (Table 3). The proportion of each cation in dried honeydew changes with the state of growth of the plant on which the aphid feeds (Fig. 3). However, it is unknown whether this is due to changes in the concentration of the particular cation in phloem sap, or to changes in the concentration of sugar, the major constituent of sap.

Table 3. Quantity of various minerals present in aphid honeydew

Mineral	*Megoura viciae* Buckt. (EHRHARDT, 1965a)	*Drepanosiphum platanoides* (Schr.) (DIXON and GREEN, unpublished)		*Eucallipterus tiliae* L. (DIXON and GREEN, unpublished)	
	mg/ml	mg/ml[a]	mg/g (dry wt)	mg/ml[a]	mg/g (dry wt)
Potassium	13.0–14.1	1.6 –4.2	6.2 –16.6	2.4 –3.6	9.6 –14.2
Sodium	0.04– 0.05	0.4 –1.4	1.6 – 5.7	0.07–0.15	0.28– 0.58
Magnesium	1.8 – 2.3	0.03–0.16	0.12– 0.62	0.12–0.21	0.5 – 0.85
Calcium	0.07– 0.09	0.05–0.18	0.20– 0.72	0.27–1.66	1.08– 6.63
Copper	trace	0.025–0.125	0.10– 0.50	0.10–0.15	0.40– 0.62

[a] Estimated; honeydew of *D. platanoides* and *E. tiliae* consists of 80% water by weight.

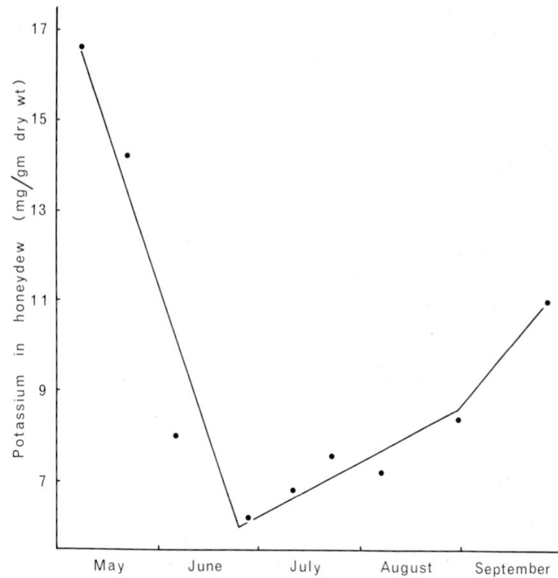

Fig. 3. The quantity of potassium in honeydew of the sycamore aphid at different times of the year

Of the minerals present in honeydew, calcium is the most interesting when considering phloem transport. It has been claimed that calcium is either not translocated in phloem sap (ZIEGLER, 1956), or moves only very poorly in the phloem (ZIMMERMANN, 1969). Calcium is present in honeydew and may accumulate as granules in the epithelial cells of the mid-gut of aphids like *A. fabae*. These granules are thought to be reserves of calcium utilized later when the diet of the aphid is poor in calcium (EHRHARDT, 1965b). Certain aphids reared on artificial diets grow better when calcium is incorporated in the diet than when calcium is omitted (RETNAKARAN and BECK, 1967). Therefore, the presence of calcium in honeydew and the need shown by some aphids for calcium are strong pointers to its presence also in phloem sap, at least in some plants.

4. Plant Hormones

Abscisic acid, gibberellic acid, indole acetic acid, cytokinins and hormonal factors controlling flowering can pass through the gut of aphids and appear in the honeydew without any apparent loss of biological activity (BOWEN and HOAD, 1958; MAXWELL and PAINTER, 1962; HUSSAIN et al., 1974, and CLELAND, 1972). Thus by collecting honeydew from aphids feeding on various parts of plants one could determine which plant hormones are being translocated, and also any changes in the level of these hormones with the state of growth of the plant. However, plants on which aphids feed show marked disturbances in growth (DIXON, 1971a, b; FORREST et al., 1973) as well as in the balance between the various growth hormones (HUSSAIN et al., 1973). Therefore, the results may not indicate what happens in uninfested plants (p. 166). The analysis of honeydew can thus provide a useful and convenient way of determining some of the substances present in phloem sap.

D. Growth Efficiency of Aphids

Aphids are wasteful feeders because much of the food they ingest is excreted. This is a consequence of the low level of amino nitrogen and high level of sugar present in the phloem sap they ingest. For an aphid:

$$\text{Gross Growth Efficiency (GGE)} = \frac{\text{Growth (calories)}}{\text{Food Consumed (calories)}}$$

Aphids which live on woody plants excrete most of the food they ingest and have a low growth efficiency, in the range of 4–20% (Table 4). However, aphids that live on herbaceous plants have a higher GGE of approximately 43–65%. Host-alternating aphids which live on woody primary hosts and herbaceous secondary hosts also show a lower growth efficiency while on the woody host than on its secondary herbaceous host (Table 4), so growth efficiency would appear to be a function of the plant species rather than of the aphid species. Such a marked difference in the GGE of an aphid living on herbaceous and woody host plants indicates a big difference in the quality of the aphid's food. The phloem sap of herbaceous plants could contain either more amino-nitrogen or less sugar than the phloem sap of woody plants. VON DEHN (1961) in her detailed study of the feeding biology of aphids living on herbaceous plants showed by stylet cutting that the sugar content of the phloem sap of herbaceous plants (*Centaurea*, *Campanula* and *Cirsium*) is between 10–15%. The sugar content of the phloem sap of *Heracleum*

Table 4. Growth efficiencies of aphids living on herbaceous (H) and woody (W) plants

	Host plant	Aphid	Growth efficiency	Source
H	*Vicia faba* L.	*Megoura viciae* Buckt.	65	QURESHI (1973)
H	*Vicia faba* L.	*Aphis fabae* Scop.	60	QURESHI (1973)
H	*Vicia faba* L.	*Acyrthosiphon pisum* (Harris)	55	RATHCHE (1968)
H	*Avena sativa* L.	*Rhopalosiphum padi* L.	43	DIXON (1971c)
W	*Prunus padus* L.		8–20	
W	*Acer pseudoplatanus* L.	*Drepanosiphum platanoides* (Schr.)	4	DIXON (1970)
W	*Salix* sp.	*Tuberolachnus salignus* (Gmelin)	5	DIXON (1970)
W	*Tilia* sp.	*Eucallipterus tiliae* L.	5	LLEWELLYN (1972)

is 24% (ZIEGLER and MITTLER, 1959). Thus the range in sugar concentration of 10–24% that has been recorded for some herbaceous plants is similar to the range of 10–25% recorded for woody plants by ZIMMERMANN (1960). Therefore the big difference in the growth efficiencies shown by aphids living on herbaceous and woody plants suggests that the concentration of amino-nitrogen is higher in the phloem sap of herbaceous plants than in woody plants.

E. Damage Done to Plants by Aphids

1. Galling

Some aphids induce the development of local structural abnormalities of their host plants. The form of these is characteristic for the species of aphid. Blisters or pocket galls on the leaves of red currant, *Ribes rubrum* L., are caused by the currant aphid, *Cryptomyzus ribis* (L). Young leaves of apple, infested with the rosy leaf-curling aphid, *Dysaphis devecta* Wlk. twist and develop a red coloration. These malformations of the plants never completely enclose the aphids and are called pseudo-galls. In true galls, like the petiole gall induced on poplar by *Pemphigus bursarius* (L.), plant tissue grows around and completely encloses the aphid and its progeny. Aphids can only induce actively growing plant tissue to form a gall. The form of a gall can mainly be attributed to the behavior of the aphid (DUNN, 1960), and the variety of plant parts available to aphids, rather than to a difference in the cecidogenic substance injected by aphids.

The process of galling has been described in detail by DUNN (1960) although the chemistry of the process is not known. There are two components in the saliva exuded from the tip of the aphid's stylet bundle: that which forms the salivary sheath already described and is deposited in the plant tissue around the aphid's stylets, and a watery saliva that is secreted directly into the sieve tube on which the aphid is feeding. Some factor as yet unidentified in the saliva appears to induce the development of a gall. MILES (1968a) has suggested that aphids produce their own specific chemical organizer of plant growth, or even unspecific plant hormones. It has also been reported that indole acetic acid (IAA) is present in the saliva of gall-forming aphids (SCHÄLLER, 1968). However, much of the work that has been done on the biochemical aspects of galling by aphids is contradictory and needs repeating. This fascinating field of aphid-induced galls still lies open for biochemical exploration and experimental analysis.

Apart from local changes caused by galling, extensive although often less conspicuous damage occurs in other parts of the plant. In addition to galled leaves, apple seedlings infested with the rosy leaf-curling aphid have thickened stems and abnormal root and shoot growth (FORREST, unpublished). Non-galling aphids markedly retard the growth of their host plants, which exhibit similar symptoms to the general symptoms exhibited by host plants attacked by galling aphids (FORREST et al., 1973). If aphids are made radioactive by feeding them on radioactive plants, and these radioactive aphids are transferred to feed on normal plants, the new plants also become radioactive (FORREST and NOORDINK, 1971; LAWSON et al., 1954). Substances in aphid saliva can therefore be translocated throughout a plant from the topmost leaves to the smallest roots, so it is not surprising if the growth of all parts of an aphid-infested plant are affected. The removal of a ring of phloem from around the stem of a plant prevents the radioactivity introduced by the aphids spreading through the plant, which illustrates that it is translocated in the phloem (GREEN, 1971).

2. Premature Senescence of Plant Tissue

Both the black bean aphid (*Aphis fabae* Scop.) and the cabbage aphid (*Brevicoryne brassicae* L.) are capable of changing the metabolism of their host plants in the aphid's favor. Although there are none of the outward signs of galling there are restricted local changes in the plants' metabolism similar to those that occur when a plant approaches senescence. As with galling, these changes are to the aphids' advantage, and as a result the aphids which develop are larger and more fecund (WAY and CAMMELL, 1970; DIXON and WRATTEN, 1971). These changes induced in a plant by certain aphids can result in a localized yellowing of the tissues in the region where the aphids are feeding. This is particularly well marked when the privet aphid, *Myzodes ligustri* Mosl., and *Periphyllus acericola* (Wlk.) feed on mature privet and sycamore leaves, respectively. This localized senescence makes the tissue attractive to other species of aphid also which feed on the same host but cannot induce senescence.

3. Death of Plant Tissue

Aphids may cause the death of parts or even the whole of a plant. Feeding on radish *(Raphanus sativus)* the aphid *Myzus persicae* induces the development of necrotic patches, resulting from the death of the cells immediately around the stylet sheath (FORREST et al., 1973). Other studies have also revealed widespread disorganization and destruction of cells near stylet sheaths (SMITH, 1926; CHATTERS and SCHLEHUBER, 1951; DIEHL and CHATTERS, 1956). Aphids which induce changes of this sort will, if abundant, cause the death of part or the whole of a plant. However many aphids, such as the sycamore aphid, do not inflict injury resulting in the death of plant cells even when the aphid is very numerous, although damaged cells secrete callose which is incorporated in the stylet sheath (HORSFALL, 1923; EVERT et al., 1968).

4. Speed of Response of Plants to Aphid Infestation

Plants respond to aphid attack very rapidly. Within 24 h of a rosy leaf-curling aphid beginning to feed on an apple seedling there is either a noticeable bend in the stem or roll in a leaf of the seedling according to where the aphid is feeding. Within 48 h the stem will show a 90° bend or the leaf roll will be very marked and deposits of anthocyanin will have appeared along the veins in the region of the leaf where the aphid is feeding (FORREST, unpublished). The development of true galls, like those induced by *Pemphigus bursarius* (L.) on the petioles of the leaves of poplar, is also extremely rapid. The aphid inducing the gall can be completely enclosed within 4 days by the growth of the plant tissue which has been stimulated by the probing of the aphid (DUNN, 1960).

After 10 days of infestation by the leaf-feeding aphid *Myzus persicae* the volume of sap bleeding from the stumps of cut stems of infested radish seedlings was only 4% of that exuding from the stumps of uninfested control seedlings of the same age (FORREST et al., 1973). After three days of infestation the volume of exuding sap was 45% of that collected from uninfested seedlings (FORREST, unpublished). Therefore the response to aphid attack was rapid even in parts of a plant some distance from where the aphid was feeding.

5. Hormonal Changes Induced by Infestation

In the above-ground parts of radish seedlings aphid infestation results in an increase in the level of growth inhibitors and a decrease in the level of substances with growth-promoting properties, such as cytokinins, gibberellins and auxins. In the roots aphid infestation results in a slight decrease in the level of growth inhibitors and a marked increase in the level of cytokinins. These changes in the hormonal balance can be related to disturbances in growth and translocation shown by the aphid infested radish seedlings (HUSSAIN et al., 1973).

F. Aphids as "Sinks"

MILES (1968b) has suggested that IAA could be produced in aphid saliva after its injection into a plant. This could account for the proliferation and enlargement of cells, and stimulation of cambial activity and xylem differentiation in the tissue observed immediately around stylet sheaths (SMITH, 1967; EVERT et al., 1968). In addition to the effect of IAA on the growth and differentiation of plant cells it is also known to direct the transport of nutrients. If auxins can indeed direct transport, as some propose, an increased supply of nutrients may be delivered to an organ in response to a high auxin concentration and not just because it is a nutrient sink (DAVIES and WAREING, 1965; SETH and WAREING, 1967). Therefore, it may not be correct to regard aphids solely as nutrient sinks as hitherto thought (KENNEDY and STROYAN, 1959; PEEL and HO, 1970; WAY and CAMMELL, 1970). Increasing the number of aphids may therefore not only increase the size of the sink but could also increase the level of auxin and thus of auxin-directed transport into the area attacked by the aphids. This highlights the danger of regarding aphids as a simple and rather delicate way of tapping the translocating system of a plant without damaging or disturbing it.

G. Aphid Stylets and Phloem Transport

Aphids can no longer be regarded as merely imbibing phloem sap from plants. They secrete substances into plants which rapidly induce changes in growth and translocation. Many of these changes in plant metabolism are to the aphid's advantage. Studies of phloem transport in which aphid stylets have been used rather than aphid honeydew are affected by this same criticism. As stylet cutting is difficult, several aphids are allowed to settle and commence feeding before an attempt is made to cut their stylets. The stylets of only a few of the aphids will be cut successfully. After the stylets are severed no more saliva flows into the plant. However, there already exists in the plant large quantities of saliva in the form of salivary sheaths that surround the stylet bundles and of watery saliva that was injected into the plant when the aphids commenced feeding. Therefore, the plant system one is studying is to some degree a disturbed system. Some aphids have apparently relatively little effect on the plant they are exploiting. However, from the evidence available it is reasonable to claim that all species of aphid probably disturb the physiology of their host plants significantly.

The changes induced in a plant do not always improve conditions for the aphid, and one can still only guess some of the functions of the saliva. ZIMMERMANN'S claim (1969) that "aphids have learned to tap sieve tubes gently" is a view widely held even by aphid biologists. However, aphid stylets are very wide compared with the phloem elements they tap. In certain species of aphid the stylets may be as wide (4.6–7.7 μ) as the narrowest sieve elements of their host plant (EVERT et al., 1968). Therefore especially when aphids are numerous, they could be regarded as inflicting severe wounds. It is possible that one function of the watery component of aphid's saliva is to prevent or reduce the intensity of the normal response of a plant to a wound, in a way comparable to the action of the anticoagulant present in the saliva of blood-sucking insects. In doing this an aphid would be assured of a more continuous flow of phloem sap, but indirectly it could adversely affect the growth processes of its host plant.

However, providing it is realized that one is dealing with an aphid-plant interaction rather than simply using aphids to monitor changes in a plant, aphids should continue to provide a useful means of studying translocation in plants. Under natural conditions in temperate regions few plants are free from aphids throughout the year, so that in any event one is investigating a relatively natural aphid-plant unit.

H. Summary

The dependence of aphids on phloem sap as a source of food has been exploited by many people in an attempt to solve problems of phloem transport. Analysis of the sap that exudes from the cut ends of aphid mouthparts left embedded in the host plant has revealed the nature of some of the substances translocated in plants. A study of where aphids feed on a plant, the chemical composition of their excreta (honeydew), and the damage they do to plants are also relevant to understanding phloem transport and supplement the information obtained from cutting aphid stylets.

Aphids select a feeding site according to the quality and quantity of food it will yield. Therefore, changes in the distribution of an aphid on a plant with time could indicate changes in concentration gradients within the phloem system.

Many substances ingested by aphids pass through their gut unchanged. The identification of substances present in honeydew can provide a useful indication of the substances present in phloem sap, especially as honeydew is very easily collected and can be obtained in large quantities. Analysis of honeydew has revealed that sterols, phenols, minerals and plant hormones are translocated on phloem sap.

Aphids are wasteful feeders as much of the food they ingest is excreted. This is a consequence of the low level of amino-nitrogen and high level of sugar present in phloem sap they ingest. Aphids which live on woody plants have a low growth efficiency, in the range 4–20%. However, aphids that live on herbaceous plants have a higher growth efficiency, of approximately 43–65%. This big difference in the growth efficiencies shown by aphids living on herbaceous and woody plants, in which the sugar content of the phloem sap does not differ, indicates that the concentration of amino nitrogen is higher in the phloem sap of herbaceous plants than in woody plants.

Many aphids damage their host plants. This damage can take the form of galls, premature senescence and death of tissue. Plants respond to aphid attack very rapidly, often within a few hours, and even in parts of a plant some way from the site where the aphid is feeding. Aphid feeding therefore can no longer be regarded as a simple and rather delicate way of tapping the translocating system of a plant without damaging or disturbing it.

References

AKEY, D.H., BECK, S.D.: Continuous rearing of the pea aphid on a holidic diet. Ann. Entomol. Soc. Am. **64**, 353–356 (1971).

AUCLAIR, J.L.: Aphid feeding and nutrition. Ann. Rev. Entomol. **8**, 439–490 (1963).

BANKS, C.J.: Aphid nutrition and reproduction. Rep. Rothamsted exp. Stn., 1964, 299–309 (1965).

BOWEN, M.R., HOAD, G.V.: Inhibitor content of phloem and xylem sap obtained from willow (*Salix viminalis* L.) entering dormancy. Planta **81**, 64–70 (1968).

BRAGDON, J.C., MITTLER, T.E.: Differential utilization of amino-acids by *Myzus persicae* (Sulzer) fed on artificial diets. Nature **198**, 209–210 (1963).

CHATTERS, R.M., SCHLEHUBER, A.M.: Mechanics of feeding of the greenbug (*Toxoptera graminum* Rond.) on *Hordeum, Avena* and *Triticum*. Oklahoma Agr. Expt. Sta. Tech. Bull. T-40 (1951).

CLELAND, C.F.: The use of aphids in the search for the hormonal factors controlling flowering. In: Plant growth substances 1970 (ed. D.J. CARR), p. 753–757. Berlin-Heidelberg-New York: Springer 1972.

DADD, R.H., KRIEGER, D.L.: Continuous rearing of aphids of *Aphis fabae* complex on sterile synthetic diets. J. Econ. Entomol. **60**, 1512–1514 (1967).

DADD, R.H., MITTLER, T.E.: Permanent culture of an aphid on a totally synthetic diet. Experientia **22**, 832–833 (1966).

DAVIES, C.R., WAREING, P.F.: Auxin-induced transport of radio-phosphorus in stems. Planta **65**, 139–156 (1965).

DIEHL, S.G., CHATTERS, R.M.: Studies on the mechanics of feeding of the spotted alfalfa aphid on alfalfa. J. Econ. Entomol. **49**, 589–591 (1956).

DIXON, A.F.G.: Reproductive activity of the sycamore aphid, *Drepanosiphum platanoides* (Schr.) (Hemiptera, Aphididae). J. Anim. Ecol. **32**, 33–48 (1963).

DIXON, A.F.G.: Aphids as root-fluid feeders. In: Methods of study in soil ecology, p. 243–247. Paris: UNESCO 1970.

DIXON, A.F.G.: The role of aphids in wood formation. I. The effect of the sycamore aphid, *Drepanosiphum platanoides* Schr. (Aphididae) on the growth of sycamore *Acer pseudoplatanus* L. J. Appl. Ecol. **8**, 165–179 (1971a).

DIXON, A.F.G.: The role of aphids in wood formation. II. The effect of the lime aphid *Eucallipterus tiliae* L. (Aphididae) on the growth of lime *Tilia* × *vulgaris* Hayne. J. Appl. Ecol. **8**, 393–399 (1971b).

DIXON, A.F.G.: The life-cycle and host preferences of the bird cherry-oat aphid, *Rhopalosiphum padi* L., and their bearing on the theories of host alternation in aphids. Ann. Appl. Biol. **68**, 135–147 (1971c).

DIXON, A.F.G.: Biology of aphids. London: Edward Arnold 1973.

DIXON, A.F.G., LOGAN, M.: Leaf size and availability of space to the sycamore aphid *Drepanosiphum platanoides*. Oikos **24**, 58–63 (1973).

DIXON, A.F.G., WRATTEN, S.D.: Laboratory studies on aggregation, size and fecundity in the black bean aphid, *Aphis fabae* Scop. Bull. Entomol. Res. **61**, 97–111 (1971).

DUNN, J.A.: The formation of galls by some species of *Pemphigus* (Homoptera: Aphididae). Marcellia **30**, 155–167 (1960).

DUSPIVA, F.: Der Kohlehydratumsatz im Beitrag zum Problem der stofflichen Wechselbeziehungen zwischen saugenden Insekten und ihren Wirtspflanzen. Mitt. Biol. Zent. Anst. Berlin **75**, 82–88 (1953).

EHRHARDT, P.: Die anorganischen Bestandteile des Honigtaues von *Megoura viciae* Buckt. Experientia **21**, 472–473 (1965a).

EHRHARDT, P.: Speicherung anorganischer Substanzen in den Mitteldarmzellen von *Aphis fabae* Scop. und ihre Bedeutung für die Ernährung. Z. Vergleich. Physiol. **50**, 293–312 (1965b).

EHRHARDT, P.: Nachweis einer durch symbiontische Mikroorganismen bewirkten Sterinsynthese in künstlich ernährten Aphiden (Homoptera, Rhynchota, Insecta). Experientia **24**, 82–83 (1968a).

EHRHARDT, P.: Einfluß von Ernährungsfaktoren auf die Entwicklung von säftesaugenden Insekten unter besonderer Berücksichtigung von Symbionten. Z. Parasitenk. **31**, 38–66 (1968b).

ESAU, K.: Minor veins in *Beta* leaves: Structure related to function. Proc. Am. Phil. Soc. **111**, 219–233 (1967).

EVERT, R.F., ESCHRICH, W., MEDLER, J.T., ALFIERI, F.J.: Observations on penetration of linden branches by stylets of the aphid *Longistigma caryae*. Am. J. Bot. **55**, 860–874 (1968).

FISCHER, A.: Studien über die Siebröhren der Dikotylenblätter. Ber. Verhandl. Sächs. Akad. Wiss. **37**, 245–290 (1885).

FORREST, J.M.S., HUSSAIN, A., DIXON, A.F.G.: Growth and wilting of radish seedlings, *Raphanus sativus*, infested with the aphid, *Myzus persicae*. Ann. Appl. Biol. **75**, 267–274 (1973).

FORREST, J.M.S., KNIGHT, B.A.: Presence of phytosterols in the food of the aphid, *Myzus persicae*. J. Insect Physiol. **18**, 723–728 (1972).

FORREST, J.M.S., NOORDINK, J.PH.W.: Translocation and subsequent uptake by aphids of ^{32}P introduced into plants by radioactive aphids. Entomol. Exptl. Appl. **14**, 133–134 (1971).

GIBSON, R.W.: The distribution of aphids on potato leaves in relation to vein size. Entomol. Exptl. Appl. **15**, 213–223 (1972).

GREEN, A.ST.J.: Translocation of aphid saliva in plants. M.Sc. thesis Glasgow University 1971.

HOAD, G.V., BOWEN, M.R.: Evidence for gibberellin-like substances in phloem exudate of higher plants. Planta **82**, 22–32 (1968).

HORSFALL, J.L.: The effect of feeding punctures of aphids on certain plant tissues. Penn. State Coll. School of Agric. Bull. **182**, 3–22 (1923).

HUSSAIN, A., FORREST, J.M.S., DIXON, A.F.G.: Changes in growth regulator content of radish seedlings, *Raphanus sativus*, infested with the aphid *Myzus persicae*. Ann. Appl. Biol. **75**, 275–284 (1973).

HUSSAIN, A., FORREST, J.M.S., DIXON, A.F.G.: Sugar, organic acid, phenolic acid and plant-growth regulator content of the honeydew of the aphid *Myzus persicae* and of its host plant, *Raphanus sativus*. Ann. Appl. Biol. **78**, 65–73 (1974).

KENNEDY, J.S., BOOTH, C.O.: Host alternation in *Aphis fabae* Scop. I. Feeding preferences and fecundity in relation to the age and kind of leaves. Ann. Appl. Biol. **38**, 25–64 (1951).

KENNEDY, J.S., FOSBROOKE, I.H.M.: The plant in the life of an aphid. In: Insect/plant relationships (ed. H.F. VAN EMDEN), p. 129–140. Oxford: Blackwell 1973.

KENNEDY, J.S., MITTLER, T.E.: A method for obtaining phloem sap *via* the mouth-parts of aphids. Nature **171**, 528 (1953).

KENNEDY, J.S., STROYAN, H.L.G.: Biology of aphids. Ann. Rev. Entomol. **4**, 139–160 (1959).

KOLLMANN, R., DÖRR, I.: Lokalisierung funktionstüchtiger Siebzellen bei *Juniperus communis* mit Hilfe von Aphiden. Z. Pflanzenphysiol. **55**, 131–141 (1966).

LAMB, K.P.: Composition of the honeydew of the aphid *Brevicoryne brassicae* (L.) feeding on swedes (*Brassica napobrassica* DC.). J. Insect Physiol. **3**, 1–13 (1959).

LAMB, K.P., EHRHARDT, P., MOERICKE, V.: Labeling of aphid saliva with Rubidium-86. Nature **214**, 602–603 (1967).

LAWSON, F.R., LUCAS, G.B., HALL, N.S.: Translocation of radioactive phosphorus injected by the green peach aphid into tobacco plants. J. Econ. Entomol. **47**, 749–752 (1954).

LLEWELLYN, M.: The effect of the lime aphid, *Eucallipterus tiliae* L. (Aphididae) on the growth of the lime *Tilia × vulgaris* Hayne. I. Energy requirements of the aphid population. J. Appl. Ecol. **9**, 261–282 (1972).

MAXWELL, F.G., PAINTER, R.H.: Auxin content of extracts of host plants and honeydew of different biotypes of the corn leaf aphid, *Rhopalosiphum maidis* (Fitch). J. Kansas Entomol. Soc. **35**, 219–233 (1962).

MCALLAN, J.W., ADAMS, JEAN B.: The significance of pectinase in plant penetration by aphids. Canad. J. Zool. **39**, 305–310 (1961).

MILBURN, J.A.: Phloem transport in *Ricinus*. Pestic. Sci. **3**, 653–665 (1972).

MILES, P.W.: Insect secretions in plants. Ann. Rev. Phytopath. **6**, 137–166 (1968a).

MILES, P.W.: Studies on the salivary physiology of plant-bugs: experimental induction of galls. J. Insect Physiol. **14**, 97–106 (1968b).

MITTLER, T.E.: Studies on the feeding and nutrition of *Tuberolachnus salignus* (Gmelin) (Homoptera, Aphididae). 1. The uptake of phloem sap. J. Exptl. Biol. **34**, 334–341 (1957).

MITTLER, T.E.: Sieve-tube sap *via* aphid stylets. In: Physiology of forest trees (ed. K.V. THIMANN), p. 401–405. New York: Ronald Press 1958.

MITTLER, T.E.: Studies on the feeding and nutrition of *Tuberolachnus salignus* (Gmelin) (Homoptera, Aphididae). 111. The nitrogen economy. J. Exptl. Biol. **35**, 626–638 (1958).

MÜNCH, E.: Die Stoffbewegungen in der Pflanze. Jena: Gustav Fischer 1930.

PEEL, A.J., HO, L.C.: Colony size of *Tuberolachnus salignus* (Gmelin) in relation to mass transport of ^{14}C-labeled assimilate from the leaves in willow. Physiol. Plantarum **23**, 1033–1038 (1970).

POLLARD, D.G.: Plant penetration by feeding aphids (Hemiptera, Aphidoidea): a review. Bull. Entomol. Res. **62**, 631–714 (1973).

PRIDHAM, J.B.: Low molecular weight phenols in higher plants. Ann. Rev. Plant Physiol. **17**, 13–36 (1966).

QURESHI, A.L.: The ecological energetics of *Aphis fabae* Scopoli and *Megoura viciae* Buckton reared at various feeding sites on plant *Vicia faba* L. M. Phil. thesis University of London 1973.

RATHCHE, B.: Energy utilization of *Acyrthosiphon pisum* (Harris) (Hemiptera: Aphididae). M.Sc. thesis University of London 1968.

RETNAKAREN, A., BECK, S.D.: Aspects of mineral nutrition of the pea aphid, *Acyrthosiphon pisum* (Harris). J. Nutr. **92**, 43–52 (1967).

SCHÄLLER, G.: Biochemische Analyse des Aphidenspeichels und seine Bedeutung für die Gallenbildung. Zool. Jahrb. Physiol. **74**, 54–87 (1968).

SETH, A.K., WAREING, P.F.: Hormone-directed transport of metabolites and its possible role in plant senescence. J. Exptl. Botany **18**, 65–77 (1967).

SMITH, F.H.: Effect of balsam woolly aphid (*Adelges piceae*) infestation on cambial activity in *Abies grandis*. Am. J. Botany **54**, 1215–1223 (1967).

SMITH, K.M.: A comparative study of the feeding methods of certain Hemiptera and of the resulting effects upon the plant tissue, with special reference to the potato plant. Ann. Appl. Biol. **13**, 109–139 (1926).

SRIVASTAVA, P.N., AUCLAIR, J.L.: An improved chemically-defined diet for the pea aphid *Acyrthosiphon pisum*. Ann. Entomol. Soc. Am. **64**, 474–478 (1971).

VAN SOEST, W., DE MEESTER-MANGER CATS, V.: Does the aphid *Myzus persicae* (Sulz.) imbibe tobacco mosaic virus? Virology **2**, 411–414 (1956).

VON DEHN, M.: Untersuchungen zur Ernährungsphysiologie der Aphiden die Aminosäuren und Zucker im Siebröhrensaft einiger Krautgewächsarten und im Honigtau ihrer Schmarotzer. Z. Vergleich. Physiol. **45**, 88–108 (1961).

WAY, M.J., CAMMELL, M.: Aggregation behavior in relation to food utilization by aphids. In: Animal populations in relation to their food resources (ed. A. WATSON), p. 229–247. Oxford: Blackwell 1970.

WEATHERLEY, P.E., PEEL, A.J., HILL, G.P.: The physiology of the sieve tube. Preliminary experiments using aphid mouth parts. J. Exptl. Bot. **10**, 1–16 (1959).

ZIEGLER, H.: Untersuchungen über die Leitung und Sekretion der Assimilate. Planta **47**, 447–500 (1956).

ZIEGLER, H., MITTLER, T.E.: Über den Zuckergehalt der Siebröhren- bzw. Siebzellensäfte von *Heracleum mantegazzianum* und *Picea abies* (L.) Karst. Z. Naturforsch. **14**, 278–281 (1959).

ZIMMERMANN, M.H.: Absorption and translocation: Transport in the phloem. Ann. Rev. Plant Physiol. **11**, 167–190 (1960).

ZIMMERMANN, M.H.: Translocation of nutrients. In: Physiology of plant growth and development (ed. M.B. WILKINS), p. 383–417. London: McGraw Hill 1969.

7. Investigations with Aphid Stylets into the Physiology of the Sieve Tube

A.J. PEEL

A. Introduction

From the earliest days of the study of phloem transport, investigators have attempted to probe the mysteries of the sieve-tube system by obtaining samples of the nutrient stream which moves through it. Though many plants have not provided samples of sieve-tube sap from incisions in the phloem, exudate has been obtained from a considerable number of species. For example, careful incisions into the bark of certain trees, e.g. *Fraxinus americana* (ZIMMERMANN, 1957a, b), and *Robinia pseudoacacia* (ZIEGLER and KLUGE, 1962) will provide samples, whilst a number of herbaceous species often produce copious amounts of sap, e.g. *Yucca* (TAMMES and VAN DIE, 1964), *Cucurbita* (CRAFTS, 1932), and *Ricinus* (MILBURN, 1970). (See Chapters 3,8).

Studies using incision exudation have given, and are still giving most valuable information on the physiology of phloem; not only do they provide samples of the translocation stream for chemical analyses, but inferences can also be drawn about the mechanism of sap movement in intact sieve tubes from various characteristics of the exudation process. However, exudation from incisions has limitations. Many species fail to provide exudate. In others exudation is a short-lived phenomenon and repeated cutting of the tissues is needed to maintain the flow of sap. Incisions are rather imprecise, so it is difficult to evaluate certain parameters of the sap flow process quantitatively.

Ideally a very small, inert tube is required to pierce a single sieve element to obtain sap. If the dimensions of this tube were small enough, then it might be expected that sieve-tube sap would issue from it for extended periods, since the fall in turgor of the pierced element would not be large enough to cause collapse of the element, not to trigger plugging mechanisms. Thus far, we have not yet attained this ideal. The nearest approach to it is to utilize severed stylets of various species of aphids, a technique for which we are indebted to the work of KENNEDY and MITTLER (1953).

Though it is certainly possible to obtain exudate for lengthy periods from stylets, the use of aphids is not without problems. Aphids secrete substances into the phloem which may interfere with the functioning of the sieve elements (see Chapter 6). Nonetheless, as we shall see later, many of the parameters of transport induced by stylet puncture are quantitatively similar to those of transport through intact phloem. The tapping of sieve tube by aphids is a frequent but unnatural event for the plant (a situation which can hardly be said to be novel in biological research) a point which must be kept in mind. Only then can meaningful data be extracted about sieve-tube function by the use of aphids, a point of view supported by the work of the author and his colleagues, as well as a number of other investigators (ZIMMERMANN, 1963; KOLLMANN and DÖRR, 1966; ESCHRICH, 1967, 1968; EVERT et al., 1968; KLUGE et al., 1970).

B. The Aphid Technique as a Method of Obtaining Samples of Sieve-Tube Sap

I. Severed Stylets

It now appears firmly established that a number of aphids feed by inserting the tip of their stylets into a *single* sieve element in the phloem (e.g. *Longistigma caryae* on *Tilia americana*, ZIMMERMANN, 1963, EVERT et al., 1968, *Cupressobium juniperi on Juniperus communis*, KOLLMANN and DÖRR, 1966, and *Tuberolachnus salignus* on various species of *Salix*, MITTLER, 1954; the present author unpublished results).

Thus it would seem that a severed stylet provides an ideal technique for sampling the contents of a sieve element. However, the technique has disadvantages. Stylets can be very unreliable. It is usually an easy matter to get individuals of *Tuberolachnus salignus* to settle and excrete honeydew from 2–3-year-old branches of *Salix* and to cut stylets from CO_2 anesthetised aphids with fine scissors (stylectomy) is not usually difficult. However, exudation from one stylet often produces only a single droplet and then stops, while another may exude for an hour or so before exudation ceases suddenly. It is not known why stoppage occurs, though it seems probable that the sudden release of pressure in the sieve elements following stylectomy may cause partial collapse of the pierced sieve element or trigger some sieve-tube plugging mechanism.

Freshly collected stem segments from field-grown plants are best for successful work on willow, when exudation from cut stylets (1–2 μm inner diameter) at a rate of 4 μl h^{-1} will continue for periods up to five days.

Although the exudate contains certain solutes such as sucrose and potassium (PEEL and WEATHERLEY, 1959) and ATP (GARDNER and PEEL, 1969) in high concentration, many other solutes are present at relatively low levels. Since only microliter volumes of sap are obtained, the assay of certain constituents is difficult or even impossible. Thus though the amino acids in the sap can be assayed without too much difficulty, especially during September and October when they reach their highest concentrations, quantitative estimations of inorganic and organic phosphates and of chloride have not yet been achieved. To study changes in the relative concentration of important constituents such as phosphates in response to environmental conditions it is necessary to use radioactive tracers (GARDNER and PEEL, 1972b). Likewise, investigation of growth hormone transport necessitates the use of labeled materials (LEPP and PEEL, 1971).

Evaporation can cause spurious changes in concentration, especially when the volume flow rate falls below 1 μl h^{-1}, as it frequently does in inhibitor studies. Despite a number of attempts, no successful experimental system has yet been devised to obviate the problem of sample evaporation.

II. Whole Aphids

Frequently whole aphids have been used to collect sieve-tube sap in the form of excreted honeydew (PEEL, 1963, 1965; FORD and PEEL, 1967a). Though this technique clearly has the disadvantage that the sap must pass through the aphid gut and is therefore exposed to possible digestion, it nevertheless has certain advantages over severed stylets, the most notable being that aphids will settle and feed over extended periods on plant material which will not support continued exudation from stylets (See Chapter 6). Moreover, since large quantities of honeydew can be collected from a modestly-sized aphid colony, detection of trace constituents in the sieve-tube sap can be made, an example of this being the finding of abscisic acid by HOAD (1967) in exudate from willow.

Though aphids certainly remove some constituents of the sap, particularly amino acids (MITTLER, 1958), and enzymically change others such as sucrose (MITTLER, 1954, and the present author, unpublished data), probably most solutes ingested are excreted unchanged. For instance, though the sucrose from sieve-tube sap is largely hydrolyzed, only 1 to 5 percent of the total sugar ingested is actually absorbed by the aphid (present author, unpublished data). Thus though whole aphids cannot be used to investigate the metabolism of sugars within the phloem, they are most useful in measuring changes in the specific activity of the sieve-tube sugars, after for instance the administration of labeled carbon dioxide to the leaves (FORD and PEEL, 1967a).

In most experiments utilizing whole aphids, the honeydew is collected on pieces of aluminum foil, and dried before radioactivity assay, or analysis. Such a procedure does not, of course, allow the measurement of the solute concentration within the sap. It is possible, however, to collect individual drops of honeydew from an aphid, weigh these quickly on a microbalance, then assay the samples for solutes known not to be removed to any great extent by the aphids. HOAD and PEEL (1965) used this procedure to follow changes in the concentration of potassium and sodium in sieve-tube sap from willow.

III. Comparison of Aphid Stylet Technique with Incision Methods

Probably the most obvious difference between exudation from stylets and that from stem incisions is the lack of a dilution effect in the former. The dilution effect, due to an osmotic ingress of water into sieve elements after the turgor pressure has been released is marked in trees—*Fraxinus americana* (ZIMMERMANN, 1957b) and also some herbaceous plants such as cucurbits (TINGLEY, 1944). However, not all plants exhibit this effect (see Chapter 14).

Results shown in Table 1 for prolonged exudation from a severed *Tuberolachnus* stylet show no evidence of dilution. However, stylets are cut only when an aphid

Table 1. Volume flow rates, sucrose concentrations and fluxes, over an extended period from a severed stylet of *Tuberolachnus* sited on an isolated length of willow stem. From PEEL (1959)

Time (h)	Volume flow rate ($\mu l\ h^{-1}$)	Sucrose concentration ($\mu g\ \mu l^{-1}$)	Sucrose exudation rate ($\mu g\ h^{-1}$)
0–6	1.73	100	173
6–12	1.72	125	215
12–24	1.75	133	230
24–30	1.88	120	226
30–48	1.53	142	217
48–60	1.74	131	228

is established. A sieve element may, therefore, have been producing exudate for some time. Presently we have no data to indicate whether the dilution effect occurs following the initial aphid puncture before the stylet is excised.

Exudation from incisions differs from that obtained *via* severed stylets in other important respects. It is difficult to ensure that the same number of cells are severed by incisions into the phloem of trees. It is, therefore, difficult to compare sap-flow rates from different incisions quantitatively. In contrast, since it is known that a stylet pierces a single sieve element, quantitative data can be extracted from sap-flow rates concerning the velocity and mass transfer rates down a single sieve tube (Section E). Also, since the dimensions of stylets (their length and the diameter of the food canal) can be measured, it is possible to compare directly certain data (e.g. hydrostatic pressures in the pierced element) between one stylet and another.

Another difference between the two methods of obtaining phloem sap is in the composition of the exudate. Sap from incisions, at least initially, may contain substances absent in the sieve elements but which are released from other cells by cutting. It would be most instructive to discover whether the concentrations of certain solutes differed between incision and stylet sap. So far we have no firm data on these questions. However, recently it has been shown (ROGERS, unpublished data) that willow stems in certain stages of their development will support both a short-lived incision exudation as well as supplying sap *via* the severed stylets of the aphid *Tuberolachnus*. This observation should enable direct comparisons of the sap obtained by both techniques from the same plant material.

C. Evidence That Exudation from Stylets Involves Longitudinal Transport through the Sieve Tubes

Following the work of KENNEDY and MITTLER (1953), it became clear that the severed stylets of *Tuberolachnus salignus* provided a precise and convenient technique for obtaining phloem sap from willow. Their work did not show whether stylet exudation involved longitudinal movement of materials along the sieve tubes, through the sieve plates. If longitudinal transport did not occur in response to stylet puncture, then clearly the technique would lose much of its usefulness, for it would be inapplicable to investigations of the mechanism of movement along sieve tubes. Subsequently stylet exudation *was* shown to depend principally on longitudinal transport (WEATHERLEY et al., 1959).

I. Incision Experiments

MÜNCH (1930) showed that exudation from incisions could be reduced by making a second incision some distance above the first. Apparently the incision prevented a long-distance longitudinal component supporting the exudation rate. HILL (1955) repeated the experiment using stylet exudation in place of incisions. To his surprise exudation continued unchanged when the leafy willow cutting was girdled between the stylet and leaves. Furthermore, normal exudation rates from stylets could be established on isolated stem segments or pieces of bark provided with a supply of water. These experiments indicated either that the sap exuded was produced locally by lateral water and solute fluxes or that lateral flow could be rapidly substituted for longitudinal flow if the latter were interrupted by incisions.

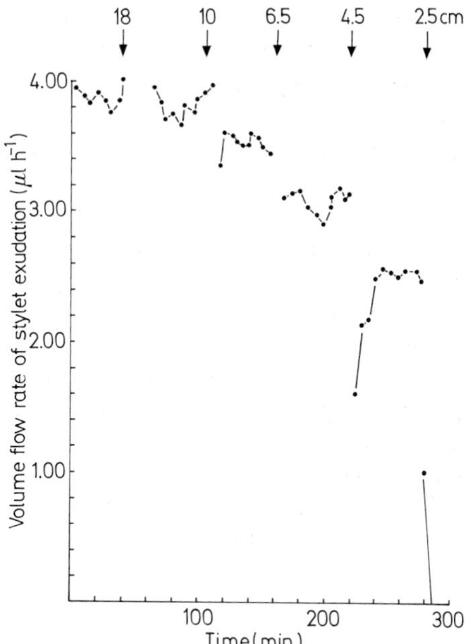

Fig. 1. The effect on the rate of exudation of sap from severed stylets of *Tuberolachnus*, of incisions in the bark made progressively nearer to the stylets, the latter being sited near one end of an isolated segment of willow stem, 40 cm in length. Distances at the top of figure refer to the length of bark in which stylets were sited after each incision. (From WEATHERLEY et al., 1959)

Incision experiments (Fig. 1) showed that exudation rates could be sustained at maximum rates providing it was supported by a minimum length of willow bark corresponding to about 15 cm representing some 1,000 sieve elements (WEATHERLEY et al., 1959). This length of 15 cm was subsequently termed the "contributory length" (PEEL and WEATHERLEY, 1962). Incisions closer to the stylet than 15 cm reduced the flow. It now seems that longitudinal transport does occur over distances greater than 15 cm, indeed FORD and PEEL (1966) showed that radioactive phosphates had an apparent contributory length of 25 cm, but the distance may vary depending on experimental conditions imposed.

It should be observed that exudation from an aphid stylet is not the same as that from incisions in two respects. The drain of stored solutes is relatively much less and it is removed from a single sieve tube contrasting with removal from practically the whole sieve-tube population in a bark sector. These factors probably explain the apparent conflict between MÜNCH'S (1930) results and those of WEATHERLEY et al. (1959).

II. Experiments with Radioactive Tracers

The incision experiments described above provided cogent evidence that exudation from severed stylets of *Tuberolachnus* sited on willow, is not just a localized phenomenon involving the cells immediately around the site of puncture, but also concerns sieve elements and associated cells some 15 to 25 cm distant. Most incision experiments were performed on isolated lengths of stem (lacking roots and leaves), and thus it could be argued that the results obtained bear little relation to the situation within an intact plant.

However, this criticism was met by the use of $^{14}CO_2$, applied to the leaves of potted cuttings of willow by PEEL and WEATHERLEY (1962). Radioactivity appeared in the honeydew produced by an aphid colony, sited 50 or more cm below the leaves within a few hours from $^{14}CO_2$ application. This proved beyond reasonable doubt that exudation from stylets is intimately associated with events taking place in the leaves.

D. The Pattern of Fluxes into and along the Sieve Tube in Relation to Stylet Puncture

In an isolated segment of stem, which lacks "natural" sources and sinks such as leaves and roots, it might be expected that translocation does not take place, and that a uniformity of water and sugar potential exists throughout the phloem cells. However, when a sieve element is pierced, the contents of the lumen being under a considerable positive hydrostatic pressure, escape through the stylet. Thus, the punctured element suffers a "leak" which rapidly lowers the turgor pressure and decreases its water potential. Consequently, water enters the element along a gradient of diffusion potential, diluting the cell sap and initiating a lateral flux of solutes into the punctured element represented by f_1 in Fig. 2 (PEEL and WEATHERLEY, 1962).

Concomitantly, another set of fluxes (F_1, F_2 ...) is initiated by the fall in turgor within the punctured element. These fluxes pass through the sieve plates from adjacent sieve elements, and give rise to further lateral fluxes (f_2, f_3 ...). It was envisaged by PEEL and WEATHERLEY (1962) that the disturbance caused by puncture would spread along the sieve tube on either side of the stylet, and that under steady-state conditions f_1 and F_1 would have the highest values, whilst the series f_2, f_3 ... and F_2, F_3 ... would contribute progressively less on each side until beyond a given distance (the contributory length) they would make no contribution to the total flux.

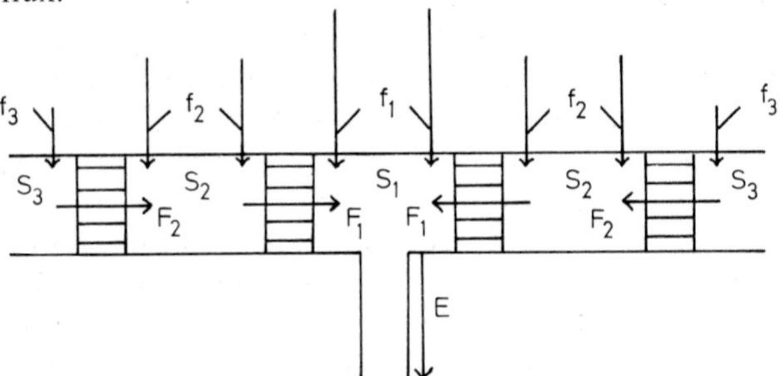

Fig. 2. Illustration of the pattern of fluxes during stylet exudation. (From PEEL and WEATHERLEY, 1962) *S* sieve elements, *F* longitudinal fluxes, *f* lateral fluxes, *E* exudation

This is the situation as pictured in isolated segments, where the stylet acts as the major sink-inducing cells surrounding the punctured sieve tube to act as sources for a distance of about 15 cm. How then does the concept of contributory length apply to the intact plant, where the leaves must constitute the primary source of sugars and where demonstrably this sugar moves towards the stylets from distances considerably greater than 15 cm? PEEL and WEATHERLEY (1962) considered that the involvement of the contributory length represented an artificial steady-state condition in the isolated segment/stylet system. However, when assimilating leaves are present, a sugar potential would build up in their immediate vicinity, which could itself initiate translocation away from the leaves. In this case cells surrounding the sieve tube some distance away from the leaves, and at a lower sugar potential than the leaf cells, would act as sinks (see Chapter 14). That is, the length of sieve tube involved in transport would probably depend entirely upon the "activities" of sources and sinks, and if there is a source of solutes in one place and a sink for them in another, then translocation will occur between them. Thus the concept of contributory length as having a fixed longitudinal dimension has no relevance in the context of the whole plant; the value of 15 cm merely relates to the sink "activity" of a single stylet in an isolated stem segment.

PEEL and HO (1970) demonstrated that in the intact plant the contributory length of an aphid colony depended upon the latter's size (and hence sink activity). Experiments were conducted on willow cuttings with leaves and roots in which the bark had been incised downwards along its entire length from the point of insertion of the leafy shoot. Two aphid colonies of different sizes were sited on either side of the incision at equal distances from the leaves. $^{14}CO_2$ was supplied to leaves, and honeydew was collected from each colony for 15 h.

Not only did the large aphid colony produce more honeydew and more labeled sugars than the small colony, but the specific activity of honeydew from the large colony was also markedly greater than that from the small one. This must have been caused by the considerable "sink" effect of the large colony drawing on labeled sugars from the leaves in contrast with a more local supply to the smaller colony.

E. Severed Stylets and Aphids as Sinks

From the previous section it is clear that both whole aphids and severed stylets act as powerful sinks for solutes. In isolated stem segments the storage cells of the stem act as the source, whilst in leafy cuttings aphids and stylets draw in the main directly upon assimilates from the leaves. HO and PEEL (1969a) showed that up to 75 percent of the sugars in the honeydew of aphids feeding on potted cuttings of willow were supplied by the assimilating leaves.

If stylets were shown to be quite different in their characteristics from normal sinks then clearly their usefulness in the study of phloem translocation would be severely diminished. Whilst it must be admitted that exudation through stylets is an abnormal process as far as the sieve tube is concerned, there is considerable evidence to substantiate the view that transport of solutes in response to puncture by stylets bears many points of similarity to movement in the intact sieve tube.

I. No Polarity in Movement Initiated by Stylets

During their classical researches with cotton, MASON and MASKELL (1928) investigated the factors controlling the rate and direction of transport. They showed that the sieve tubes did not appear to exhibit any degree of polarity, for defoliation techniques revealed that transport would proceed either acropetally or basipetally in the stem, the direction being determined solely by the relative positions of sources and sinks.

In a similar manner, sieve-tube transport in willow stems, brought about due to puncture by the stylets of *Tuberolachnus*, shows no evidence of polarity. WEATHERLEY et al. (1959) sited stylets at the morphological apex and base of 40-cm-long segments of stem. Measurements of the volume flow rates and sucrose concentrations revealed no significant difference in either of these parameters between stylets established at the base when compared to those at the apex (Table 2).

Table 2. Volume flow rates and sucrose concentrations of stylet exudate obtained from the morphological apex and base of stem segments of willow 40 cm in length. L.S.D. = least significant difference. From WEATHERLEY et al. (1959)

Segment	Mean volume flow rate ($\mu l\ h^{-1}$)		L.S.D.	Mean sucrose conc. ($\mu g\ \mu l^{-1}$)		L.S.D.
	base	apex		base	apex	
1	1.19	1.21	0.82	126	130	33
2	1.99	1.74	0.77	133	135	41

II. Velocity of Transport and Specific Mass Transfer of Sucrose in Sieve Tubes Pierced by Aphid Stylets

If the puncture of sieve elements by aphids initiated processes within these cells completely divorced from the intact condition, then it seems probable that two of the most fundamental parameters of the transport system, velocity and specific mass transfer, would be markedly changed. It is possible to conceive either that puncture would damage the sieve elements, in which case the magnitude of both these parameters might be lower than in the intact system, or possibly aphids might even enhance transport by injecting some promotive substance into the phloem system (see Chapter 6).

The range of values quoted in the literature for the velocity of sieve-tube transport is remarkably wide, from a few centimeters per hour to several meters per hour (CRAFTS and CRISP, 1971). However, despite the criticisms of CANNY (1960), it appears that values between 10 and 100 cm h^{-1} are reasonable for tree species, especially in view of ZIMMERMANN'S (1969) work on "concentration ratio waves" in white ash.

Two methods have been used for assessing transport velocity in willow sieve tubes in response to stylet puncture, the first of which is indirect in that the velocity was calculated. WEATHERLEY et al. (1959) measured the dimensions of willow sieve elements, finding these to be on average 170 μm long by 23 μm in diameter, thus they were able to calculate the volume of these cells. For a moderate stylet exudation rate of 1 µl h^{-1}, this meant that some 235 sieve elements were emptied per minute, which in turn led to the conclusion that the exudate must be flowing through the pierced sieve element at a velocity of around 120 cm h^{-1} from each direction.

An experimental approach was also made by PEEL and WEATHERLEY (1962) using potted cuttings of willow. Two aphid colonies were established on these, an apical one just below the leaves, and a basal one some 30–65 cm lower down the stem. $^{14}CO_2$ was supplied to the leaves when the colonies were producing honeydew, the time taken for activity to move from the apical to the basal colony being measured. Values for the velocity of transport were found to be around 30 cm h^{-1}, well within the range measured on intact systems.

CANNY (1973) compiled data from the literature which shows that sucrose mass transfer in the intact stems (mainly of fruit or tubers) are about 4 g sucrose cm^{-2} phloem h^{-1} (see also Chapter 5). Assuming that the sieve tubes occupy one fifth of the phloem cross-sectional area (a figure which may be far too low in some species according to LAWTON and CANNY, 1970). CANNY (1973) arrived at a specific mass transfer for sucrose in these stem systems of about 20 g cm^{-2} sieve tube h^{-1} and used the data of WEATHERLEY et al. (1959) to calculate that the specific mass transfer of sucrose in a stylet-pierced sieve tube is 24 of these units, i.e. a value very similar to those found for intact plant systems. In fact this latter figure should probably be only half that which CANNY's calculations suggest; in stylet exudation, movement would normally be taking place in two directions towards the site of puncture. However, the figure of 12 g cm^{-2} sieve tubes is clearly reasonable in view of the range of data given by CANNY (1973).

From the results reviewed in this section, the conclusion must be reached that stylets initiate transport in sieve elements, the characteristics of which as far as is known are essentially the same as those of movement in intact cells.

F. The Control of Solute Loading into Sieve Elements

The observation that exudation of sap takes place through aphid stylets for considerable periods of time makes the aphid technique, apart from any considerations on the mechanism of longitudinal movement, particularly suitable for studies on the movement of solutes into the sieve elements. Since PEEL (1972b) reviewed this topic, virtually no new data have been obtained, so the following section is a condensation of that review.

I. General Considerations, Solute "Potential" and Specificity

WEATHERLEY et al. (1959) suggested that the rate of movement of a solute between the sieve elements and surrounding cells was governed by differences in the "potential" of that solute. The term potential rather than concentration was used since it is most probable that movement is an active process (PHILLIS and MASON, 1933), it being envisaged by WEATHERLEY et al. that potential is related to, though not necessarily equated with, concentration.

WEATHERLEY et al. (1959) bathed the cambial surface of an isolated bark strip, bearing an exuding stylet, with osmotica. Upon increasing the strength of the osmotic solution, the sap-flow rate from the stylets decreased, the sucrose concentration in the exudate increased, and the sucrose flux into the pierced sieve element decreased. The data shown in Fig. 3 are from such an experiment in which successive increases in sucrose concentration within the stylet exudate were brought about by the application of mannitol solutions of increasing concentration. As the sucrose potential in the sap increased, so the flux rate of this solute into the sieve elements declined.

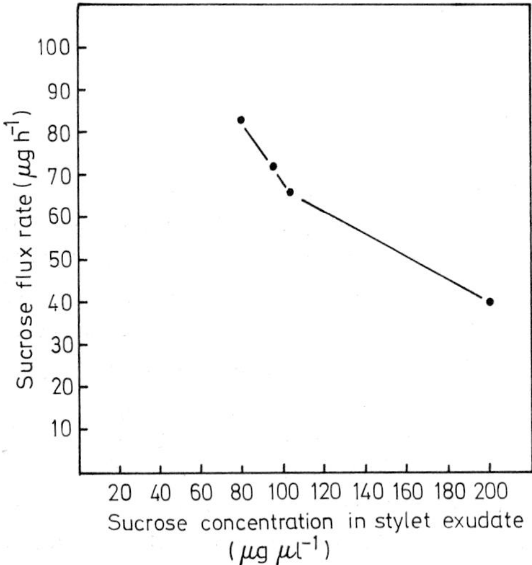

Fig. 3. Relationship between the flux rate of sucrose into willow sieve elements and the concentration of this solute in sieve-element sap obtained *via* severed stylets of *Tuberolachnus salignus*. Changes in sucrose concentration were produced by application of mannitol solutions to cambial surface of a bark strip. (From PEEL, 1972b)

Clearly therefore in some situations at least, "potential" is very closely related to solute concentration. However, PEEL (1963) showed that when the xylem of stem segments of willow were perfused with solutions of potassium, its concentration increased in the stem tissues, but not always in the sieve-tube sap.

PEEL (1972b) has given some comparative data on the movement of calcium, a relatively immobile cation in the phloem, and of the mobile cation caesium. His

Table 3. The distribution of activity (cpm) in stylet exudate and ethanolic bark extracts 24 h after the application of ^{14}C-labeled sugars to the cambial surface of a bark strip of willow. From PEEL and FORD (1968)

		Labeled sugar applied to strip		
		Sucrose	Glucose	Fructose
Stylet exudate	Organic phosphates	None	500	None
	Sucrose	5,000	12,000	5,000
	Glucose	None	None	None
	Fructose	None	None	None
Ethanolic bark extract	Organic phosphates	4,500	7,000	2,500
	Sucrose	7,000	2,000	6,500
	Glucose	13,000	24,000	13,000
	Fructose	11,000	16,000	19,500

results indicated that calcium moved into sieve elements much less readily than did caesium, i.e. the relatively long-distance immobility of the former cation was probably a consequence of its inability to enter the sieve elements, rather than of its failure to move longitudinally through the sieve tubes. This work illustrates the specificity of the sieve-element loading mechanisms. Specificity is to be expected with active mechanisms, and occurs with closely related chemical species.

PEEL and FORD (1968) applied labeled sugars to the cambial surface of willow-bark strips for several hours, then removed the excess activity by washing. Stylet exudate, obtained from the strip 24 h later, showed radioactivity which was virtually confined to sucrose, though hexoses and organic phosphates in the bark as a whole were heavily labeled (Table 3).

II. Metabolism and Solute Loading

Sucrose movement into the sieve elements appears to involve inversion by a free space invertase, the hexose moieties then traversing the plasmalemma (GARDNER and PEEL, 1971 a). By following changes in the radioactivity of certain components of the stylet exudate after application of ^{14}C-sucrose to bark strips, GARDNER and PEEL were able to infer that resynthesis of sucrose from the hexose moieties was probably accomplished by a uridine diphosphate (UDP) -uridine diphosphate-glucose (UDPG) system.

^{14}C-labeled glutamic and aspartic acids were also extensively metabolised. Much activity in the stylet exudate appeared in sucrose (GARDNER and PEEL, 1971 b).

FIELD and PEEL (1971) in a study of the movement of the chlorophenoxy herbicides into willow sieve elements, found large differences in the relative mobilities of methyl chloro-(MCPA), 2.4-dichloro (2.4-D) and 2.4.5-trichloro (2.4.5.-T) phenoxy acetic acids; MCPA was highly mobile, 2.4-D was less so, whilst 2.4.5-T had a very low relative mobility.

G. The Nature of the Longitudinal Movement Produced in Response to Stylet Puncture

Though the stylet technique is clearly useful in studying solute movement into sieve elements, the most pressing question in phloem physiology concerns the mechanism of longitudinal sieve-tube transport. The technique has not yet produced any unequivocal answers on this subject, but has opened up interesting areas of research on this topic.

I. Water Movement

Most phloem physiologists believe that transport through sieve tubes takes place as a bulk flow of solution. Indeed, it is difficult to visualize the enormous mass-transfer rates which occur in phloem being accomplished by any other means (MACROBBIE, 1971), and bulk flow is the central feature of the hypotheses of pressure flow (MÜNCH, 1930) and electroosmotic (SPANNER, 1958).

Though the phenomenon of exudation from sieve tubes, either through incisions or severed stylets (particularly the experiments detailed in Section C I) would appear to provide cogent evidence of extensive longitudinal water movement in sieve tubes, corroborative data from tracer studies with labeled water is somewhat equivocal. BIDDULPH and CORY (1957) and TRIP and GORHAM (1968b) showed movement of tritiated water in phloem, but GAGE and ARONOFF (1960), CHOI and ARONOFF (1966) could find little evidence for movement of this tracer.

All these workers employed non-exuding phloem, thus it seemed reasonable to employ the aphid technique on this problem; surely water movement should be at its height through a pierced sieve tube, for water patently exudes through the severed stylets. Accordingly PEEL et al. (1969) conducted experiments with double-chambered bark strip systems, a stylet being established on the bark below each chamber. Introduction of tritiated water and ^{14}C-labeled sugars into one of the chambers was quickly followed by the appearance of both tracers in exudate from the stylet sited below that chamber. However, though ^{14}C-activity rapidly moved into the exudate from the other stylet, tritium activity took considerably longer, small quantities only appearing after 4–6 h from tracer application. PEEL and his colleagues considered that tritium activity could have moved along the bark by diffusion in this length of time and thus suggested that a bulk flow of water might not occur in willow sieve tubes.

Of course labeled water is a difficult tracer to use, not only does it rapidly equilibrate with unlabeled water, but activity can be lost from the sieve-tube due to tritium exchange. The data of PEEL et al. (1969) could therefore be explained in these terms (in fact very recent unpublished work by COULSON at Hull has demonstrated that water labeled with ^{18}O moves more rapidly along bark strips than does water labeled with ^{3}H).

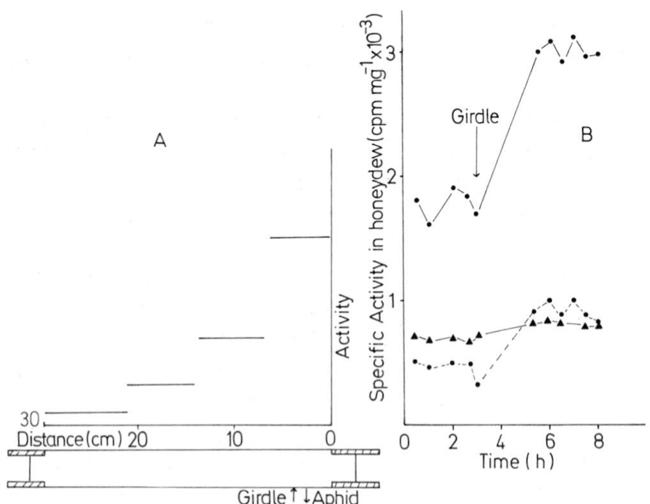

Fig. 4. (A) Diagram illustrating the procedure used to study the movement of water along the sieve tube towards the site of puncture by an aphid stylet. (B) The effect of girdling a labeled segment on the specific activities of tritium (triangles solid lines), ^{35}S (closed circles dashed lines), and ^{32}P (closed circles solid lines) in the honeydew from an aphid feeding at the high activity end. (From PEEL, 1970)

However, in a further publication, PEEL (1970) again failed to discover evidence in favor of rapid longitudinal water movement, using a technique which reduces the effect of loss of tritium activity through exchange. Gradients of tritiated water, ^{35}S-sulphate and ^{32}P-phosphate were established in isolated stem segments, a single aphid being sited at the high-activity end (Fig. 4A). Thus the aphid would excrete honeydew containing all three tracers, the activities of these being "diluted" by unlabeled solutes and water from the low activity end of the segment if a bulk flow occurred towards the point of puncture. Thus if the supply of unlabeled water and solutes to the honeydew was removed by girdling the segment near to the aphid (Fig. 4A), then the specific activities of the three tracers in the honeydew should rise. Conversely, if the honeydew was not receiving unlabeled water or solutes from beyond the girdle, then the specific activity of the label in the honeydew should remain constant.

In fact, PEEL found that although the specific activities of ^{35}S and ^{32}P in the honeydew rose after girdling, that of tritium did not (Fig. 4B). Thus it was inferred that puncture of a willow sieve element by the stylet of an aphid does not induce a rapid flux of unlabeled water along the sieve tube. However, in view of the difficulties connected with the use of tritiated water, it cannot be unequivocally claimed that a bulk flow does not occur along the sieve tube in response to puncture by a stylet. Indeed until further evidence is obtained, it must still be considered that some type of mass flow is responsible for longitudinal transport in pierced sieve tubes. (For a calculation of radial diffusional exchange of water see Appendix II).

II. Hydrostatic Pressures in Sieve Tubes

Measurements of the osmotic potential of sieve-tube sap have been performed by PEEL and WEATHERLEY (1959) using a vapor pressure micro-osmometer. Since the values obtained by these workers were in the range of 15 to 25 atm, it is clear that the sieve tube has the potential to develop considerable internal hydrostatic pressures. This observation is of some significance for the mechanism of movement; the pressure-flow hypothesis would require high pressures within the sieve tube at the source end of the system in order to move solutes over the long distances found in tree species.

Evidence that the sieve tube not only has the potential, but can actually produce high internal pressures has been provided by the work of MITTLER (1954) and PEEL (1959). These workers made measurements of the dimensions of the canal within the stylets through which the sap flows, both finding the diameter of the food canal to be between 1–2 μm, and the length to be between 1–2 mm. Now if the volume flow rate and sucrose concentration in the exudate from a given stylet are measured, and the dimensions of the canal through this stylet subsequently determined, then it is possible, assuming flow obeys the Poiseuille equation, to calculate the hydrostatic pressure within the sieve tube at the point of puncture. Calculations by both MITTLER and PEEL have given values within the range 10–30 atm.

Another feature of the sieve-tube system which has emerged from stylet studies is that the sieve tubes are not only capable of generating high internal pressures, but can maintain them in the face of considerable water stress (see Chapter 14). WEATHERLEY et al. (1959) found that perfusing the xylem of stem segments of willow or the cambial surface of bark strips with strong osmotic solutions slowed down but did not stop exudation from stylets. This observation is of some importance with regard to the situation within intact plants where high water stresses can develop.

These observations do not necessarily favor the pressure flow hypothesis; presumably all mechanisms would require that the sieve tubes do not collapse under conditions of an adverse water balance within the plant. However, they are certainly not inimical to the pressure-flow concept.

The pressure-flow hypothesis requires not only high hydrostatic pressures, but also a gradient in the direction of movement. At the present time we have no unequivocal data on whether a gradient is present. Though KAUFMAN and KRAMER (1967) could find no evidence of a pressure gradient in certain tree species, HAMMEL (1968) using a micromanometer has adduced some evidence for a gradient down the trunks of red oaks. Clearly, therefore, it would be interesting to site aphid stylets at the top and bottom of trees and to calculate the hydrostatic pressures at these points using the method previously described. Very recently ROGERS working at Hull (unpublished) has performed such studies, both on willow trees growing in the field and on long potted cuttings. The preliminary indications are that pressure gradients may exist in the presumed direction of movement, the magnitude of these possibly being as great as 1–2 atm m^{-1}.

III. The Effect of Hydrostatic Pressure Gradients in the Xylem upon Stylet Exudation

If movement through sieve tubes is indeed a mass flow along hydrostatic pressure gradients, then it might be possible to affect transport by altering the gradient. PEEL and WEATHERLEY (1963) investigated the effect of raising the hydrostatic pressure in the xylem of stem segments of willow upon exudation from the severed stylets of *Tuberolachnus*. A uniform increase in xylem pressure did indeed raise the hydrostatic pressure within the punctured sieve tube as evidenced by a rise in the volume flow from the stylets, i.e. an effect opposite to that produced by perfusing the xylem with osmotic solutions (WEATHERLEY et al., 1959). Furthermore, by raising the hydrostatic pressure in the xylem at one end of a stem segment, a rise in the rate of sap flow from a stylet, located at the other end, was observed. This result was observed in intact segments as well as in segments with severed xylem in which no possibility existed of a rise in pressure in the xylem adjacent to the stylet (Fig. 5). Although this pattern of data seems in excellent accord with a pressure-flow mechanism, in other experiments in which stylets were sited at the high-pressure end of a segment, the rate of exudation declined, i.e. there was a fall in hydrostatic pressure in the sieve tube in the region where the water potential had been raised. It was also shown that when stylets were sited at the low-pressure end of a segment, the increase in the rate of exudation was greater the longer the length of the segment. This is difficult to reconcile with a simple effect upon a pressure-flow mechanism where it would be expected that increases in the rate of stylet exudation would be proportional to the steepness of the added pressure

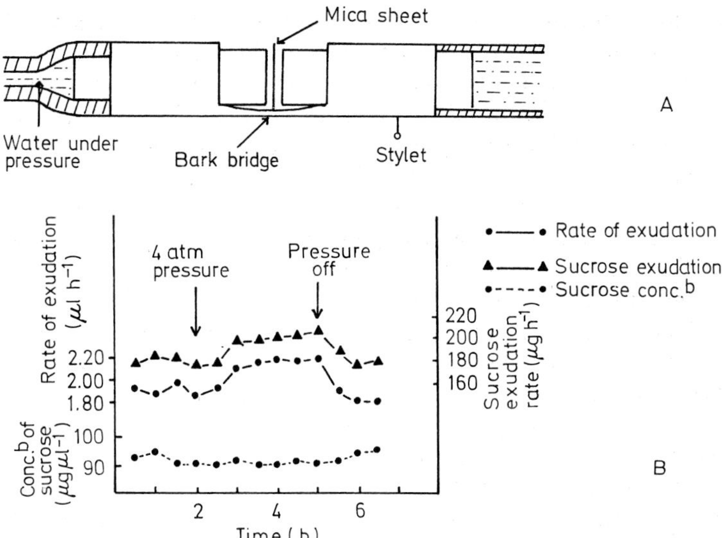

Fig. 5A and B. The effect of raising the hydrostatic pressure in the xylem of one part of a willow-stem segment on exudation from a stylet sited on another part, in the xylem of which the pressure was not raised (B). The two parts of the segment were connected only by a bark bridge (A). (From PEEL and WEATHERLEY, 1963)

gradient, i.e. exudation rates should increase proportionately more with short segments.

From the results of incision experiments, PEEL and WEATHERLEY (1963) concluded that pressure gradients in the xylem affected stylet exudation by changing the length of bark which contributed to the stylet sap, a conclusion supported by the work of PEEL (1965). It seems clear from this that pressure gradients do not act simply by enhancing a pressure-flow mechanism in the sieve tubes; some of their effects on exudation from stylets appear to be indirect and are probably complex. Thus it does not seem justified to conclude from these experiments that sieve-tube transport in willow, in response to stylet puncture, is necessarily mediated by a simple pressure-flow system.

IV. Simultaneous Bidirectional Movement

For a considerable number of years, certainly since the work of PHILLIS and MASON (1936), phloem physiologists have been concerned with the problem of simultaneous bidirectional movement in sieve tubes, i.e. the capacity of the sieve tube to conduct two solutes simultaneously in opposite directions from their respective sources to their sinks. Such a demonstration would be difficult to reconcile the mass flow hypotheses. However, despite the extensive use of radiotracers (CHEN, 1951; TRIP and GORHAM, 1968a) such an unequivocal demonstration has not been made.

The main difficulty which has to be overcome in any investigation of simultaneous bidirectional movement is the complexity of the vascular system. TRIP and GORHAM (1968a) attempted to circumvent this problem by the use of histoautoradiography, and some phloem physiologists seem to believe that they have indeed demonstrated simultaneous movement in opposite directions in the same sieve tube.

Since aphids tap single sieve elements it is possible to detect the presence, in a single sieve tube, of two tracers applied at spatially separated sites on the plant. The first to use aphids in such experiments was ESCHRICH (1967), working with *Vicia* plants and the aphid *Acyrthosiphon pisum* (Harris). The honeydew excreted by a colony fell onto a rotating disc (see Chapter 10). $NaH^{14}CO_2$ and fluorescein were applied to mature leaves, one to a leaf above the colony, the other to a leaf below it. ESCHRICH showed that a large proportion of the honeydew drops contained both tracers, from which he concluded that either simultaneous bidirectional movement had occurred, or what he termed a "homodromous loop path" had operated (see Chapter 10). He dismissed the possibility that movement of the tracers in opposite directions towards the common stylet sink had occurred, for he considered the sink "capacity" of a single aphid to be insufficient to change the direction of transport to the aphid.

Somewhat more detailed experiments were performed by HO and PEEL (1969b) using the aphid *Tuberolachnus* to sample sieve-tube sap from both 2- to 3-year-old stems and 5- to 6-week-old shoots of willow. ^{14}C and ^{3}H-labeled sugars and ^{32}P-phosphates were employed as tracers. Fig. 6 shows a typical series of experiments with young shoots in which individual drops of honeydew were collected from single aphids sited between the tracer applications points. As can be seen from the data presented in Table 4, all the honeydew samples which became labeled eventually contained both tracers and some aphids produced honeydew including the two tracers from the first drop. Thus, simultaneous bidirectional movement

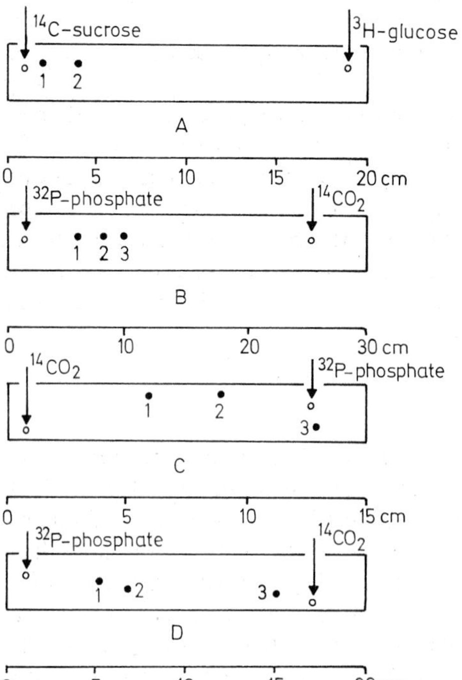

Fig. 6. Diagrams showing the position of feeding individuals of *Tuberolachnus* in relation to the tracer application sites on young willow shoots. Data from these experiments are presented in Table 4. (From HO and PEEL, 1969b)

might have occurred, though as in the case of ESCHRICH's study the aphid technique did not preclude the possibility of lateral movement between sieve tubes transporting in opposite directions. They also confirmed ESCHRICH's observation that a single aphid is only a minor sink, for some aphids (Number 3 in experiments A and C, Table 4 and Fig. 6) did not produce labeled honeydew. In one extreme case an aphid feeding only one centimeter from the site of tracer application failed to produce labeled honeydew during a period of 38 h. However, the anatomical situation is so complex that it is uncertain how meaningful these conclusions are.

Table 4. Time taken (h) from application of tracers to young willow shoots to their appearance in the honeydew of individuals of *Tuberolachnus salignus*. From HO and PEEL (1969b)

Experiment	Duration from tracer application (h)	Aphid					
		1		2		3	
		^{3}H or ^{32}P	^{14}C	^{3}H or ^{32}P	^{14}C	^{3}H or ^{32}P	^{14}C
A	28	4	4	1	25	—	—
B	24	7	6	16	10	7	1
C	24	5	3	12	12	—	—
D	24	9	7	11	11	9	7

Experiments A–D refer to those shown in Fig. 6.

V. Metabolism and Movement of Solutes

A conclusive demonstration of simultaneous bidirectional movement would eliminate the possibility that translocation is a flow of solution. A demonstration that metabolic energy is necessary for sap movement through each sieve element would eliminate the pressure-flow concept. The aphid technique is proving useful in investigations of this aspect. However, aphid techniques have their limitations, one of the major ones being the difficulty of differentiating between the effect of metabolic depressants upon longitudinal, as opposed to lateral, movement in sieve tubes. In an isolated segment-stylet system for instance, a temperature reduction or treatment with inhibitors would certainly reduce stylet exudation by affecting active solute-loading processes.

1. The Effect of Localized Low Temperatures

The first investigations on localized low temperature effects upon sieve tube transport, utilizing an aphid technique, were carried out by FORD and PEEL (1966). Willow stems (40 cm long, 2–3 years old) were used, in which a gradient of radioactive phosphate was established by introducing the label into one end of the xylem. A colony of *Tuberolachnus* was established at the high activity end, then after a period of honeydew collection with the whole of the segment at normal temperature (20° C), a portion in the middle of the segment was cooled to −1° C. From the data on the changes in honeydew specific activity induced by alteration in temperature, FORD and PEEL concluded that low temperature had a marked effect upon sieve-tube loading but little or no effect upon longitudinal transport. Indeed it seemed that this localized low-temperature treatment actually increased the length of bark contributing to the honeydew.

FORD and PEEL (1967a) investigated the effect of localized low temperature upon the transport of ^{14}C-labeled assimilates from the leaves of rooted willow cuttings. Not only were portions of 2–3-year-old stems cooled, but also lengths of 5–6-week-old leafy shoots. The surprising result was that low temperature reduced movement through leafy shoots, but appeared to enhance movement in older stems (Fig. 7). FORD and PEEL rejected the idea that this could be due to fundamental differences in the mechanism of transport in the same organ at two different stages of differentiation. Instead they based their explanation of the data upon differences in the diameter of the sieve tubes in leafy shoots (12.6 μm) and older stems (19.0 μm). Assuming a pressure-flow mechanism, the increase in sap viscosity on lowering the temperature would have a much more marked effect upon movement through the sieve tubes of leafy shoots than through those of older stems, the resistance to flow of the former being about 5 times that of the latter.

In fact, FORD and PEEL were measuring not total sugar mass transfer, but merely relative movement of the ^{14}C-label. Thus if localized low temperature affected sieve-tube loading in the cooled portion of old stems, it could also increase the contributory length of the aphid colony. This in turn could cause sugars of high specific activity

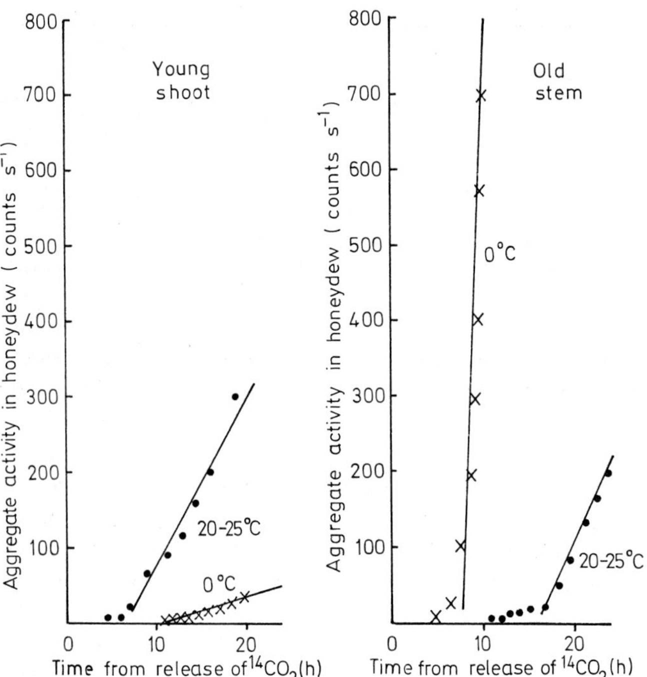

Fig. 7. Plots illustrating the effect of cooling young shoots or old stems of willow to 0° C on the relative mass transfer of ^{14}C-labeled assimilates to colonies of the aphid *Tuberolachnus*. (From FORD and PEEL, 1967a)

to move towards the colony, and the specific activity of the honeydew would rise, i.e. an effect very similar to that found by FORD and PEEL (1966) with isolated stem segments. In young, rapidly growing leafy shoots however, it is more than probable that the cells of the stem would compete as sinks for solutes, rather than become sources for an aphid colony. Thus it could well be that the reduction of ^{14}C-assimilate transport in these shoots by low temperature represents the "true" situation in that the data are not complicated by temperature effects upon solute loading systems in the cells adjacent to the sieve tubes.

GARDNER and PEEL (1972a) showed that low temperatures retard longitudinal transport in willow sieve tubes pierced by aphid stylets. By using severed stylets rather than whole aphids, these workers were able to measure the effect of localized low temperature upon the mass transfer of sucrose, ATP and potassium along the sieve tubes. Since they did not use radiotracers as an indicator of transport, their work is uncomplicated by effects upon contributory length. Even in the sieve tubes of old stems (cf. FORD and PEEL, 1967a), low temperatures markedly reduced the mass transfer of sucrose and the other solutes towards the stylet (Table 5).

Table 5. The effect of cooling a 10 cm portion of an isolated stem segment or leafy cutting of willow to 0° C for a period of 24 h, on volume flow rate, sucrose, ATP and potassium concentrations and fluxes from severed stylets of the aphid *Tuberolachnus salignus*. From GARDNER and PEEL (1972a)

Experiment		Volume flow rate ($\mu l\ h^{-1}$)	Concentration ($\mu g\ \mu l^{-1}$)			Flux ($\mu g\ h^{-1}$)		
			Sucrose	ATP	K^+	Sucrose	ATP	K^+
1.	A	1.33	73	0.77	2.9	96	1.02	3.9
	B	1.33	34	0.71	1.5	45	0.95	2.0
2.	A	1.11	56	1.50	4.6	62	1.67	5.1
	B	1.02	31	1.41	3.8	31	1.43	3.9
3.	A	1.54	80	1.30	2.7	123	2.00	4.2
	B	1.34	50	1.55	4.4	67	1.76	5.0
4.	A	2.07	143	0.31	4.4	148	0.34	4.6
	B	2.17	89	0.31	3.9	97	0.35	4.2

A—before cooling, B—during cooling. Experiments 1 and 2 performed on isolated stem segments, 3 and 4 on leafy cuttings.

For technical reasons, a 5 cm length of the bark immediately around the stylets had to be left at normal temperatures. Possibly the low-temperature treatment (0° C) virtually stopped longitudinal transport in the cooled bark but the stylets did not stop exuding because they were supplied with solutes from the short length of uncooled bark in which they were sited.

2. Respiratory Breakdown of Sugars in Transporting Sieve Tubes

An interesting problem arising in connection with the relationship of metabolic energy to transport, is that of the site of energy production. Data from a number of studies show the phloem to be a tissue of high metabolic potential (cf. KURSANOV, 1963). Of course, this does not necessarily mean that large quantities of energy are directly necessary for movement; associated processes such as lateral solute transfer are undoubtedly vigorous with an energy requirement. Just as it is not proper to argue from a metabolically active phloem to an active longitudinal transport mechanism, so it is unjustified to argue in the opposite sense. One cannot conclude that an energy-requiring mechanism does not exist from observations which suggest the sieve element is a metabolically moribund cell. There is no reason why energy could not be supplied, for instance, by the companion cells. Therefore, the question of the metabolic potential of the sieve element is a somewhat academic one, though if an answer could be found it might prove to be very useful.

With this aim in mind, COULSON and PEEL (1968) examined the respiratory breakdown of labeled sugars in willow phloem. They sampled both sieve-tube sap (obtained as aphid honeydew), and the respiratory gas given off by the stem after $^{14}CO_2$ application to the leaves of rooted cuttings. If the labeled sugars were respired in transit through the sieve elements, then the slopes of the increase in radioactivity in the sieve-tube sap and respiratory CO_2 should match. On the other hand, if these radioactive sugars were respired in phloem cells adjacent to the sieve elements, then the slope of the respiratory gas activity plot should be less than that of the honeydew. However, the results of this study were not clear.

In other similar experiments, COULSON and PEEL (1971) investigated the effect of temperature upon the respiration of labeled sugars in willow phloem. They demonstrated that in both young, leafy shoots and old stems, respiration of the translocated sugars did not cease at temperatures as low as 0.5° C. Moreover, in the old stems, the relative rate of breakdown at this temperature was greater than at 25° C. It is difficult to draw any detailed inferences from these observations, but at all events it is clear that even at temperatures around 0° C, energy is available if required to power an active transport process in the sieve tubes.

3. ATP in Stylet Exudate

Analyses of stylet exudate from willow by GARDNER and PEEL (1969) showed ATP levels in this to be as high as 1 $\mu g\ \mu l^{-1}$. This confirmed the earlier findings of KLUGE and ZIEGLER (1964) of ATP in sieve-tube exudate from trees. ATP appears to be a normal constituent of the sap, its level in the stylet exudate is constant over periods of hours, and it can readily be transported through the sieve tubes (GARDNER and PEEL, 1972b). This does not necessarily mean that its function is to power an active transport mechanism, it may well be required for other purposes. Whatever its role in the sieve tubes, it has a rapid turnover. Both KLUGE et al. (1970) working with stylet exudate from *Salix triandra* stems, and GARDNER and PEEL (1972b) using bark strips of *Salix viminalis*, have demonstrated rapid incorporation of labeled phosphate into the sieve-tube ATP. Moreover enzymes able to mediate this incorporation must be present in the stylet sap for GARDNER and PEEL (1972b) have shown *in vitro* incorporation of ^{32}P-phosphate into ATP. Further, GARDNER and PEEL (1972b), have measured ATP/ADP ratios as high as 2:1 in stylet exudate from willow. These observations support the idea of an "active" role for ATP, i.e. it is probably not just a solute in transit through the sieve tubes.

4. Metabolic Inhibitors and Stylet Exudation

The use of metabolic inhibitors in the study of longitudinal sieve tube movement in response to stylet puncture, has not so far proved a very useful technique. Since in stem and bark strips storage cells supply solutes to the stylet sink, if the whole of the tissue is treated with metabolic inhibitors, the exudation rate will be reduced by interference with the active sieve-tube loading processes and the plugging of sieve tubes is probable also.

The relationships of the stylet sink to its sources in willow are, therefore, too complex for the application of inhibitors to provide a satisfactory method of attacking the problem of the mechanism of transport. If the inhibitor were applied between the stylet and the leaves, and affected longitudinal movement, there could be a switchover in the source of solutes from the leaves to the storage cells of the stem. No effect upon the volume flow rate or concentration of the exudate would be shown, unless the inhibitor actually moved down the stem to the site at which the stylet was established. Furthermore, one is never certain that an inhibitor has penetrated into the functioning sieve elements.

Stylet exudation is very sensitive to certain inhibitors, such as 10^{-4} dinitrophenol, phloridzin and cyanide at 10^{-4} M to 10^{-6} M which slow down or stop exudation completely and irreversibly (PEEL and WEATHERLEY, 1963). But in view of what has been said, it can hardly be concluded from these experiments that longitudinal sieve-tube transport is the process primarily affected.

Inhibitors were used in conjunction with a stylet technique by GARDNER and PEEL (1972b) who were particularly concerned with the role of the sieve-tube ATP in transport. They tried to determine whether certain inhibitors would simultaneously affect both exudation and ATP levels using the antibiotic oligomycin which stops energy from oxidative phosphorylation being utilized in the formation of ATP. It caused abrupt stoppage of exudation within 4–6 h from application when applied to a bark strip at a concentration of 20 μg ml^{-1}. Inhibition could be reversed by replacing the inhibitor with water, or better, with solutions of ATP. Similar effects were shown with dinitrophenol at a concentration of 10^{-4} M. Sodium fluoride at a concentration of 10^{-3} M frequently did not have any discernible effect upon exudation. In certain experiments it was shown that exudation could still proceed even in the apparent absence of ATP in the sieve tube (Table 6). GARDNER and PEEL (1972b) summarized their results as follows: though ATP is ultimately necessary

Table 6. The effect of applying 10^{-3} M sodium fluoride solution to the cambial surface of a bark strip of willow, on volume flow rate and ATP concentration in stylet sap. From GARDNER and PEEL (1972b)

Time (h)	Volume flow rate (μl h^{-1})	ATP conc. in stylet sap (μg $μl^{-1}$)
0–1	0.99	0.70
1–2	0.81	0.96
2–3	1.61	1.20
NaF applied		
3–4	0.80	0.40
4–5	0.42	none detected
5–6	very slow	—

for stylet exudation (at least in so far as lateral transport is concerned), ATP may not have to be present within the sieve-tube sap. They concluded that ATP in the sap was formed by glycolysis rather than in oxidative phosphorylation because fluoride reduced its concentration, whilst oligomycin and dinitrophenol did not.

H. Conclusions

The tapping of sieve elements by aphid stylets initiates processes in these cells which are not localized around the point of puncture, but extend longitudinally for considerable distances. Movement towards stylets involves long distance transport in sieve tubes, and changes in the exudate are intimately and immediately related to changes in the primary source of sugars, i.e. the assimilating leaves. It has been shown that though stylet exudation from sieve tubes is an unnatural state, it causes transport in the phloem conduits at velocity and specific mass-transfer values within the generally accepted range for intact phloem systems.

Stylet techniques should be of particular value in providing answers to the seemingly intractable problems found in the field of phloem physiology. However, stylets present difficulties, both technically and in the interpretation of data from their use, some of these being general in phloem work, others more particularly associated with aphid studies. In the latter category are included those experiments with low temperatures and inhibitors, in which it is particularly difficult to differentiate between effects upon lateral as opposed to longitudinal movement. If some way could be discovered to get around this problem effectively, then stylets would prove immensely more valuable.

Though aphid work has been proceeding in the hands of a number of investigators for some twenty years, I am certain the technique still has much to offer. It is possible to visualize many more studies on metabolic processes in sieve tubes in relation both to loading and to longitudinal transport. Work on hydrostatic pressure gradients in the phloem conduits is still in its infancy and much more remains to be done. Moreover, stylets could be of some value in the area of sieve-element ultrastructure. It would be most interesting if someone could produce a picture with the electronmicroscope of a sieve element, which at the time of sampling had been pierced by an exuding stylet. At least we should then know without any shadow of doubt that the particular element had been translocating prior to its fixation.

References

BIDDULPH, O., CORY, R.: An analysis of translocation in the phloem of the bean plant using THO, ^{32}P and $^{14}CO_2$. Plant Physiol. (Lancaster) **32**, 608–619 (1957).

CANNY, M.J.: The rate of translocation. Biol. Rev. Cambridge Phil. Soc. **35**, 507–532 (1960).

CANNY, M.J.: Phloem translocation. Cambridge: University Press 1973.

CHEN, S.L.: Simultaneous movement of ^{32}P and ^{14}C in opposite directions in phloem tissue. Am. J. Botany **38**, 203–211 (1951).

CHOI, I.C., ARONOFF, S.: Photosynthate transport using tritiated water. Plant Physiol. (Lancaster) **41**, 1119–1129 (1966).

COULSON, C.L., PEEL, A.J.: Respiration of ^{14}C-labeled assimilates in stems of willow. Ann. Botany N.S. **32**, 867–876 (1968).

COULSON, C.L., PEEL, A.J.: The effect of temperature on the respiration of ^{14}C-labeled sugars in stems of willow. Ann. Botany N.S. **35**, 9–15 (1971).

CRAFTS, A.S.: Phloem anatomy, exudation, and transport of organic nutrients in cucurbits. Plant Physiol. (Lancaster) **7**, 183–225 (1932).

CRAFTS, A.S., CRISP, C.E.: Phloem transport in plants. San Francisco: Freeman and Co. 1971.

ESCHRICH, W.: Bidirektionelle Translokation in Siebröhren. Planta **73**, 37–49 (1967).

ESCHRICH, W.: Translokation radioactivmarkierter Indolyl-3-Essigsäure in Siebröhren von *Vicia faba*. Planta **78**, 144–157 (1968).

EVERT, R.F., ESCHRICH, W., MEDLER, J.T., ALFIERI, F.J.: Observations on the penetration of linden branches by stylets of the aphid *Longistigma caryae*. Am. J. Botany **55**, 860–874 (1968).

FIELD, R.J., PEEL, A.J.: The movement of growth regulators and herbicides into the sieve elements of willow. New Phytologist **70**, 997–1003 (1971).

FORD, J., PEEL, A.J.: The contributory length of sieve tubes in isolated segments of willow and the effect on it of low temperatures. J. Exptl. Botany **17**, 522–523 (1966).

FORD, J., PEEL, A.J.: Preliminary experiments on the effect of temperature on the movement of ^{14}C-labeled assimilates through the phloem of willow. J. Exptl. Botany **18**, 406–415 (1967a).

FORD, J., PEEL, A.J.: The movement of sugars into the sieve elements of bark strips of willow. I. Metabolism during transport. J. Exptl. Botany **18**, 607–619 (1967b).

GAGE, R.S., ARONOFF, S.: Translocation III: Experiments with Carbon-14, Chlorine-36 and Hydrogen-3. Plant Physiol. (Lancaster) **35**, 53–64 (1960).

GARDNER, D.C.J., PEEL, A.J.: ATP in sieve-tube sap from willow. Nature **222**, 774 (1969).

GARDNER, D.C.J., PEEL, A.J.: Transport of sugars into the sieve elements of willow. Phytochemistry **10**, 2621–2625 (1971a).

GARDNER, D.C.J., PEEL, A.J.: Metabolism and transport of ^{14}C-labeled glutamic and aspartic acids in the phloem of willow. Phytochemistry **10**, 2385–2387 (1971b).

GARDNER, D.C.J., PEEL, A.J.: The effect of low temperature on sucrose, ATP and potassium concentrations and fluxes in the sieve tubes of willow. Planta **102**, 348–356 (1972a).

GARDNER, D.C.J., PEEL, A.J.: Some observations on the role of ATP in sieve tube translocation. Planta **107**, 217–226 (1972b).

HAMMEL, H.T.: Measurement of turgor pressure and its gradient in the phloem of oak. Plant Physiol. (Lancaster) **43**, 1042–1048 (1968).

HILL, G.P.: A technique for the study of the physiology of the sieve tube. M.Sc. thesis, University of Nottingham 1955.

HO, L.C., PEEL, A.J.: The relative contributions of sugars from assimilating leaves and stem storage cells to the sieve tube sap in willow cuttings. Physiol. Plantarum **22**, 379–385 (1969a).

HO, L.C., PEEL, A.J.: Investigation of bidirectional movement of tracers in sieve tubes of *Salix viminalis* L. Ann. Botany N.S. **33**, 833–844 (1969b).

HOAD, G.V.: (+)-Abscissin II, ((+)-Dormin) in phloem exudate of willow. Life Sci. **6**, 1113–1118 (1967).

HOAD, G.V., PEEL, A.J.: Studies on the movement of solutes between the sieve tubes and surrounding tissues in willow. I. Interference between solutes and rate of translocation measurements. J. Exptl. Botany **16**, 433–451 (1965).

KAUFMANN, M.R., KRAMER, P.J.: Phloem water relations and translocation. Plant Physiol. (Lancaster) **42**, 191–194 (1967).

KENNEDY, J.S., MITTLER, T.E.: A method for obtaining phloem sap *via* the mouth-parts of aphids. Nature **171**, 528 (1953).

KLUGE, M., BECKER, D., ZIEGLER, H.: Untersuchungen über ATP und andere organische Phosphorverbindungen im Siebröhrensaft von *Yucca flaccida* und *Salix triandra*. Planta **91**, 68–79 (1970).

KLUGE, M., ZIEGLER, H.: Der ATP-Gehalt der Siebröhrensäfte von Laubbäumen. Planta **61**, 167–177 (1964).

KOLLMANN, R., DÖRR, I.: Lokalisierung funktionstüchtiger Siebzellen bei *Juniperus communis* mit Hilfe von Aphiden. Z. Pflanzenphysiol. **55**, 131–141 (1966).

KURSANOV, A.L.: Metabolism and the transport of organic substances in the phloem. Advan. Bot. Res. **1**, 209–274 (1963).

LAWTON, J.R.S., CANNY, M.J.: The proportion of sieve elements in the phloem of some tropical trees. Planta **95**, 351–354 (1970).

LEPP, N.W., PEEL, A.J.: Patterns of translocation and metabolism of ^{14}C-labeled IAA in the phloem of willow. Planta **96**, 62–73 (1971).

MACROBBIE, E.: Phloem translocation. Facts and mechanisms: a comparative survey. Biol. Rev. Cambridge Phil. Soc. **46**, 429–481 (1971).

MASON, T.G., MASKELL, E.J.: Studies on the transport of carbohydrates in the cotton plant. II. The factors determining the rate and the direction of movement of sugars. Ann. Botany (London) **42**, 571–636 (1928).

MILBURN, J.A.: Phloem exudation from caster bean: Induction by massage. Planta **95**, 272–276 (1970).

MITTLER, T.E.: Studies on the feeding and nutrition of *Tuberolachnus salignus* (Gmelin). Ph.D thesis, University of Cambridge 1954.

MITTLER, T.E.: Studies on the feeding and nutrition of *Tuberolachnus salignus* (Gmelin). II. The nitrogen and sugar composition of ingested phloem sap and excreted honeydew. J. Exptl. Biol. **35**, 74–84 (1958).

MUNCH, E.: Die Stoffbewegungen in der Pflanze. Jena: G. Fischer 1930.

PEEL, A.J.: Studies on the physiology of the sieve tube in higher plants. Ph.D thesis University of Nottingham 1959.

PEEL, A.J.: The movement of ions from the xylem solution into the sieve tubes of willow. J. Exptl. Botany **14**, 438–447 (1963).

PEEL, A.J.: The effect of changes in the diffusion potential of the xylem water on sieve-tube exudation from isolated stem segments. J. Exptl. Botany **16**, 249–260 (1965).

PEEL, A.J.: Further evidence for the relative immobility of water in sieve tubes of willow. Physiol. Plantarum **23**, 667–672 (1970).

PEEL, A.J.: The control of the rate and direction of phloem transport. In: Crop processes in controlled environments (eds. A.R. REES et al.), p. 265–278. London: Academic Press 1972a.

PEEL, A.J.: The control of solute movement into sieve elements. Pestic. Sci. **3**, 631–641 (1972b).

PEEL, A.J., FIELD, R.J., COULSON, C.L., GARDNER, D.C.J.: Movement of water and solutes in sieve tubes of willow in response to puncture by aphid stylets. Evidence against a mass flow of solution. Physiol. Plantarum **22**, 768–775 (1969).

PEEL, A.J., FORD, J.: The movement of sugars into the sieve elements of bark strips of willow. II. Evidence for two pathways from the bathing solution. J. Exptl. Botany **19**, 370–380 (1968).

PEEL, A.J., HO, L.C.: Colony size of *Tuberolachnus salignus* (Gmelin) in relation to mass transport of ^{14}C-labeled assimilates from the leaves in willow. Physiol. Plantarum **23**, 1033–1038 (1970).

PEEL, A.J., WEATHERLEY, P.E.: Composition of sieve-tube sap. Nature **184**, 1955–1956 (1959).

PEEL, A.J., WEATHERLEY, P.E.: Studies in sieve-tube exudation through aphid mouthparts. I. The effects of light and girdling. Ann. Botany N.S. **26**, 633–646 (1962).

PEEL, A.J., WEATHERLEY, P.E.: Studies in sieve-tube exudation through aphid mouthparts. II. The effects of pressure gradients in the wood and metabolic inhibitors. Ann. Botany N.S. **27**, 197–211 (1963).

PHILLIS, E., MASON, T.G.: Studies on the transport of carbohydrates in the cotton plant. III. The polar distribution of sugar in the foliage leaf. Ann. Botany **47**, 585–634 (1933).

PHILLIS, E., MASON, T.G.: Further studies on transport in the cotton plant. IV. On the simultaneous movement of solutes in opposite directions through the phloem. Ann. Botany (London) **50**, 161–174 (1936).

SPANNER, D.C.: The translocation of sugar in sieve tubes. J. Exptl. Botany **9**, 332–342 (1958).

TAMMES, P.M.L., VAN DIE, J.: Studies on phloem exudation from *Yucca flaccida* Haw., I. Some observations on the phenomenon of bleeding and the composition of the exudate. Acta Botan. Neerl. **13**, 76–83 (1964).

TINGLEY, M.A.: Concentration gradients in plant exudates with reference to the mechanism of translocation. Am. J. Bot. **31**, 30–38 (1944).

TRIP, P., GORHAM, P.R.: Bidirectional translocation of sugars in sieve tubes of squash plants. Plant Physiol. (Lancaster) **43**, 877–882 (1968a).

TRIP, P., GORHAM, P.R.: Translocation of sugar and tritiated water in squash plants. Plant Physiol. (Lancaster) **43**, 1845–1849 (1968b).

WEATHERLEY, P.E., PEEL, A.J., HILL, G.P.: The physiology of the sieve tube. Preliminary investigations using aphid mouth parts. J. Exptl. Botany **10**, 1–16 (1959).

ZIEGLER, H., KLUGE, M.: Die Nucleinsäuren und ihre Bausteine in Siebröhrensaft von *Robinia pseudoacacia* L. Planta **58**, 144–153 (1962).

ZIMMERMANN, M.H.: Translocation of organic substances in trees. I. The nature of the sugars in the sieve-tube exudate of trees. Plant Physiol. (Lancaster) **32**, 288–291 (1957a).

ZIMMERMANN, M.H.: Translocation of organic substances in trees. II. On the translocation mechanism in the phloem of white ash. Plant Physiol. (Lancaster) **32**, 399–404 (1957b).

ZIMMERMANN, M.H.: How sap moves in trees. Sci. Am. **208**, 132–142 (1963).

ZIMMERMANN, M.H.: Translocation velocity and specific mass transfer in sieve tubes of *Fraxinus americana* L. Planta **84**, 272–278 (1969).

8. Phloem Exudation from Monocotyledonous Axes

J. VAN DIE and P.M.L. TAMMES

A. Introduction

The peculiarity of some groups of woody monocotyledons of producing sugar-rich exudates after wounding of certain stem tissues has been known from time immemorial to the populations of tropical areas all over the world. They made use of this property and often set up local industries for the production of sugar and alcoholic beverages. Such is the use in Asia of palms of the genera *Arenga, Borassus, Caryota, Cocos, Corypha, Nypa* and *Phoenix*, in Africa of *Elaeis* and *Raphia* and in South America of *Copernicia, Jubaea* and *Mauritia*. The only other monocotyledonous plant group outside the family of the Palmae known to be thus utilized is the genus *Agave* (Agavaceae), while also at least one species of the genus *Yucca*—also belonging to the Agavaceae, namely *Y. flaccida* HAW.—produces a similar juice experimentally.

The fresh sweet juice from palms is called *toddy* in India and several parts of Malaya, and *tuba* in the Philippines. Palm sugar is made by boiling and evaporating the unfermented palm sap in open pans in much the same way as maple sugar is prepared in North America. The beverage resulting from the distillation of fermented juice (*sagoer* in Indonesia) is called *arrack* in India, Malaya and Indonesia, and *alak* in the Philippines.

Production data show that during the first decades of this century, hundreds of thousands of tons of palm sugar were produced annually in Southeast Asia and even exported to other countries. In later years the economic significance of toddy as a source of refined sugar gradually declined (CHILD, 1964). Nevertheless the production of fermented toddy remains very profitable, though often limited by legislation (WOODROOF, 1970).

During the fiscal year 1910, over 90 million l of palm exudate were distilled in the Philippines (GIBBS, 1911). In 1916 the production of palm sugar on the Indonesian islands Java and Madura amounted to about 40 million kg (HEYNE, 1927, 1950). In India, palm sugar was annually produced to the extent of 500,000 tons (MORRIS, 1920). In the Madras Presidency (India) annually about 1.2 million coconut trees were tapped for fermented or sweet toddy (PATEL, 1938). 36 million l of coconut toddy were handled by 9 distilleries in Ceylon in 1952 (WOODROOF, 1970).

It is remarkable that—with some exceptions (e.g. FREY-WYSSLING 1929, 1945; KRAMER, 1949; HUBER, 1953; ZIMMERMANN and BROWN, 1971)—this bleeding phenomenon has hardly attracted the attention of plant physiologists, in contrast to most bleeding phenomena, which can be studied in temperate regions of the world. As a result most plant physiology treatises either ignore or hardly mention bleeding from palms or agaves, although they deal extensively with the very much less substantial bleeding following incisions in the phloem of some temperate trees, with exudates from aphid stylets, or with the xylem exudates from the root systems of many herbaceous plants after decapitation. Apparently plant physiology, like plant anatomy (cf TOMLINSON, 1970), suffers from being mainly practised outside the tropics, indissolubly bound to the relatively scarce and less diverse number of objects available in temperate regions. The objectives of this chapter are the following: to present for the first time a review of the scattered, mainly older literature on the subject; and more intensively, to direct attention to the unravelling of the physiological background of the bleeding phenomenon in question, and to experiments with *Yucca flaccida* carried out in the last twelve years, that have demonstrated clearly the sieve-tube origin of the exudates mentioned. The study of these exudates, therefore, is actually a study of the physiology of vascular bundles and of phloem metabolism. It may throw its own light on present-day problems of sieve-tube translocation.

B. Exudation from Wounded Palms and *Agaves*

I. Sugar-Rich Saps Collected in Tropical and Subtropical Areas

1. History and Methods Applied

a) Palms. The tapping of sugar-rich juices from palms in order to make sugar or fermented beverages was already known in ancient times. The first known written records of the use of such saps are medical Sanskrit texts. In a script from the first centuries AD, an alcoholic beverage made from *Phoenix* is mentioned (Sutrasthana-Section, Chapter 45, Verse 174). In a Tamil script from Southern India, probably from the 6th century AD, the same is mentioned for *Cocos* (Manimekalai, Chapter 3, Verses 98–99). From old Chinese literature of the Tang Dynasty (618–906), a period in which the Chinese had contacts with the Indonesian island of Java, the following translation is quoted from GROENEVELDT (1880): "Wine is made out of the flowers of the coconut tree; the flowers of this tree are more than three feet long and as large as a man's arm, they are cut and the juice is collected and made into wine, which is sweet and intoxicating" (cf. BURKILL, 1935). The description of the flowers fits the unopened spathe which is still used for tapping today.

MARCO POLO, who in 1293 stayed for some time on the Indonesian island of Sumatra (MARCO POLO, ed. 1972), mentions the tapping of a palm, which according to his description was almost certainly *Arenga saccharifera*. This palm is still the most tapped tree in the Malaysian area.

RUMPHIUS (1741) gives a detailed description of tapping of *Cocos, Arenga* and *Borassus* and mentions tapping of *Nypa*. In tapping, the whole young inflorescence or its stalk are used. In *Cocos* the entire spathe is used before opening, or the enwrapping bracts are carefully removed and the inflorescence (s.s.) tied with a few strings. In *Arenga, Nypa* and *Corypha* the stalks of the inflorescences are used; in *Arenga* only of the male ones. Tapping of the upper stem parts after removal of parts of the foliage is carried out in India with wild and cultivated *Phoenix*, in the Philippines with *Corypha*, and in African countries with *Raphia*.

A remarkable procedure has been described by DARWIN (1845) for palms in Chile. The stems of *Jubaea* species were first cut down, the leaves were lopped off, and then the sap was tapped from the apex of the felled stem. KOORDERS (1898) describes a similar procedure for *Arenga* in the Indonesian island of Celebes (Sulawesi), but this was undoubtedly an exceptional case. In Brazil, sap is tapped from holes made into the stem of *Mauritia* during the development of inflorescence (WARBURG, 1922).

All tapping procedures in palms have one thing in common: it is essential to renew the exuding wound by shaving off a thin slice of a few mm thick once or several times a day. If this is not done, flow stops.

The preparation of the plant parts to be tapped shows some variation: sap can appear directly after wounding without any manipulation, but regular renewal of the wound surface is usually necessary (DARWIN, 1845 for *Jubaea;* MOLISCH, 1898, and TAMMES, 1933 for *Cocos;* BOSE, 1927 for *Phoenix;* GIBBS, 1911 for *Corypha*). Sometimes the sap exudes immediately after wounding, as mentioned by GIBBS (1911) for *Corypha*. Usually, however, it takes a few days before bleeding starts: 3–4 days in *Corypha* (TAMMES, 1933), 4–5 days in *Cocos* (MOLISCH, 1898), or a week in *Phoenix* (BOSE, 1927). Very often the plant parts to be tapped receive a special treatment before wounding, consisting of kneading or pounding at regular intervals. It may take up to a month before a coconut spathe (in Ceylon) is ready for tapping (BROWNING and SYMONS, 1916). In Celebes the stalk of an *Arenga* inflorescence is beaten at regular intervals with a wooden stick. From time to time small incisions are made to see if any sap comes out, and as soon as it occurs the inflorescence is cut from its stalk and tapping is started (TAMMES, 1933). In India wounds in *Cocos* are pounded and smeared with clay or mucilage from certain leaves (PATEL, 1938). In more modern works full descriptions of the method of collecting palm exudate and the uses of the toddy, have been given by NATHANAEL (1955), MENON and PANDALAI (1958), HODGE (1963) and by CHILD (1964).

b) Agaves. In the highlands of Mexico, Agaves are cultivated for tapping. The custom appears to be very old and was known to the Aztecs when the Spaniards arrived (EGELING, 1895). The main species used is *Agave salmiana* OTTO, in several varieties (BERGER, 1915). SÁNCHEZ-MARROQUÍN and HOPE (1953) mention *Agave atrovirens* and *A. americana* as main producers of the "aquamiel" or its fermentation product ("pulque"); the alcoholic beverage "tequila" is obtained by distillation of the fermented juice of *A. tequilana*.

Plants can be tapped 7 years (usually 8–10 years) after planting, when they have reached full maturity. An entrance is cut through the spiny leaves, the central spike with leaves is destroyed, and the plant is left for a year. Then a hollow basin is made in the heart of the plant and tapping is started. With the "respador"—a spoon-like implement with a sharp edge—the wall of the basin is scraped every time the sap is collected, usually three times a day (HOUGH, 1908).

In Mexico about 1,500 to 2,000 farms mainly or exclusively produce pulque. A reliable estimate of their annual production report 400–500 million l (LÜCK, 1968).

The manner of tapping Agaves implies that even freshly-collected aquamiel may be slightly fermented as the wall of the basin in which it is collected is far from sterile. The presence of some lactic acid (SÁNCHEZ-MARROQUÍN and HOPE, 1953) is readily explained by the activity of *Lactobacillus* species "naturally" present in the juice.

2. Duration and Amounts of Sap Flow

Darwin (1845) writes that from a cut-down palm stem (*Jubaea*) 90 gallons (409 l) can be obtained during a tapping period of several months. From the stem apex of *Corypha elata* ROXB. the astonishing amount of 45.2 l per day was reported by GIBBS (1911); during the tapping period of 132 days he registered 2,699 l of sap from one tree. BOSE (1927) gives a maximum of 19 l per day from the stem of *Phoenix*. Sap flow starts slowly in *Cocos* and *Arenga*, increases to a maximum and then gradually decreases again. From *Cocos*, of which successive spathes are tapped, each lasting for about a month, average production records are given for 8 trees in Kuala Lumpur, Malaya, by MARSDEN and SKILTON (1931). For the first 100 days the average yield was 3.2 pints (1.8 l) per spathe per day. For the second period this value was 2.1 pints (1.2 l). The total average was 2.6 pints (1.5 l) per day per spathe.

In *Arenga* only a limited number of inflorescences can be tapped during the lifetime of the tree, but the daily harvest of exudate is large. TAMMES (1933) gave a maximum of 5.96 l per day from a single stalk. The tapping period was 62 days and the average 3.3 l per day. Larger values, however, are also reported for *Arenga*. BARNABY LAUTIER (quoted by HEYNE, 1927, 1950) gave a total average of 5.5 to 7 l per day. The tapping period of *Arenga* depends on the thickness of the slices that are shaved off the wound. The tapping period can be extended as long as 6 months.

Fewer data are available for *Agave*. MOLISCH (1916) reported that one plant can yield up to 1,100 l of sap. A good producer yields 45 gallons (204 l) of "aquamiel" during a tapping period of three months (EGELING, 1895). LÜCK (1968) mentioned a daily production of 5–8 l of juice during the 4 to 5-month season.

II. The Use of *Yucca flaccida* in Experimental Studies on the Bleeding Phenomenon

1. The Taxonomic Status of the Genera *Yucca* and *Agave*

The genera *Yucca* and *Agave* were formerly placed in different families, the *Liliaceae sensu* KRAUSE (subfamily *Dracenoideae)* and the *Amaryllidaceae* sensu PAX and HOFFMANN (subfamily *Agavoideae*) respectively (ENGLER-PRANTL, 1930). However, both genera have many characteristics in common. They have an almost identical chromosome pattern with 5 pairs of large and 25 pairs of small chromosomes (MCKELVEY and SAX, 1933). Phytochemical evidence also favors a close relationship between *Yucca* and *Agave* (e.g. their sapogenins possess C-27 steroid skeletons; HEGNAUER, 1963). HUTCHINSON (1959) placed both genera in the new family of the Agavaceae, whose representatives originally all occur in arid regions of the tropics and sub-tropics, although some of them, e.g. *Yucca flaccida* HAW. can also be cultivated in a temperate climate. Although the genera *Agave* and *Yucca* belong to different subfamilies of the Agavaceae, the exudation studies reported in this chapter strongly support their close mutual relationship. HUTCHINSON regards the Agavaceae "as a half-way house between the Liliaceous stock and the climax group of the palmae". One could raise the question whether the large degree of similarity of the bleeding process of *Yucca* and *Agave* on the one hand and that of the Palmae on the other, can also act as physiological evidence for a more close taxonomic relationship between these two plant groups.

2. Methods of Tapping Used

a) Attached Inflorescences. The method of tapping *Yucca* inflorescences still attached to the plants has changed somewhat since the first experiments reported by TAMMES and VAN DIE (1964). When, in the early summer, the *Yucca* plants growing outside start flowering and the young inflorescence has obtained a height of about 60 cm, its bracts and buds are removed with the exception of the apical 10 cm. The inflorescence stalk is bent and the upper end fixed horizontally and left thus for a day. The next day the 10 cm tip is cut off and the stalk end inserted into a test tube of sufficient width placed in a plastic bag, and the whole placed in a Dewar bottle filled with crushed ice (Fig. 1). Sometimes exudation starts immediately but slowly,

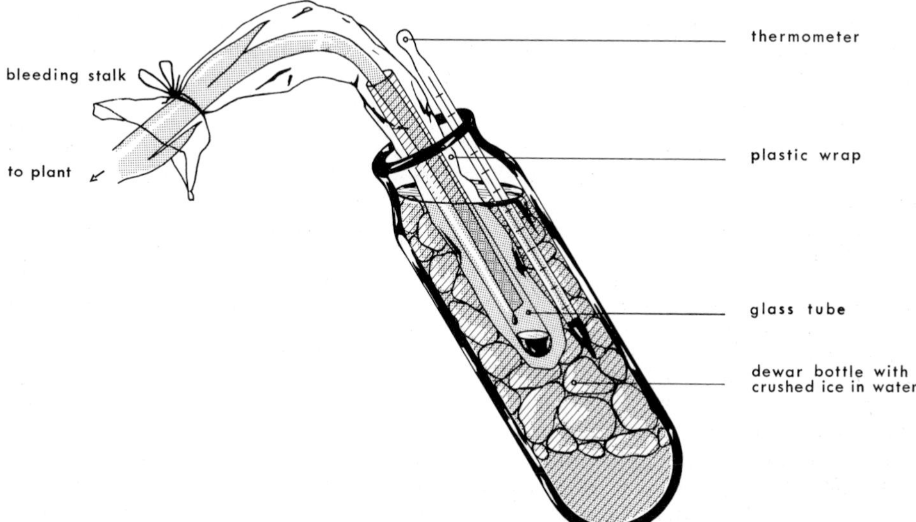

Fig. 1. Cooling an exuding stalk end of a *Yucca* plant (TAMMES et al., 1969)

but in other cases it may take as long as 48 h before the first drops can be collected. The flow rate increases to a maximum within a few days. Stalks can be tapped continuously for about three weeks, provided slices of a few mm thickness are cut off twice a day. The length of the tapping period is determined by the length of the inflorescence part that remains attached to the plant and eventually becomes too short for cooling.

Each time a fresh slice is cut off the wound surface is washed with distilled water and dried with paper tissue. Tubes with exudate are taken to the laboratory in a vessel with ice and stored at −20° C.

Fresh *Yucca* sap is almost as clear as water but with a very faint buff hue. When standing at room temperature it soon deteriorates by microbial activity and by some remaining metabolic activity of its own.

b) Detached Inflorescences. Detached inflorescences are able to produce small amounts of exudate (VAN DIE and TAMMES, 1966). They were prepared by breaking off bracts and buds with the exception of the apical 10 cm. The next day the apical 40 cm part of the inflorescence stalk was cut off and stored in a plastic bag at 2° C, in which it can be held for at least two weeks without losing its ability to bleed if maintained in favorable conditions. The stalk parts from 10 to 30 cm from the apex used for the experiments were placed into a small beaker containing some water at room temperature, in such a way that only a few cm of the stalk part is actually inserted. Exudation takes place from both stalk ends, usually within one or two hours (VAN DIE and TAMMES, 1966; VEEN and TAMMES, 1971).

Clonal differences exist with regard to exudation from *Yucca flaccida;* some clones bleed distinctly better than others and there are even some clones whose inflorescence stalks are too thick to be bent for tapping.

III. The Composition and Nature of the Exudates

1. Palms

GIBBS (1911), who analyzed the exudates of *Nypa fruticans* WURMB., *Cocos nucifera* LINN., *Arenga saccharifera* LABILL. and *Corypha elata* ROXB., found a remarkable uniformity of composition. He found about 17.5% total solids, which was practically all sucrose (about 16.5%). Reducing sugars appeared to be almost absent. For *Arenga* the variation in total solids and sucrose during entire tapping periods of 50–64 days has been presented by TAMMES (1933). Although the amounts of exuding juice showed considerable fluctuations, its concentration remained remarkably constant. In later years additional analyses were made (TAMMES, 1951, 1958). A compilation of these data is presented in Table 1. It is remarkable that more detailed modern analytical data are not reported in literature so far as the authors are aware.

One of the striking aspects of the palm exudate is its alkaline pH. For *Arenga* TAMMES (unpublished) found a pH of 8.0–8.2. The fresh juices of *Phoenix sylvestris* ROXB. (PATWARDHAN, 1920) and of *Borassus flabellifer* L. (GHOSE, 1920) also gave an alkaline reaction at a pH around 8.

Other typical properties of the palm exudates analyzed are: the predominant presence of sucrose, the virtual absence of reducing sugars, the high K^+ and the very low Ca^{2+} content.

Table 1. The composition of the exudate of *Arenga saccharifera* (TAMMES, 1933, 1951, 1958)

Total solids (1st infl. stalk)	14.5–15.6%
Sucrose (1st infl. stalk)	13.5–14.8%
Total solids (2nd infl. stalk)	16.6–18.0%
Sucrose (2nd infl. stalk)	14.9–17.0%
Nitrogen	410 μg/ml
Potassium	1,200 μg/ml
Phosphorus	100 μg/ml
Magnesium	96 μg/ml
Calcium	10 μg/ml
Copper, Iron, Zinc and Manganese, each	1–4 μg/ml
Molybdenum	0.03 μg/ml

2. *Agave*

Only a few records exist on the composition of unfermented exudate of *Agave* species. SÁNCHEZ-MARROQUÍN and HOPE (1953) reported pH-values of 7.0 and 7.4, a dry-matter content of 15.29%, a sucrose content of 7.6%, "direct reducing sugars, in glucose" 2.40%, protein 0.17% and ash 0.31%. The presence of some lactic acid (which probably indicates some fermentation), and of phosphates is mentioned. EGELING (1895) reported the presence of a trace of Ca. The ash of the juice mainly consists of potassium salts.

3. *Yucca flaccida*

a) Metabolites and Ionic Composition. An extensive analysis of *Yucca* exudate was reported by TAMMES and VAN DIE (1964). In later years many other, and more refined, analyses were made. Table 2 gives an average composition of the exudate so far as organic substances are concerned together with some other features. An analysis of the free amino-acid fraction is presented in Table 3.

Table 2. Amounts of organic substances in the exudate of *Yucca flaccida* (TAMMES and VAN DIE, 1964, slightly modified and supplemented)

Total dry substances	17.1–19.2%
pH	8.0–8.2
Sucrose	150–180 mg/ml
Fructose	2–4 mg/ml
Glucose	2–4 mg/ml
Hexose phosphates	+
Total amino acids and amides	0.05–0.08 M
Total protein	0.5–0.8 mg/ml
Allantoin, allantoic acid and urea	±
Invertase activity	–
Malic acid	ca. 2.7 μEq/ml
Oxalic acid	ca. 1.4 μEq/ml
Other known di- and tricarboxylic acids	ca. 2.9 μEq/ml

Table 3. Free amino acids and amides (mole percentages) of three exudate samples from *Yucca flaccida* (VAN DIE and BORSTLAP, unpublished results)

Glutamine and glutamic acid	54.2%	56.1%	58.5%
Asparagine and aspartic acid	9.4	9.2	7.4
Valine	8.0	8.0	5.5
Proline + threonine	9.2 ± 0.5	4.4 ± 0.8	6.5
Serine	5.7	5.4	6.1
Lysine	4.0	3.6	2.7
Isoleucine	2.8	2.8	1.8
Leucine	2.4	2.2	1.9
Glycine	1.5	1.6	1.0
α-Alanine	1.3	1.0	1.5
Phenylalanine	2.0	1.9	1.6
Ornithine	0.3	0.3	+
Tyrosine	+	+	5.5

Table 4. Balance account of the positive and negative charges (pH 8.0–8.2) of the exudate solutes from *Yucca flaccida* (VAN DIE, unpublished results). Exudate collected in 1971 (*figures derived from TAMMES and VAN DIE, 1964)

Cations	μg/ml	μEq/ml	Anions		μEq/ml
K^+	1,650	42.2	Total carboxylate		30.8
Mg^{2+}	95	7.0	Excess negative charges of amino acids/amides	12.5	
Ca^{2+}	12	0.6	Known carboxylates (non-N)	7.0	
Zn^{2+}	2*	0.07	Unknown carboxylates (incl. bicarbonate)	11.3	
Na^+	1.2	0.05	Total P (as R-PO_4^{2-})		16.2
Fe	1.4*		Organic P (as R-PO_4^{2-})	12.0	
Mn	0.5*		HPO_4^{2-}	4.2	
Cu	0.4*		SO_4^{2-}		0.7
Mo	0.01*		Cl^-		ca. 1.0
			Unknown		1.3
Positive charges		50.0	Negative charges		50.0

The inorganic constituents were determined on a large composite volume of exudate and in consequence the data obtained (TAMMES and VAN DIE, 1964) are believed to represent good average values for the substances involved. Table 4 shows the ionic composition of the sap as a balance-account of the positive and negative charges of the solutes. The phosphorus-containing substances, which contribute considerably to the number of negative charges in the exudate, have not been determined in detail by the authors. An average ATP content of 615 μg/ml was reported for *Yucca* exudate by KLUGE et al. (1970).

From both sides of detached *Yucca* inflorescence stalks small amounts of exudate can be collected over a period of several days, provided the wounds are regularly renewed. Since in this case the exudate solutes must find their origin in the inflorescence itself, it was obvious to compare the composition of the exudate with that of the detached inflorescence part. Table 5 gives some features of both. It shows that the exudate apparently has its own characteristics, as far as high pH and carbohydrate composition is concerned. In these respects there is no fundamental

Table 5. A comparison of the composition of the inflorescence of *Yucca flaccida* with that of its exudate collected several hours after the inflorescence had been cut off the plant (VAN DIE and TAMMES, 1966)

	Inflorescence	Exudate
Reducing sugars, mg/g(ml)	27.4	1.1–2.5
Sucrose, mg/g(ml)	18.2	55–75
Amino acids, µMol/g(ml)	81	83–115
pH of pressed-out juice, or exudate	5.7	8.2

difference between inflorescence exudate and that from the intact plant. However, attention should be drawn to the relatively low sucrose content of the exudate of the detached stalk.

b) Enzymatic Activities of the Exudate. The protein content of the *Yucca* exudate is low. Surprisingly however, several enzyme-systems concerned with phosphorus and polysaccharide metabolism are apparently present in freshly collected sap. If incubated with $^{32}PO_4^{3-}$, *Yucca* exudate and phloem exudate of *Tilia* catalyze a very rapid incorporation of the label in a number of organic phosphorus compounds (BECKER et al., 1971). ATP appeared as one of the first products. Fractions of exudate sampled over a $7^1/_2$-hour period showed a remarkably constant synthetic ability, indicating that enzymes and substrates needed for the phosphorylations are continuously secreted into the lumen of the sieve tubes. Enzymic synthesis of callose in *Yucca* exudate was reported by ESCHRICH et al. (1972). When exudate is kept at room temperature for 24 h—with a drop of toluene for conservation—a flocculate formed, which gave positive reactions for the presence of callose. The presence of the enzyme system for callose synthesis in the exudate could biochemically be proved with UDP^{14}C-glucose and pachyman as a primer. The exudate catalyzed the incorporation of the label in a callose-like polysaccharide.

4. Other Monocotyledonous Plants

Small amounts of exudate can be obtained after cutting stalks or leaves of several genera of Liliaceae and Amaryllidaceae. MEYER-MEVIUS (1959) analyzed a number of these exudates from *Allium, Clivia, Asparagus, Lilium* and *Hemerocallis* species. Their composition deviates considerably from that found in palms, *Yucca* and *Agave*. The total solids content is low and reducing sugars are the main carbohydrates present. These often viscous exudates almost certainly originate in the large slime cells, slime tubes or some kind of laticiferous systems which are characteristic for the plant groups involved (cf MOLISCH, 1901; HEGNAUER, 1963). It would certainly be interesting to learn more about origin and composition of these exudates. But so far as can be judged now there is little reason to believe that the exudates investigated by MEYER-MEVIUS (1959) are homologous with those of palms and *Yucca*.

5. Evidence in Favor of a Phloem Origin of the Exudates from Palms and *Yucca*

Continuous bleeding requires a continuous transport of the fluid to the site of bleeding. Of the several structures able to provide such a flow in stems the xylem vessels at first sight seem the most likely pathway for its conduction. MOLISCH (1898) tried to explain bleeding in palms as xylem bleeding. He observed many plugged xylem vessels in the bleeding stalk. Removing these obstacles by regular wound renewal would be a prerequisite for an unhampered flow. In bleeding *Cocos* and *Arenga*, TAMMES (1933) also observed xylem plugging, but he related it with the bleeding phenomenon in quite a different manner. He found that a solution of acid fuchsin was able to move through the xylem of a bleeding inflorescence twig, but it did not reach the wound surface and its exudate. Potassium ferrocyanide, however, could enter the exudate when it was localized in the sieve-tube lumina. TAMMES (1933) concluded that the palm exudate was of phloem origin. The plugging of the xylem vessels prevents the sap from being sucked into the xylem, and consequently is a prerequisite for bleeding.

It should be recalled that drops of phloem exudate can also be obtained from incisions in the bark of some woody Angiosperms (e.g. *Quercus rubra*). When the knife goes too deep and pierces the cambium the drop immediately disappears because it is sucked in by the xylem. This is accompanied by a faint hissing sound (MÜNCH, 1930). In monocotyledons the xylem is adjacent to the phloem in the vascular bundles. They are cut together and any phloem sap that would normally exude is sucked directly into the xylem.

Apart from substantial physiological and biochemical support for the view presented by TAMMES—which will be amply discussed below—several additional observations can be regarded as circumstantial evidence.

(a) Air could be sucked through short pieces of coconut inflorescence, provided they were not bleeding (TAMMES, 1933).

(b) As mentioned above (p. 198), in some methods used in palm tapping the inflorescence is pounded regularly before sap production starts. This treatment possibly enhances the plugging of the xylem vessels (cf. MILBURN, 1972).

(c) Alternatives to pounding seem to treat the wound surface with clay (PATEL, 1938), or with a mucilageous substance (BROWNING and SYMONS, 1916; PATEL, 1938).

VAN DIE and TAMMES (1966) could unequivocally demonstrate that in *Yucca flaccida* the bleeding sap comes out of the phloem part of the vascular bundles and thus, by definition, represents phloem exudate. They could also demonstrate that a negative pressure may exist in the xylem system of a bleeding plant. On sunny days water was sucked into a wounded *Yucca* leaf tip at the same time as the inflorescence produced exudate.

6. Phloem Exudates from Other Plants

a) Short-Term Exudation. Although phloem exudate can be obtained from a number of temperate trees by means of an incision in the bark (MÜNCH, 1930; see additional literature cited in CRAFTS and CRISP, 1971) in most of them prolonged exudation does not occur. The drops of fluid exude more or less momentarily and owing to the small amount that can be collected in this way, are undoubtedly contaminated with the contents of other damaged cells. Nevertheless, much of the early knowledge on phloem translocation has been obtained by this method.

b) Prolonged Exudation. Prolonged exudation is known from incisions in a few dicotyledons. In Sicily *Fraxinus ornus* is tapped during the hot season. The dried sap is harvested for commercial purposes as "manna" (HUBER, 1953). Each day an incision is made in the bark a few mm above that of the previous day. Clonał differences apparently exist. For propagation the best yielding trees are selected by the local population (HUBER, 1953).

Fraxinus americana is frequently used as an experimental object due to the relatively large amounts of exudate it can deliver (ZIMMERMANN, 1960).

MILBURN (1970) described the tapping of phloem exudate from the bark of *Ricinus*. Initially he reported that massage of the stem was needed to induce a prolonged exudation, a very interesting parallel with the previously described habit of pounding or kneading in commercial palm-tapping. However massage—just as in palms and *Yucca*—is apparently not always necessary to produce an exudate flow from the phloem (MILBURN, 1972).

Continuous exudation from cut-off stylets of the aphid *Tuberolachnus salignus*, which lives on the stem of several *Salix* species, was first described by KENNEDY and MITTLER (1953). In recent years much research on sieve-tube translocation using several species of Aphidae or Coccidae has been carried out with this method, which may continuously deliver microamounts of exudate over periods of many hours (see Chapter 7).

A comparison of the composition of phloem exudates of dicotyledonous plants, obtained either after incisions or from aphid stylets, with the palm/ Yucca exudates shows an amazing degree of similarity (e.g. ZIMMERMANN, 1960; CRAFTS and CRISP, 1971). The large amounts of exudate produced by palms and agaves seem the only significant difference from the well-known phloem exudates of woody dicotyledons. But even this appears to be only a relative difference in view of the large quantities that can be produced by clones of *Fraxinus ornus* (HUBER, 1953).

7. Comparison of Bleeding from Palms with Xylem Bleeding from Dicotyledonous Trees

One often encounters the suggestion that palm exudation may be of xylem origin. A comparison with xylem bleeding in dicotyledons may therefore be useful. In early spring several deciduous trees such as *Betula, Carpinus, Alnus, Populus,* and *Acer* species yield a bleeding sap following wounding of roots, stems or branches, that usually contains up to a few percent of reducing sugars (e.g. LÖHR, 1953), small amounts of nitrogenous substances (POLLARD and SPROSTON, 1954) and traces of several enzymes (MEEUWSE, 1949). *Acer* seems an exception in so far as it produces a sap with sucrose as the main sugar, usually in a concentration of 3–5% (e.g. MEEUWSE, 1949).

In spite of much research carried out on this exudation process, its mechanism is not yet fully understood (KRAMER, 1949, 1959; FISCHER, 1967; ZIMMERMANN and BROWN, 1971). Root pressure plays an important role but in *Acer* bleeding is rather brought about by local conditions within the stem or branches themselves (Papers by SAUTER and by MILBURN in preparation). The phenomenon is obviously connected in some way with the onset of bud growth. Although in former years the xylem was often regarded as the principle tissue involved in the translocation of C, N, and P compounds from the stem to the developing buds, it is now generally recognized that the substances involved move upwards through the phloem and *not* through the xylem (SWANSON, 1959; FISCHER, 1967).

In palms with terminal inflorescences (VAN DIE, 1974) and in deciduous trees, the stored carbohydrates are localized in the stem—mainly in the pith and in the secondary xylem parenchyma respectively. In the intact non-bleeding plants of both groups the reserves are mobilized and translocated through the phloem to the inflorescence or the growing buds. In bleeding palm inflorescences the sap exudes from the phloem and has the general composition of sieve-tube exudate. Moreover, phloem exudation takes place usually in the presence of mature leaves. The fact that sugar does not accumulate in the transpiring leaves indicates that we are not dealing with xylem sap. Exudation of sugar solution that can be clearly seen to emerge from the xylem of dicotyledonous trees takes place at a time when there are no leaves. In both xylem and phloem exudation, sugars originate from mobilization of carbohydrate resources; they are secreted into either the symplastic or the apoplastic transport system (for *Acer* see SAUTER et al., 1973).

C. Experimental Analyses of the Exudation Process

I. Translocation to the Site of Bleeding

1. Palms

In palms like *Corypha* and some *Metroxylon* species which form terminal inflorescences and afterwards die, starch accumulation in the trunk increases with age and reaches a considerable level. An average sago palm, *Metroxylon Rumphii* MART., contains ca. 600 kg of starch (HEYNE, 1927, 1950) which becomes mobilized with the formation of the inflorescence. The sago palm is therefore cut down for starch production just before the developing inflorescence becomes visible; this usually happens at an age of 9 to 20 years (for details e.g. HEYNE, 1927, 1950; BARRAU, 1959). Consequently, the tree is not used for tapping, in contrast to *Corypha* species, which are frequently tapped from their developing inflorescence. In these trees, as the bleeding goes on, the starch of the trunk disappears from the top downwards, and also perhaps more slowly, from the outside towards the center (GIBBS, 1911).

A *Corypha elata* ROXB. specimen, 30–35 years old, with a volume of 2.71 m^3 had produced 2,699 l of sap over a period of 130 day (GIBBS, 1911). The sap contained 252 kg of sucrose (reported average yields per tree range from 180–324 kg). After the flow had stopped almost all starch had disappeared from the trunk. The starch content of a non-mature tree (1.6 m^3) was reported by GIBBS to be 6%. A mature tree undoubtedly has a higher content, thus a low estimate of the amount of starch in the tree—if not tapped at all—would be 166 kg. According to MANIS, quoted by ZIMMERMANN (1973), the terminal inflorescence of a 44-year-old specimen of *Corypha elata* ROXB. produced fruits of a total dry weight of ca. 600 kg. This tree was considerably larger than the one used by GIBBS. From the size mentioned by ZIMMERMANN a volume has been estimated by the authors of about 7.0 m^3, which would correspond with at least 420 kg of starch.

The starch accumulated in the trunk of these palms with terminal inflorescence can consequently be utilized as such (sago from *Metroxylon*), for the production of exudate sucrose (*Corypha*), or of course for the formation of the huge inflorescences such trees have (DOUGLAS and BIMANTORO, 1956), and ultimately for the production of fruits.

In *Cocos,* which continuously forms lateral inflorescences during its lifetime, starch accumulation in the stem (with the exception of the stem apex) or elsewhere does not occur to a significant extent (REIJNE, 1948). It is primarily the current products of photosynthesis from which the nuts are formed, or alternatively, which supply the exudate sucrose.

According to GIBBS (1911), a 40-year-old *Cocos* tree forms about 10 fruit stalks per year, each of which exudes for about two months. They produce a total of about 400 l of exudate with 66 kg of sucrose per year. A productive palm has an annual yield of 60–100 coconuts, which may contain about 16–27 kg (dry weight) of copra (HEYNE, 1927, 1950). Keeping in mind that the other fruit parts (solutes of the fruit water, the shell and the husk with its fibers) constitute 77% of the total dry weight of the fruit (REIJNE, 1948), it becomes clear that tapping a *Cocos* tree withdraws the photosynthates which otherwise would be translocated to the developing fruits (400–500 l of exudate with 72–90 kg of total solids, versus 70–117 kg of dry nuts, both per year and per tree). The existence of a positive and significant correlation between the yields of exudate obtained from many individual *Cocos* trees, and the yields of nuts from these trees, obtained during two years prior to tapping (PATEL, 1938), is in accord with this view.

Arenga saccharifera LABILL. forms a small number of inflorescences a few years before the tree dies, at an age of 15–20 years. In times of food shortage the tree may be used for starch production (HEYNE, 1927, 1950), when it can deliver about 150 kg of starch. Normally, however, it is used for exudate production. The total quantity of palm sugar obtained in this way is reported to amount to about 345 kg. Since the inflorescence of *Arenga* may be considered a transition between the terminal and the lateral one, the origin of the exudate sucrose may be starch reserves as well as the current products of photosynthesis. If an *Arenga* has been tapped it becomes unfit to produce sago (TAMMES, 1933, information from local tappers).

2. *Yucca flaccida*

Yucca flaccida exudate resembles that of palms in many ways. It cannot all be derived from the inflorescence itself (cf. TAMMES, 1933). The total volume of exudate that can be collected from an inflorescence with a dry weight of about 35 g may be as high as 400 ml, containing ca. 70 g of sucrose. Thus a very considerable part of the sucrose has to be withdrawn from other plant parts (VAN DIE, 1968). With $^{14}CO_2$-feeding of a single leaf it could be shown that a large proportion of the label exuded as ^{14}C-sucrose and to a considerably smaller extent as ^{14}C-amino and carboxylic acids from the inflorescence (VAN DIE and TAMMES, 1964). In a later study (VAN DIE et al., 1973) more detailed analyses were carried out on the movement of photosynthates from a leaf to the bleeding site. Within one hour following the supply of $^{14}CO_2$ to a leaf, labeled sucrose started to exude and rapidly increased in specific activity, its maximum value being reached after about 7 h (Fig. 2). The second part of the curve, relating activity with bleeding time, showed a gradually decreasing specific activity of the sap. Just as has been found in the experiments of 1964 here too the exudation of labeled sucrose continued for more

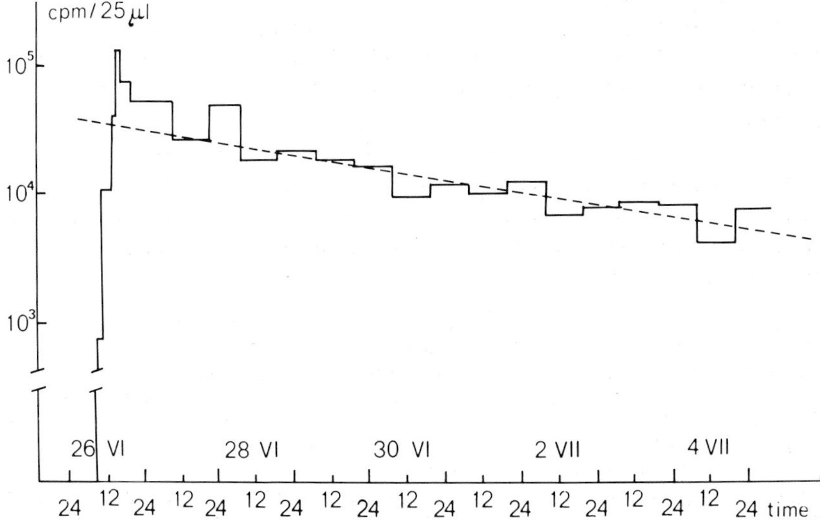

Fig. 2. The ^{14}C content of phloem exudate from the wounded inflorescence top of a *Yucca* plant during a 215-h bleeding period following the supply of $^{14}CO_2$ to a single leaf. Note the daily periodicity in ^{14}C concentration. During the nights more exudate (with higher ^{14}C content) was collected than during the daylight periods (VAN DIE et al., 1973)

than a week. This points to the existence of a pool of photosynthates in the plant, from which the exudate sucrose was continuously withdrawn. From the slope of the second part of the curve the turnover rate of this pool of mobile ^{14}C-labeled carbohydrates could be calculated to be about 21% per day. Since the removal of the labeled leaf from a bleeding *Yucca* rapidly stopped the exudation of labeled sucrose (VAN DIE, TAMMES and VONK, unpublished results) this pool is apparently localized in the treated leaf.

When the sieve tubes had transported labeled assimilates for $22^1/_2$ hours, the removal of the treated leaf resulted in a rapid drop in exudate activity (Table 6). Within 3 hours the level of exudate activity decreased to two percent of the average ^{14}C level of the exudate collected before leaf removal. Structural components of the sieve tubes that could hypothetically be involved in the conduction of the labeled substances apparently do not receive substantial amounts of label available for exchange with the moving sugar. In a similar experiment in which the leaf was removed 48 h after its labeling the activity drop was less rapid (Table 6). It took 7 and 10 h respectively to reach a 12 and 2% activity level in the exudate. This more gradual decline may be explained by some lateral translocation of assimilates out of the transport channel, followed by a loading process possibly induced by the leaf removal. It may be compared with the secretion of sucrose from detached inflorescences, which normally behave as a sink for translocated assimilates but become a source region after detachment (cf. page 202).

Table 6. Time-course of ^{14}C exudation following $^{14}CO_2$ pulse-labeling of a leaf. Two *Yucca* plants were used. After one day (left) and two days (right) the treated leaf was removed and exudate sampling was continued. The distances from the leaf bases to the bleeding sites were (left) 30 cm (start of the experiment) to 28 cm (end of the experiment) and 41 cm to 39 cm (right)

Time from application of $^{14}CO_2$ to leaf or time from leaf removal	Exudate activity (dpm/25 µl)	Time from application of $^{14}CO_2$ to leaf or time from leaf removal	Exudate activity (dpm/25 µl)
		22 h	8,560
$10^1/_4$ h	13,840	36	5,120
$22^1/_4$	20,220	48	7,060
leaf removed		leaf removed	
1 h	7,360	$^1/_4$ h	5,580
3	378	$^3/_4$	5,230
7	235	$1^3/_4$	1,830
10	231	$3^3/_4$	2,310
22	141	$7^3/_4$	835
46	138	$10^3/_4$	140
70	83	$94^1/_2$	101

The size of the pool could be approximately 7 to 8% of the dry weight of the leaf (VAN DIE, VONK and TAMMES, 1973), which means that it is very probably identical with the soluble carbohydrate fraction of the leaf. An important observation seems to be that the maximum specific activity of the sucrose reached in the sap was a few percent of the maximum specific activity of the sucrose that could theoretically be formed from the supplied label in the leaf. Since the bleeding *Yucca* shoot had 25 leaves and assuming that all the leaves contribute in a similar manner to the exudate sucrose, this could mean that the number of labeled sucrose molecules exported by the parenchyma cells to the sieve tube of the treated leaf remains constant during movement from leaf to bleeding site (a distance of 41 cm). The ^{14}C-sucrose became diluted only with the inactive sucrose exported by the other 24 leaves. Apparently lateral transport of sucrose out of the sieve tubes of the *Yucca* axis is a slow process, a conclusion in accord with results of VAN DIE et al. (1970) and TIETEMA et al. (1972) obtained with *Fritillaria imperialis* (Liliaceae). The experiments with the labeled CO_2 thus demonstrate that in *Yucca* the major part of the exudate sucrose is derived from the daily production of photosynthates, which is transiently stored in the leaves.

The second important organic substance in *Yucca* bleeding sap is glutamine. With a concentration of about 0.03–0.04 M it occupies roughly 50% of the amino acid fraction, which constitutes about 7% of the total exudate solutes (VAN DIE and TAMMES, 1964). The origin of these amino acids seems to be different to that of the exudate sucrose. Although in the pulse-labeling experiments reported by VAN DIE et al. (1973) the maximum specific activity of the exudate-sucrose was reached at the same time as that of the amino acid and amide fraction (unpublished results) the latter was much lower than the former as is shown in Table 7. Moreover,

Table 7. The distribution of ^{14}C among the amino acid and amide and the sucrose fraction of a number of exudate samples collected over a period of 9 days following pulse-labeling of a single leaf. Average sucrose concentration: 0.50 M; average amino acid and amide concentration: 0.08 M. The amino acids and amides are assumed to have a C_5 skeleton (cf. Table 3)

Time of collection of exudate fraction (hours from application of $^{14}CO_2$)	Amino acid and amide fraction		Sucrose fraction dpm/μmole Carbon
	dpm/μmole Carbon	% of total ^{14}C in the exudate fraction	
1			65
4	6	0.3	139
5	29	0.3	658
7	125	0.8	1,057
11	38	0.4	649
$22^1/_2$	37	0.4	658
$34^1/_2$	19	0.7	179
$70^1/_2$	22	0.8	182
130	17	1.3	87
$166^1/_2$	16	1.6	67
202	10	1.9	35
$214^1/_2$	24	2.6	62

the specific activity of the amino acids and amides in the exudate decreased more slowly with time than that of the exudate sucrose. The specific activity of the amino acids and amides was initially 5 to 12% of the corresponding values of the exudate sucrose (both on a μmole of Carbon basis) and increased distinctly during later stages of bleeding. This means that only a small part of the amino acids of the exudate is directly available for export after their production from photosynthates in the labeled leaf. More than 90% of the amino acids and amides in the exudate are therefore derived from sources already present at the time of the supply of the $^{14}CO_2$.

An increase in amino acids and the appearance of amides in sieve-tube exudates from several deciduous trees of temperate regions occurs in the autumn during the period of leaf senescence (ZIEGLER, 1956; GARDNER and PEEL, 1971; for reviews FISCHER, 1958, 1967). Moreover a high amide content of tissues in general strongly points to ammonium uptake or production; the latter often accompanies protein hydrolysis (e.g. MOTHES, 1958).

Although the exudate sucrose in *Yucca* originates largely directly from photosynthesis, the sources of glutamine and amino acids in the exudate are apparently mainly proteins which become hydrolyzed either as a result of the created artificial sink or in connection with the onset of flowering. Moreover, amides and amino acids possibly enter the sieve tubes along their whole lengths. The high amino acid and amide content of the exudate from detached *Yucca* inflorescences (VAN DIE and TAMMES, 1966) and the seemingly unhampered entrance of glutamine into the sieve tubes (TAMMES et al., 1973) favor this view.

3. Rates of Translocation

Since the sap of *Yucca* exudes directly from the phloem part of the vascular bundle (VAN DIE and TAMMES, 1966) and knowing that the xylem vessels are plugged, a calculation could be made on the velocity of the fluid flow through the phloem to the site of bleeding. After having measured the percentage of phloem per cross-sectional area of the bleeding stalk end, and after having observed that all the bundles take part in bleeding, a velocity of the assumed flow could be calculated from the observed bleeding rate in ml/h. A velocity of 37 cm/h was found if the whole cross-section of the phloem were available for streaming. The corresponding specific mass-transfer value—the most useful parameter in measuring phloem translocation as long as it remains a matter for controversy whether sugar molecules and water are moving together or independently of one another (CANNY, 1960, 1962)—was 5.7 g dry matter per cm^2 phloem cross-section per hour. The specific mass-transfer values calculated by CANNY from available literature data, for several plant species ranged between 2.1 and 4.8 g dry substance per cm^2 phloem, per hour.

It should be stressed that the velocity calculated for an assumed streaming in the *Yucca* sieve tubes is that in a bleeding plant and in the sieve tubes only. In trying to compare or verify this value with data derived from tracer experiments in which the label has been supplied to a leaf, one has to realize that in that case the labeled sugar has to move through several metabolic compartments before it reaches the sieve-tube lumen. The overall translocation rate is determined by the slowest component of the series of translocation processes. This probably is a diffusion-like movement of the sugar through the parenchyma cells around the sieve tubes. Out of these border cells the tracer enters the sieve tube by an active mechanism. In the tracer experiment described above (VAN DIE et al., 1973) the logarithmic profile apparently moved with a velocity of approximately 41 cm in 7 h or 6 cm/h from chloroplasts to bleeding site.

TAMMES (1952) has made a calculation for the velocity of the assumed streaming in the sieve tubes of a bleeding *Arenga* inflorescence. With a flow of 5–6 l per day he arrived at the astonishingly high value of 7 m/h. In appreciating this high value, one has to be aware that it is brought about by simple, straightforward measurements, which hardly allow another interpretation. Moreover, the value represents a streaming velocity in an artificially opened sieve-tube system and thus will probably approximate the highest velocity fluid mechanically possible in the tubes involved. At the source site an intensive mobilization of carbohydrates occurs; at the other, the wounded site of the sieve-tube system, the turgor must be almost zero.

Since bleeding and fruit growth depend on the same carbohydrate resources, it is interesting to compare the length of the period the inflorescence of *Corypha elata* can be tapped before the tree dies (130 days, 252 kg sucrose; GIBBS, 1911) with the time the fruits need for complete development (13 months; DOUGLAS and BIMANTORO, 1956). The difference in rates of both alternative translocation processes might point to an enhanced rate of carbohydrate withdrawal from the stem in the case of bleeding.

II. Feeding Experiments with Detached Inflorescence Axes

1. Sugars and Some Other Compounds

The solutes of the exudate produced from detached inflorescences differ considerably in composition from those of the stalk tissues (Table 5). Therefore exudate formation is possibly preceded by a number of transformations. Those leading to the formation of the exudate sucrose were considered to be of major importance and have been studied in more detail. ^{14}C-labeled sugars and some other substances were supplied to the basal end of detached young *Yucca* inflorescences of about 20 cm in length. The exudates were collected from the cut top ends and analyzed.

Experiments with acid fuchsin showed that in such experiments the solution enters the stalk through the xylem vessels. All transformations leading to the formation of exudate solutes from the supplied substances must occur in xylem parenchyma or in the phloem, because passage through other tissues before reaching the sieve tubes seems unlikely. Although exudate from detached inflorescence stalks very much resembles that from attached ones (Tables 2, and 5), the possibility cannot be completely ruled out that it may gradually become contaminated with substances moving passively through apoplasmic compartments to the wound surface. All the experiments with detached inflorescences, therefore, should be appreciated for what they are: an endeavor to study vascular metabolism in relation with the mechanism of sieve-tube loading.

The results obtained in two studies on the synthesis of the exudate sucrose (TAMMES et al., 1967, 1973) may be grouped as follows:

1. D-glucose, D-fructose, D-galactose, maltose, lactose, fructose, fructose-1:6-diphosphate, and fructose-6-phosphate were converted to, and exclusively exuded as sucrose. The fed substance itself was absent from the exudate. The feeding of UDP-glucose not only gave rise to the appearance of mainly sucrose, but also of a small amount of glucose in the exudate.

2. D-sorbitol and K-glycerate led to the exudation of these substances themselves, together with small amounts of sucrose.

3. L-sorbose, glycerol, glycollic acid and glutamine were not converted at all to sucrose but exuded as such.

4. ^{14}C(U)-sucrose feeding led to the exudation of asymmetrically labeled sucrose, with about 75% of the label in the glucose parts of the molecules.

The results underline the exclusive position of the sucrose in the exudate. Of a number of naturally occurring sugars, sucrose apparently is the sole carbohydrate permitted to move into the sieve tube. The one hexose which could enter the exudate in appreciable amounts was L-sorbose, a substance very probably not occurring in higher plants (KARRER, 1958). This points to the existence of a metabolic barrier between the vascular parenchyma cells and the sieve tubes. Only a hexose not "recognized" by the enzymes involved can enter the locked up sieve tubes, probably by diffusion.

Disaccharides are hydrolyzed and converted to sucrose, even lactose which is rather rare in higher plants (KARRER, 1958). Sucrose supplied exogenously through the xylem, does not enter the exudate without being (partly?) hydrolyzed and resynthesized.

2. Indoleacetic Acid and Maleic Hydrazide

^{14}C-indole-3-acetic acid (IAA) supplied to the distal or the proximal ends of detached inflorescence stalk parts gave rise to labeled exudates. A kind of polar movement of the label (more acropetally than basipetally) could be observed, but only during the first hours of the experiments (VEEN and TAMMES, 1971). It is, however, a non-specific polar movement since sucrose and maleic hydrazide showed similar patterns. Probably anatomical differences between both ends of the stalk are responsible for this phenomenon. The small amounts of the IAA label that were secreted into the sieve-tube exudates were almost exclusively localized in two chromatographically less mobile IAA derivatives. IAA itself was virtually absent from the exudate. This contrasts with results reported by ESCHRICH (1968), obtained with the aphid-stylet technique and *Vicia faba* plants. ESCHRICH concluded that applied IAA moves in the sieve tubes and that the derivatives found by him are phloem-immobile.

III. Cooling Experiments with *Yucca flaccida*

1. Attached and Detached Inflorescences

When 10 to 15 cm of the tip of a bleeding inflorescence attached to a plant is brought to the temperature of melting ice the exudate flow continues at a speed hardly differing from that at a normal temperature. Apparently the flow is not driven along the translocation pathway in the cooled part by metabolic processes (e.g. electroosmosis, microperistalsis), but by a force localized outside the cooled region (TAMMES et al., 1969). The flow through the inflorescence consequently has the characteristics of a mass flow driven by a mechanism centered outside the inflorescence. It is of special note that the sucrose content of the exudate obtained in such chilling experiments is 10 to 20% higher than in sap collected at normal outside temperatures (20 to 25° C). This might be the result of a reduction in metabolic activity in the chilled inflorescence part and the concomitant reduction in its sink function. But possibly the explanation should be found on a more physical level. The osmotic pressure exerted by a solution is proportional to the absolute temperature. This means that a locally cooled part needs a higher solute concentration in its cells than the non-cooled part to reach osmotic equilibrium.

The observation of an unhampered longitudinal transport of sucrose along a cooled *Yucca* stem part of considerable length is in accord with evidence from studies with chilling-resistant plants as *Helianthus annuus* (BOWLING, 1968), sugar beet (SWANSON and GEIGER, 1967; GEIGER and SOVONICK, 1970; GIAQUINTA and GEIGER, 1973), willow (GARDNER and PEEL, 1972), *Lolium temulentum L.* (WARDLAW, 1972) and cold-acclimated *Cucurbita melopepo* (WEBB, 1971), although in most of these plants a temporary inhibition in longitudinal translocation has been found.

With detached inflorescences cooling rapidly reduces the exudation from both ends. Within 45 min bleeding has completely stopped, but it resumes within a few minutes when the stalks are returned to room temperature. The sugar concentrations of exudate samples collected during the warming period showed a distinct tendency to increase with time (TAMMES et al., 1969). Detached stalks stored for 23 days at 0° to 2° C could produce ample exudate after wounding and subsequent return to room temperature. The dry-matter content of exudate samples rose from an initial average of 8.8% (7.6, 9.6, 9.2) to 14.6% (16.3, 14.5, 13.1) after 2 h at room temperature (unpublished results).

The translocation system involved in the exudation of sucrose apparently contains two components:

(1) A longitudinal movement of the sugar from the leaves through the sieve tubes, driven by a mechanism centered outside the inflorescence axis.

(2) A radial movement of sucrose from sieve-tube surrounding cells into the sieve-tube lumen. This process of sieve-tube loading is a strongly temperature-dependent and rather selective secretion process. Although studied in the detached inflorescence, in that part of the plant it apparently does not contribute detectably to the driving force of the longitudinal flow. But there is little reason to assume that the secretion process in the source regions of the exudate sucrose, i.e. the phloem of the leaves, is different.

Literature data on assimilate translocation through sieve tubes point to a vein-loading process in various plant species comparable with the secretion process postulated for bleeding *Yucca*. In *Lolium temulentum* (WARDLAW, 1972) lateral movement of ^{14}C in leaves was extremely sensitive to temperature, in contrast to the longitudinal movement. In willow (FORD and PEEL, 1966) lateral translocation of solutes was more dependent on temperature than longitudinal flow, while in *Cucurbita melopepo* (WEBB, 1971) the radial component of assimilate transport out of the leaf appeared to be far more stressed by low temperature than the long-distance transport. These experiments emphasize the active mechanism of phloem loading in the source areas as a part of normal assimilate movement through the sieve tubes. The parallel with the loading of the sieve tubes of *Yucca* with exudate sucrose is evident.

Bleeding experiments at low temperature have also thrown light on the nature of the closing mechanism of the sieve tubes involved. The sealing process responsible for the gradual decline and ultimate cessation of exudation, which takes about 7 h at normal temperature, needs about 24 to 36 h to be completed under low temperature conditions (TAMMES et al., 1969). It is a chemical process and possibly involves the formation of callose, which has been demonstrated to occur in *Yucca* exudate (ESCHRICH et al., 1972).

D. The Exudation Process and Its Relation to Phloem Transport

I. Exudate Flow between Source and Artificial Sink

The sugar-rich sap which exudes from the phloem of palm and *Yucca* inflorescences could be taken as the aqueous phase of the sieve tubes which, in the intact plant, is immobile and in equilibrium with more static structures involved in assimilate translocation (cf. the translocation model of CANNY and PHILLIPS, 1963). This phase would exude after wounding (for a critical view on the significance of exudates for our knowledge on translocation the reader is referred to SCHUMACHER, 1967). Such an explanation of bleeding would mean that the exudate would have much in common with the flow of latex from a wounded latex plant.

During the tapping of latex from *Hevea brasiliensis* the flow rate decreases in a characteristic manner and approaches zero within a few hours. At the beginning of the flow, elastic contraction of the latex tubes predominates (exponential decrease of the discharge) whereas after a while the latex flow is regulated by Poiseuille flow in capillaries with increasing length (hyperbolical decrease of the flow rate). The decrease of the turgor pressure in the latex tubes is followed by an infiltration of water which causes a dilution of the latex of at least 10% (last drops compared with the first ones) (FREY-WYSSLING, 1952).

The prolonged bleeding from palms and *Yucca* cannot be explained as an exudation of such a static liquid phase, as its flow pattern distinctly differs from that of a latex (TAMMES, 1933; TAMMES et al., 1969). The remarkably constant sugar concentration in palm saps has always surprised workers in this field. In palms the source of the exudate sugars is not the inflorescence itself but either (1) mainly the pith of the trunk (*Corypha* and *Metroxylon* species), or (2) both the trunk and the leaves (*Arenga saccharifera*), or (3) presumably the leaves only (*Cocos nucifera*). In *Yucca* it is the pool of photosynthates localized in the leaves.

When sugar enters the sieve tubes at the source sites, water is osmotically attracted and both will move together from source to exudation site. Of course, the water is easily exchanged with water molecules in surrounding cells (cf. Appendix II), and consequently the sugar molecules in the sieve tubes will have continuously changing companions. But in essence both move together *en masse*.

II. The Structure of the Sieve Plate in Relation to Flow

The exuding fluid moves through the sieve tubes and demonstrates the existence of easily permeable longitudinal connections between the sieve-tube members.

In *Yucca* the sieve plates contain numerous small pores with an average radius of 0.26 μm (IE et al., 1966; TAMMES and IE, 1971). At least a considerable number of them are open pores, or are partly obstructed by 10–20 filaments of 20–25 nm diameter running through them. But apparently they allow a velocity of exudate flow of 0.44 m h^{-1} (VAN DIE and TAMMES, 1966). The calculated resistance of the sieve plates with open or partly obstructed pores appeared to be low (TAMMES et al., 1971). Assuming all the pores free of any obstruction, and a pressure difference between the intact sieve-tube members and the exuding ones of 16 atm—at an assumed distance of one meter—the fluid-mechanical capacity of the *Yucca* sieve tubes would allow an exudate velocity of 20 m h^{-1}. Since from the rate of bleeding a velocity of the exudate transport in the sieve tubes of 0.44 m h^{-1} was calculated, only a small part of the pores need to be open during bleeding. Assuming all the pores obstructed by the filaments, a pressure difference of $5\,^1/_2$ atm m^{-1} would be sufficient to explain the velocity of the exudate flow in the *Yucca* sieve tubes.

The main causes of the relatively low resistance of the sieve plates are the extreme thinness of the plates (ca. 0.4 μm) and their oblique position with regard to the axis of the sieve tube, which makes the total surface area of the ca. 1,760 pores in one plate as large as the cross section of the sieve tube (TAMMES et al., 1971). Calculations showed that notwithstanding the 0.26 μm radius of the sieve pores and the presence of filaments there is no reason for such a pessimistic view as that expressed by CANNY (1973) that flow of sieve-tube contents will not be easy for a system with sieve pores smaller than about 2 μm radius.

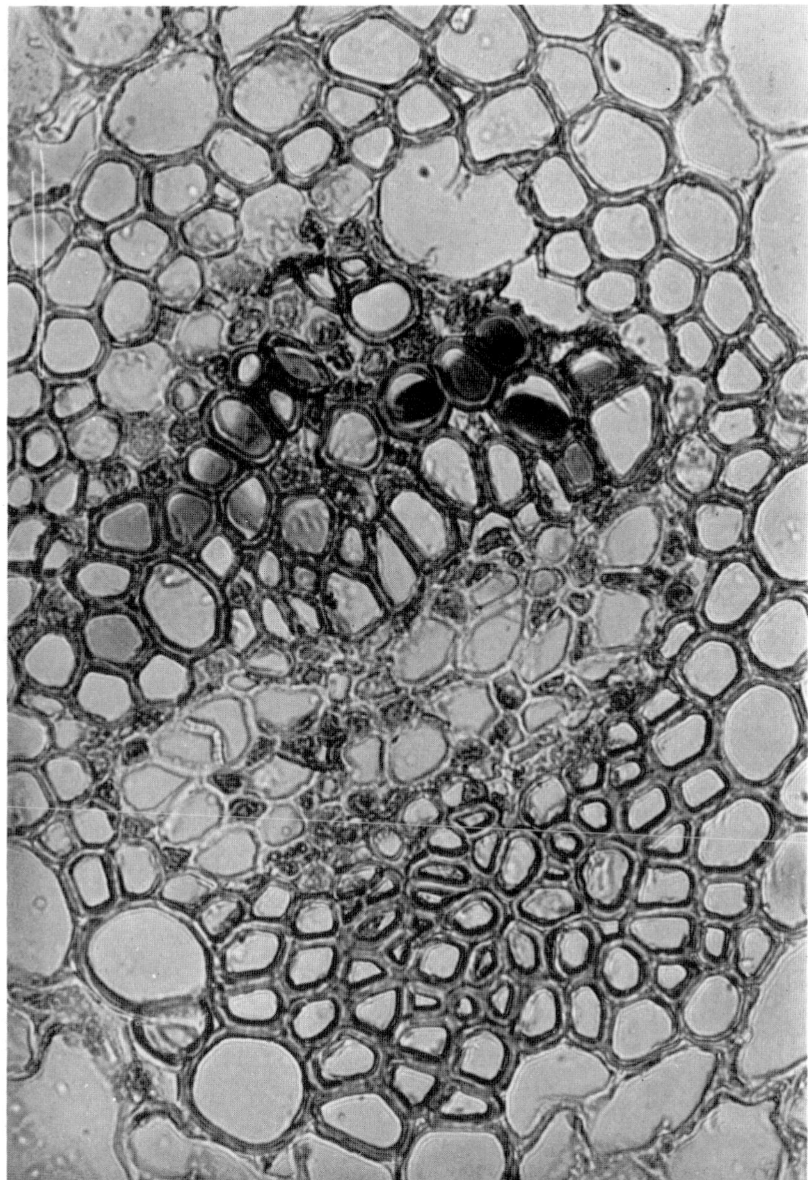

Fig. 3. Vascular bundle of a *Yucca* inflorescence stalk with plugged xylem vessels

Mature sieve tubes are living structures. Their contents must have retained a number of vital functions (for a review e.g. ESCHRICH, 1970), therefore a number of cytoplasmic structures must be present in them. Protoplasmic filaments or P-protein (THAINE, 1964, 1969; KOLLMANN et al., 1970; ROBIDOUX et al., 1973) running through the sieve pores are the main visible structures and therefore one would expect that they are engaged in keeping the sieve tubes in a vital state. There is little reason to believe that they play a role in the translocation process itself. On the contrary, available evidence is unfavorable to the view that they resemble known contractile proteins found elsewhere (WILLIAMSON, 1972). It would be more logical to connect the presence of the longitudinally oriented fibrils in the pores (if not an artifact, e.g. ANDERSON and CRONSHAW, 1970) with, for example, rapid pore closing and opening, one of the vital functions a sieve tube can carry out. Increased resistance to flow through the sieve plates owing to constriction of the pores by slime plugs and callose seems an important factor in the blockage of sieve-tube transport (TAMMES et al., 1970). In cotton, callose deposition and decallosing have been shown to be related with blocking and recovery of sieve-tube transport (MCNAIRN and CURRIER, 1968). According to MILBURN (1970) repeated formation and dissolution of callose may make the closing mechanism insensitive to wounding. Possibly the common practise of pounding the inflorescence of palms before tapping may have a similar physiological basis, just as frequent cutting of slices over a number of days, which may also induce bleeding. Another explanation of the various pretreatments mentioned in the literature (see p. 197) may be that the repeated pressure release and build-up which will consequently occur, ejects possibly present slime or P-protein plugs from the sieve pores and prevents their re-establishment (SPANNER, 1971). The presence of protein fibrils in some sieve-tube exudates (THAINE, 1969; STONE and CRONSHAW, 1973) points in that direction.

In bleeding monocotyledons plugged xylem vessels are a *conditio sine qua non* for sieve-tube bleeding. Both in bleeding palms (TAMMES, 1933) and in *Yucca* (Fig. 3) such plugging could be observed. Plugging of the xylem is a major effect of the various pretreatments, although it should be emphasized that sometimes in palms and often in *Yucca* a pretreatment is unnecessary to obtain bleeding. In these cases the xylem vessels might already be blocked, or back suction of the phloem exudate occurs relatively slowly. The highly concentrated exudate and its high pH irritates the xylem and causes plugging of the vessels.

In *Yucca flaccida* the ability to bleed depends on the clone used, as has also been found to be the case in the Sicilian manna ash (HUBER, 1953), while in *Ricinus communis* it depends on the sub-species (MILBURN, 1972). Within these plant species there apparently exists a pool of genetic diversity in the rate of the sieve-pore closing reaction out of which new genotypes can be selected. It may be possible to select better bleeding lines from plant species from which at present sieve-tube exudate cannot be obtained, because of rapid sieve-plate closure.

III. Concluding Remarks

If mass flow is possible in sieve tubes during exudation one wonders why this should not in fact be the way by which assimilates are translocated in the intact plants. In palms the amounts of carbohydrates translocated to the bleeding sites, or in the intact plants to the developing fruits, appear to be of the same order of magnitude. In *Yucca* photosynthates are almost quantitatively exported from the leaves to the bleeding inflorescence. During their movement through the sieve tubes there appears to be little exchange with more static structures inside or outside the translocation channel. Moreover, the sucrose arrives at the bleeding site with a specific activity that could be predicted on the ground of the specific activity of the photosynthates in the labeled leaf and an assumed mass flow from leaf to inflorescence top (VAN DIE et al., 1973).

WIERSUM (1966) has shown that during the period of fast growth of tomatoes and apples only traces of Ca enter these fruits. The influx of N, P and K into growing apple, however, is correlated with the weight increase (ASKEN, 1960, quoted by WIERSUM, 1966). Early thinning of apple fruits, which increases the leaf/fruit ratio, results in significantly higher levels of P, K and Mg in mature fruits, while the Ca level is not affected (SHEARPLES, 1964, quoted by BOLLARD, 1970). Strong evidence exists for an assumed phloem immobility of Ca (e.g. WIERSUM, 1966, 1967; FISCHER, 1967, Chapter 3). It leads to the conclusion that the phloem sap stream is the principle supplier of N, P, K, Mg and carbohydrates as well as of the water needed for fruit development. Additional support for this view comes from observations on the very low Ca-contents and the high K/Ca ratios of fruits like date, apple, peach and tomato (BOLLARD, 1970). The supply of nutrients to fruits apparently involves the influx through the phloem of a carbohydrate *solution* with a high K/Ca ratio (see also Chapter 19). Such a solution is very similar in composition to the bleeding sap from palms and *Yucca* (cf. VAN DIE, 1974).

A rather persistent argument often raised against mass flow is based on observations of different velocities of movement of ^{14}C-labeled compounds and tritiated water in the sieve tubes of more or less intact plants (CHOI and ARONOFF, 1966; PEEL et al., 1969; PEEL, 1970). Such evidence, however, is in no way in conflict with the mass-flow model. Different velocities of solutes and THO have also been shown to occur during flow through xylem vessels (VAN DIE and VONK, 1967; VAN BEL, 1974). Moreover, CATALDO et al. (1972) have shown that a lower apparent velocity of THO as compared to ^{14}C-sucrose is primarily due to an extensive lateral exchange of the former along the translocation path (see also Appendix II). Thus the velocity of tritiated water flow cannot be used as a critical test for mass flow.

The secretion of sucrose into the sieve-tube lumina in the source areas is the main driving force of the exudate flow in *Yucca*. It is a rather specific process as far as the nature of the carbohydrate is concerned, although some other substances seem to have relatively free access to the sieve-tube lumen. What cell types are involved in the secretion process is still uncertain. A role may possibly be reserved for the companion cells, or for "transfer cells" (PATE and GUNNING, 1972). The *Yucca* experiments so far have not given any clue to the solution of this problem. Each nucleate cell bordering the sieve tubes is probably able to secrete sucrose into the tube lumen even if localized in a sink region, as the experiments with the detached inflorescences have shown.

The *Yucca* experiments have not demonstrated any need for a driving mechanism located along the translocation pathway itself. The temperature insensitivity of the longitudinal component of the exudate-sucrose translocation process, together with the observed unpolarized secretion of exudate from inflorescence stalk parts, argue strongly against electroosmotic pumping (SPANNER, 1971) as the main or an additional driving mechanism. The temperature insensitivity also makes superfluous the postulation of other additional driving mechanisms as muscle-like protein filaments or micro peristalsis (THAINE, 1969; FENSOM, 1972; THOMPSON and THOMPSON, 1973), filaments resembling flagella (WOODING, 1971) or filaments like those implicated in cytoplasmic streaming (MACROBBIE, 1971), although these hypotheses undoubtedly have the advantage of resting upon increasing evidence that movement in many cells may be explained by the activity of tubules and protein filaments (e.g. FREY-WYSSLING, 1973). Several theories and views on sieve-tube translocation mentioned above are based on investigations with isolated phloem strands, thus on a translocation system that beside a longitudinal component also contains a radial one. Evidence presented by these authors for a metabolically-driven translocation of assimilates is therefore not *per se* in conflict with evidence obtained with *Yucca*. But the *Yucca* experiments have made it possible to deal separately with the longitudinal and the radial component of translocation. In *Yucca* the metabolic part of assimilate translocation seems restricted to the loading and unloading of the sieve tubes, thus to the radial components of the transport process. The longitudinal movement of sucrose through the sieve-tube lumen is the consequence of the secretion of sucrose in the source regions and its disappearance in the sink regions of the transport channel. Whether the sink is an artificial or a natural one, a bleeding site or a developing fruit, is very probably not essential for the phloem-transport system in *Yucca* or other bleeding monocotyledons.

References

ANDERSON, R., CRONSHAW, J.: Sieve-plate pores in tobacco and bean. Planta **91**, 173–180 (1970).

BARRAU, J.: The sagopalms and other food plants of marsh dwellers of the South Pacific Islands. Econ. Botany **13**, 151 (1959).

BECKER, D., KLUGE, M., ZIEGLER, H.: Der Einbau von $^{32}PO_4^{3-}$ in organische Verbindungen durch Siebröhrensaft. Planta **99**, 154–162 (1971).

BERGER, A.: Die Agaven. Beiträge zu einer Monographie. Jena: Fischer 1915.

BOLLARD, E.G.: The physiology and nutrition of developing fruits. In: The biochemistry of fruits and their products (ed. A.C. HULME), vol. I, p. 387–425. London-New York: Academic Press 1970.

BOSE, J.C.: Plant autographs and their revelations. London: Longmans, Green and Co. 1927.

BOWLING, D.J.F.: Translocation at 0° C in *Helianthus annuus*. J. Exptl. Botany **19**, 381–388 (1968).

BROWNING, K.C., SYMONS, C.T.: Coconut toddy in Ceylon. J. Soc. Chem. Ind. **35**, 1128–1142 (1916).

BURKILL, I.H.: A dictionary of the economic products of the Malay Peninsula. Vol. I. London 1935.

CANNY, M.J.: The rate of translocation. Biol. Rev. **35**, 507–532 (1960).

CANNY, M.J.: The mechanism of translocation. Ann. Botany (London) **26**, 603–617 (1962).

CANNY, M.J.: Phloem translocation. Cambridge University Press 1973.

CANNY, M.J., PHILLIPS, O.M.: Quantitative aspects of a theory of translocation. Ann. Botany (London) **27**, 379–402 (1963).

CATALDO, D.A., CHRISTY, A.L., COULSON, C.L., FERRIER, J.M.: Solution-flow in the phloem. I. Theoretical considerations. Plant Physiol. **49**, 685–689 (1972).

CATALDO, D.A., CHRISTY, A.L., COULSON, C.L., FERRIER, J.M.: II. Phloem transport of THO in *Beta vulgaris*. Plant Physiol. **49**, 690–695 (1972).

CHILD, R.: Coconuts. London: Longmans, Green and Co. 1964.

CHOI, I.C., ARONOFF, S.: Photosynthate transport using tritiated water. Plant Physiol. **41**, 1119–1129 (1966).

CRAFTS, A.S., CRISP, C.E.: Phloem transport in plants. San Francisco: Freeman and Co. 1971.

DARWIN, C.: A naturalist's voyage (1845). London: Edition of 1897.

DOUGLAS, J., BIMANTORO, R.R.: Identification of the *Corypha* palms which flowered in the Hortus bogoriensis during 1953–1955. Ann. Bogor. **2**, 137–146 (1956).

EATON, B.J.: Coconut toddy in Ceylon. Agr. Bull. Fed. Malay States **5**, 193–199 (1917).

EGELING, B.F.G.: Aquamiel, pulque und mezcal. Abhandl. u. Ber. des Vereins f. Naturk. zu Kassel **40**, 1–14 (1895).

ENGLER, A., PRANTL, K.: Die natürlichen Pflanzenfamilien. Bd. 15a. Leipzig: Engelmann 1930.

ESCHRICH, W.: Translokation radioaktiv markierter Indolyl-3-Essigsäure in Siebröhren von *Vicia faba*. Planta **78**, 144–157 (1968).

ESCHRICH, W.: Biochemistry and fine structure of phloem in relation to transport. Ann. Rev. Plant Physiol. **21**, 193–214 (1970).

ESCHRICH, W., HUTTERMANN, A., HEYSER, W., TAMMES, P.M.L., VAN DIE, J.: Evidence for the synthesis of "callose" in sieve tube exudate of *Yucca flaccida*. Z. Pflanzenphysiol. **67**, 468–470 (1972).

FENSOM, D.S.: A theory of translocation in phloem of *Heracleum* by contractile protein microfibrillar material. Can. J. Botany **50**, 479–497 (1972).

FISCHER, H.: Transport von organisch gebundenem Stickstoff. In: Encyclopedia of Plant Physiology (ed. W. RUHLAND), vol. VIII, p. 610–636. Berlin-Göttingen-Heidelberg: Springer 1958.

FISCHER, H.: Der Mineralstofftransport. In: Encyclopedia of plant Physiology (ed. W. RUHLAND), vol. XIII, p. 200–268. Berlin-Heidelberg-New York: Springer 1967.

FISCHER, H.: Phloemtransport und Stoffaufnahme. Z. Pflanzenernähr. u. Bodenk. **118**, 100–111 (1967).

FORD, J., PEEL, A.J.: The contributory length of sieve tubes in isolated segments of willows, and the effect of low temperatures. J. Exptl. Botany **17**, 522–533 (1966).

FREY-WYSSLING, A.: Theorie des Blutens. Ber. Deut. Botan. Ges. **47**, 434–450 (1929).

FREY-WYSSLING: Ernährung und Stoffwechsel der Pflanzen. Zürich: Büchergilde Gutenberg 1945.

FREY-WYSSLING, A.: Latex flow. In: Deformation and flow in biological systems (ed. A. FREY-WYSSLING), p. 322–343. Amsterdam: North Holland Publ. Comp. 1952.

FREY-WYSSLING, A.: Comparative organellography of the cytoplasm. Wien-New York: Springer 1973.

GARDNER, D.C.J., PEEL, A.J.: Metabolism and transport of ^{14}C-labeled glutamic and aspartic acids in the phloem of willow. Phytochemistry **10**, 2385–2387 (1971).

GARDNER, D.C.J., PEEL, A.J.: The effect of low temperature on sucrose, ATP and potassium concentrations and fluxes in the sieve tubes of willow. Planta **102**, 348–356 (1972).

GEIGER, D.R.: Effect of sink region cooling on translocation of photosynthate. Plant Physiol. **41**, 1667–1672 (1966).

GEIGER, D.R., SOVONICK, S.A.: Temporary inhibition of translocation velocity and mass transfer rate by petiole cooling. Plant Physiol. **46**, 847–849 (1970).

GHOSE, M.: A neglected source of sugar in Bihar. Agr. J. India **15**, 32–39 (1920).

GIAQUINTA, R.T., GEIGER, D.R.: Mechanism of inhibition of translocation by localized chilling. Plant Physiol. **51**, 372–377 (1973).

GIBBS, H.D.: The alcohol industry of the Philippine Islands. The Phil. J. Sci.; A. Chem. and Geol. Sci. and Ind. **6**, 99–206 (1911).

GROENEVELDT, W.P.: Notes on the Malay archipelago and Malacca compiled from Chinese sources. Verh. Bat. Genootsch. **39**, 1–144 (1880).

HEGNAUER, R.: Chemotaxonomie der Pflanzen. Vol. II: Monocotyledonae. Basel-Stuttgart: Birkhäuser 1963.

HEYNE, K.: De nuttige planten van Nederlands Indië. Batavia: Ruygrok 1927.

HEYNE, K.: De nuttige planten van Indonesië. Wageningen: Veenman 1950.

HODGE, W.H.: Toddy collection in Ceylon. Principes (J. Palm Soc.) **7**, 70–79 (1963).

HOUGH, W.: The pulque of Mexico. Proc. U.S. nation. Museum **33** (1579), 577–592 (1908).

HUBER, B.: Die Gewinnung des Eschenmanna — Eine Nutzung von Siebröhrensaft. Ber. Deut. Botan. Ges. **66**, 340–346 (1953).

HUTCHINSON, J.: The families of flowering plants. Vol. II: Monocotyledons—arranged according to a new system based on their probable phylogeny. Oxford: Clarendon Press 1959.

IE, T.S., TAMMES, P.M.L., VAN DIE, J.: Studies on phloem exudation from *Yucca flaccida* HAW. V. Electron-microscopy of sieve-plate pores. Proc. Koninkl. Ned. Akad. Wetenschap. **C69**, 660–663 (1966).

KARRER, W.: Konstitution und Vorkommen der organischen Pflanzenstoffe (exclusive Alkaloide). Basel-Stuttgart: Birkhäuser 1958.

KENNEDY, J.S., MITTLER, T.E.: A method of obtaining phloem sap *via* the mouth-parts of aphids. Nature **171**, 528 (1953).

KLUGE, M., BECKER, D., ZIEGLER, H.: Untersuchungen über ATP und andere organische Phosphorverbindungen im Siebröhrensaft von *Yucca flaccida* und *Salix triandra*. Planta **91**, 68–79 (1970).

KOLLMANN, R., DÖRR, I., KLEINIG, H.: Protein filaments—Structural components of the phloem exudate. I. Observations with *Cucurbita* and *Nicotiana*. Planta **95**, 86–94 (1970).

KOORDERS, S.H.: Verslag ener botanische dienstreis naar de Minahassa. Meded. 's Lands Plantent. **19**, 286–289 (1898).

KRAMER, P.J.: Plant and Soil Water Relationships. New York-Toronto-London: McGraw-Hill 1949.

KRAMER, P.J.: Transpiration and the water economy of plants. In: Plant Physiology (ed. F.C. STEWARD), vol. II, p. 607–726. New York-London: Academic Press 1959.

LÖHR, E.: Die Zuckerarten im Blutungssaft von *Betula* und *Carpinus*. Physiol. Plantarum **6**, 529–532 (1953).

LÜCK, E.: Pulque. Gordian (Hamburg) **68**, 303–304 (1968).

MACROBBIE, E.: Phloem translocation. Facts and mechanisms: a comparative survey. Biol. Rev. **46**, 429–481 (1971).

MARCO POLO: The travels: English translation by R. LATHUM, p. 254–255. Penguin Classics Edition 1972.

MARSDEN, H., SKILTON, F.L.: Yields of toddy from coconut palms. Malayan Agr. J. **19**, 287–290 (1931).

MCKELVEY, S.D., SAX, K.: Taxonomic and cytological relationships of *Yucca* and *Agave*. J. Arnold Arbor. **14**, 76–81 (1933).

MCNAIRN, R.B., CURRIER, H.B.: Translocation blockage by sieve-plate callose. Planta **82**, 369–380 (1968).

MEEUWSE, B.J.D.: Observations on the enzymatic action of maple and birch saps. New Phytologist **48**, 125–142 (1949).

MENON, K.P.V., PANDALAI, K.M.: The coconut palm: A monograph. Ernakulam—S. India: Indian Central Coconut Committee 1958.

MEYER-MEVIUS, U.: Vorkommen und Transport von Kohlenhydraten und Stickstoffverbindungen in den pflanzlichen Leitungsbahnen. Flora (Jena) **147**, 553–593 (1959).

MILBURN, J.A.: Phloem exudation from castor bean, exudation by massage. Planta **95**, 272–276 (1970).

MILBURN, J.A.: Phloem physiology and protective sealing mechanisms. Nature **236**, 82 (1972).

MILBURN, J.A.: Phloem transport in *Ricinus*. Pest. Sci. **3**, 653–665 (1972).

MOLISCH, H.: Botanische Beobachtungen auf Java. III. Die Sekretion des Palmweins und ihre Ursachen. Sitzber. Kais. Akad. Wiss. Wien **107**, 1247–1271 (1898).

MOLISCH, H.: Studien über Milchsaft und Schleimsaft der Pflanzen. Jena: Fischer 1901.

MOLISCH, H.: Pflanzenphysiologie als Theorie der Gärtnerei. Jena: Fischer 1916.

MORRIS, D.: Botany and its economic applications in the empire. Agr. J. India **15**, 207–216 (1920).

MOTHES, K.: Ammoniakentgiftung und Aminogruppenvorrat. In: Encyclopedia of Plant Physiology (ed. W. RUHLAND), vol. VIII, p. 716–762. Berlin-Göttingen-Heidelberg: Springer 1958.

MÜNCH, E.: Die Stoffbewegungen in der Pflanze. Jena: Fischer 1930.

NATHANAEL, W.R.N.: Toddy yields from coconut palms in Ceylon. Ceylon Coconut Quart. **4**, 8–17 (1955).

PATE, J.S.: The coconut, Madras 1938.

PATE, J.S., GUNNING, B.E.S.: Transfer cells. Ann. Rev. Plant Physiol. **23**, 173–196 (1972).

PATWARDHAN, V.G.: Gur-making from the juice of the date palm (*Phoenix sylvestris*) in the Thana district of the Bombay Presidency. Agr. J. India **15**, 525–532 (1920).

PEEL, A.J.: Further evidence for the relative immobility of water in sieve tubes of willow. Physiol. Plantarum **23**, 667–672 (1970).

PEEL, A.J., FIELD, R.J., COULSON, C.L., GARDNER, D.C.L.: Movement of water and solutes in sieve tubes of willow in response to puncture by aphid stylets. Evidence against a mass flow of solution. Physiol. Plantarum **22**, 768–775 (1969).

POLLARD, J.K., SPROSTON, T.S.: Nitrogenous constituents of sap exuded from the sapwood of *Acer saccharum*. Plant Physiol. **29**, 360–364 (1954).

REIJNE, A.: De cocos palm. In: De Landbouw in den Indischen Archipel (eds. C.C.J. VAN HALL and C. VAN DE KOPPEL), vol. IIa, p. 427–525. 's Gravenhage-Bandoeng: Van Hoeve 1948.

ROBIDOUX, J., SANDBORN, E.B., FENSOM, D.S., CAMERON, M.L.: Plasmatic filaments and particles in mature sieve elements of *Heracleum sphondilium* under the electron microscope. J. Exptl. Botany **24**, 349–359 (1973).

RUMPHIUS, G.E.: Amboinse Kruydboek (Herbarium Amboinense), vol. I. Amsterdam 1741.

SÁNCHEZ-MARROQUIN, A., HOPE, P.H.: *Agave* juice. Fermentation and chemical composition. Studies of some species. J. Agr. Food Chem. **1** (3), 246–249 (1953).

SAUTER, J.J., ITEN, W., ZIMMERMANN, M.H.: Studies on the release of sugar into the vessels of sugar maple (*Acer saccharum*). Can. J. Botany **51**, 1–8 (1973).

SCHUMACHER, W.: Die Fernleitung der Stoffe im Pflanzenkörper. In: Encyclopedia of Plant Physiology (ed. W. RUHLAND), vol. XIII, p. 61–177. Berlin-Heidelberg-New York: Springer 1967.

SPANNER, D.C.: Transport in the phloem. Nature **232**, 157–160 (1971).

STONE, D.L., CRONSHAW, J.:Fine structure of P-protein filaments from *Ricinus communis*. Planta **113**, 193–206 (1973).

SWANSON, C.A.: Translocation of organic solutes. In: Plant physiology (ed. F.C. STEWARD), vol. II, p. 481–551. New York-London: Academic Press 1959.

SWANSON, C.A., GEIGER, D.R.: Time course of low temperature inhibition of sucrose translocation in sugar beets. Plant Physiol. **42**, 751–756 (1967).

TAMMES, P.M.L.: Observations on the bleeding of palm trees. Rec. Trav. Bot. Neerl. **30**, 514–536 (1933).

TAMMES, P.M.L.: Bleeding of and sieve tube transport in palm trees. Proc. Koninkl. Ned. Akad. Wetenschap. **C54**, 30–31 (1951).

TAMMES, P.M.L.: On the rate of translocation of bleeding sap in the fruit stalk of *Arenga*. Proc. Koninkl. Ned. Akad. Wetenschap. **C55**, 141–143 (1952).

TAMMES, P.M.L.: Micro and macro-nutrients in sieve-tube sap of palms. Acta Botan. Neerl. **7**, 233–234 (1958).

TAMMES, P.M.L., IE, T.S.: Studies on phloem exudation from *Yucca flaccida* HAW. IX. Passage of carbon black particles through sieve-plate pores. Acta Botan. Neerl. **20**, 309–317 (1971).

TAMMES, P.M.L., VAN DIE, J.: Studies on phloem exudation from *Yucca flaccida* HAW. I. Some observations on the phenomenon of bleeding and the composition of the exudate. Acta Botan. Neerl. **13**, 76–83 (1964).

TAMMES, P.M.L., VAN DIE, J.: IV. Translocation of macro and micro-nutrients by the phloem sap stream. Proc. Koninkl. Ned. Akad. Wetenschap. **C69**, 655–659.(1966).

TAMMES, P.M.L., VAN DIE, J., IE, T.S.: Studies on phloem exudation from *Yucca flaccida* HAW. VIII. Fluid mechanics and exudation. Acta Botan. Neerl. **20**, 245–252 (1971).

TAMMES, P.M.L., VONK, C.R., VAN DIE, J.: Studies on phloem exudation from *Yucca flaccida* HAW. VI. The formation of exudate sucrose from supplied hexoses in excised inflorescence parts. Acta Botan. Neerl. **16**, 244–246 (1967).

TAMMES, P.M.L., VONK, G.R., VAN DIE, J.: VII. The effect of cooling on exudation. Acta Botan. Neerl. **18**, 224–229 (1969).

TAMMES, P.M.L., VONK, C.R., VAN DIE, J.: XI. Xylem feeding of ^{14}C-sugars and some other compounds, their conversion and recovery from the phloem exudate. Acta Botan. Neerl. **22**, 233–237 (1973).

THAINE, R.: The protoplasmic-streaming theory of phloem transport. J. Exptl. Botany **15**, 470–484 (1964).

THAINE, R.: Movement of sugars through plants by cytoplasmic pumping. Nature **222**, 873–875 (1969).

THOMPSON, R.G., THOMPSON, A.D.: Inhibition by cytochalasin B of sucrose transport in isolated phloem strands of *Heracleum*. Can. J. Botany **51**, 933–936 (1973).

TIETEMA, T., HOEKSTRA, S.M.R., VAN DIE, J.: Translocation of assimilates in *Fritillaria imperialis* L. II. Downward movement of ^{14}C-labeled photosynthates into the developing bulb and their subsequent distribution among the scale parts. Acta Botan. Neerl. **21**, 395–399 (1972).

TOMLINSON, P.B.: Monocotyledons—Towards an understanding of their morphology and anatomy. In: Advances in botanical research (ed. R.D. PRESTON), vol. III, p. 207–292. London-New York: Academic Press 1970.

VAN BEL, A.J.E.: Different translocation rates of ^{14}C-α-alanine and tritiated water in the xylem vessels of tomato plants. Acta Botan. Neerl. **23**, 715–722 (1974).

VAN DIE, J.: The use of phloem exudates from *Yucca flaccida* HAW. in the study of translocation of assimilates. Vortr. Gesamtgebiet Botan. N.F. **2**, 27–30 (1968).

VAN DIE, J.: The fruits of *Cocos nucifera* and *Phoenix dactylifera* as physiological sinks importing and assimilating the mobile aqueous phase of the sieve-tube system. Acta Botan. Neerl. **23**, 521–540 (1974).

VAN DIE, J., LEEUWANGH, P., HOEKSTRA, S.M.R.: Translocation of assimilates in *Fritillaria imperialis* L.I. The secretion of ^{14}C-labelled sugars by the nectaries in relation to phyllotaxis. Acta Botan. Neerl. **19**, 16–23 (1970).

Van Die, J., Tammes, P.M.L.: Studies on phloem exudation from *Yucca flaccida* Haw. II. The translocation of assimilates. Acta Botan. Neerl. **13**, 84–90 (1964).

Van Die, J., Tammes, P.M.L.: III. Prolonged bleeding from isolated parts of the young inflorescence. Proc. Koninkl. Ned. Akad. Wetenschap. **C69**, 648–654 (1966).

Van Die, J., Vonk, C.R.: Selective and stereo-specific absorption of various amino acids during xylem translocation in tomato stems. Acta Botan. Neerl. **16**, 147–152 (1967).

Van Die, J., Vonk, C.R., Tammes, P.M.L.: Studies in phloem exudation from *Yucca flaccida* Haw. XII. Rate of flow of ^{14}C-sucrose from a leaf to the wounded inflorescence top. Evidence for a primary origin of the major part of the exudate sucrose. Acta Botan. Neerl. **22**, 446–451 (1973).

Veen, H., Tammes, P.M.L.: Studies on phloem exudation from *Yucca flaccida* Haw. X. Translocation of indole-3-acetic acid. Acta Botan. Neerl. **20**, 356–366 (1971).

Warburg, O.: Die Pflanzenwelt. Bd. III, p. 383. Leipzig: Bibliographisches Institut 1922.

Wardlaw, S.F.: Temperature and the translocation of photosynthate through the leaf of *Lolium temulentum*. Planta **104**, 18–34 (1972).

Webb, J.A.: Translocation of sugars in *Cucurbita melopepo*. VI. The reversible low temperature inhibition of ^{14}C-movement and cold acclimation of phloem tissue. Can. J. Botany **49**, 717–733 (1971).

Wiersum, L.K.: Calcium content of fruits and storage tissues in relation to the mode of water supply. Acta Botan. Neerl. **15**, 406–418 (1966).

Wiersum, L.K.: The mass-flow theory of phloem transport; a supporting calculation. J. Exptl. Botany **18**, 160–162 (1967).

Williamson, R.E.: An investigation of the contractile protein hypothesis of phloem translocation. Planta **106**, 149–157 (1972).

Wooding, F.B.P.: Phloem. Oxford Biology Readers, No. 15. Oxford University Press 1971.

Woodroof, J.G.: Coconuts: production, processing, products. Westport, Conn. Avi 1970.

Ziegler, H.: Untersuchungen über die Leitung und Sekretion der Assimilate. Planta **47**, 447–500 (1956).

Zimmermann, M.H.: Transport in the phloem. Ann. Rev. Plant Physiol. **11**, 167–190 (1960).

Zimmermann, M.H.: The monocotyledons: their evolution and comparative biology. IV. Transport problems in arborescent monocotyledons. Quart. Rev. Biol. **48**, 314–321 (1973).

Zimmermann, M.H., Brown, C.L.: Trees: Structure and function. Berlin-Heidelberg-New York: Springer 1971.

9. Work with Isolated Phloem Strands

D.S. FENSOM

A. Introduction

When WILLIAM HARVEY was studying the circulation of blood in mammals three and a half centuries ago, his work was aided by his being able to separate arteries and veins both because of their appearance and their manner of function. Plant physiologists are not so fortunate in that their long distance phloem and xylem vessels are very intimately connected. They are also minute and usually protected by other tissues which makes their isolation in the living state difficult. Nonetheless the analogy between conductivity in plants and in animals leads one to suppose that there could be advantages in using isolated sieve tubes or other conducting tissue if the isolation could be performed without damage to the functioning tissue itself. In most cases, for example in trees, the difficulty of isolating phloem from xylem in small discrete bundles without killing the tissue in the process is enormous compared to isolation of arteries and veins in animals. However, the very close proximity of phloem and xylem in most of the higher plants which makes separation difficult seems not only to be a part of the morphological development of the two tissues, but also seems to indicate a functional feed-back relationship between the two.

It has long been recognized that studies on unisolated phloem are subject to some great uncertainties. Most studies feeding $^{14}CO_2$ to leaves cannot be done in times shorter than 10 or 15 min and often extend up to several hours (CANNY, 1960; FISHER, 1970). Therefore, if the work is carried out using tracer elements, lateral translocation and feed-back in cells adjacent to the sieve tubes add to the complexity of the observations. Long-term experiments may tell little about the actual front of advancing tracer, partly because of the feed-back and side effects mentioned above and partly because of the random action of many sieve tubes. On the other hand, short time experiments of less than 5 min duration usually involve loading of the leaf, photosynthesis, translocation and perhaps other processes which means that at the moment of examination of intact tissue there is either very little tracer at all or its distribution is too complex to sort out by a simple model. Nonetheless CANNY (1962) and others have long recognized that very short-term tracer studies would be useful, as would studies in which the lateral dispersion of translocated tracer is minimized. Both of these advantages occur in isolated phloem strands and therefore the evidence arising from such studies must be carefully considered.

Many people have studied fixed but isolated phloem tissue. The importance of this work, however, is to give information as it now stands on phloem which has been isolated while still alive. Some of the most successful earliest developments of this technique were done by ZIEGLER (1958), who found that the central hollows of the petioles of *Heracleum mantegazzianum* often contained isolated conducting bundles of phloem and xylem, surrounded by a parenchyma sheath, which were 1 or 2 mm across and which had separated from the wall of the surrounding petiole into the central hollow because of their rate of growth. This finding led to considerable advance in techniques of studying material translocated in phloem tissue (see previous section).

Meanwhile, SPANNER and PREBBLE (1962) had found that in the long petiole of the water plant *Nymphoides* the central phloem bundle is particularly well developed and fairly free of associated xylem or parenchyma. They developed a technique of exposing this bundle and studying it in partially isolated state using tracers, electrical techniques (FENSOM and SPANNER, 1969) and studies with the electronmicroscope (SIDDIQUI and SPANNER, 1970). This is to be compared with work by THAINE (1961) who did quick dissections of *Primula* and made observations under the light microscope of isolated phloem tissue, but the sections were relatively short, always excised from a living petiole. Therefore we may consider THAINE's work to be on strands which were possibly subject to more damage than strands attached to the plant at each end.

In the studies described below the phloem strand is either isolated by nature as in ZIEGLER's work, as a vascular strand, or else isolated by manipulation so that it is freed from much of the parenchyma and perhaps all of the xylem in the case of *Heracleum* and *Nymphoides*, and more recently, sugar beet. But in every case the tissue is allowed to remain attached to the parent petiole at each end so that it is in a sense part of, but also gently displaced from, its surrounding environment over a given length. In doing these manipulations it is hoped that minimal damage occurs to the actual phloem itself and that the preparation, at least in its early stages, will still conduct in the normal manner. Various findings with isolated strands will now be reviewed.

B. Studies of Heat-Pulse Movement

Isolated phloem strands from the central cavity of *Heracleum* were set up using sensitive thermo-couples above and below a central heating location. Then, when the small heat pulse was fed into the strand, the time taken for the thermo-couples to record the pulse was noted. In this way, ZIEGLER and VIEWEG (1961) found that their heat pulse moved from apex towards base in the petiole at a velocity between 30 and 80 cm h^{-1}. The heat movement in reverse direction was not appreciable. This work has been quoted frequently and it is indeed important, for it indicates a mass flow. The sensitivity of the detector is the most crucial part of the experiment. The main objection to the technique is that it was unable to indicate small flow components or the clear profile of flow with time. But in view of the frequent references to the work it would seem desirable to repeat it with more replicates upon tissue of various ages.

C. Electrical Studies

If an electroosmotic force were important in motivating translocation it was argued that the electroosmotic component should be detectable in isolated phloem strands, that the magnitude of the electroosmotic component should be big enough to move sugar, and finally that as sugars began to move down the petiole the driving force, namely the electrical potential difference across individual sieve plates or along the system should show an increase. The possibility was investigated by FENSOM and SPANNER in *Nymphoides* (1969), and they did indeed find some evidence that changes in potential might occur down a petiole as the sugar flow moved through. The changes that they found were changes that occurred after the petiole had been kept in the dark for 12 h when its leaf was given strong light (Fig. 1). But while changes were detected in some cases, there was little uniformity between them and explanations other than electroosmosis could be advanced. This led to measurement of Onsager coefficients in cut strands of phloem of *Nymphoides* and later in *Heracleum mantegazzianum*. TYREE and FENSOM (1970) published measurements on excised tissue, electrical conductivity, hydraulic conductivity, Onsager cross coefficients, and a few measurements done on the intact isolated bundles. These values are given in Table 1. It was deduced from this work that there might be a small electroosmotic component in the phloem tissue. On the other hand it was clearly

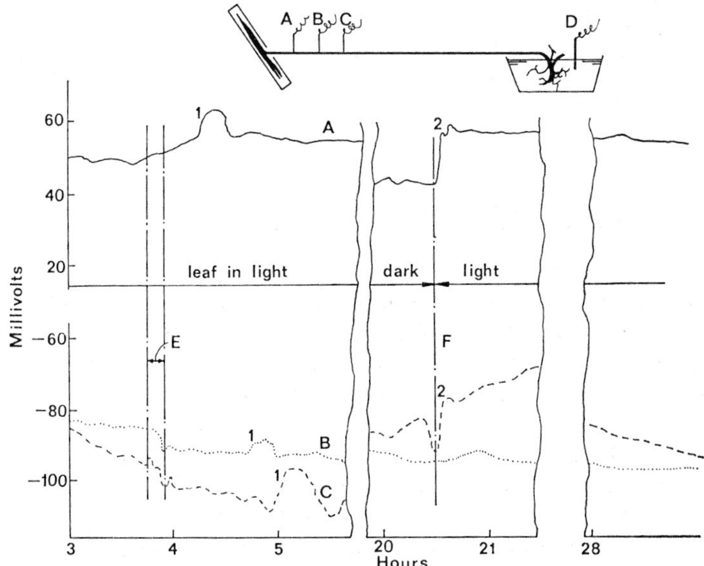

Fig. 1. Potential difference—time curves between electrodes *A*, *B*, and *C* in the phloem of *Nymphoides* and reference salt bridge electrode *D*. The distances leaf–*A*, *A*–*B*, *B*–*C*, and *C*–*D* were 5, 5, 5 and 30 cm respectively. Petiole covered with black polythene, but leaf illuminated in the daylight at time 0. At *E* about 3,000 lux additional illumination was added to the leaf for 10 min. The biopotential change possibly associated with *E* is marked 1–1–1. At *F* the leaf was again exposed to daylight after 14 h dark, on the following day. This time the associated potential changes seemed to occur on curves *A* and *C* at 2–2, but were not picked up on *B*. (From FENSOM and SPANNER, 1969)

Table 1. Thermodynamic coefficients of flow in *Heracleum* vascular bundles. (From TYREE and FENSOM, 1970)

No. of samples	Date of work	Observer and location	Solution and conditions	$(J/I \times 10^2$ $cm^3 Coul^{-1}$	$L_{PP} \times 10^2$ $cm^3 s^{-1} cm^{-2}$ $(J cm^{-3})^{-1} cm$	$L_{EE} \times 10^3$ $mho\ cm^{-1}$	$L_{PE} \times 10^5$ $cm^3 s^{-1} cm^{-2}$ $V^{-1} cm$	$L_{EP} \times 10^5$ $A\ cm^{-2}$ $(J cm^{-3})^{-1} cm$
4	1–10 July 1964	D.S.F. (A)	0.1 mN KCl, 22°–23° C, excised phloem	1.34 ± 0.12	—	—	—	—
7	1–10 July 1964	D.S.F. (A)	10 mN KCl+0.3 N sucrose 22–23° C, excised phloem	0.52 ± 0.04	—	—	—	—
5	July 1964	D.S.F. (A)	10 mN KCl+0.3 N sucrose 22–23° C, excised phloem	$0.59 + 0.04$	4.5 ± 0.7*	5.8 ± 1.7	4.0 ± 1.2	—
2	July 1964	D.S.F. (A)	0.1 mN KCl, 22–23° C excised phloem	1.2, 1.8	4.1, 8.2	0.9, 3.0	1.1, 5.1	—
6	3 July 1967	M.T.T. (B)	Freshly excised strands 2 cm long, no bathing medium	—	—	5.0 ± 0.5	—	—
5	19–23 June 1967	M.T.T. (B)	1 mN KCl+0.3 N sucrose, 22° C, excised phloem	1.7 ± 0.3	16 ± 2	0.52 ± 0.05	0.9 ± 0.15	—
5	8–15 Aug. 1967	P.I.	1 mN KCl+0.3 N sucrose, 22° C, excised phloem	0.64	1.9 ± 0.7	0.92 ± 0.1	0.59 ± 0.12	—
5	21 Aug. 1967	M.T.T. (B)	1 mN KCl+0.3 N sucrose, 22° C, excised phloem	—	—	0.77 ± 0.09	—	0.57 ± 0.13
5	24–31 Aug. 1967	P.I. (B)	0.1 N NaCl+0.1 N sucrose, 22° C, excised phloem	0.56	3.5 ± 1.5	7.5 ± 0.6	3.1 ± 0.8	—
5	22 Aug. 1967	M.T.T. (B)	0.1 NaCl+0.05 N sucrose, 22° C, excised phloem	—	—	7.1 ± 1.6	—	2.4 ± 0.6
6	Aug. 1968	M.B.A. (B)	Fresh strand *in situ* (uncut) no bathing medium	—	—	0.9 ± 0.2	—	—
5	5–8 Sept. 1967	M.T.T. (B)	2 mN KCl, excised xylem	6.2 ± 1.1	—	3.6 ± 0.6	23 ± 8	—
3	June 1967	M.T.T. (B)	2 mN KCl+2 mN NaCl, excised xylem	—	0.5, 1.8, 2.3 $\times 10^4$	—	—	—

Observers: D.S.F. = D.S. FENSOM; M.T.T. = M.T. TYREE; P.I. = P. INGRAM; M.B.A. = M. BRIGHT ASARE. Locations: (A) = Bedford College, Univ. London; (B) = Mount Allison University. All values reported are mean ± standard deviation of the mean whenever more than three samples are used.
* At Bedford College D.S.F. observed volume flows under a sucrose concentration difference. The hydraulic conductivity for two sample computed

evident that the electroosmotic movement, if any, was a very small proportion of the whole sugar flow. It was hoped that these measurements would permit discrimination between a mass-flow mechanism and an electro-kinetic one, but the artifacts of preparation were too great. It was realized at the time that callose formation might be considerable in the tissue prepared in this fashion, and this has subsequently been substantiated. The data of Table 1 are included because they are the first of their kind, and offer a base for more refined work. They also give values for electrical conductivity and electro-kinetic coefficients which can be used as a first approximation of *in vivo* values. This work showed that an approach using irreversible thermodynamics was a possible way to study the system and it lead to measurements such as electroosmotic efficiencies which permitted an electro-kinetic model to be tested theoretically and to some extent empirically.

Table 2. Electric biopotential gradients across sieve plates in phloem of *Heracleum*. (From D.R. LEE's Ph.D. thesis; to be published by LEE and BOWLING)

Sieve Element Potentials. Displaced phloem, intact plant, in 10^{-3} M KCl

ASP (mV)	BSP (mV)	TSP (mV)
−20	−20	0
− 4.5	− 3.0	1.5
−30	−30	0
−32	−28	4
−12	−12	0
− 7	−14	7
−14	−22	8
Mean		
−17.1 mV	−18.4 mV	2.9 ± 3.0 mV
Grouped Mean	−17.1 ± 9.9 mV	

ASP = apical side of sieve plate, polarity of tissue known. BSP = basal side of sieve plate. TSP = trans-sieve plate potential (referred to in text as trans-plate potential).

The possibility that circulation of potassium ions occurred around individual sieve plates needed further examination (SPANNER, 1970). This was done by BOWLING (1968, 1969) by putting microelectrodes across individual sieve plates in *Vitis*. Later the technique was improved by LEE (1972b) using isolated phloem strands of *Heracleum* still attached at each end (Table 2). In this way LEE (1972) was able to calculate the resistance of an individual sieve plate, the potential difference across it, and the pattern of potential along several plates. They concluded that no consistent electrical polarity occurred across successive sieve plates, and the plate resistances made an electro-kinetic mechanism highly improbable. They also found that with the techniques used for their preparation the strand was not appreciably conducting photosynthate. This electrical type of study has been useful in testing some of the possibilities advanced concerning electroosmotic models. And while the studies have convinced most people that electroosmotic mechanisms are unlikely, it must be admitted that the greater amount of evidence now lies on theoretical grounds (MACROBBIE, 1971; FENSOM, 1972) rather than on measurements in fully-operating sieve tubes.

Like many pieces of work, however, this rather negative conclusion has led to other ways of looking at the problem. For example, further investigation by direct microscopy and the use of tracers and dyes in isolated strands. These will now be discussed.

D. Light Microscopy of Isolated Phloem Strands

THAINE (1961) had already shown that it was possible to examine sieve tubes which he considered fully viable under the light microscope and in which he claimed he could detect particles passing from one sieve element to another along tubular inclusions. The heat studies and the electrical work suggested that sieve tubes should be re-examined, using the system of *Heracleum* where strands of isolated phloem could be displaced, yet left relatively intact and observed under very high magnification with the light microscope. The key to this problem appeared to lie partly with the plant material, partly with the use of Nomarski optics which are particularly suited for work in cells of several layers' thickness. Early among the findings by this method was the presence of the plastids about 1 μ across or smaller, which moved inside sieve tubes in a peculiar saltatory manner. These have often been called "marker" particles, for in phloem tissue their movement is characteristic of the sieve tubes and they may be seen in Fig. 2. Their movement and behavior was studied by FENSOM et al. (1968) and LEE, ARNOLD and FENSOM (1971) over a 3-year period and a cine-film was also taken by LEE, FENSOM and COSTERTON (1970). These particles can be found throughout the sieve-tube lumen, particularly in the state of minimal injury to tissue (Fig. 2b). As the tissue is damaged, the particles tend to collect near the plate (Fig. 2a and c) and eventually form aggregation with slime so that particles are particularly evident around each side of damaged plates. But this is not always the case; it appears from very careful work that the marker particles are distributed throughout the lumen of the sieve elements when the surrounding cells undergo normal protoplasmic streaming and when negligible aggregation occurs near the sieve plate (Fig. 2b). Under these conditions, indeed under both conditions, these particles appear to be attached to strands which are invisible when the tissue is in undamaged condition. There is further evidence that these particles themselves are restricted in their movement. They move rather as though they were in Brownian motion and yet around a locus so that they never wander very far from a point, yet their motion is about three times Brownian when the sieve tubes are in an undamaged state. If the tissue be progressively and very gently damaged, long strands of slime, also called aggregates of plasmatic filaments, form from one sieve plate to another and the marker particles are attached to these (see Fig. 2c). Upon further damage, the interplate strands break or snap as they may do at any time and the strands of marker particles themselves are found close to the plate. This leads eventually to what is known as a "slime plug".

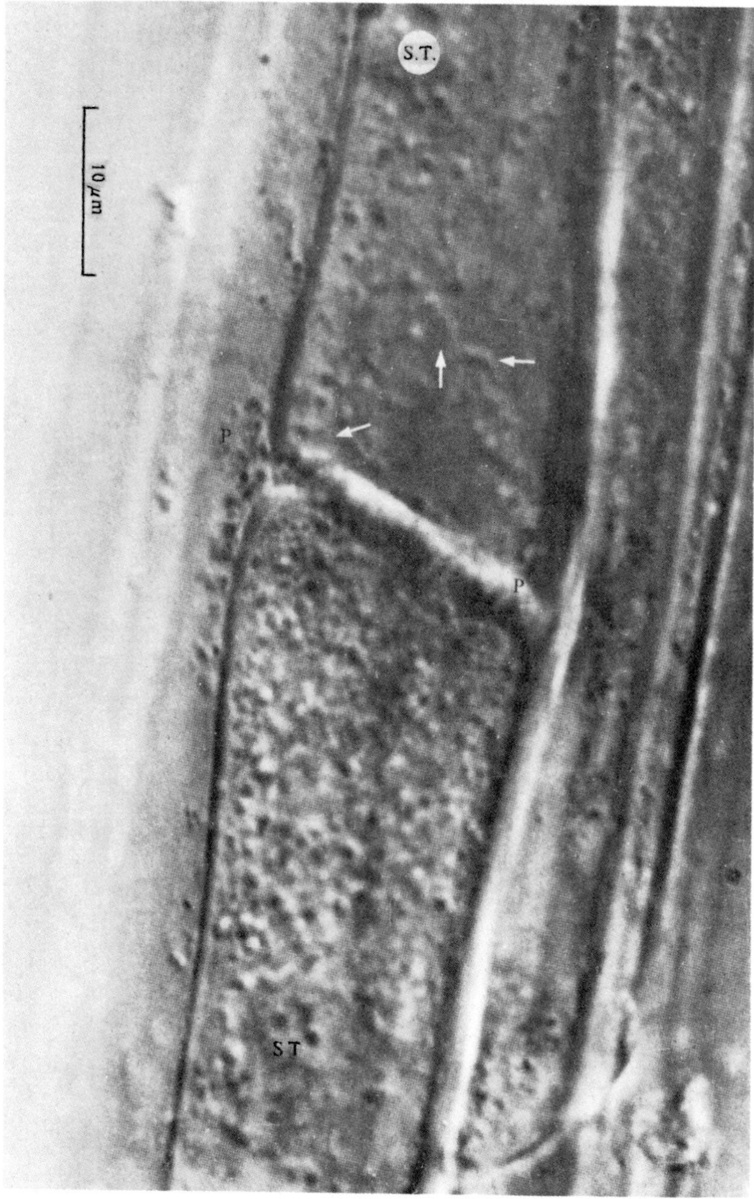

Fig. 2a. A sieve tube of *H. mantegazzianum, S.T.*, showing sieve plate *P*. Nomarski-interference optics. Exposure time $^{1}/_{5,000}$ sec. Particle aggregation indicates some damage. Some alignment of particles (arrows). (From LEE et al., 1971)

Cooling the strand upstream a technique which is known to stop translocation for a time (GEIGER, 1969), leads to great reduction in the motion of the marker particles after two minutes, whereas the same sort of cooling "downstream" did not give so readily detectable an effect. Feeding sucrose to the strand upstream externally caused the marker particles 2 cm away to move very rapidly indeed; certain poisons either caused their aggregation or a reduction in movement.

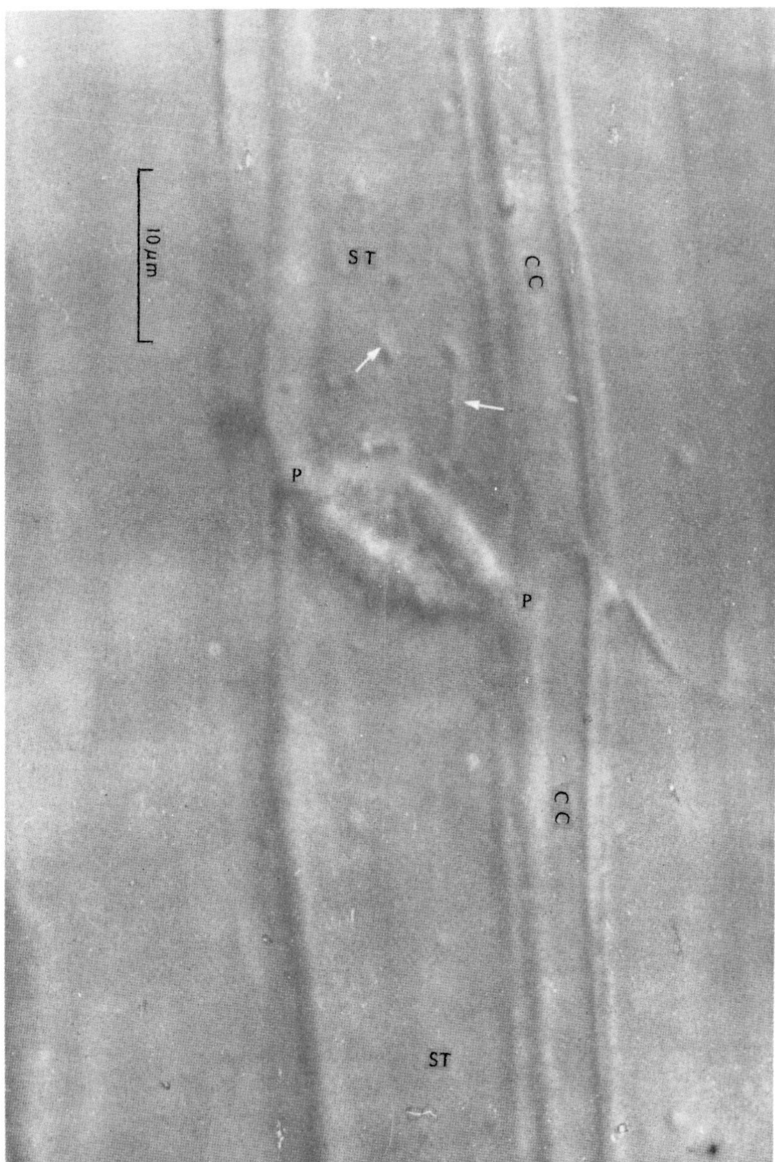

Fig. 2b. Relatively undamaged sieve tube *S.T.*, of *H. mantegazzianum*, transmitted flash $^{1}/_{2,000}$ sec. Companion cell, *CC*, sieve plate, *P*. Even distribution of particles in lumen of sieve tube, with particle alignment and strand of fibrils suggested (arrows). (From LEE et al., 1971)

It therefore appeared that at least some of the work, using the light microscope method technique, was actually disclosing a system that might be translocating. In some cases callose could be seen to develop around the sieve plates but in other cases the work was done with a minimum of callose in the early stages of it. In none of these preparations were particles observed to move from one element to another, as THAINE (1961) had reported. In very young tissue, protoplasmic

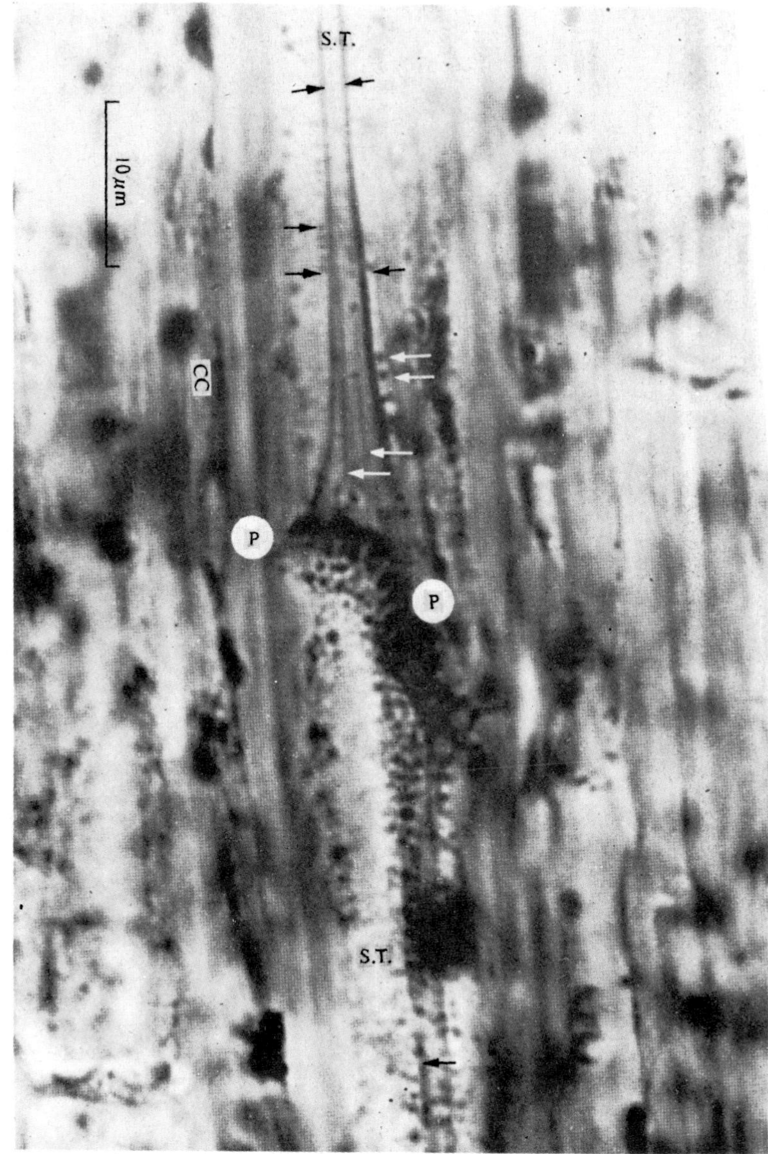

Fig. 2c. Nigrosin fixation of sieve tube of *H. mantegazzianum*. Transmitted light. Note strands above the plate *P* with particles (arrows) along the outer surface. *CC*, companion cell; *S.T.*, sieve tube. (From LEE et al., 1971)

streaming was seen inside the sieve element, but after mid-June or late June this was not visible. Essentially similar results were found by WILDON (1971).

Two further developments of considerable importance using light microscopy may also be described here. BARCLAY and FENSOM (1973), were able to inject carbon black into a sieve element prepared in this way and have shown that the carbon black could actually pass an uncallosed sieve plate. A picture of such an injection

Fig. 3a

Fig. 3a and b. Flash photographs of a carbon black injection into a sieve tube of *H. sphondylium*. The injection was done apically to a sieve plate. Successive flashes were 5 sec apart $^{1}/_{2,000}$ sec. Carbon black clearly passed through the plate. Scale lines 10 μm

Fig. 3c. A microinjection flash photograph showing carbon black passing through a sieve plate. The plate is at right angles to the page, but carbon black may be seen in several pores. Note marker particles, apparently intact in this case; also that the injection passes through one side of the plate only. Scale line 10 μm. (From BARCLAY and FENSOM, 1973)

Fig. 3b

Fig. 3c

is shown in Fig. 3a–c. This particular preparation was prepared using an anti-callose buffer and therefore it is suggested that when callosing is minimal, a kind of mass-flow movement does occur across a sieve plate when prepared in this fashion in isolated phloem strands. If the microfibrillar material on which the marker particles are attached actually goes through the plates, as seems possible, then either this must be very easily broken so that the plates can be penetrated by the pressure across them, or else it must be of such a fine nature that carbon black particles and the water solution carrying them can move externally to it. Both these possibilities must be seriously considered.

The other important finding is concerned with the microscopy of intact strands in *Heracleum sphondylium*, made by MITTON et al. (in preparation). It was observed that in September an isolated phloem strand had very little callose as detected by resorcinol blue staining technique, but when the strand was cut, callose showed up immediately in appreciable quantities. Subsequent studies confirmed that this condition of low callose was associated with plants in the late summer or early autumn in the case of *Heracleum sphondylium*. Callose occurred on all plates in the early part of the summer unless the plants were previously kept for 24 h in the dark. Subsequent work with various solutions led to the finding that when the buffer (7.0×10^{-2} mM Na_2CO_3, 4.5×10^{-2} mM KH_2PO_4, all in 0.1 M sucrose at pH 8.0) was used for the strands, callose detected by resorcinol blue was either minimal or absent in this species. On the other hand callose was always revealed in some quantity by the aniline-blue ultraviolet technique, but the quantity was considerably less than that present when the strands were damaged. With the use of this buffer it has been possible to make preparations which not only gave minimal callose as determined visually by the resorcinol blue microscope technique, but also appeared to conduct readily tracers applied from a feeding well or by micro-injection as described below (cf. Figs. 4 and 7).

In the course of the cine-film study of isolated phloem strands several instances have been noticed in which strands of marker particles appeared to be moving in a very different way from their neighbors inside a single sieve tube. For instance, in the film of LEE, FENSOM, COSTERTON (1970) one strand of marker particles is entirely at rest, while others surrounding it are moving in normal rapid motion. Later in the same film when the tissue was cooled upstream, two-thirds of the marker particles seemed to slow down in long ribbons or strands, whereas the remainder moved in regular fashion. FENSOM (1972) has suggested that this is evidence for a bi-directional movement within a single sieve element (see TRIP and GORHAM, 1968). While this is by no means proven, it is an interesting point which should be kept in mind by other workers.

E. Micro-Injection of Tracers

As soon as it was known that micro-pipettes could be inserted into sieve tubes of isolated phloem strands, the techniques of micro-injection and micro-manipulation were explored. Of particular interest is the micro-injection of tracers ^{14}C, THO, ^{32}P and ^{42}K. The technique used here by FENSOM and DAVIDSON (1970) and KNIGHT et al. (1974) has been to isolate the strand, leaving it attached to the petiole at both ends, if possible under an anti-callose buffer. The micropipette is inserted and the micro-injection made. The pipette is withdrawn and after 2 to 5 min the tissue is quickly excised, lifted onto dry ice and then cut into small sections, assayed by a scintillation counter. Several things are noticeable. One is that ^{14}C tracer

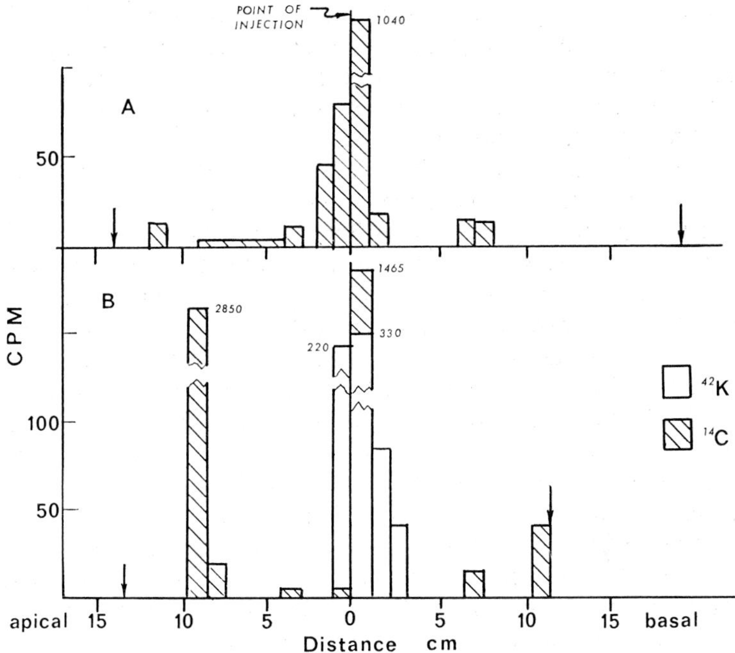

Fig. 4A and B. Microinjection of single sieve tubes in intact phloem strands. (A) histogram of cpm per cut section. ^{14}C injected as 4×10^{-4} µl of 0.3 M ^{14}C sucrose. (B) a similar experiment in which 0.1 M ^{42}KCl was simultaneously injected in 3×10^{-1} µl. In both cases the strands were frozen on dry ice and cut into sections 2 min after the microinjection. (From FENSOM, 1972)

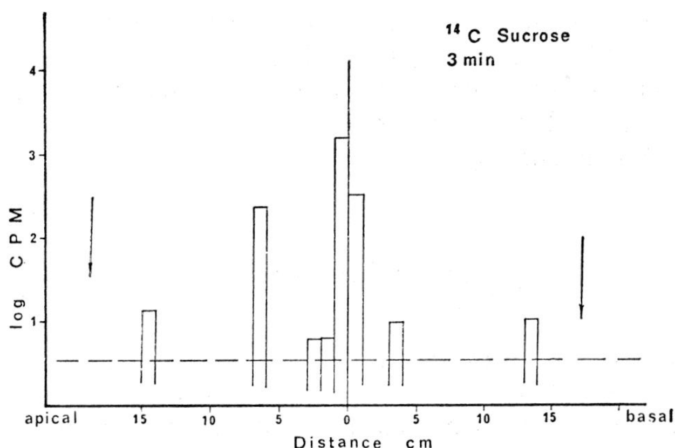

Fig. 5. A histogram of the radioactivity recovered in an isolated phloem strand after microinjection into a sieve tube at position "0" and run for 3 min before excision (at arrows). The strand was immediately frozen and then cut into 1 cm portions, each of which was assayed. Log cpm is plotted against distance from point of injection. 3.0×10^{-4} µl of 0.3 M ^{14}C-sucrose were injected without buffer. The broken line represents the 95% confidence limit. (From KNIGHT et al., 1974)

is found in apparent aggregates or pulses, both upstream and downstream from the point of injection after 2 to 5 min (Figs. 4 and 5). Secondly, the tracer near the point of injection is often found in a completely different pattern which would imply some sort of mass flow near this point. Thirdly, small amounts of tracer are often detected between the so-called pulses (Fig. 6). It may be that small amounts of tracer lie up- and downstream from the point of injection everywhere, but only those that are significantly different from the background have been reported. But it is thought that this implies some kind of movement which might be surface-active. At times no movement at all was obtained; this is thought to be associated with

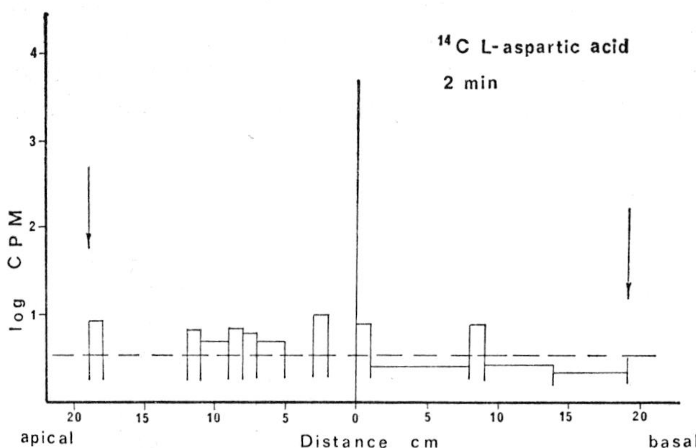

Fig. 6. Similar to Fig. 5. A 2-min run in which 2.4×10^{-3} µl of 10^{-4} M ^{14}C L-aspartic acid were injected. The long full lines represent tracer along five successive segments of the strand; the whole significantly above background by the method of paired variates. (From KNIGHT et al., 1974)

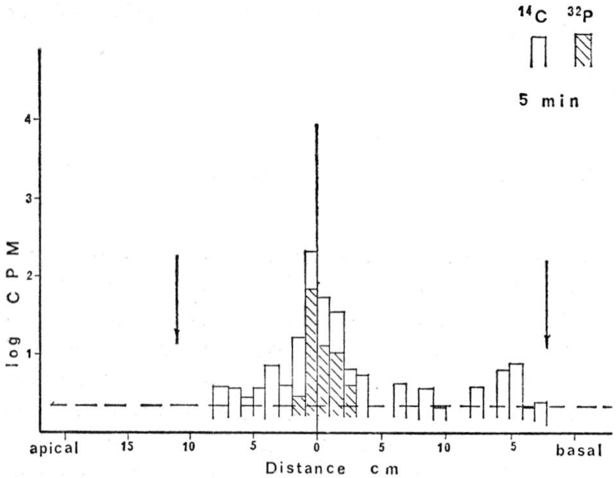

Fig. 7. Similar to Fig. 5. 4.5×10^{-3} µl of 0.5 M ^{14}C-sucrose were microinjected together with $K_3{}^{32}PO_4$ using anti-callose buffer. Note the restricted movement of ^{32}P. (From KNIGHT et al., 1974)

internal damage in the sieve-tube system. At other times the pulse movement was very evident and at positions along the strands which imply rates of translocation of the order of 300–400 cm h^{-1}. Of particular interest is the separation of movement of tracers: ^{42}K often moved independently from ^{14}C sucrose, tritiated water moved in a different pattern and ^{32}P again moved differently than did the ^{14}C (Fig. 7). Pulses did not move through areas of cold around 1° C nor through sections soaked in cytochalasin B (Fig. 8). Calculations by KNIGHT et al. (1974) and LEE (1972a) have shown that the tracer in the amounts observed could have been moving along the surface of many small microfilamentous strands inside the sieve element or they could have been moving in some sort of pulse in a larger channel. If the former is the case, then it is surprising that more tracer is not found everywhere in the tissue; if the latter, then the pulses must be moving. This would seem to support the latter view, but it is not yet certain. But it would be an important point to establish. L-aspartic acid moved very rapidly in pulse fashion (Fig. 6).

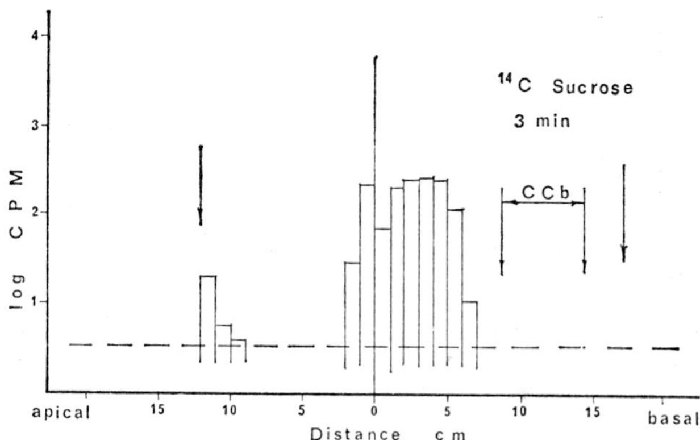

Fig. 8. A histogram similar to Fig. 5. Microinjection of ^{14}C-sucrose (without buffer) into a parenchyma cell adjacent to a sieve tube. The strand ran through a cytochalasin-B solution at "CCb" set 10 min before the run. (From KNIGHT et al., 1974)

F. Feeding Sucrose Solution to Isolated Phloem Strands

Objection has been raised to the possibility of damage to strands during micro-injection and to their subsequent abnormal functioning. To reduce this possibility, a drop of labeled sucrose solution was added to isolated strands by FENSOM and DAVIDSON (1970) and after a short interval the strands were excised, frozen and assayed in cm long portions. At first the drop was added to the strand surface; surface conductivity of the solution was then reduced by passing the strand through barriers of vaseline or, better, lanolin. The efficiency of the barrier was checked with the use of dye (indol-phenol red) added to the feeding well. THOMPSON and THOMPSON (1973), and THOMPSON et al. (1975) have found that ^{14}C moves along the strands in both directions from the feeding well in three types of pattern: near the well a slow movement (50–120 cm h^{-1}) carrying most of the tracer with an

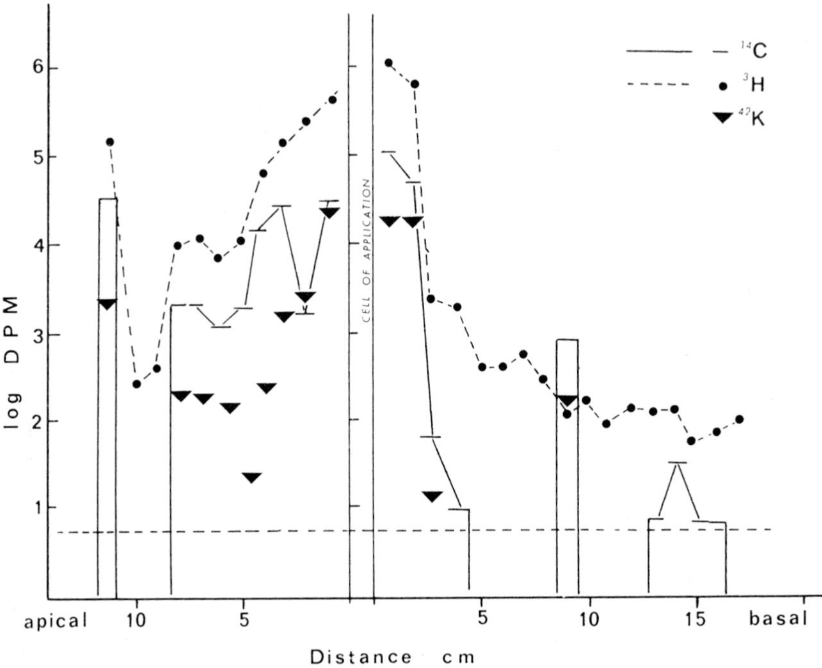

Fig. 9. Histogram of log net cpm against distance showing simultaneous movement of triple isotopes in an intact, but isolated phloem strand of *Heracleum*, 3 min after feeding a mixture of ^{14}C-sucrose, ^{42}KCl and ^{3}HHO to the cell of application. Note that the three isotopes travelled together near the feeding well, but were preceded by pulses and isotope separation. (From FENSOM, 1972)

apparent mass flow profile; further out a type of pulse flow with intervals of no detectable tracer (100–400 cm h^{-1}) (Fig. 9); fastest of all a trace or radioactivity in small amounts was at times detected (>500 cm h^{-1}). Damaged strands used as controls did not translocate. Nor did the tracer translocation pass cold areas (within 10 min of application) (Fig. 10) or through freshly prepared solutions of cytochalasin-B. In other words, the feeding technique gave results similar to micro-injection and having properties similar in most respects to the techniques using $^{14}CO_2$ on intact plants.

Finally, it should be noted that similar translocation patterns can be obtained with isolated strands which are completely detached from the parent plant. The three modes of flow are less in extent and quantity, but are still evident. THOMPSON et al. (1975) have interpreted this as meaning that completely detached strands contain their own loading and conducting system, even if separated from the parent plant. The system is clearly affected by callose, but when this is minimized, translocation may be considerable. They argue that the mass flow portion appears to be blocked by (a) callose or (b) by a process which hinders the action of microfibrillar material in the elements (cold or cytochalasin-B). They further argue that the small pulse-flow portion of translocation which precedes the mass flow is itself a key part of translocation and intimately connected with its mechanism.

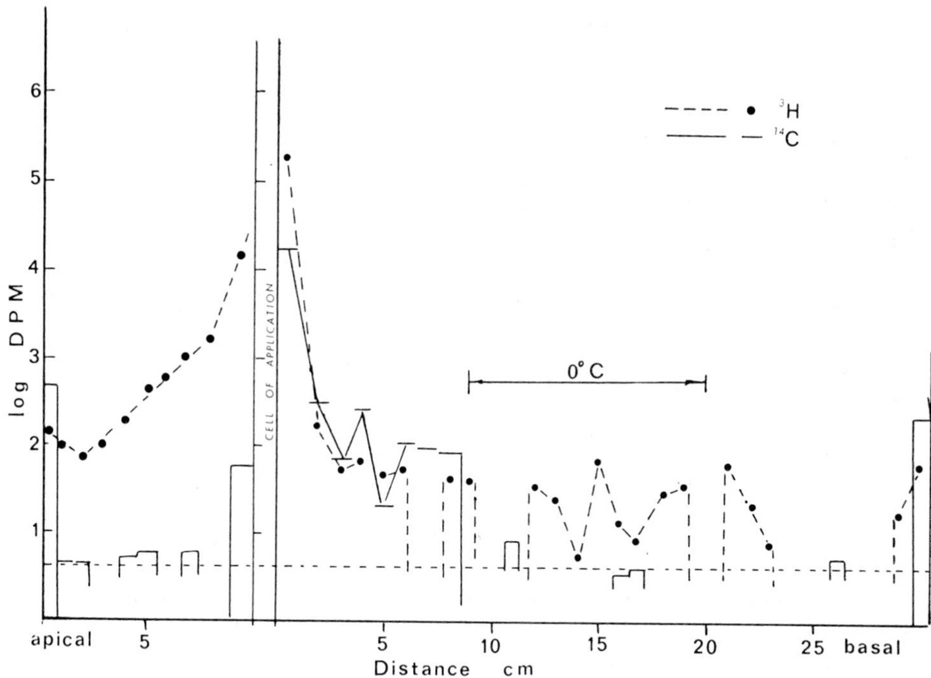

Fig. 10. Similar to Fig. 9, except that a "cold block" was applied 5 min before the run. Strand cut and frozen 3 min after tracer application. Note that practically no ^{14}C pulses went through the cold block, yet an appreciable quantity was detected at the extreme ends of the strand. The dashed line represents the 95% confidence level. (From FENSOM, 1972)

But care is obviously needed when this technique is used, for not only may spurious conductivities be obtained when tracer leaks from the well, but the strand must be kept moist at all times. The application of mineral oil or of a direct current appeared to prevent translocation (AIKMAN, CALDWELL and FENSOM personal communication). On the other hand the use of high sucrose concentration in the well of application and anti-callose buffer along the strand markedly enhanced it. HODDINOTT and GORHAM (1974) think that the mechanisms for translocation in these isolated strands are different than for those in the intact plant.

LEE (1972b) has found that dry-ice frozen strands also conduct tracer in somewhat similar fashion (but without the pulse flow mode). However, THOMPSON et al. (1975) obtained no appreciable translocation using liquid nitrogen-killed strands in their experiments. This anomaly has not yet been resolved at the time of writing.

As in the case of the micro-injection experiments, ^{14}C sucrose moved in a different pattern than did ^{3}HHO, and very different from ^{42}K, $^{32}PO_4$ and ^{137}Cs, but identical to ^{3}H sucrose. All tracers moved in larger amounts in tissue prepared in the late summer when callose was minimal, or when anti-callose buffer was used (at any time). The $^{137}Cs^{+}$ and most of the $^{42}K^{+}$ and $^{32}PO_4^{\equiv}$ were confined to the mass flow modes, but pulses have been obtained in advance of the mass flow which contained some K and P in small amounts. In general, however, the ^{14}C seemed to move ahead of K and P pulses and separate from them.

G. Electronmicroscopy of Isolated Strands

Since isolated phloem strands are much more rapidly fixed than larger thicknesses of living tissue, they were clearly suitable material to examine under the electronmicroscope. ZIEGLER (1960) using glutaraldehyde fixatives found that the plate pores of his preparations contained plasmatic filaments with occasional portions of endoplasmic reticulum. SPANNER (personal communication) and JOHNSON (1968 and 1973) studying isolated strands of *Nymphoides* have also found much plasmatic filamentous material in both the lumina and plate pores of the sieve elements. The work upon *Heracleum* was repeated by ROBIDOUX et al. (1973) using dimethyl sulphoxide as a penetrant to speed up the action of glutaraldehyde. They have found plasmatic filaments (p.f.) stretching axially through the sieve elements from plate to plate and seeming to carry through the plate pores (Fig. 11a). They have found that isolated portions of p.f. are helical in appearance 6–7 nm diam. and occasionally exist in aggregates of about 20–40 nm diameter along which small swellings or vescicles are visible (Fig. 11b). They have not found membrane-bound tubules of the type described by THAINE et al. (1967). JOHNSON (1973), using freeze-etching technique on strands known to be translocating, has also found evidence for continuous plasmatic filaments axially located, though he has not found evidence of strings of vescicles (Fig. 12b).

Two other advances using electron microscopy on isolated strands have recently appeared. SABNIS and HART (1973) and HART and SABNIS (1973) have found that neither colchicine nor vinblastine cause discernible effects on ultrastructure of sieve elements, nor is the translocation of photosynthate affected by these chemicals. They do find that binding of colchicine and sieve-tube protein can occur. This implies that the translocatory mechanism is not linked with microtubular action—as opposed to the plasmatic filaments which are found dispersed in mature sieve tubes and which are probably implicated because of the inhibitory action on translocation of cytochalasin-B (THOMPSON and THOMPSON, 1973).

The first scanning electronmicrographs of sieve tubes have now appeared (SANDBORN et al., in preparation). They show that the marker particles are indeed tied to a reticulum of fine strands, some of which stretch axially from plate to plate, but many lead towards companion cells presumably *via* plasmadesmata (Fig. 12a).

▶

Fig. 11a. Transmission electronmicrograph of phloem of *H. sphondylium;* injection technique with cold fixative *in vivo* (DMSO + glutaraldehyde + acrolein). Sieve plate sectional axially. Filamentous material △ in strands through the lumen, swellings along strands ▲. (×48,000)

Fig. 11b. Possible microperistaltic swelling ▲ along transplate microfilamentous strands from the lumen of a sieve tube of a petiole of mature *H. sphondylium*. Injection and fixation as in 11a (×48,000). The line in (a) and (b) is 0.5 μm. (Figs. 11a and b from ROBIDOUX et al., 1973)

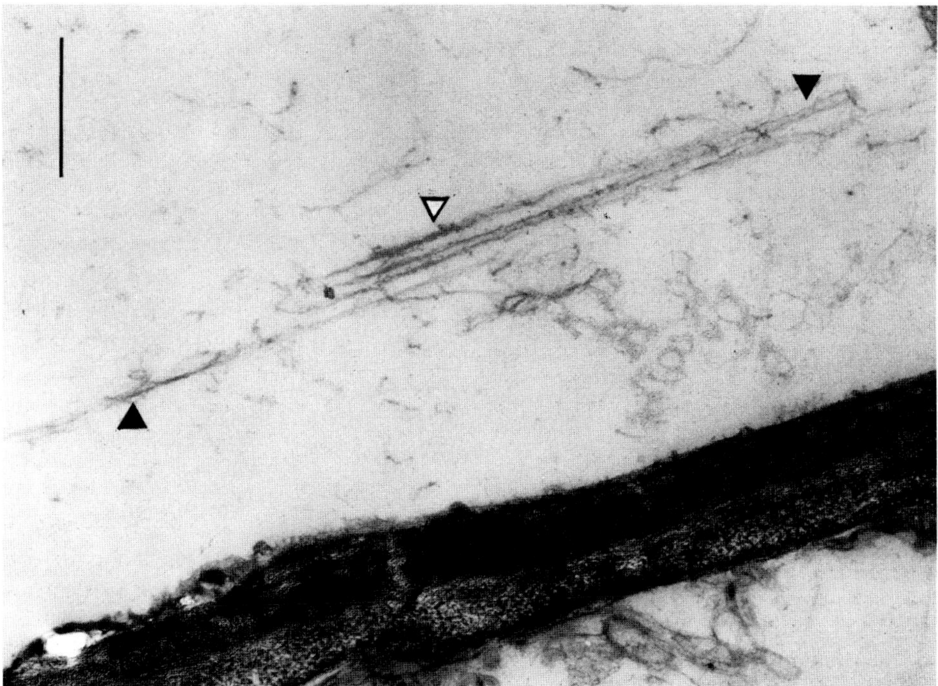

Fig. 11 a. Legend see opposite page

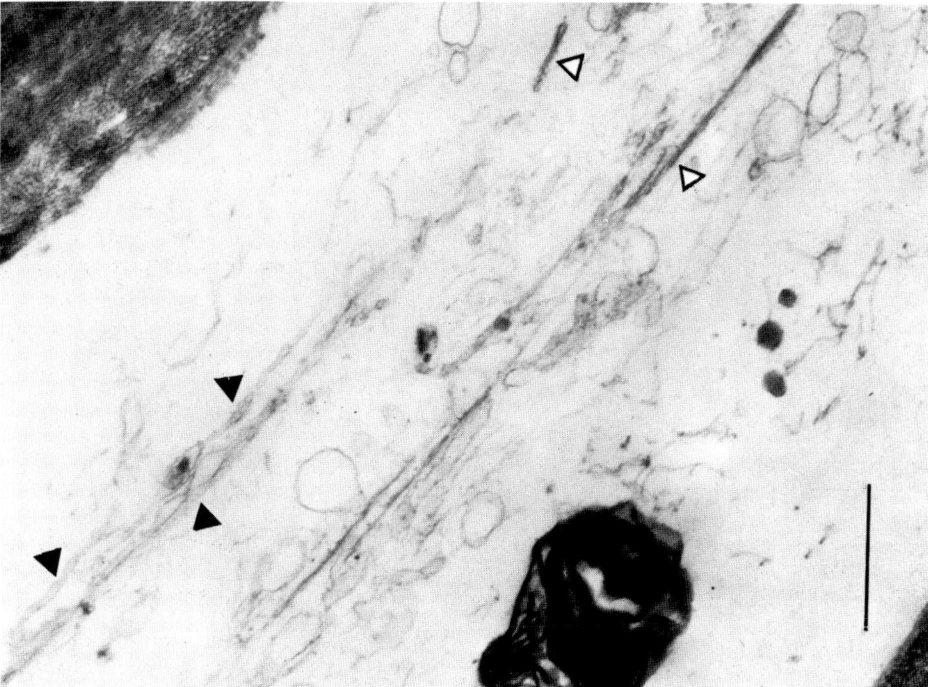

Fig. 11 b. Legend see opposite page

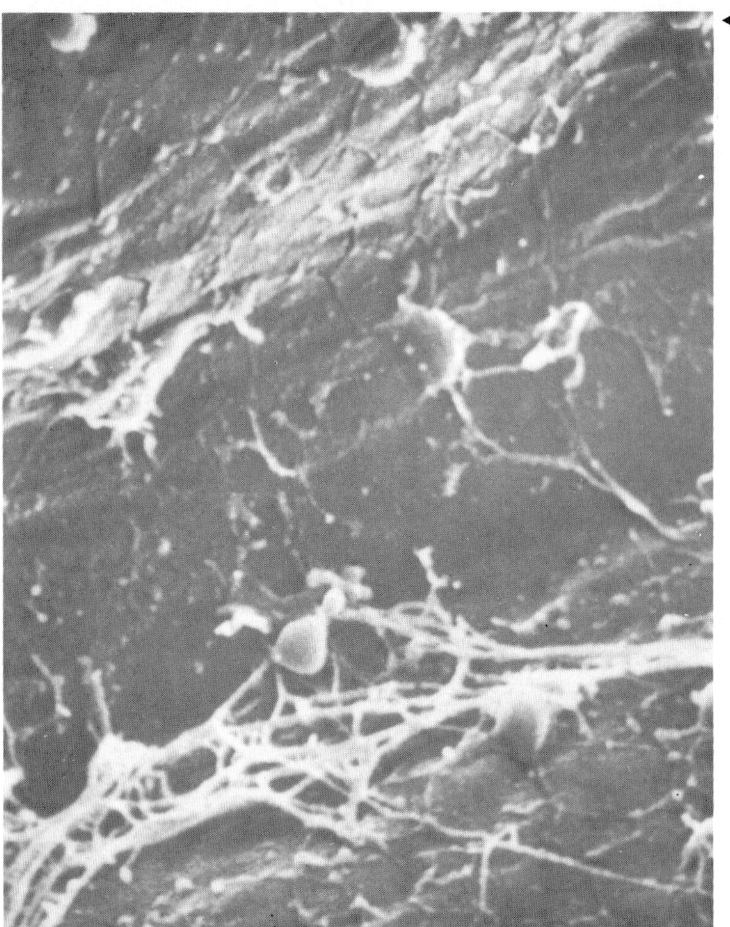

◀ Fig. 12a. Scanning electron micrograph of mature phloem of *H. sphondylium*, prepared by the injection technique using cold fixative *in vivo* as in Fig. 11. Sieve tube is shown in axial section, shadowed and scanned (× 10,000 approx). Fibrillar reticulum and some marker particles in the lumen of the tube to show axial and transverse attachments. (From SANDBORN et al., in prep.)

Fig. 12b. Electron micrograph of a sieve tube and sieve plate of translocating *Nymphoides* prepared by freeze-etching technique. The plate is to the right, showing part of three pores (1, 2, 3) with banded filaments near pores (for example at small arrowheads) and bundles or strands of filaments in the lumen (between broken lines). *P* (Plasmalemma), large arrow shows in which direction platinum carbon was applied. (From JOHNSON, 1973)
▼

H. Summary

The use of isolated phloem strands has added an important new method to the study of translocation phenomenon in the last decade. Where the strands are prepared by gentle detachment from other living tissue they are still subject to injury effects and perhaps to excessive oxidation after displacement. Yet these problems and other artifacts are slowly being surmounted. The advantages of examining the translocation patterns in a very few or even a single sieve tube are obvious.

Meanwhile this new technique has made possible direct observations of living sieve tubes, direct measurements of transplate parameters—such as biopotential or resistance, and to the exciting use of microcanulation for either injection or sampling of the contents of sieve-tube sap. It has also led to a way to observe and to control callose formation and to improved electronmicrograph technology. If the recent findings be accepted as valid, the mechanism of translocation includes a mass flow portion and also a pulse flow moiety. The first is particularly sensitive to the amount of callose in the plates, the second to the integrity and active functioning of axially-oriented microfibrillar material known as P-protein. FENSOM (1972) has suggested that the second and faster portion involves contractile proteinaceous material, and is of much greater importance than hitherto realized.

References

BARCLAY, G.F., FENSOM, D.S.: Passage of carbon black through sieve plates of unexcised *Heracleum sphondylium* after micro-injection. Acta Botan. Neerl. **22**(3), 228–232 (1973).

BOWLING, D.J.F.: Measurements of the potential across the sieve plates in *Vitis vinifera*. Planta **80**, 21–26 (1968).

BOWLING, D.J.F.: Evidence for the electro-osmotic theory of transport in the phloem. Biochim. Biophys. Acta **183**, 230–232 (1969).

CANNY, M.J.: The rate of translocation. Bio. Rev. **35**, 507–532 (1960).

CANNY, M.J.: The mechanism of translocation. Ann. Botany (London) **25**, 152–167 (1962).

CANNY, M.J.: Phloem translocation. London: Cambridge University Press 1973.

FENSOM, D.S.: A theory of translocation in phloem of Heracleum. Can. J. Botany **50**, 479–497 (1972).

FENSOM, D.S., CLATTENBURG, R., CHUNG, T., LEE, D.R., ARNOLD, D.C.: Moving particles in intact sieve tubes of *Heracleum mantegazzianum*. Nature **219**, 531–532 (1968).

FENSOM, D.S., DAVIDSON, H.R.: Micro-injection of ^{14}C sucrose into single living sieve tubes of *Heracleum*. Nature **227**, 857–858 (1970).

FENSOM, D.S., SPANNER, D.C.: Electro-osmotic and biopotential measurements in phloem strands of *Nymphoides*. Planta **88**, 321–331 (1969).

FISHER, D.B.: Kinetics of C-14 translocation in soybean. I. Kinetics in the stem. Plant Physiol. Lancaster **45**, 114–118 (1970).

GEIGER, D.R.: Chilling and translocation inhibition. Ohio J. Sci. **69**, 356–366 (1969).

HART, J.W., SABNIS, D.D.: Colchicine-binding protein from phloem and xylem of a higher plant. Planta **109**, 147–152 (1973).

HODDINOTT, J., GORHAM, P.R.: Translocation of ^{14}C labelled assimilates in petioles and phloem loops of *Heracleum lanatum*. Can. J. Botany **52**, 349–354 (1974).

JOHNSON, R.P.C.: Microfilaments in pores between frozen etched sieve elements. Planta **81**, 314–332 (1968).

JOHNSON, R.P.C.: Filaments but no membranous transcellular strands in sieve pores in freeze-etched translocating phloem. Nature **244**, 464–466 (1973).

KNIGHT, B.K., MITTON, G.D., DAVIDSON, H.R., FENSOM, D.S.: Microinjection of ^{14}C sucrose and other tracers into isolated phloem strands of Heracleum. Can. J. Botany **52**, 1491–1499 (1974).

LEE, D.R.: Possible significance of filaments in sieve elements. Nature **235**, 286 (1972a).

LEE, D.R.: Ph.D. Thesis, Dept. of Botany, University of Aberdeen (1972b).

LEE, D.R., ARNOLD, D.C., FENSOM, D.S.: Some microscopical observations of functioning sieve tubes of *Heracleum* using Nomarski Optics. J. Exptl. Botany **22**, 25–38 (1971).

LEE, D.R., FENSOM, D.S., COSTERTON, J.W.: Particle movement in intact phloem of *Heracleum*. Can. Natl. Film Library, Ottawa, Canada (1970).

MACROBBIE, E.A.C.: Phloem translocation Facts and Mechanisms: A comparative survey. Biol. Rev. **46**, 429–481 (1971).

MITTON, G.D., KNIGHT, B.K., FENSOM, D.S.: In preparation.

ROBIDOUX, J., SANDBORN, E.B., FENSOM, D.S., CAMERON, M.L.: Plasmatic filaments and particles in mature sieve elements of *Heracleum sphondylium* under the electron microscope. J. Exptl. Botany **24**, 349–359 (1973).

SABNIS, D.D., HART, J.W.: P-protein in sieve elements. I. Ultrastructure after treatment with vinblastine and colchicine. Planta **109**, 127–134 (1973).

SANDBORN, E.B., BLAIS, P., ROBIDOUX, S.J., FENSOM, D.S.: Sieve tubes of *Heracleum* by scanning electron microscope. (In preparation.)

SIDDIQUI, A.W., SPANNER, D.C.: The state of the pores in functioning sieve plates. Planta **91**, 181–189 (1970).

SPANNER, D.C.: The electro-osmotic theory of phloem transport in the light of recent measurements of *Heracleum* phloem. J. Exptl. Botany **21**, 325–333 (1970).

SPANNER, D.C., PREBBLE, J.N.: The movement of tracers along the petiole of *Nymphoides peltatum*. I. A preliminary study with 137-Cs. J. Exptl. Botany **13**, 294–306 (1962).

THAINE, R.: Transcellular strands and particle movement in mature sieve tubes. Nature **192**, 772–773 (1961).

THAINE, R., PROBINE, M.C., DYER, P.Y.: The existence of transcellular strands in mature sieve elements. J. Exptl. Botany **18**, 110–127 (1967).

THOMPSON, R.T., THOMPSON, A.D.: Inhibition by cytochalasin-B of sucrose transport in isolated phloem strands of *Heracleum*. Can. J. Botany **51**, 933–936 (1973).

THOMPSON, R.T., THOMPSON, A.D., FENSOM, D.S.: Translocation of ^{14}C sucrose and ^{3}HHO fed to isolated phloem strands of *Heracleum*. Can. J. Botany (in press).

TRIP, P., GORHAM, P.R.: Bidirectional translocation of sugars in sieve tubes of squash plants. Plant Physiol. **43**, 877–882 (1968).

TYREE, M.T., FENSOM, D.S.: Some experimental and theoretical observations concerning mass flow in the vascular bundles of *Heracleum*. J. Exptl. Botany **21**, 304–324 (1970).

WILDON, D.C.: Cine film. School of Biological Sciences, University of East Anglia, Norwich, U.K. (1971).

ZIEGLER, H.: Über die Atmung und den Stofftransport in den isolierten Leitbündeln der Blattstiele von *Heracleum mantegazzianum*. Som. et Lev. Planta **51**, 186–200 (1958).

ZIEGLER, H.: Untersuchungen über die Feinstruktur des Phloems. I. Mitteilung. Die Siebplatten bei *Heracleum mantegazzianum*. Somm. et Lev. Planta **55**, 1–12 (1960).

ZIEGLER, H., VIEWEG, G.H.: Der experimentelle Nachweis einer Massenströmung in Phloem von *Heracleum mantegazzianum* Somm. et Lev. Planta **56**, 402–408 (1961)

10. Bidirectional Transport

W. ESCHRICH

A. Introduction

I. Brief Historical Survey

Experimental work on bidirectional transport was motivated to elucidate the mechanism of assimilate translocation. At a time when "ascending" (water) and "descending" (assimilates) sap streams were still spoken of by most botanists, CURTIS (1920a, b) suggested that carbohydrates may be transferred longitudinally through the phloem in either direction. Later MASON et al. (1936) and PHILLIS and MASON (1936), suggested that carbohydrates and nitrogenous compounds in cotton plants could move through the phloem simultaneously in opposite directions. They advanced the concept of source-to-sink movement of assimilates (MASON and PHILLIS, 1937), to replace that of a "descending sap stream". Meanwhile, potassium fluorescein was found to be a valuable tracer for sap movement in sieve tubes (SCHUMACHER, 1933). PALMQUIST (1938) used it to try to demonstrate simultaneous movement of carbohydrates and fluorescein in opposite directions in the phloem. Experimental times then were still very long (two days in Palmquist's case), which made interpretation difficult. When radioactive tracers became available as tools for biological research, shorter experiments with two different tracers became possible. CHEN (1951) applied ^{14}C and ^{32}P to an upper and lower *Pelargonium* leaf respectively and found both tracers in bark strips, separated from the xylem, in the stem between the two points of application, and concluded that bidirectional movement had taken place in the phloem. But his experimental times were still 12 to 17 h, ample time for repeated upward movement in xylem and downward movement in phloem. BIDDULPH and CORY (1960), utilizing the same tracers, were able to differentiate between ^{14}C- and ^{32}P-radiation in autoradiographs of bean plants. This provided the first evidence that bidirectional movement could occur in a single vascular bundle. With BIDDULPH and CORY's paper, investigations were initiated which, besides their original purpose of elucidating the problem of bidirectional transport, introduced new and valuable techniques for the study of sieve-tube translocation.

II. Aims

The aim of investigations on bidirectional transport is to determine whether simultaneous movement of solutes in opposite directions can take place in a single sieve tube. If such movement does occur it would be difficult to explain in terms of the concept of pressure flow (see Chapter 14), as originally proposed by MÜNCH (1930). On the other hand, the occurrence of bidirectional movement in a single sieve tube would not be incompatible with some alternative hypotheses of sieve-tube translocation. So far, evidence for bidirectional movement in a single sieve tube is still inconclusive.

III. Anatomical Aspect

Long-distance translocation of assimilates is restricted to plants equipped with phloem or other specialized conducting tissues as in mosses, or red and brown algae. Among these plants there are apparently no species or plant organs with solitary sieve tubes. With the exception of a few organs—for example, the midveins of submersed aquatic plants like *Elodea* (CURRIER and SHIH, 1968)—sieve tubes or equivalent rows of cells are branched and interconnected as a system which traverses the whole plant having numerous terminations.

Thus, it is questionable whether one should refer to a "single sieve tube" when a single part of the sieve-tube system is intended. In addition, the sieve-tube system is composed of sieve elements of varying age and stages of differentiation. Even in monocotyledons with only primary phloem, differentiation of conducting tissues proceeds simultaneously acropetally and basipetally, as for example in a leaf vein and its trace (ESAU, 1965b).

B. Experiments

I. Analysis of Sieve Tubes between Two Sources

1. Gross Autoradiography

BIDDULPH and CORY (1960) applied $^{14}CO_2$ to the lowest ternate leaf of a bean plant (*Phaseolus vulgaris*) and $^{32}PO_4$ to the next higher leaf. After 30 min, the bark was peeled off, frozen and dried. The cambial surface of the flattened bark was exposed to X-ray film with or without an aluminium filter to reduce almost completely the ^{14}C-radiation. In addition, autoradiographs were prepared after the decay (10 half-lives) of ^{32}P.

Acropetal transport of ^{14}C and basipetal transport of ^{32}P were recorded in separate phloem bundles. In addition, movement of both tracers in opposite directions in the same bundle was also observed. The authors concluded after resolving the traces on the X-ray film that, within a single bundle, bidirectional movement occurred only in the most recently-formed sieve tubes of the secondary phloem. In a subsequent paper BIDDULPH and CORY (1965) reported the pattern of distribution of ^{14}C metabolites provided by a single leaf. Phloem bundles were located with the fluorescence method of callose detection (CURRIER and STRUGGER, 1956). Comparison of the pictures published in this article does not reveal complete correlation between labeled and fluorescing strands. The reader therefore must depend upon the authors' description to learn the exact results of their experiments. According to this, labeled assimilates exported by a single leaf moved downward in the stem. At the next lower node, part of the labeled assimilates entered other bundles, which carried them upward beyond the node of the source leaf. In younger parts of the stem, upward transport sometimes began at the node of the fed leaf.

The results of BIDDULPH and CORY's study (1965) confirm the premise that assimilates can recycle in the stem. For the moment, it is of little importance whether this happens in separate or single bundles. In either case, such a cycle appears to start with a downward movement. This is in agreement with anatomical features and developmental processes, and apparently it is related to the age of the bundle.

2. Microautoradiography

TRIP and GORHAM (1968) administered glucose-6-^{3}H solution to a mature leaf of a 3-week old *Cucurbita* plant (*C. melopepo* BAILEY, var. *torticollis*), and after 160 min a half-grown leaf of the same plant was allowed to assimilate $^{14}CO_2$. 20 min later the plant was frozen and parts of it were processed for liquid scintillation counting. The latter showed that tritium had entered the petiole of the $^{14}CO_2$-fed leaf and that ^{14}C-assimilates, exported basipetally, had passed the tritium label. From that region freeze-dried petiole tissue was infiltrated with paraffin and 10 μm sections were exposed to Kodak NTB-10 plates. Part of the emulsion had been coated previously with gelatine to screen out ^{3}H-radiation. The microautoradiographs showed diffusely labeled external phloem bundles in cross sections.

By comparing screened and unscreened microautoradiographs of radial sections, the authors concluded that both tracers occurred in the same sieve tube and, therefore, a transport mechanism other than mass flow must have been operative in the sieve tubes. This conclusion was based on 3 microautoradiographs of heavily damaged phloem tissue, with not a single sieve element of normal appearance. In addition, discrimination between screened and unscreened label, as well as grain counting, was performed in different radial sections. The evidence that both tracers were present in the same sieve tube is not convincing. However, this experiment does show convincingly that the tracers moved in opposite directions in the same phloem bundle.

3. Aphid Techniques

Aphid techniques for tapping single sieve tubes are described in Chapters 6 and 7. It was the purpose of two investigations (ESCHRICH, 1967; HO and PEEL, 1969) to determine whether a single aphid could produce doubly-labeled honeydew when feeding in a sieve tube situated between two sources of differing tracers. In one case (ESCHRICH, 1967), *Vicia faba* plants with 4 primary leaves were investigated, and individuals of the aphid species *Acyrthosiphon pisum* were applied to the internode below the 3rd leaf. The honeydew was collected on a turntable rotating once in 24 h (Fig. 1).

The leaves of *Vicia faba* are arranged in two orthostichies, leaf 3 positioned over leaf 1. The latter was supplied with K-fluorescein, while leaf 3 was fed with ^{14}C-labeled urea or bicarbonate. In preliminary experiments it was shown by fluorescence microscopy and microautoradiography that both tracers were present in the same phloem bundles of the stem part between the two source leaves.

In 12 experiments, 68 aphids produced rows of honeydew drops which were recorded by photographing the "honeydew chronogram" under UV-light, as well as by exposing it to X-ray film.

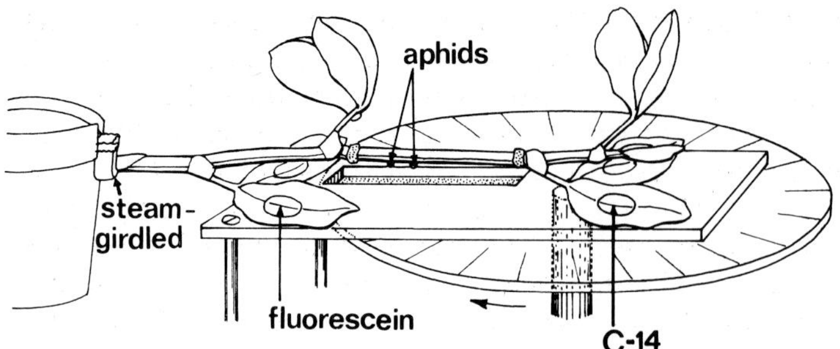

Fig. 1. Setup used by ESCHRICH (1967) for recording honeydew production of individual aphids. The stem of the *Vicia faba* plant was steam-girdled. Fluorescein and ^{14}C-compounds were applied to abraded areas of the lower side of midveins of both leaflets. Aphids were encaged on one internode by 2 rings of grease. The turntable was covered with a sheet of celluloid 24 cm in diameter. (From ESCHRICH, 1967)

The results showed that 42% of the rows of droplets were doubly-labeled from the first drop. 7% first labeled singly, later became doubly-labeled. 21% were only fluorescein-labeled. 28% were only ^{14}C-labeled, and 2% were unlabeled.

At first glance, the results suggest that bidirectional transport occurred in a single sieve tube. However, as pointed out, no plant contains solitary sieve tubes. Lateral sieve plates connect adjacent sieve tubes of a branched system, making possible the recycling of tracers not only at the nodes but also in the internodes. This was taken into account, and the concept of the "homodromous loop-path" was advanced (Fig. 2). If one tracer moves basipetally in one sieve tube and the second tracer acropetally in an adjacent sieve tube, both tracers can merge without

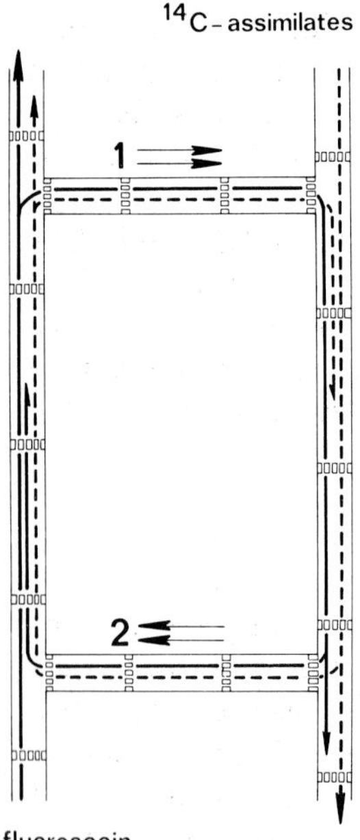

Fig. 2. Model explaining the "homodromous loop-path". When two anastomoses (*1, 2*), or lateral sieve plates, connect two longitudinal sieve tubes, transporting different tracers in opposite directions, both tracers can merge without change of direction of flow. (From ESCHRICH, 1967)

change of the direction of flow, provided the sieve tubes are connected by lateral sieve plates or anastomoses. An alternative, even simpler explanation, is that the two tracers each move toward a stylet sink from opposite directions as is generally assumed (see Chapter 6). A similar setup was used by HO and PEEL (1969) (see Chapter 7). Their results confirm those found in *Vicia faba* (ESCHRICH, 1967). Arguments against transport in a single sieve tube are the same for both investigations. Since 2 to 3-year-old branches of willow were used in some of the experiments by HO and PEEL, there must have been at least 2 increments of secondary phloem. Branch-feeding aphids are known to utilize sap of young as well as older (17 months!) sieve tubes in *Tilia americana* (EVERT et al., 1968). It is not known whether secondary sieve tubes of different age are connected by anastomoses. In *Tilia*, for example, groups of sieve tubes are separated by tangential bands of fibres. Even in herbaceous plants (e.g. *Impatiens*), it was found that newly formed longitudinal sieve tubes, produced after severing a bundle, ran parallel to the sieve tubes of the metaphloem, but did not become connected with them by lateral sieve plates (ESCHRICH, 1953). And as pointed out, bidirectional transport in bean plants seemed to be restricted to phloem with newly formed secondary sieve tubes (BIDDULPH and CORY, 1960).

Since most of the honeydew droplets obtained in the experiments of HO and PEEL were doubly-labeled, the aphids apparently fed in the same increment of sieve tubes. The situation was essentially similar to that in *Vicia faba*, in which only primary phloem was present and an exchange of tracers *via* a homodromous loop path (Fig. 2) was possible. Another important question to be considered is whether a single aphid can influence the direction of solute transport or whether it constitutes only a relatively minor sink. Calculations based on the amount of honeydew produced by different aphids (MITTLER, 1957; HILL, 1963) indicate that sap flow in a sieve tube would have to be raised to a velocity of 300 to 500 cm/h to deliver the measured volume of honeydew.

During the *Vicia faba* experiments 49% of the rows of honeydew droplets were singly labeled. Since an aphid should be able to attract its food from both directions, it might be questioned why only 42% of the aphids produced doubly-labeled honeydew. Possibly the aphid simply extracts what is available at its stylet tips. However, its sink must cause enhanced secretion (phloem loading either at one or the other source, or at both sources simultaneously).

Summarizing the results of the aphid experiments with *Vicia faba* and *Salix viminalis*, it can be concluded that (1) bidirectional transport can occur both in vascular bundles containing only primary phloem and in strips of bark in which only the secondary phloem is functional, and (2) lateral movement between sieve tubes is possible but does not result in an overall redistribution of assimilates.

II. Bidirectional Spreading from a Single Source

It is well established by numerous experiments that tracers introduced over a single leaf spread in the stem in both acropetal and basipetal directions (CRAFTS and CRISP, 1971, and literature cited therein). The direction of transport in the stem depends on the developmental stage of the source leaf. In general, young, mature leaves supply the top region of the shoot, old leaves supply the basal parts of the stem and the roots, and middle-aged leaves supply both regions. Since more than one leaf belongs to the group of middle-aged leaves, bidirectional transport must occur in that part of the stem situated between such leaves.

Vicia faba has at least 3 primary leaves which simultaneously are middle-aged. Two of these are situated in the same orthostichy (Fig. 1). In addition, the vascularization of the nodes is fairly simple and makes this species especially suitable for studies on bidirectional transport. This plant has been used for such experiments by PETERSON and CURRIER (1969) and by FRITZ (1973).

Since the movement of K-fluorescein was recorded in free-hand transverse sections by PETERSON and CURRIER, it was not possible to determine the capacity of single sieve tubes to transport bidirectionally. The buffered dye solution was supplied from a trough around the stem and fluorescing phloem bundles were recorded in camera-lucida drawings from transverse sections above and below the site of dye application. Of 130 bundles (from 13 treated plants) only 6 were found in which the dye was located in both apical and basal sections. Similar results were obtained with other plant species.

The conclusion of PETERSON and CURRIER that bidirectional transport is restricted to separate bundles is contrary to those of the experiments outlined above, which indicate clearly that a bidirectional transport does occur in individual bundles. It is pertinent to note that PETERSON and CURRIER did observe acropetal transport in small bundles and basipetal transport mainly in the leaf traces extending downward from that leaf, which was inserted just above the internode where the tracer was introduced.

FRITZ (1973) concentrated his studies on internodes of *Vicia faba*, which showed in gross autoradiographs a bidirectional spreading of the ^{14}C-labeled tracer. He applied very low concentrations (0.04–0.08 μM) of 1-^{14}C-DL-3-phenylalanine (spec. activity 48 mCi/mM) to small abraded areas outside a lateral leaf trace in the middle of an internode. Isolated from the ring of stem bundles for more than one length of an internode, the lateral leaf traces traverse the two ridges of the stem (Fig. 4). Stem parts above and below the site of tracer application were freeze-dried and embedded in resin, and microautoradiographs of cross sections 1 to 1.5 μm thick were prepared as described by FRITZ and ESCHRICH (1970). This technique, more extensively described by ESCHRICH and FRITZ (1972), allows the exact localization of soluble radioactivity in any sieve tube of a bundle.

The results obtained by FRITZ from experiments with 26 plants showed bidirectional transport in the same bundle in 12 plants. 6 plants showed only acropetal transport, and 8 only basipetal transport. Of the 12 plants in which bidirectional transport was observed, 5 had labeled sieve tubes in the same region of the phloem above and below the site of application of the label. In the remaining 7 plants, the acropetally and basipetally transporting sieve tubes were located in different regions of a cross-sectional area.

C. Bidirectional Transport in Relation to Vascular Differentiation

I. Anatomical Aspect

Vicia faba has been the main object for investigations on bidirectional transport (Section B). Its pattern of primary vascularization is relatively simple and may be ventured for possible pathways of assimilate transport. Fig. 3 shows a series of cross sections of the stem of *Vicia faba*, starting above (A) and ending below (J) one of the nodes. If the five prominent bundles of the petiole are followed backwards into the stem, it is found that only three bundles, the median (*med*) and two lateral (*lat*) leaf traces supply each leaf. In Fig. 4 the pathways of lateral leaf traces of one side (A) and the median leaf traces of one orthostichy (B) are illustrated diagrammatically.

Comparing A and B of Fig. 4, one can see that the median leaf trace traverses two internodes below its associated leaf, then branches to provide room for the median leaf trace of the next lower leaf of that orthostichy. The two branches continue downward through two more internodes and eventually lose their identity by joining similar branches derived from lateral leaf traces of a younger leaf.

The course of the lateral leaf traces is essentially the same as that of the median trace, except that the first two internodes are traversed in complete isolation inside the wings of the stem.

From the number of bundles in any cross section of Fig. 3 we can estimate that 4 to 5 leaves of one orthostichy are represented by leaf traces at a given level. This means that the leaf traces of each leaf extend as far as 8 to 10 internodes below its node of insertion.

The size of the leaf traces diminishes continuously in the downward direction. In the first and second internodes below the leaf, the associated traces are represented by primary phloem and primary xylem, including protophloem and protoxylem. In the seventh and eighth internodes below the leaf the branches of the leaf traces are represented only by metaphloem (open circles in Fig. 3). Xylem is not present at that level until secondary growth is initiated there.

II. Differentiation

Translating the anatomical pattern into developmental terms, it can be stated that the leaf traces of a given leaf are initiated 8 to 10 plastochrons prior to the formation of the primordium of that leaf. Accordingly, the procambium appears in the stem before it does in the leaf and it differentiates acropetally (ESAU, 1965b). Within the growing primordium acropetal differentiation, in general, proceeds until formation of the leaf blade is initiated.

Concomitantly with the elongating primordium, protophloem elements differentiate acropetally. It is not known how far back in the stem leaf traces are established with protophloem.

With increasing size of the leaf and elongation of the internodes, formation of protophloem sieve tubes is discontinued and metaphloem elements differentiate.

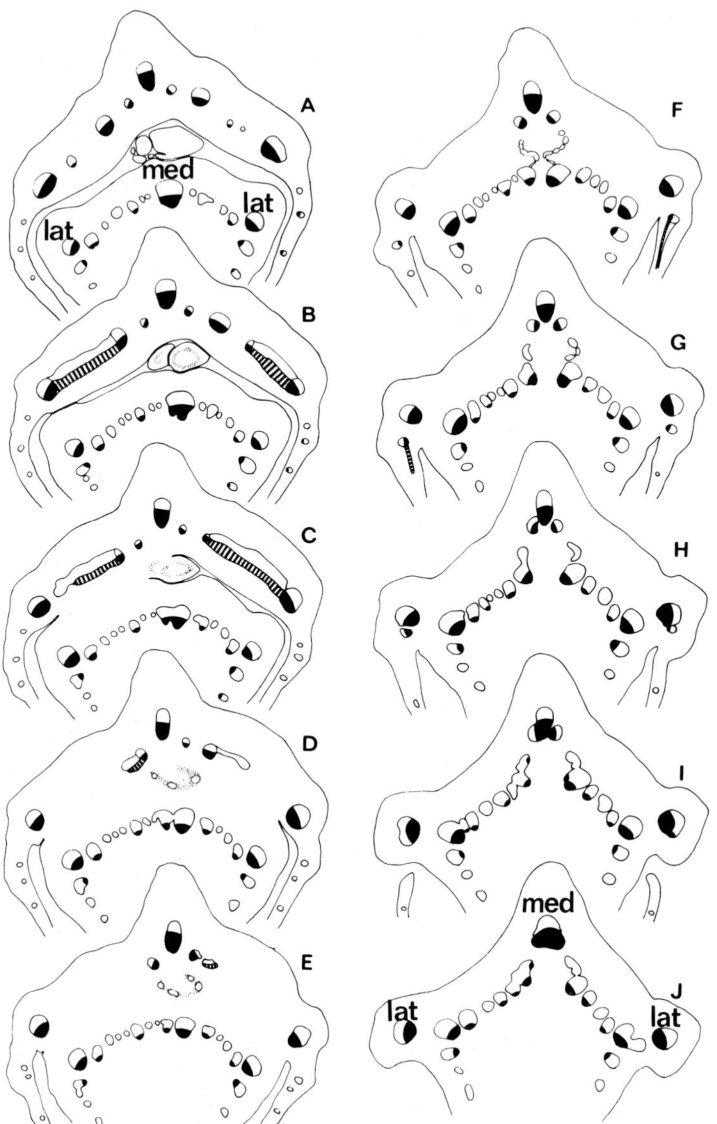

Fig. 3. Vascular pattern of the stem of *Vicia faba,* represented by selected cross sections of a series starting above (A) and ending below (J) a node. Open circles, phloem; black parts of the bundles, xylem. (From FRITZ, 1973)

Metaphloem develops both acropetally and basipetally, beginning at the level of the stem where the leaf is inserted (ESAU, 1965a).

Before the leaf reaches maturity, it passes through a developmental stage involving overall basipetal maturation of the leaf blade. The upper limit of this stage has been characterized for *Populus deltoides* leaves by LARSON et al. (1972): Leaf plastochron index 4, the pattern of smallest veins can be recognized and the mesophyll exhibits intercellular spaces.

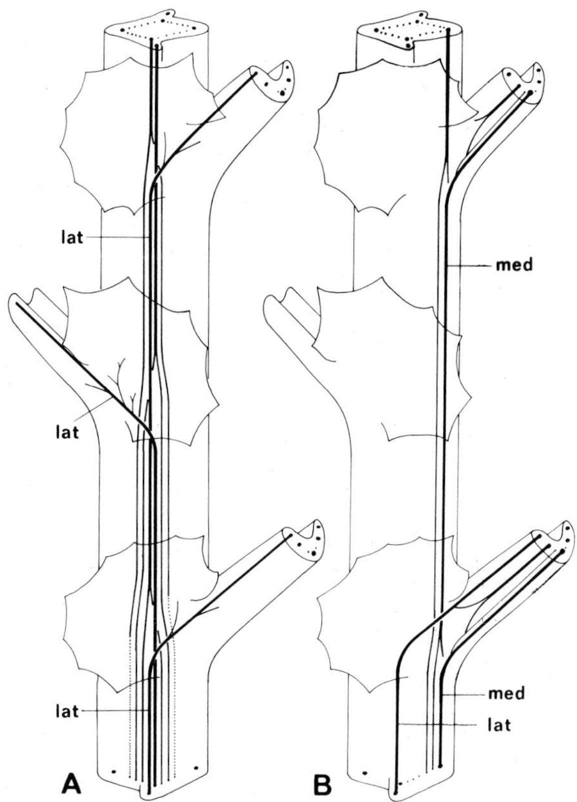

Fig. 4. Diagrams of the course of lateral leaf traces (*lat*) of one side (A) and median leaf traces (*med*) of one orthostichy (B) in the stem of *Vicia faba* (From FRITZ, 1973)

III. Transport

The shoot tip and all growing leaves import assimilates, which are provided by exporting leaves.

According to the pattern of leaf traces (Section C.I), exported assimilates move basipetally. Acropetal transport results when the leaf traces of the exporting leaf come into contact with leaf traces of a younger leaf, which is still importing. This can occur just below the node of insertion of the exporting leaf, when the median leaf trace is used for export. The two lateral leaf traces join the ring of bundles two internodes below the node of leaf insertion.

A reversal from basipetal to acropetal transport can occur as far as 10 internodes below the exporting leaf, provided leaf traces of importing leaves are available. If the exporting leaf is the oldest of 5 mature leaves of its orthostichy, no acropetal transport occurs because all leaf traces at this level of the stem belong to exporting leaves. Thus, the shoot tip and growing leaves of *Vicia faba* draw assimilates from 8 recently matured leaves and in part from partly mature leaves, which are exporting and importing simultaneously.

The latter deserve a special consideration, because their leaf traces show simultaneous basipetal and acropetal transport (TURGEON and WEBB, 1973). Such bidirectional transport within a single bundle is restricted to sieve tubes of the metaphloem (FRITZ, 1973). Apparently the first-formed sieve tubes of the metaphloem are concerned primarily with acropetal transport. Since differentiation of the sieve elements progresses basipetally in the leaf traces and acropetally in the leaf, imported assimilates first move against the gradient of sieve-tube differentiation. After entering the leaf, imported assimilates move with the differentiation gradient. Exported assimilates, in turn, have first to move against, and then, after entering the stem, with the gradient of sieve-element differentiation. Thus, there seems to be no relation between direction of sieve-element differentiation and direction of transport.

The number of metaphloem sieve tubes transporting in the acropetal direction is relatively small, one to three in the pictures published by FRITZ (1973). It is not known whether these sieve tubes later can switch over to basipetal transport. Microautoradiographs of leaf traces of a mature leaf which previously was exposed to $^{14}CO_2$ are depicted in FRITZ and ESCHRICH (1970, Fig. 2) and ESCHRICH and FRITZ (1972, Figs. 4, 6). Although many labeled sieve tubes of the metaphloem indicate basipetal transport, some appear unlabeled. It is unknown whether the unlabeled sieve tubes represent those which initially transported in an acropetal direction.

D. Conclusions

Acropetal and basipetal transport occur in separate bundles when basipetally exported assimilates are transferred to a bundle supplying a growing organ.

Simultaneous bidirectional transport in a single bundle has been confirmed for herbaceous dicotyledons in leaves. This phenomenon seems to be restricted to a certain developmental stage. This stage encompasses the period from the initiation of assimilate export to the cessation of assimilate import as a requirement for growth. No data are available which unequivocally show simultaneous bidirectional transport in a single sieve tube (i.e. a part of the sieve-tube system composed of one row of sieve elements).

The pattern of bidirectional transport in separate bundles, as well as in single bundles, seems closely related to the pattern of vascularization and its mode of differentiation. *Vicia faba*, the main object of investigations on bidirectional transport, has a primary bundle system entirely composed of sympodia of leaf traces. With increasing age, a continuous change from acropetal, to mixed acropetal/basipetal, to basipetal-transporting sieve tubes occurs in such sympodia.

This would seem to imply that assimilates synthesized in the roots move acropetally in the xylem until they come into contact with acropetal-transporting sieve tubes of a more recently formed sympodium. It is, however, uncertain whether all sieve tubes of the roots transport only toward the root tip. Nor is it known whether transport through sieve tubes of the secondary phloem is only basipetal or whether the direction of transport may reverse as in metaphloem.

References

BIDDULPH, O., CORY, R.: Demonstration of two translocation mechanisms in studies of bidirectional movement. Plant Physiol. **35**, 689–695 (1960).

BIDDULPH, O., CORY, R.: Translocation of ^{14}C metabolites in the phloem of the bean plant. Plant Physiol. **40**, 119–129 (1965).

CHEN, S.L.: Simultaneous movement of ^{32}P and ^{14}C in opposite directions in phloem tissue. Am. J. Botany **88**, 203–211 (1951).

CRAFTS, A.S., CRISP, C.E.: Phloem transport in plants. San Francisco: W.H. Freeman and Company 1971.

CURRIER, H.B., SHIH, C.Y.: Sieve tubes and Callose in *Elodea* leaves. Am. J. Botany **55**, 145–152 (1968).

CURRIER, H.B., STRUGGER, S.: Aniline-blue and fluorescence microscopy of callose in bulb scales of *Allium cepa* L. Protoplasma **45**, 552–559 (1956).

CURTIS, O.F.: The upward translocation of foods in woody plants. I. Tissues concerned in translocation. Am. J. Botany **7**, 101–134 (1920a).

CURTIS, O.F.: The upward translocation of foods in woody plants. II. Is there normally an upward transfer of storage foods from the roots or trunk to the growing points? Am. J. Botany **7**, 286–295 (1920b).

ESAU, K.: Plant anatomy, 2. ed. New York-London-Sydney: John Wiley and Sons 1965a.

ESAU, K.: Vascular differentiation in plants. New York-Chicago-San Francisco-Toronto-London: Holt, Rinehart and Winston 1965b.

ESCHRICH, W.: Beiträge zur Kenntnis der Wundsiebröhrenentwicklung bei *Impatiens holsti.* Planta **44**, 37–74 (1953).

ESCHRICH, W.: Bidirectionelle Translokation in Siebröhren. Planta **73**, 37–49 (1967).

ESCHRICH, W., FRITZ, E.: Microautoradiography of water-soluble organic compounds. In: Microautoradiography and electron probe analysis: Their application to plant physiology (ed. U. LÜTTGE), p. 99–122. Berlin-Heidelberg-New York: Springer 1972.

EVERT, R.F., ESCHRICH, W., MEDLER, J.T., ALFIERI, F.J.: Observations on penetration of linden branches by stylets of the aphid *Longistigma caryae.* Am. J. Botany **55**, 860–874 (1968).

FRITZ, E.: Microautoradiographic investigations on bidirectional translocation in the phloem of *Vicia faba.* Planta **112**, 169–179 (1973).

FRITZ, E.:, ESCHRICH, W.: ^{14}C-Mikroautoradiographie wasserlöslicher Substanzen im Phloem. Planta **92**, 267–281 (1970).

HILL, G.P.: The sources of sugars in sieve-tube sap. Ann. Botany (London) **27**, 79–87 (1963).

HO, L.C., PEEL, A.J.: Investigation of bidirectional movement of tracers in sieve tubes of *Salix viminalis* L. Ann. Botany (London) **33**, 833–844 (1969).

LARSON, P.R., ISEBRANDS, J.G., DICKSON, R.E.: Fixation patterns of ^{14}C within developing leaves of eastern cottonwood. Planta **107**, 301–314 (1972).

MASON, T.G., MASKELL, E.G., PHILLIS, E.: Further studies on transport in the cotton plant. III. Concerning the independence of solute movement in the phloem. Ann. Botany (London) **50**, 23–58 (1936).

MASON, T.G., PHILLIS, E.: The migration of solutes. Botan. Rev. **3**, 47–71 (1937).

MITTLER, T.E.: Studies on the feeding and nutrition of *Tuberolachnus salignus* (Gmelin) (Homoptera, Aphididae). I. The uptake of phloem sap. J. Exptl. Biol. **34**, 334–341 (1957).

MÜNCH, E.: Die Stoffbewegungen in der Pflanze. Jena: Gustav Fischer 1930.

PALMQUIST, E.H.: The simultaneous movement of carbohydrate and fluorescein in opposite directions in the phloem. Am. J. Botany **24**, 97–105 (1938).

PETERSON, C.A., CURRIER, H.B.: An investigation of bidirectional translocation in the phloem. Physiol. Plantarum **22**, 1238–1250 (1969).

PHILLIS, E., MASON, T.G.: Further studies on transport in the cotton plant. IV. On the simultaneous movement of solutes in opposite directions through the phloem. Ann. Botany (London) **50**, 161–174 (1936).

SCHUMACHER, W.: Untersuchungen über die Wanderung des Fluoresceins in den Siebröhren. Jahrb. Wiss. Bot. **77**, 685–732 (1933).

TRIP, P., GORHAM, P.R.: Bidirectional translocation of sugars in sieve tubes of squash plants. Plant Physiol. **43**, 877–882 (1968).

TURGEON, R., WEBB, J.A.: Leaf development and phloem transport in *Cucurbita pepo:* transition from import to export. Planta **113**, 179–191 (1973).

11. Effects of Temperature, Anoxia and Other Metabolic Inhibitors on Translocation

D.R. GEIGER and S.A. SOVONICK

A. Introduction

I. The Importance of Translocation Modification by Metabolic Inhibitors

Localized application of chemicals which inhibit metabolism, anoxia and low temperature have been used as tools in basic research to assess the role of energy metabolism in the various stages of the translocation process. The results of these studies are reviewed in this chapter. In addition to their theoretical implications, these studies of the relationship between energy metabolism and translocation have a number of direct practical applications. There are numerous studies relating altered energy metabolism to the rate and pattern of assimilate translocation in crop plant productivity (NELSON, 1963; WARDLAW, 1968; LOOMIS, WILLIAMS and HALL, 1971). Unfortunately the role of energy from metabolism in assimilate translocation in relation to crop productivity is not well understood. Another practical area supported by studies of metabolic inhibitors and translocation is that of the effect of atmospheric pollutants on translocation of assimilates. Little work has been done to investigate the effect of these agents on assimilate distribution resulting from metabolic inhibition. These and other potentially practical applications depend on a precise understanding of the effect of metabolic inhibitors on translocation.

II. Possible Difficulties Encountered in Studying the Effect of Metabolic Inhibitors on Translocation

1. Undesirable Effects of Treatments Designed to Inhibit Energy Metabolism

One of the major difficulties encountered when the effects of metabolic inhibitors on translocation are studied is the inability to confine the effect of the treatment to the specific process we wish to modify. Several precautions should be noted in analyzing the physiological effects caused by enhancement or inhibition of energy metabolism. Agents which alter metabolism usually have non-specific effects in addition to raising or lowering of the energy state of the tissue. In this review an attempt is made to discuss known secondary effects of the various treatments that are used to alter energy metabolism and to determine which mechanisms predominately affect translocation. Emphasis is placed on those studies in which the primary role of the inhibitor is known with some certainty.

Because membrane integrity and membrane transport play key roles in translocation it is helpful to distinguish the various functions of membranes. Maintenance of differential permeability is one aspect of membrane function which determines what enters or leaves a cell and at what rate. Metabolic energy plays a key role in maintenance of membrane integrity and differential permeability. Translocation may be affected by changes in energy metabolism through permeability changes rather than more direct inhibition of a process which drives translocation. Disruption of membrane structure may be induced by treatments with inhibitors. The various models of membrane transport stress the key role of electrochemical gradients, of absorption on protein-binding sites or of mobile proteins capable of changes in orientation in the membrane. While in all cases free energy input, usually in the form of ATP, is important, the models also include mechanisms to account for secondary effects of metabolic inhibitors which do not affect energy metabolism directly. These other unwanted effects add an element of complexity to inhibitor studies and require cautious interpretation.

Low-temperature treatments have been used widely to study the mechanism of translocation but documentation of the effects of chilling has lagged considerably. In addition to lowering the turnover rate of ATP and other intermediates of energy metabolism, low-temperature treatment reduces membrane fluidity (LYONS et al., 1964; RAISON, 1972), increases the viscosity of solutions, affects water relations of tissues (MILBURN and WEATHERLEY, 1971; WRIGHT and SIMON, 1973) and causes morphological changes of cell structure (DAS et al., 1966). A recent review by LYONS (1973) discusses a number of the physiological manifestations of chilling. RAISON (1972) demonstrated increased activation energy for succinate oxidation and other membrane-associated reactions in isolated mitochondria as the temperature was lowered below a critical level. By extension, it is likely that low-temperature treatments affect all processes which are dependent in some way on the structural or fluid state of cell membranes.

Chemical inhibitors such as 2,4-dinitrophenol (DNP) are thought to affect energy metabolism directly by uncoupling phosphorylation from terminal electron transport. The mechanisms are not generally agreed upon and the mode of action may have secondary effects in addition to those intended. DNP uncouples oxidative phosphorylation at relatively low concentrations, 10^{-5} to 10^{-6} M with isolated organelles. Advocates of the Mitchell hypothesis believe that proton or ion gradients present across membranes drive synthesis of ATP, and that uncoupling agents act by enhancing passive proton conductivity (BIELAWSKI et al., 1966) which dissipates the proton gradient. Other schools of thought postulate uncoupling by destruction of high energy intermediates, modification of protein structure and catalytic breakdown of high energy bonds (TING et al., 1970). The various mechanisms proposed to explain uncoupling also help to explain damage to cellular metabolism caused by concentrations above 10^{-5} M and by long treatments at lower concentrations. Low DNP concentrations increase oxygen uptake while long treatment times, higher DNP concentrations and low pH produce lower oxygen uptake compared to the control and tend to produce effects in addition to lowered energy metabolism. A crucial factor in concentration-related effects is the ease with which the DNP is able to penetrate to the desired site of inhibition of energy metabolism.

A number of the effects of DNP other than direct inhibition of metabolism are discussed here as indicating the complexity generally found when using chemical inhibitors in physiological studies. Effects on membrane permeability and integrity commonly accompany treatments with chemical uncoupling agents (GLINKA and REINHOLD, 1972; STUART, 1973). LOTT and ROSENE (1956) found that 4,6-dinitro-o-cresol (DNC) at 10^{-6} M increased both oxygen consumption and water influx whereas at 10^{-3} M, DNC decreased both parameters. Other studies generally confirm these observations. BIELESKI (1960) found that 10^{-5} M DNP caused sugar uptake in carrot storage tissue to decrease to near zero and caused leakage to increase approximately 250% over the control. Increasing the concentration of DNP caused a 10-fold increase in leakage over the control. To summarize, it appears that treatment with levels of DNP sufficiently low to uncouple respiration causes inhibition of membrane transport, a slight to moderate increase in leakage of solutes, an increase in permeability to water along with the decrease in ATP level in the tissue. Increasing the concentration or the duration of treatment generally decreases oxygen uptake and causes a decrease in permeability to water and a much higher rate of leakage of solutes. The dimensions of the piece of tissue treated and the accessibility of DNP help to determine what effect a given concentration will have. Faced with the variety of responses to treatment by chemical inhibitors one must not presume dependence on metabolic energy.

Anoxia induced by treatment with gaseous nitrogen removes oxygen physically as a terminal electron acceptor for respiration and so inhibits oxidative phosphorylation. As with other inhibitors a number of effects accompany the desired effect and these may dominate in a given case. In addition to decreasing ATP levels, anaerobiosis affects membrane permeability and gives rise to longer-term accumulation of toxic products of anaerobic metabolism. For example ethanol was shown to accumulate for at least 6 h during anoxia in buckwheat seedlings (EFFER and RANSON, 1967). Furthermore, short-term membrane changes occur within two or three minutes under a nitrogen atmosphere. Rapid effects were revealed by an almost immediate change in electrical conductivity of the sugar beet leaf tissue (GEIGER and CHRISTY, 1970). Changes in the water status of the treated leaf were also apparent within several minutes after anaerobiosis was started (SOVONICK et al., 1974). Anaerobic treatment of root tissue was shown to produce leakage of solutes (HIATT and LOWE, 1967). In this and a number of other similar studies it was difficult to decide which effects resulted from disruption of structure and which were more directly related to inhibition of energy metabolism.

Factors related to the types of effects produced by anaerobiosis in inhibition studies include the degree of oxygen depletion achieved, presence or absence of light with its effect on oxygen production and possibly on stomatal opening, the length of treatment time, the likelihood that toxic products of anaerobic glycolysis can be removed and reversibility of the changes with restoration of oxygen or addition of ATP. For various reasons tissues differ in their susceptibility to damage from anaerobiosis. To assess the dominant effects of anaerobic treatment these factors should be weighed in each experimental design.

2. Uncertainty about the Site of Action of Metabolic Inhibitors

A problem in determining the mechanism by which a given treatment exerts its effect on translocation arises from the fact that both source and sink regions contain translocation path tissue. The presence of path tissues operationally complicates analysis of experiments in which source or sink regions are treated. In addition, localized treatment of one section of the translocation system may affect another. For example, application of inhibitors to path tissue results in the inhibitor reaching the xylem and being distributed to source or sink tissue depending upon the direction of water distribution (HO and MORTIMER, 1971; QURESHI and SPANNER, 1973). Steps should be taken to evaluate the effect on regions outside the zone under study as was done in these two studies.

3. Other Precautions

In addition to the problems discussed above, several other difficulties have been encountered in attempting to develop consistent data for analyzing the mechanisms of the translocation process and the effects of energy metabolism thereon. One source of variability and of apparently contradictory results from experimental treatment lies in the difference in response of different species or ecotypes of plants (GEIGER, 1969) or of plant organs of different ages (FORD and PEEL, 1967) to a treatment such as chilling. Yet another problem results from the time dependence. A number of effects on translocation increase or decrease in severity with time of treatment. Before the advent of radiotracer methods, much of the work on low temperature effects produced variable results, because only indirect, low-precision means of measuring translocation were available. Usually a long time was required to complete the measurements and under these circumstances subtle differences between treatments and transient changes in translocation were difficult to detect or to measure accurately.

Appreciation of the problems described here has led to data which are useful in resolving many of the earlier contradictions and have resulted in progress toward elucidating the mechanisms by which metabolic inhibitors affect translocation.

4. Subdivision of the Translocation System

A method of analysis which has helped to clarify the relationship between energy metabolism and translocation was suggested by NELSON (1963) in a study of the effect of various climatic factors on translocation. He proposed that the effects of a treatment on the component steps of the translocation process be analyzed. This division has assisted in both experimental design and interpretation of results.

In the sections which follow, the translocation process will be subdivided into a) short distance transport and vein loading in the minor veins of the *source* region, b) long distance movement in the phloem of the *path*, c) accumulation of translocated assimilates in *sink* tissue. In the final sections, data from studies focusing on each segment of the translocation system will be synthesized and considered in terms of whole plant function.

B. Effects of Temperature, Anoxia and Metabolic Inhibitors on Translocation

I. Whole-Plant Experiments

1. Temperature Treatments

When an entire plant is subjected to a change in temperature there is generally an optimal range for translocation between 20 and 30° C, with a diminished rate above and below this range (Fig. 1a; HEWITT and CURTIS, 1948; SWANSON, 1959). Below 10° C the reduction is often particularly drastic but shows evidence of recovery after many hours. HEWITT and CURTIS (1948) measured loss of dry weight from exporting leaves during a 13-h dark period and observed similar curves for milkweed, tomato and bean. CURTIS and HERTY (1936) made the significant observation that treating a short portion of the petiole at 0.5 to 5° C has the same marked inhibitory effect on translocation as treating the entire plant (of Figs. 1a, 1b). At 40° C and above, translocation is severely inhibited, but the effect increases with treatment

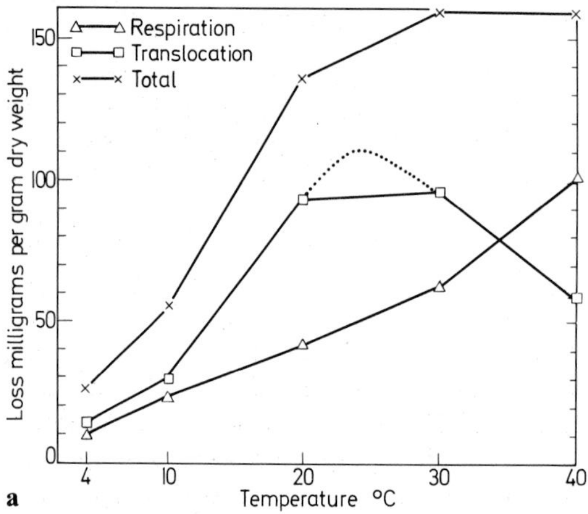

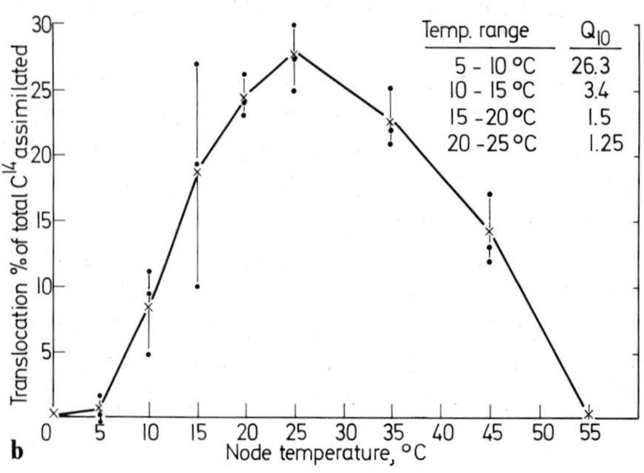

Fig. 1a and b. Effect of temperature on translocation. (a) Whole plant treated at the indicated temperature (HEWITT and CURTIS, 1948). (b) Translocation through the primary node held at the indicated temperature (WEBB and GORHAM, 1965)

time rather than showing recovery (SWANSON and BÖHNING, 1951). While providing indications, treatment of the whole plant tends to combine effects of several different inhibitory mechanisms in the different translocation subsystems, at both high and low temperature extremes. For this reason, detailed discussion will be restricted to localized rather than whole-plant treatments.

II. Results of Path Treatment

1. Low-Temperature Treatment

As early as 1919, CHILD and BELLAMY reported the striking effect of chilling a few centimeters of the translocation path in inhibiting translocation. In a study designed to follow up the work of CHILD and BELLAMY (1919), CURTIS (1929) observed a significant inhibition of translocation in red kidney bean plant below 6 to 8° C but not above this temperature and concluded that the effect of chilling becomes apparent only below a rather definite threshold temperature. Subsequent workers confirmed his observations including the fact that inhibition lessened with time of chilling. For the reasons indicated above, considerable variation in response marked this work. The advent of radiotracers allowed the time course of adjustment during chilling to be studied in detail. In bean, chilling a portion of the stem or petiole to temperatures below 10 to 12° C causes a marked inhibition of translocation (Fig. 2). Below 4 to 5° C this blockage is almost complete and resumption is very gradual, requiring many hours for a significant level of recovery (Fig. 2a). The almost complete inhibition near 0° C is characteristic of many plants, which as a class can be referred to as chilling-sensitive. Most of the early studies of path chilling were done with this class of plants.

The extensive data of WEBB (1967, 1970, 1971) and WEBB and GORHAM (1965) for temperature dependence of translocation in squash (*Cucurbita melopepo*) are representative of chilling-sensitive species. In the range from 15 to 40° C, localized path treatment has little or no effect on translocation of labeled assimilates. Inhibition is rather marked above 40° C and below 10° C; below 5° C and above 50° C translocation practically ceases (WEBB, 1970). Near 15° C, which is close to the threshold of marked inhibition, there is considerable variability between plants. Stem, petiole, hypocotyl and nodes all respond similarly to temperature (WEBB, 1967). The effect of low temperature is reversible, while the high temperature inhibition is reversed slowly or not at all. The velocities of the major translocation species were affected to the same extent (WEBB, 1971).

SWANSON and WHITNEY (1953) observed similar temperature dependence curves for translocation of foliar-applied ^{32}P, ^{42}K, ^{45}Ca and ^{137}Cs through a temperature-treated region of a petiole. During 4 h at 5° C, translocation was inhibited by 85% or more when compared with the 30° C optimum. Between 40 and 45° C translocation dropped to between 25 to 60% of the optimal rate.

While localized path-chilling can reduce translocation for many hours or days in chilling-sensitive plants, in other plants translocation continues undiminished after a short period of inhibition, even at 0° C (SWANSON and GEIGER, 1967). Plants in this group show transient inhibition (Fig. 2b); this initial drop is reversed completely with 1 to 2 h of cooling (SWANSON and GEIGER, 1967; GEIGER and SOVONICK, 1970). Plants such as sugar beet and willow which show this adjustment are referred

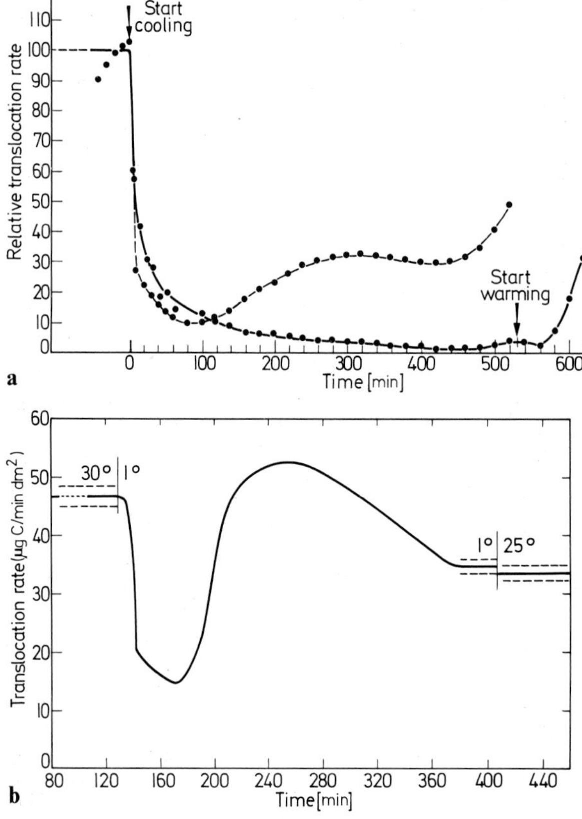

Fig. 2a and b. Time course of translocation through a 2-cm zone of petiole held at the temperatures indicated. (a) Bean petiole cooled to 7° C (upper curve) or 3° C (lower curve) showing effect on a chilling-sensitive plant. (b) Sugar beet petiole cooled to 1° C, showing effect on a chilling-insensitive plant

to as chilling-insensitive (GEIGER, 1969). WEATHERLEY and WATSON (1969) studied the effect of 24- to 48-h low-temperature treatment of a 10-cm length of willow stem on translocation of labeled assimilates. Translocation regularly continued at temperatures down to −4° C and in one case to −4.5° C; when translocation stopped during low-temperature treatment, the tissues showed indications of cell damage as evidenced by reduced Q_{O_2} values and dark brown discoloration. The respiratory rate at −4° C was about 5% of the control rate at 25° C. WARDLAW (1972), who treated a zone of the leaf of the chilling-insensitive plant *Lolium temulentum* at 0° C, noted no reduction in translocation through the cooled zone of the leaf after 4 or 24 h but lateral retention of assimilates along the translocation path was reduced to 1.5 to 2% of the controls. TAMMES et al. (1969) observed that exudation from an inflorescence stalk of *Yucca* continued for 24 h at 0° C; lateral loss from the assimilate stream was inhibited resulting in a higher solute content of the exudate.

A detailed analysis of the effect of stem or petiole temperature on translocation in bean (Fig. 3) reveals a break in the curve at about 10° C. Below this threshold, cooling brings about a more severe and long-lasting effect. Comparison with a similar curve for sugar beet reveals the absence of a threshold of onset of severe damage until the temperature reaches the sub-zero range in the chilling-insensitive sugar beet.

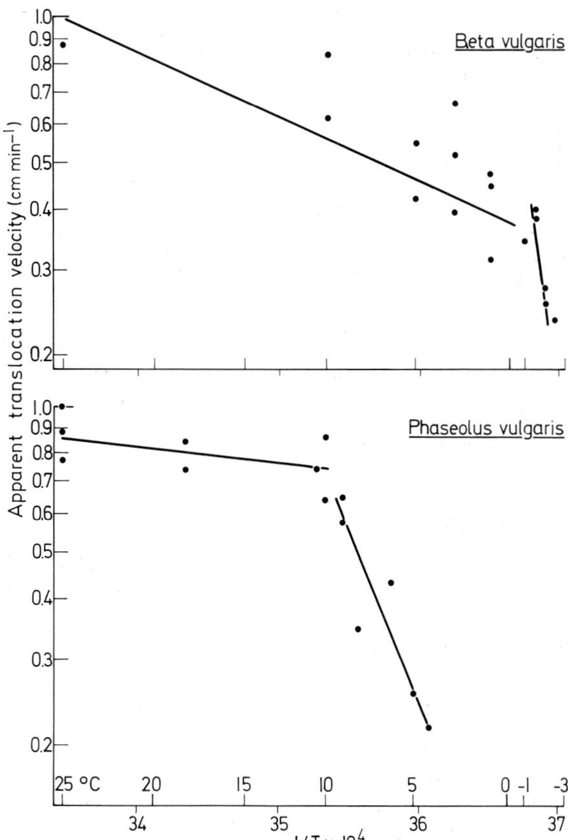

Fig. 3. Temperature-dependence curve (Arrhenius plot) comparing response of sugar beet, *Beta vulgaris* and bean, *Phaseolus vulgaris* to cooling (GIAQUINTA and GEIGER, 1973)

This difference in response occurs even between ecotypes of a species. Plants of *Cirsium arvense* from Montana respond to chilling to 5° C in a manner similar to sugar beet while the southern ecotype from California responds like the bean plant (BAYER, in GEIGER, 1969). BOWLING (1968) used K^+ uptake by the roots of sunflower plants as a measure of translocation of sugar to the roots. Chilling 12 cm of the stem to 0° C sometimes produced a rapid decline in potassium uptake which in some cases lasted for 24 h. In most cases (5 in 8) the initial decrease was followed by a rapid rise over 5 h, to a level above the initial rate prior to stem cooling.

FORD and PEEL (1967) compared young (3 to 5 weeks) and older (2 to 3 years old) willow shoots in their response to localized low-temperature treatment. The young shoot showed a marked decrease in translocation at 5° C to 2 to 15% of the control. In the mature stem the rate generally varied from 100 to 500% of the control. The young shoot resembles chilling-sensitive plants and the older shoot chilling-insensitive (see Chapter 7, p. 188). Although the mechanism is not as yet clear, the fact of a significant difference in response even between tissues of different age in the same plant is of interest in terms of the mechanism of translocation as well as plant growth.

A number of the apparent contradictions in the older literature regarding the effect of temperature on translocation can be explained on the basis of difference in chilling-sensitivity. For example HULL (1952) cites the general pattern of temperature effect on translocation and then goes on to point out a number of studies which indicate a Q_{10} less than 1. He found no difference after either 1 or 3 h between the export of ^{14}C activity from tomato leaves with a zone of the petiole at 1° C and from leaves with petioles at 20° C. The petioles had been treated for 7 h prior to application of ^{14}C-sucrose. A similar result was obtained for sugar beet leaves with petioles at 3° C or 21° C for 6 h prior to labeling. Sugar beet is a chilling-insensitive plant and the 6-h period was more than adequate for recovery as shown above. Presumably the variety of tomato used may also have been chilling-insensitive. Depending on the selection of material for experimental use, it is possible to demonstrate either a high Q_{10} or one near unity.

From the time of CHILD and BELLAMY (1919) there has been evidence that the low-temperature effect is time-dependent. SWANSON and BÖHNING (1951) measured translocation by following the rate of stem and leaf elongation during 65 to 135 h of petiole temperature treatment. In the optimal range, translocation appears steady with time while at 40° C it decreases with time, probably as the result of cellular damage. At 10° C the translocation rate gradually increases with treatment time.

Low-temperature treatment produces two different time-course patterns depending on whether the plant is chilling-sensitive or chilling-insensitive (Fig. 2a and b). Using squash, WEBB (1971) investigated the pattern for chilling-sensitive plants. When a portion of the path was cooled to 0° C, a new transport equilibrium was established within 60 min with the petiole and other path tissue above the cold block acting as a sink for translocate (WEBB and GORHAM, 1965, WEBB, 1971). There appeared to be slight delay in vein loading as a result of path cooling (WEBB, 1971; WARDLAW, 1972) although assimilation in the source leaf is not slowed. Translocate continued to move out of the source leaf but did not pass the chilled region. By acclimatizing the petiole for periods of up to 19 h, WEBB (1971) determined the time course of adjustment at 1.5° C. After 5 h of chilling, the translocation rate had reached about 12% of the control; by 19 h 85% recovery had occurred. Radial movement of translocate in the chilled region was strongly inhibited and failed to show acclimation. After removal of a 1° C chilling block, translocation began within a few minutes and increased steadily. Full rate of translocation was not achieved until some 90 min after the treated path region had been rewarmed.

In chilling-insensitive plants, recovery during cooling takes place within one to several hours after the start of cooling. If the treated region is rewarmed, recovery occurs almost immediately, often with a small overshoot (SWANSON and GEIGER, 1967). LANG (1974) studied the time course of adjustment of translocation rate following a sudden change in temperature of a treated zone petiole of *Nymphoides peltata*. The time course of translocation to the rootstock was monitored continuously before and after temperature changes in a 30-cm petiole segment, a region slightly less than half the translocation path. A sudden decrease in temperature caused an abrupt but temporary inhibition of translocation followed by subsequent recovery. There was no evidence of a severe-damage threshold below approximately 10° C indicating that the plants of *Nymphoides peltata* were chilling insensitive. A 20° C drop, in which the final temperature was near 0° C produced a longer-lasting inhibition than when the second temperature was near 20° C. The Q_{10} of the former treatment was also somewhat larger than for the latter case.

Suddenly raising the temperature caused an immediate and sustained increase in the rate of translocation through the treated region. This increase occurred both when the initial temperature was near 0° C and when it was near 20° C and had a Q_{10} of approximately 1.2. Reimposing cooling after a 75-min period at the original, higher temperature revealed a reduced effect of the cooling treatment. A warm period of 225 min before resumption of cooling treatment restored the usual full degree of inhibition upon cooling. As was the case with previous studies of a similar type, the patterns observed are indicative of a physical rather than a metabolic mechanism for producing the observed changes in translocation rate.

The difference in degree of response and time-course of recovery between types of plants and between temperature-treatment patterns is of importance in designing and interpreting temperature experiments. Generally it is desirable to observe the time course of the temperature effect. If this is not done, it is crucial to take the recovery transient into account when designing the length of the measuring periods and sampling times. Failure to take the transients into account has given rise to apparently anomalous results as noted above for the data of HULL (1952).

The existence of two significantly different patterns of response in the two classes of plants suggests that there may indeed be two different mechanisms for producing inhibition during cooling. GIAQUINTA and GEIGER (1973) compared the path-temperature dependence curves for sugar beet and bean as a means of determining possible mechanisms for low temperature inhibition (Figs. 3a and b). Analysis of the Q_{10} obtained from the slope of the Arrhenius plots can be used to indicate the nature of the mechanism responsible for a temperature effect (GIESE, 1973). A Q_{10} of 1.2 to 1.5 indicates a mechanism limited by a physical process such as diffusion or viscosity while a Q_{10} of 2 to 4 indicates a thermochemical process as the basis of the mechanism. Denaturation of protein or other disruptions of a system result in a large Q_{10} of 4 and above. When analyzed in this manner the translocation-temperature curve for bean (Fig. 3), a chilling-sensitive plant, showed a Q_{10} of 1.3 for temperatures between 10 and 25° C and a Q_{10} of approximately 6 below 10° C. Sugar beet, a chilling-insensitive plant, showed a Q_{10} of 1.3 throughout the same range (Fig. 3).

TAMMES et al. (1969) suggest that in yucca, the decrease in flow through a cooled inflorescence stalk can be explained by the increased viscosity. They note that a 20% sucrose solution increases from a viscosity of 2.0 centipoise at 20° C to 3.8 at 0° C. The fact that translocation occurs for long periods at pretreatment rates through a petiole at 0° C (SWANSON and GEIGER, 1967; FORD and PEEL, 1967; BOWLING, 1968; GEIGER, 1969; TAMMES et al., 1969; GEIGER and SOVONICK, 1970; WARDLAW, 1972) is a strong argument against the existence of a metabolically-dependent driving force being generated in the sieve-tube element of the translocation path.

When the time course is followed closely, the inhibition of translocation by chilling which does not go below the temperature damage extreme is reversed within 60 to 90 min of the start of cooling (SWANSON and GEIGER, 1967; GEIGER and SOVONICK, 1970; GIAQUINTA and GEIGER, 1973). The kinetics suggest operation of a feedback system in response to increased resistance to flow. Resistance to flow should be directly proportional to viscosity according to the Poiseuille relationship. In a test of this hypothesis, sieve-tube sap from castor bean, a chilling-sensitive plant, was subjected to low-temperature treatment. With cooling, an increase in viscosity similar to that shown by a 10% sucrose solution was observed (GIAQUINTA and GEIGER, 1973). Analysis of the change in fluidity (the inverse of viscosity) with temperature revealed a Q_{10} of 1.3. From this analysis it appears that the effect of temperature in chilling-insensitive plants between 0° C and the point of high temperature damage can be explained on the basis of changes in fluidity of the sieve-tube sap. The adjustment back to pretreatment rates at low temperature probably is the result of increased pressure behind the treated region. The overshoot in translocation rate which is often observed upon returning the chilled region of the stem or petiole to a higher temperature supports the pressure build up concept.

A study of the relationship between translocation velocity and mass transfer during petiole cooling also supports the above mechanisms (GEIGER and SOVONICK, 1970). They found that the temporary reduction of mass transfer rate brought about by petiole cooling in sugar beet, a chilling-insensitive plant, is the result of inhibition of translocation velocity (GEIGER and SOVONICK, 1970). Recovery at low temperatures was found to be the result of restoration of the original velocity. In a related study, GARDNER and PEEL (1972) found from exudate studies that recovery of translocation during chilling is not the result of increased sucrose or solute concentration in response to lower velocity of sieve-tube sap movement. In summary, it appears that an increase in the resistance to flow and feedback adaptation to it are sufficient to explain inhibition and recovery above the damage threshold in both chilling-insensitive and sensitive plants.

It can be argued that the effect on translocation of inhibition of energy metabolism in a relatively small proportion of the total path may be overcome by an active mechanism in the uninhibited portion of the path. WATSON (1975) has tested this possibility by chilling a 65- to 70-cm portion of a willow shoot with a leafy branch attached. The translocation through treated segments, which constituted a major portion of the path, was only slightly less than through untreated segments. This finding supports the concept that energy metabolism is only indirectly responsible for maintaining translocation.

Recently FERRIER and CHRISTY (1975) have modelled the recovery of translocation in a sugar beet plant with a 10-cm segment of petiole treated by chilling. It was assumed that the initial inhibition of translocation was the result of increased resistance to flow. Very high resistances to flow were needed to produce the initial time course indicating that a mechanism other than viscosity is responsible or that a viscosity change somehow produced a large increase in resistance to flow. Clearly research is needed into the mechanism by which chilling above the threshold of severe damage inhibits translocation.

In the range below 10 to 12° C in chilling-sensitive plants and probably below 0° C in chilling-insensitive plants another mechanism prevails. Judged by its Q_{10} this mechanism involves denaturation or serious disruption of the system. This hypothesis is supported by the fact that there is a delay of 20 to 45 min before resumption of translocation after return to a higher temperature; the recovery is slow and sometimes incomplete (THROWER, 1965; GEIGER, 1969; WEBB, 1971). Physical disruption and blockage is further suggested by the results of pressure-release experiments reported by GIAQUINTA and GEIGER (1973). The displacement of protein bodies in the sieve elements of bean (*Phaseolus*) was used as an indicator of the open, unplugged condition of the sieve elements in chilled and in untreated petioles of bean plants. In the petiole at 25° C the protein bodies show displacement toward the point of incision for several cm on either side of a cut; in the chilled petiole these bodies are displaced only within the segment extending a few mm on either side of the cut. These results indicate that the high-Q_{10} region of the temperature curve results from plugging or blockage of the sieve tubes in the chilled zone of the petiole.

MAJUMDER and LEOPOLD (1967) reported increased frequency of callose plugs in bean plants exposed to low night temperature. The frequency increased with the length of treatment. There was no increase in the number of plugs in tomato plants treated in a similar way. They suggest that the long-term damage from chilling may in part result from low temperature-induced callose in the petiole. Although this mechanism may account for some of the damage at low temperature, recent studies utilizing improved methods for freeze-substitution preparation of tissue for electronmicroscopy have contributed additional evidence concerning the nature of

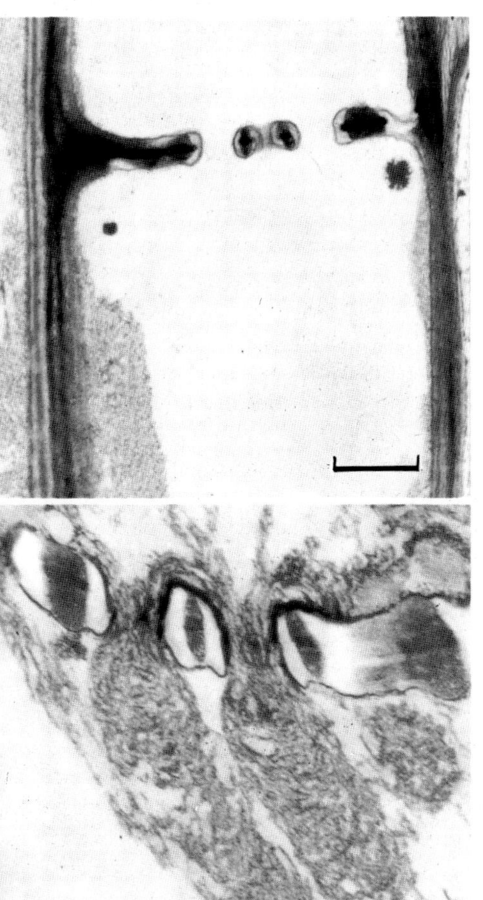

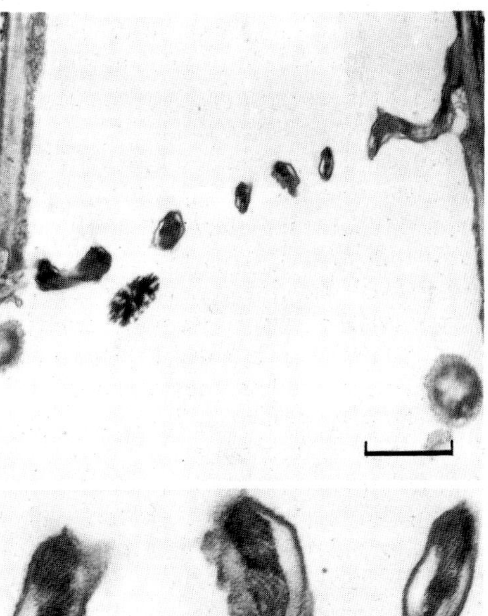

Fig. 4A–D. Longitudinal sections through sieve plates of bean petioles prepared by rapid freezing and freeze substitution. (A) Control tissue. (B) Tissue at 0° C. (C) and (D) Tissue cooled for 1 h and rewarmed for 100 min. Bars indicate 1 μ

chilling damage in relation to translocation. A comparison of sieve-element structure from rapidly frozen petiole tissue taken from adjacent petiole regions at 25° C and at 0° C reveal significant plugging of the sieve pores by cytoplasmic material in the latter tissue (Fig. 4). The mechanism by which chilling causes sieve-plate blockage in chilling-sensitive species below 10° C is not established but it appears significant that the temperature dependence curves and particularly the threshold for onset of low temperature damage (Fig. 3) resemble very closely the curves and thresholds for the effect of chilling on mitochondrial respiration in chilling-sensitive and chilling-insensitive plants (Fig. 5).

LYONS and RAISON (1970a) pointed out that the inhibition of mitochondrial respiration below 10° C in chilling-sensitive plants such as tomato, cucumber and sweet potato (Fig. 5) appears to be the result of a transition in the state of membrane lipids from liquid to a coagel (LYONS and RAISON, 1970b). BELEHRADEK (1967) reviewed the reported changes in various components of the cell in response to temperature extremes. He concluded that fats and phospholipids are the only components that undergo molecular structural changes and whose-physio-chemical behavior depends on temperature of formation. The formation of unsaturated bonds in the hydrocarbon chain is promoted by low temperature. Although the composition of natural fats is primarily genotypical, it is plastic enough to allow individual

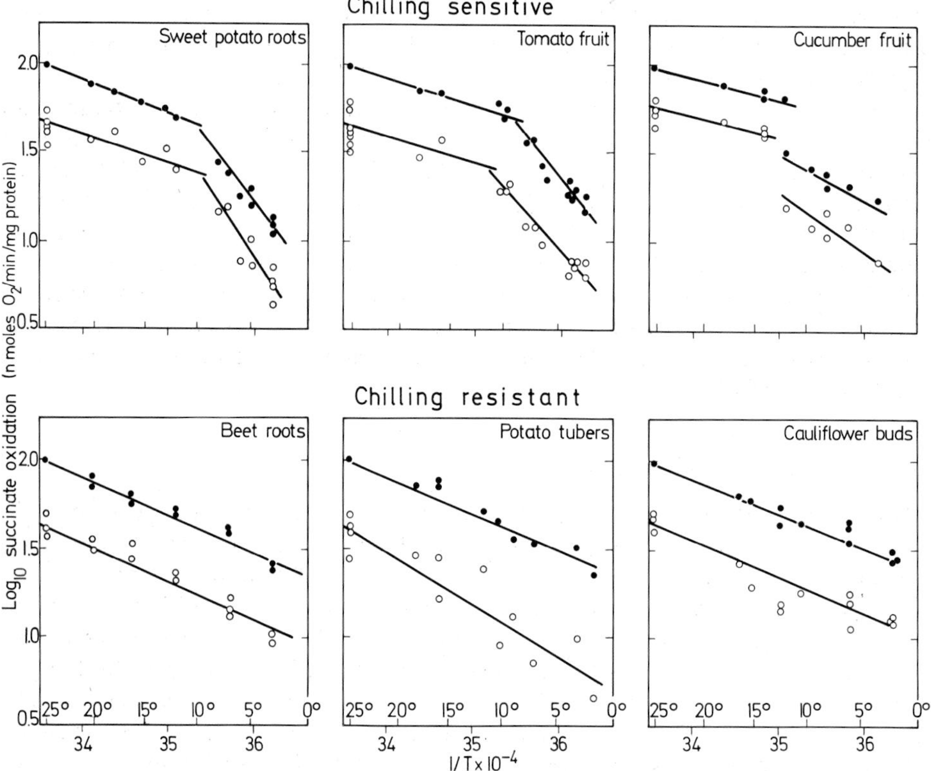

Fig. 5. Arrhenius plots showing the effect of temperature on succinate oxidation in chilling-sensitive and chilling-insensitive plants (LYONS and RAISON, 1970a)

variations, sometimes rather wide. BELEHRADEK cites evidence that functional stability of lipid-containing protoplasmic structures, such as surfaces membranes, is easily upset at temperature extremes; the effects seem to be the result of the function of lipids as "spacers" and as concomitant molecules indispensable to some enzymes.

LYONS et al. (1964) observed that mitochondrial membrane flexibility and the degree of fatty acid unsaturation in membranes was greater in chilling-insensitive than in sensitive plants. In view of the dynamic nature of membranes, the increase in membrane rigidity could conceivably result in disruption of cell structure. Cytoplasmic anomalies associated with low temperature treatment have been reported by a number of workers (GEIGER, 1969; GIAQUINTA and GEIGER, 1973; RAISON et al., 1971). NOBEL (1974) observed that permeability of the chloroplast-limiting membranes, as measured by reflection coefficients, decreased when the temperature was raised. In chilling-insensitive plants, the curves relating reflection coefficients and temperature were smooth while in chilling-sensitive plants there was a break with a shallower slope above 11° C. Inhibition at temperatures below the threshold of damage is the result of cytoplasmic changes which cause the membranes and cytoplasmic material lining the sieve-tube elements to become dislodged and block the sieve-plate pores. The different thresholds of damage in chilling-sensitive and chilling-insensitive plants correspond to their respective points of membrane lipid phase change. An ultrastructural study of recovery following warming indicates that by 60 min after rewarming, the sieve plates in the region which was treated are again clear of cytoplasmic material and debris (Fig. 4C, D). Events at the cellular level seem to explain the low temperature inhibition of translocation in terms of cytoplasmic changes in the sieve tubes of the treated region.

WALDING and WEATHERLEY (1972) pulse-labeled the translocation stream with bark-applied ^{32}P and followed the progress of the pulse past 2 GM-detectors located downstream from the applied tracer. Chilling the stem to 0° C caused a marked inhibition of translocation velocity. After 8 to 10 h the label reaching the first detector increased, apparently because of increased loading of ^{32}P rather than an increase in velocity. After another 5 or 6 h the translocate with the greater load of label reached the second detector. This "recovery" clearly differs from the restoration of velocity and mass transfer which occurs above the low-temperature damage threshold, adding evidence that the modes of inhibition are different above and below the threshold.

2. High-Temperature Treatment

Results of experiments involving localized high-temperature treatment (usually in the 40 to 60° C range) indicate that the effect is the result of changes in the structural integrity of the sieve-tube elements resulting in permanent or slowly reversible damage. The mechanism is not clear and there is a good possibility that more than one high-temperature effect produces the inhibition which is observed. MCNAIRN and CURRIER (1968) observed that translocation is inhibited by treating a 4-cm zone of the hypocotyl at 40° C for 15 min. There was no evidence of cell damage as determined by tetrazolium, neutral red or plasmolyzability below 50° C. At 40° C the increased resistance due to constriction of plasmodesmata and sieve pores appeared to be the cause of the inhibition. Sieve plates were almost completely constricted by heat-induced callose (SHIH and CURRIER, 1969). The deposits on the sieve plates showed some reversal after 6 h and virtually complete disappearance after 2 days. Translocation was inhibited for at least 3 h following the 15 min treatment but by 6 h was equal to or above normal. It appears that high phloem pressure can overcome the increased resistance to flow. Lateral movement of assimilate does not recover so quickly as longitudinal movement. In a subsequent study MCNAIRN (1972) found that translocation is inhibited when 50% or more of the sieve plates have a large amount of callose. However, even at these high callose levels, excessively high temperature had an additional effect on translocation by some other mechanism, possibly denaturation of some sieve-tube component or possibly inhibition of vein loading in the leaf blade. In this regard, DANIELL et al. (1969) attributed the primary effect of sublethal as well as lethal high temperatures in plants to structural changes in the cell membranes. They cite the lipoid liberation theory of CHAPMAN which links cytological damage to change in the membrane lipids. In this aspect, the mechanism of high- and low-temperature inhibition of translocation may be similar. Presumably the membrane effect could cause disarrangement of peripheral sieve-tube membranes resulting in plugging of sieve-plate pores. GIAQUINTA (1972) provided evidence that a number of deleterious treatments of path tissue result in plugging similar to that observed below the low-temperature damage threshold.

3. Anoxia

A number of workers measured translocation while a portion of the translocation path was maintained under anaerobic conditions for periods of up to several weeks. CURTIS (1929) reviewed the results of early experiments designed to determine whether translocation is inhibited by anaerobic treatment of the petiole or by other agents that inhibit respiratory metabolism of the translocation path. In his experiments, CURTIS produced anaerobiosis by coating the petiole with wax and by flushing nitrogen through a jacket enclosing the petiole. He found the latter treatment produced a greater retention of material by the treated leaves. The differences generally were small though they were statistically significant in the latter case. The results of experiments employing petiole treatments of chilling, anaerobiosis and chemical inhibitors led CURTIS to conclude that these treatments stopped cytoplasmic streaming which stopped translocation.

MASON and PHILLIS (1936) used elaborate precautions to exclude oxygen from a 20-cm portion of the translocation path to investigate the need for aerobic metabolism to support translocation *via* the phloem. Only by scrupulously excluding oxygen were they able to show inhibition; transport showed evidence of recovering after about a week. They attributed the need for oxygen to the maintenance of structural integrity rather than the driving of translocation. Using fluorescent materials as tracers of translocation, BAUER (1953) found that anaerobic treatment of the path did not have an inhibitory effect while treatment of the source caused marked inhibition. Measuring translocation by means of a fluorescein tracer, ULLRICH (1961) and WILLENBRINK (1957) also failed to observe a significant effect of anoxia in the path on translocation.

Utilizing a more sensitive method for measuring the translocation time course, SIJ and SWANSON (1972) reported that nitrogen-induced anoxia in a 15-cm length of petiole held in darkness caused only short-term inhibition of translocation in squash. The kinetics of adjustment, which are strikingly similar to the recovery in sugar beet during petiole chilling, suggest that the inhibition may be the result of increased viscosity with subsequent adjustment to overcome the decreased fluidity. After this transient translocation continues unimpaired for 18 to 21 h under anaerobic treatment, indicating that transport can also continue for long periods in tissue maintained by anaerobic metabolism. These data are consistent with the results of path-cooling experiments which indicate that phloem transport can occur over extended periods through a zone with a very low level of energy metabolism.

The marked inhibition of translocation found by QURESHI and SPANNER (1973a) when 10 to 30 cm of stolon was confined to an anaerobic atmosphere, as well as the transient effect noted by SIJ and SWANSON (1972) and the slight to moderate inhibition reported by earlier workers suggest that some condition imposed by very low oxygen partial pressures may cause blockage of the translocation path. It appears that oxygen production in the light will reverse the observed effects produced by nitrogen-induced anoxia (WEATHERLEY, 1955 and R.E. TOIA, personal communication). The possibility of accumulation of toxic products of anaerobic metabolism or of structural breakdown under very strict anoxia should be pursued to resolve the discrepancies. It seems unlikely that the effect is related to unavailability of ATP or metabolic energy in the path to drive translocation. This issue has been discussed in detail by COULSON et al. (1972) who found no stoichiometric relationship between sucrose transport rates in the petiole and petiolar respiration or ATP turnover. COULSON and PEEL (1971) found that chilling to near 0° C reduced respiration to 10% of the control rate.

4. Treatment with Metabolic Inhibitors

Experiments in which the translocation path is treated with chemical inhibitors, like those using anoxia and chilling, have often yielded somewhat ambiguous and contradictory data. Although the idea of inhibiting respiratory metabolism in the translocation path seems relatively straightforward, the results suggest considerable complexity in the mechanism producing the effects. An example of the complications which arise has already been discussed in relation to path-cooling studies. In general, data obtained by treatment of the translocation path with metabolic inhibitors do not present a strong case for translocation being driven directly by energy derived from path metabolism.

The inhibition which is generally observed gives evidence of being the result of secondary effects other than inhibition of energy metabolism, for example by damage to the sieve elements. Studies utilizing cyanide treatment show the complexity involving an apparently simple experiment. VERNON and ARONOFF (1952) failed to demonstrate inhibition of translocation by application of cyanide to the stem while both ULLRICH (1961) and WILLENBRINK (1957) reported inhibition of translocation of fluorescein tracer along the petiole of *Pelargonium*. WILLENBRINK (1967 and 1968) also observed inhibition of ^{14}C-assimilate transport in the same species; the inhibition was reversible with translocation starting to resume approximately 90 min after removal of the cyanide. QURESHI and SPANNER (1973c) reported similar results with *Saxifraga sarmentosa* L. HO and MORTIMER (1971) observed that application of 0.5 M cyanide to a sugar beet petiole caused inhibition of translocation from the treated leaf. Within 5 min, cyanide was found in the leaf blade and by

50 min about 40% of the applied cyanide was in the blade. However, the pattern of assimilation products in the blade was not changed by the cyanide treatment and vein loading did not appear to be inhibited judging by the heavy labeling of the minor veins of the treated blade. It is possible that aerobic respiration in mature sugar beet leaf tissue is relatively insensitive to cyanide as was observed by R.E. TOIA (personal communication). The point of blockage was clearly in the petiole near the site of treatment. To examine the mechanism of cyanide inhibition, GIAQUINTA (1972) applied potassium cyanide solutions to an exposed vascular bundle of a bean plant petiole while following translocation of ^{14}C-assimilate. Translocation continued in spite of step-wise increases in cyanide concentration until at 100 mM translocation was markedly inhibited. This tissue was then rapidly frozen and prepared by freeze substitution for examination under an electronmicroscope. The sieve tubes in this tissue showed obstructed sieve plates very similar to those found in tissue subjected to chilling damage (chilling damage shown in Fig. 4b). The appearance of the tissue and the length of time required for reversing the inhibition are similar to that found with chilling injury in chilling-sensitive plants, strongly suggesting a similar mechanism of inhibition by cytological damage. To what extent inhibition of translocation by respiratory inhibitors is due to tissue damage remains to be established, but continued investigation appears to be worthwhile. Until damage of this type, as well as inhibition of vein loading, are explicitly excluded as a cause of inhibition of translocation, claims to the effect that translocation is driven by respiratory energy derived in the path region are open to question.

A number of other respiratory inhibitors such as 2,4-dinitrophenol (DNP) have also been used to study the energetics of translocation. KENDALL (1955) found that 2 to 5 mM DNP injected into the space inside a bean petiole stopped translocation through the segment; phloem-loading in the blade did not appear to be affected. HAREL and REINHOLD (1966) concluded that DNP slowed translocation in soybean by inhibiting the loading step rather than the movement along the translocation path. QURESHI and SPANNER (1973b) observed inhibition of transport when a 30-cm length of stolon of *Saxifraga sarmentosa* was treated with 5 mM DNP. The absence of blockage of the sieve pores by cytoplasmic elements was not reported and the mechanism of inhibition was not unequivocally established. As for other path-inhibitor treatments, the results are varied and suggest multiple mechanisms of inhibition.

III. Results of Sink Treatment

1. Introduction

The conclusion that the major role of energy metabolism in the path is for maintenance of structural integrity places added emphasis on the function of energy metabolism in source and sink regions for driving translocation. Almost without exception, treatment of sink tissue with metabolic inhibitors results in decreased translocation. This consistency in the data stands in marked contrast to the situation for the path and suggests the key involvement of respiratory metabolism in moving assimilate. In a recent review, WARDLAW (1968) summarizes the functions of sink tissue in translocation of assimilates. As a generalization, it can be said that growing tissues, developing storage organs and other metabolically active tissues enhance translocation by providing good sinks and thereby determine the distribution of assimilates. Control of the rate and pattern of translocation appears to depend largely on the ability of various organs to deplete or transform the translocate, creating a concentration gradient which facilitates movement into that organ.

2. Inhibition of Translocation by Inhibiting Sink Metabolism

a) Low-Temperature Treatment. The results of a number of experiments in which the sink region of a plant was subjected to temperature treatment indicate that temperature is a significant factor in controlling rate and pattern of translocation into sink tissues. HÄRTT (1965) observed that with the air temperature at 22° C, a root temperature of 17° C significantly retards translocation from the shoot. In a study of the effect of fruit temperature on translocation to a young bean pod, LINCK and SWANSON (1960) observed that chilling to approximately 7° C resulted in less accumulation of phosphorus-32 in the pod, particularly in the seeds. At least part of the effect is probably the result of path-chilling inhibition but there is evidence of a component of inhibition resulting from the altering of the metabolic activity of the pod. Unlike the situation with path treatment sink cooling showed no 20–30° C optimum but maximum accumulation occurred with the sink tissue at 39° C.

HUSAIN and LINCK (1967) observed that chilling the shoot apex inhibited translocation of foliar-applied ^{32}P to the shoot tip and resulted in diversion to the roots. The chilling also inhibited growth and the transport of IAA from the shoot-tip region. In a study of the effect of temperature on photosynthesis, respiration and translocation in the various plant organs, FUJIWARA and SUZUKI (1961) established that translocation occurred at the maximum rate when root respiration was highest and photosynthesis was the most rapid. The tissues lateral to the sieve tubes also constitute an important sink in plants. FORD and PEEL (1966), and WARDLAW (1972) established that movement out of the sieve tubes into surrounding tissue is strongly inhibited by low-temperature treatment suggesting dependence on energy metabolism.

The use of chilling-insensitive plants enables us to make a more detailed study of the effect of localized chilling on the rate, time course and pattern of translocation. In chilling-insensitive plants the overriding effect of cooling the path is reversed in a matter of 60 to 90 min (GEIGER, 1966). After this initial adjustment period, which appears to be largely the effect of chilling on the sieve tubes, translocation gradually adjusts to a rate approximately 40% of the pretreatment rate (Fig. 6). Translocation remains inhibited throughout cooling periods of up to 24 h duration and probably indefinitely. The effect is quickly reversed upon return to a higher temperature range. It was also observed that when the beet was chilled to 0.5° C, translocation to a young uncooled leaf increased by 30%. Within 10 min after the beet was rewarmed, translocation decreased to the pretreatment level (GEIGER, 1966). These data demonstrate that temperature can also have a marked effect on pattern as well as rate of translocation. Although no systematic study of sink temperature and translocation has been made there does not seem to be a threshold for onset of the effect of chilling; the effect seems closely to parallel the effect on the level of sink-tissue metabolism. In chilling-sensitive plants, path chilling masks the more subtle effects of sink cooling resulting from inhibited metabolism.

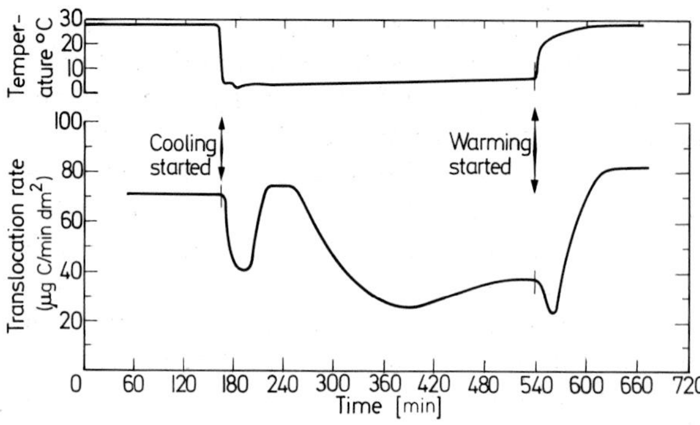

Fig. 6. Time course of translocation into a chilled sink region of sugar beet (GEIGER, 1966)

The Q_{10} of translocation inhibition caused by chilling the sink tissue is approximately 1.5 after the initial 60 to 90 min adjustment period. This value is low for an effect attributed to inhibition of energy metabolism but the Q_{10} is probably the result of the operation of a feedback mechanism which, if it were completely effective, would reduce the Q_{10} to 1. According to the activated mass flow model (MÜLLER and LEOPOLD, 1966), a "push" from the source region and a "pull" from the sink tissues, both metabolically dependent, generate forces which move the translocate stream through the path. Inhibition of the active driving process in the sink lessens the pressure gradient initially with a Q_{10} of 2 or more. A compensatory increase in the gradient in the source region from the backup of translocate solutes presumably will increase the "push", partially reversing the effect of the inhibited sink metabolism on the pressure gradient.

b) Anoxia. Inhibition of translocation by subjecting sink tissue to anaerobic conditions supports the proposed relationship between the level of metabolic activity in sink tissue and the rate of translocation into the tissue. Anaerobic treatment of the sink leaf of sugar beet results in an inhibition of translocation into the leaf to 40 to 50% of the control rate (GEIGER and CHRISTY, 1971). The decline in translocation coincides with a decrease in CO_2 output and ATP level; all three quantities return to near control levels within 2 to 3 h after treatment is discontinued. The initial decrease in translocation may be the transient inhibition resulting from path anaerobiosis noted by SIJ and SWANSON while the long-term effect is presumably the result of inhibition of sink-tissue metabolism. Recovery of translocation to 40 to 50% of the control rate occurs during continued sink anoxia without a concomitant increase in respiration rate. Presumably the increased driving force generated in the source leaf gradually compensates, in part, for the reduced sink "pull" (MÜLLER and LEOPOLD, 1966). Recently, QURESHI and SPANNER (1973a) subjected a developing daughter plant of *Saxifraga sarmentosa* to nitrogen anaerobiosis in the dark. Labeled assimilate moved down the stolon but failed to enter the sink plant during a 4-h translocation period. In view of the marked effect which is observed when the stolon is subjected to anaerobiosis, it is difficult to determine the actual effect of reduced sink metabolism in this system.

c) Treatment with Metabolic Inhibitors. Because of the effect of certain inhibitors on the sieve tubes of the path it is somewhat difficult to study the effect of chemical inhibitors on sink metabolism and translocation. For example, QURESHI and SPANNER (1973b) applied 5×10^{-3} M DNP to a developing daughter plant and then supplied $^{14}CO_2$ to the parent plant. The label was inhibited from moving into the sink plant but to what extent this was due to path blockage was not clearly demonstrated. They attributed most of the inhibition that was observed to a direct effect on the sieve tubes of the path. Under these circumstances it is difficult to assess the effect of inhibited sink metabolism on translocation unless the path effect is clearly reversed as it is with nitrogen-induced anoxia.

While it is difficult to demonstrate the effect of inhibited sink metabolism on translocation because of the path effect in intact tissue, sugar uptake studies in excised sink tissue shed some light on the subject. FINKELMAN and REINHOLD (1963) found that 10^{-4} M DNP caused leakage of actively accumulated sugars from sunflower hypocotyl segments; at 5×10^{-4} M, DNP abolished the transport process. This inhibition of active accumulation should have a marked effect on accumulation in a sink tissue and would be expected to reduce translocation into the tissue. More direct evidence seems difficult to obtain at present.

d) Mechanisms Relating Inhibition of Sink Metabolism to Inhibition of Translocation. Results of experiments with sink region cooling and anoxia support the correlation between the level of metabolic activity and the rate of translocation into the treated region. Several explanations for this correlation might be suggested. Metabolic activity may be used for unloading or actively accumulating the assimilate and, secondly, the metabolic processes themselves may serve to transform or deplete the translocate species in the sink region, steepening the translocate gradient. It seems that both mechanisms are likely to promote translocation into a sink region. When the time course of inhibition of translocation is studied by inhibition of sink metabolism, there is a gradual decline in translocation over a several-hour period (GEIGER, 1966; GEIGER and CHRISTY, 1971). Based on a pressure-flow model, translocation depends on the development of a pressure gradient to promote movement down a given file of sieve tubes. If metabolism is inhibited, active transport of the translocate molecules into the sink tissue presumably will be inhibited, lessening the osmotic pressure gradient, and as a consequence, the turgor pressure gradient.

A second mechanism, based on metabolic transformation, has been reported. Recent studies by BOWEN and HUNTER (1972) have convincingly demonstrated the role of β-fructofuranosidase in sugar transport in sugarcane sink tissue. Uptake is from the free space where sucrose is hydrolyzed to glucose prior to transport of the latter into storage space (BOWEN and HUNTER, 1972). The rate-limiting step in glucose uptake is the movement from the free space into metabolic space (GAYLER and GLASZIOU, 1972). Glucose uptake is energy-dependent and is likely to be significantly inhibited by low temperature, anoxia and other inhibitors as well as by high temperature which induces enzyme denaturation. ANAND and GALSTON (1972) found that phytochrome (P_{fr}) promotes increased uptake of ^{14}C-sucrose by the bud of pea and somewhat later increases growth. The metabolic effects are attributed to induction of higher β-fructofuranosidase activity and increased incorporation into ethanol insoluble wall fractions. Both of the latter processes would be expected to be inhibited by low temperature, anoxia and chemical inhibitors and may be another basis for the metabolic dependence of translocation into storage and growing tissue.

A further effect of inhibited metabolism or the toxic by-products thereof is reduced permeability. Nitrogen-induced anoxia, for example, causes an immediate decrease in water uptake by the treated tissue and a drastic reduction in electrical conductance across the anoxic cells (SOVONICK et al., 1974). The early effect of sink anoxia on translocation appears to result from this decrease in membrane permeability (GEIGER and CHRISTY, 1970, 1971). Another example is the inhibition of lateral transport out of sieve tubes caused by heat-induced callose formation (WEBSTER and CURRIER, 1968). It is not known whether callose deposit or altered membrane permeability in the sink tissue caused by chemical inhibitors is significant but it seems likely to be so from reports concerning cytological effects of these materials.

The causal relationships in the area of translocation and sink metabolism are in need of further study. In an extensive review, WARDLAW (1968) concludes that in growing tissues the effect of temperature is to affect growth directly, which in turn changes the rate of import of assimilates by the affected organ. Whether metabolic inhibitors primarily affect solute transport or its utilization, the effect of temperature and other processes which alter the energy metabolism and structure of sink tissues is clear. Import rates are changed and the pattern of distribution is modified in favor of those organs able to utilize the assimilates to a greater extent.

IV. Results of Source Treatment

1. Introduction

According to the proponents of activated mass-flow theories of translocation, active phloem loading is responsible for generating a major portion of the force which drives translocation. The work of CURTIS and ASAI (1939) and ROECKL (1949) first suggested the need for an active step between sugar production and translocation out of the leaf. More recent data (GEIGER et al., 1973) indicate that the site of this active step is the sieve element-companion cell (se-cc) complex of the minor veins of the source region. The phloem-loading step appears to involve active transport of sugar into the se-cc complex. If phloem loading has this crucial role, inhibition of source leaf metabolism should produce marked inhibition of translocation. Several difficulties present themselves in interpreting these experiments. In the first instance, if newly assimilated translocate is being traced, the metabolic inhibition will often inhibit assimilation, so that a lowered translocation rate may be due to decreased assimilate formation as well as inhibited phloem loading. A second problem is the presence of "path" phloem in the major veins of the source leaf. Any treatment which produces a large amount of inhibition in the path phloem will mask the effect produced on phloem loading.

2. Chilling

BAUER (1953) obviated the effect of chilling on the assimilation rate by studying the difference in response between source and path. He used a fluorescent dye to follow the velocity of translocation through the phloem of geranium petioles while the blade was held at 0.4° C or 21° C. Treating the petiole indicated that chilling the path produced inhibition to about 44% of the control. Blade chilling reduced the dye movement from 15 mm/h at 21° C to 0.4 mm/h at 0.4° C, a reduction to 2.7% of the control. Even allowing for some effect on the path phloem, chilling the blade produced a drastic reduction in translocation. FORD and PEEL (1966) found that the lateral tissues along a "contributory length" of the phloem serve as a source of solutes found in the aphid stylet exudate. They noted that lateral movement of solutes into the sieve tubes was markedly inhibited by cooling, presumably because transport of the solutes is dependent on energy metabolism. Observing the effect of cooling on the rate of exudation in *Yucca* inflorescence stalks, TAMMES et al. (1969) noted a marked inhibition when the region serving as source of exudate was cooled; cooling the path had no effect. They suggest that sugar uptake or loading into the cells surrounding the sieve tubes is a metabolic process which is markedly affected by temperature. Cooling the stalk to 0° C stopped secretion into the sieve tubes and consequently stopped movement of the sieve-tube sap. The results of those source-cooling experiments which have avoided the problems mentioned above indicate that source-region metabolism plays an important part in motivating translocation.

The effect of chilling on the sieve tubes of chilling-sensitive plants and the disruption produced by anoxia, cyanide and other respiratory inhibitors emphasize the delicate structural balance of the sieve tube system. The high flux and pressures necessitate maintenance of structural integrity for normal function. It appears that the major role of energy expenditure in the path phloem is the preservation of this highly specialized structure. The marked effects of extreme temperatures appear to relate to the alteration of structure rather than a deficit of metabolic energy.

3. Anoxia and Chemical Inhibition

Inhibition of metabolism in the sink region appears to have a more direct effect on translocation rate. Cooling of the sink tissue, as well as other treatments which lower metabolic activity, appears to exert a significant control over translocation rate. Results of sink cooling point to the existence of a force, possibly the result of active loading of sugar into the cells of the sink region, which steepens the free energy gradient that drives translocation. The presence of a force in the source region that drives translocation has not been investigated to any great extent and little data from metabolic inhibition of the source region is available to quantitate the extent to which energy metabolism is required. Viewed as a whole, the path temperature-dependence, anoxia and metabolic inhibition data for translocation suggest the operation of a pressure-flow mechanism activated by phloem loading and sink accumulation. In a discussion of the role of sink metabolism in translocation, MÜLLER and LEOPOLD (1966) propose active processes of "loading" at the source end and "unloading" at the sink end. The observation that inhibiting metabolism of either the source or sink seriously limits translocation supports the existence of both an active force-generating process in the source and an active gradient-steepening process in the sinks. Under various circumstances which alter source or sink metabolism, the suction flow or the pressure flow may predominate. Sink-chilling and sink-anoxia experiments (GEIGER, 1966; GEIGER and CHRISTY, 1971) indicate that the pressure-flow mechanism suffices to maintain translocation, but at a reduced rate, when the active sink component is inhibited.

QURESHI and SPANNER studied the effect of anoxia (1973a) and DNP (1973b) applied to the source leaf on phloem loading. In both cases phloem loading was inhibited but the effect of inhibited source metabolism on the translocation rate was obscured by the significant effect of these inhibitors on the path tissues present in the source leaf. The topic of metabolic inhibition of the source and phloem loading is discussed in Chapter 17 of this volume.

C. Significance of Effects of Various Inhibitors

I. Inhibitor Effects in Relation to the Mechanism of Translocation

Results of the various experiments employing localized chilling point to a number of generalizations regarding the role of energy metabolised in the source, path and sink regions. The ability of translocate to move at undiminished rate through 10 cm and more of path tissue at 0° C or under stringent anoxia suggests that energy input from the path is not crucial for driving translocation. COULSON et al. (1972) studied the stoichiometric relationship between path energy metabolism and the flux of translocate. They observed that cooling a sugar beet petiole to 1 to 2° C reduced respiratory carbon dioxide production to 10% of the control while translocation occurred at the pretreatment rate after an initial adjustment period. The study revealed a lack of correlation of translocation with carbon dioxide output and, by inference, with ATP turnover rates in the petiole. This lack of stoichiometry supports the conclusion that the major sites of energy input for driving translocation are elsewhere than in the sieve-tube elements of the path. At 1° C more than 600,000 molecules of sucrose were transported through a sieve-tube element per ATP molecule generated in the element.

II. Effects on Plant Growth and Productivity under Field Conditions

The various mechanisms by which metabolic inhibition affects translocation offer some insights into effects on plant growth and productivity under field conditions. Situations in which metabolic inhibition of one or more portions of the translocation system may occur include exposure to temperature extremes, flooding of the soil, and atmospheric pollutants which inhibit energy metabolism. It is advantageous to separate effects produced by localized inhibition for the purpose of studying mechanisms of translocation. However, when we wish to apply our knowledge of the mechanisms by which translocation is altered as a result of metabolic inhibition to plant growth and productivity, it is important to know which effects predominate under a given set of circumstances.

GIFFORD et al. (1973) reviewed work done to determine the relationship of the physiology of assimilation in higher plants to crop yield. They devised models to study factors which limit accumulation of assimilate in grain and found that for the barley crop studied neither source nor sink exerted an overriding limitation to grain yield. Their conclusion suggests that under field conditions, effects on assimilate transport in path, source and sink may all contribute significantly to controlling crop yield and plant growth under different circumstances. The effect of chilling can be used as a case in point.

For chilling-insensitive plants the transient effect of cool temperatures on the path probably does not affect yield significantly. In these plants the major effect of chilling will result from mechanisms acting in the source and sink regions. In chilling-sensitive plants the effects of low temperatures on source or sink components of translocation are overshadowed by the marked obstruction which occurs in the phloem. In support of this thesis, WEBB (1970) noted that the translocation rate curve for temperature treatment of the leaf blade resembles that of node, petiole, hypocotyl or stem treatments. THROWER (1965) found labeled ^{14}C in the leaf blade and petiole of bean plants held at 2 to 3° C for 5 h but found no label in the stem, roots, or apices. Assimilation occurred but translocation was severely limited by obstruction in the path.

Under field conditions the blockage of translocation by path chilling may seriously affect productivity during times of periodic low temperatures. HILLIARD and WEST (1970) studied the effect of low temperature on Pangolagrass *Digitaria decumbens* whose growth is markedly reduced by night temperatures below 10° C. Chloroplasts of these plants retain their starch during dark periods below 10° C and the leaves subsequently show reduced photosynthesis. From their data it appears that temperatures below 10° C block translocation and result in the symptoms described. The 12-h night period apparently is not sufficient for adaptation and renewed translocation. As a consequence of starch persistence and assimilate build-up caused by the intermittent chilling, assimilatory capacity and growth are limited even though favorable temperatures follow during the day period. OWEN (1972) found that cool periods of 2 h or longer delayed floral initiation, reduced grain yields and increased tiller sterility in rice. The effects may include reduction of translocation as a part of the causal mechanism but without additional experimentation it is conjectural. JONES (1969) in a review of the effects of temperature on productivity in bean, reports stoppage of leaf growth below 10° C. Below 15° C, seed set and pod growth became very erratic and, following a night at 10° C, photosynthesis does not reach its full rate until afternoon. It is difficult to determine from the report of JONES how much of the effect is a result of inhibited sugar translocation and how much is the result of direct effects on photosynthesis and growth.

High path temperatures appear to block translocation by promoting formation of sieve-tube callose (MCNAIRN and CURRIER, 1968). MCNAIRN (1972) studied sieve-tube callose and translocation rates in cotton plants under field conditions. During hot weather sieve-plate callose is present in minimal amounts in the morning and is generally more abundant in the afternoon, especially if the temperature rises above 35° C. Intermediate amounts are present in the evening. Callose maxima lag several hours behind temperature maxima with eventual recovery during the night. Breakdown is slower than synthesis. Longitudinal translocation is decreased as a result of sieve-plate callose and lateral transport from the phloem is also markedly reduced by sieve-tube callose (MCNAIRN, 1972).

In chilling-insensitive plants low temperature seems more likely to affect components of the translocation process in the sink and possibly the source regions. In a review of factors affecting rate and pattern of assimilate distribution, WARDLAW (1968) concludes that the major mechanism by which temperature affects distribution is reduction of growth. Assimilates are distributed in greater amounts to those organs able to maintain greater growth and therefore have a greater demand for assimilates. TERRY (1968) has studied the effect of temperature on distribution of assimilates in sugar beet. Because atmospheric CO_2 concentration limits photosynthesis, temperature over much of the range has a relatively minor effect on net assimilation rate in sugar beet. However, temperature does have a significant effect on plant morphogenesis. Above and below the 24° C growth optimum, the rates of cell division and cell expansion decreased in sugar beet. Distribution of assimilate between leaves and root was not affected directly by temperature but occurred according to the pattern of plant morphology; thus the root grew relatively faster than the shoot at temperatures above and below 24° C. At 15° C the roots were smaller than at 25° C even though there was a larger concentration of soluble carbohydrates in the leaves at the lower temperature. The lower root growth rate at 15° C appeared to lessen translocation to the roots even though the net assimilation rate in the leaves was not reduced.

In sugar cane, WALDRON et al. (1967) found a Q_{10} of 1.1 for photosynthesis over a range of 8 to 34° C. However, long-term treatments at low temperatures (17° C day, 10° C night) reduced photosynthetic efficiency. This treatment favored partitioning of assimilates into storage over growth. Accumulation of assimilates in the leaf with reduced translocation did not appear to be the cause of reduced photosynthetic efficiency.

Indirect effects of reduced translocation add to the complexity of temperature effects on the whole plant. BOWLING (1968) observed that uptake of K^+ from the root medium decreased rapidly and markedly when translocation to the roots is inhibited by path chilling in sunflower. In a substequent study, HATRICK and BOWLING (1973) found that root respiration was closely correlated with the rate of translocation from the shoots. They cite a number of cases where inhibition of translocation from shoots to roots dramatically reduced salt uptake and demonstrate the effect with rubidium uptake studies.

From the above data it seems likely that inhibition of translocation by chilling inhibits growth and upsets mineral ion balance in the shoot as well as decreasing the supply of assimilates to the roots. DAVIS and LINGLE (1961) reported that shoot growth of young plants decreased as root temperature decreased from 25° C to 10° C. Below 10° C root growth is nearly zero. Rapid shoot growth at higher root temperatures is accompanied by higher potassium and phosphorus concentrations in the shoot. It appears that chilling-sensitive plants would be particularly susceptible to blockage of translocation to the roots and the resulting decrease in mineral translocation.

ROVIRA and BOWEN (1973) observed that lowering root temperature of wheat plants to 10 or 5° C lowered the rate of translocation of ^{14}C assimilates to the roots. At 5° C the proportion of label entering the apex and elongating zone was reduced giving a more uniform distribution of radioactivity along the root. The observations seem to explain why roots grown at a low temperature are thicker than those grown at a higher one and have a different pattern of ion uptake.

Little or no work has been reported relating anoxic conditions in roots under submergence to inhibition of translocation. Judging from the effectiveness of sink-region anoxia in inhibiting translocation, there are probably field conditions in which low carbohydrate status in the roots is joined with changes in membrane permeability to cause the symptoms accompanying flooding of roots. Another area which may be quite significant is the effect of air-borne pollutants on metabolism and consequently on phloem loading and translocation. To date no studies in this field have come to the present authors' attention. As the relationship between metabolism and translocation is clarified, the way will be opened to work out the practical applications to plant growth and crop productivity.

III. Future Work

To understand the temperature dependence of translocation, several areas need further investigation. A more detailed study of the cause of the obstruction of sieve pores in chilling sensitive plants below the critical threshold temperature is needed.

The mechanism by which recovery occurs upon rewarming needs further study. The mechanism of feedback adjustment of rate during chilling above the damage threshold is still unresolved. Data pointing to increased pressure or some other compensatory response are needed.

The area of the mechanism of callose blockage needs further clarification. In addition, high-temperature effects such as protein denaturation need to be studied as to mechanism, time course and threshold. Freeze-substitution electron-microscopy should shed additional light on this problem.

Identification of the specific processes blocked or inhibited by inhibitors and by low-temperature treatment of the source and sink are important in view of the impact on theories of translocation. Localized inhibition of the subdivisions of the translocation system appears to be moving out of an era characterized by confusion and contradictory data into one where it may be a powerful tool for studying and testing proposed translocation mechanisms.

D. Summary

In the application of metabolic inhibitors for the study of translocation, a number of difficulties are encountered, particularly the inability to limit the treatment to the target region and uncertainty about the major mode of action of the agents. Secondary effects on processes other than energy metabolism or on regions of the system other than the site of application make interpretation difficult. Chemical inhibitors of metabolism, including commonly used ones such as DNP and cyanide, are difficult to restrict to the original treated area and have side effects which include alteration of the physical properties of membranes. Low temperature treatment can generally be restricted to one region but it has effects other than reduction of energy metabolism, particularly in chilling-sensitive plants.

Another source of difficulty which adds to the complexity of interpretation of data is the time-dependent nature of inhibitor effects. In the case of low-temperature treatment, the level of inhibition generally decreases with time while with chemical agents and anoxia long treatment often leads to progressive damage. These considerations have practical application in the interpretation of the results of translocation experiments in which metabolic inhibitors are employed.

The subdivision of the translocation system into source, path and sink regions is helpful in analyzing the role of metabolism in these subsystems. Whole-plant treatments tend to superimpose several separate effects. Path treatment with low temperature, anoxia or chemical inhibitors of respiratory metabolism have yielded data which indicate that the major role of energy metabolism in the translocation path is the maintenance of structural integrity. Treatment of chilling-sensitive plants by lowering the temperature of stems or petioles reveals a threshold of increased inhibition of translocation at approximately 12° C. Structural damage appears to be more severe below this threshold. Chilling insensitive plants do not show the increased damage until 0° C or below. The initial transient inhibition found in chilling-sensitive plants near the threshold of long-term damage may also be caused by structural damage. The long-term slight decrease in translocation by chilling above the threshold is able to be explained in terms of viscosity increase as is the decrease noted above the damage threshold in chilling sensitive plants.

The role of energy metabolism in the sink region appears to be related to the ability of growing tissues, storage organs and metabolically active regions to enhance translocation into themselves. The effect on translocation of low temperature, anoxia or chemical inhibitors when applied to sink region can be accounted for by the inhibition of cellular transport or the transformation of the translocated substances or both. Advocates of mass flow theories view the role of metabolism in the sink region in terms of a steepening of the osmotic potential gradient at that end of the translocation system.

The assessment of the effect of inhibition of metabolism in the source region is particularly difficult. There are the possible effects of these treatments on photosynthesis and on the entry of translocate in addition to effects on the process which causes movement of the translocate. In general, the results of experimental inhibition of energy metabolism in the source region are consistent with the role of the source in motivating translocation but more conclusive and incisive experiments are needed (see Chapter 17).

In addition to helping us understand the role of energy metabolism in translocation, the use of metabolic inhibitors can also provide insights into the role of translocation in plant growth and productivity under field conditions. Conditions which can inhibit energy metabolism in the translocation system, for example, anoxia, low temperature and chemical pollutants in the environment, all enter into the picture of growth and productivity. These factors are potentially critical depending on circumstances. More data on the effect of atmospheric pollution on phloem loading and export from the source as well as data on the effect of low or high temperature on the translocation path and of low temperature and anoxia on sink tissue are needed to properly assess the agronomic significance of these factors. Localized inhibition of energy metabolism has contributed to our understanding of translocation and a number of practical questions remain which can be addressed by this approach.

References

ANAND, R., GALSTON, A.W.: Further investigations on phytochrome-controlled sucrose uptake into apical buds of etiolated peas. Am. J. Botany **59**, 327–336 (1972).

BAUER, I.: Zur Frage der Stoffbewegungen in der Pflanze mit besonderer Berücksichtigung der Wanderung von Fluorochromen. Planta **42**, 367–451 (1953).

BELEHRADEK, J.: Intermolecular aspects of the structural stability of protoplasm at the temperature extremes. In: The cell and environmental temperature (ed. A.S. TAOSHEN), p. 433–443. New York: Pergamon Press 1967.

BIELAWSKI, J., THOMPSON, T.R., LEHNINGER, A.L.: The effect of 2,4-dinitrophenol on the electrical resistance of phospholipid bilayer membranes. Biochem. Biophys. Res. Commun. **24**, 948–954 (1966).

BIELESKI, R.L.: The physiology of sugar cane. IV. Effects of inhibitors on sugar accumulation in storage tissue slices. Australian J. Biol. Sci. **13**, 221–231 (1960).

BOWEN, J.E., HUNTER, J.E.: Sugar transport in immature internodal tissue of sugar cane. II. Mechanism of sucrose transport. Plant Physiol. **49**, 789–793 (1972).

BOWLING, D.J.F.: Translocation at 0° C in *Helianthus annus*. J. Exptl. Botany **19**, 381–388 (1968).

CHILD, C.M., BELLAMY, A.W.: Physiological isolation by low temperature in *Bryophyllum* and other plants. Science **50**, 362–365 (1919).

COULSON, C.L., CHRISTY, A.L., CATALDO, D.A., SWANSON, C.A.: Carbohydrate translocation in sugar beet petioles in relation to petiolar respiration and adenosine-5′-triphosphate. Plant Physiol. **49**, 919–923 (1972).

COULSON, C.L., PEEL, A.J.: The effect of temperature on the respiration of ^{14}C-labeled sugars in stems of willow. Ann. Botany **35**, 9–15 (1971).

CURTIS, O.F.: Studies on solute translocation in plants. Experiments indicating that translocation is dependent on the activity of living cells. Am. J. Botany **16**, 154–168 (1929).

CURTIS, O.F., ASAI, G.N.: Evidence relative to the supposed permeability of sieve-tube cytoplasm. Am. J. Botany **26**, 16s–17s (1939).

CURTIS, O.F., HERTY, S.D.: The effect of temperature on translocation from leaves. Am. J. Botany **23**, 528–532 (1936).

DANIELL, J.W., CHAPPELL, W.E., COUCH, H.B.: Effect of sublethal and lethal temperatures on plant cells. Plant Physiol. **44**, 1684–1689 (1969).

DAS, R.M., HILDEBRANDT, A.C., RIKER, A.J.: Cinephotomicrography of low temperature effects on cytoplasmic streaming, nucleolar activity and mitosis in single tobacco cells in microculture. Am. J. Botany **53**, 253–259 (1966).

DAVIS, R.M., LINGLE, J.C.: Basis of shoot response to root temperature in tomato. Plant Physiol. **36**, 153–162 (1961).

EFFER, W.R., RANSON, S.L.: Respiratory metabolism in buckwheat seedlings. Plant Physiol. **42**, 1042–1052 (1967).

FERRIER, J.M., CHRISTY, A.L.: Time dependent behavior of a mathematical model for Münch translocation: application to recovery from cold inhibition. Plant Physiol. **55**, 511–514 (1975).

FINKELMAN, I., REINHOLD, L.: Studies on the uptake and release of sugars by segments of sunflower hypocotyl. II. The effect of 2,4-dinitrophenol on the release of sugars and on the apparent free space of the tissue. Israel J. Botany **12**, 106–113 (1963).

FORD, J., PEEL, A.J.: The contributory length of sieve tubes in isolated segments of willow, and the effect on it of low temperature. J. Exptl. Botany **17**, 522–533 (1966).

FORD, J., PEEL, A.J.: Preliminary experiments on the effect of temperature on the movement of ^{14}C-labeled assimilates through the phloem of the willow. J. Exptl. Botany **18**, 406–415 (1967).

FUJIWARA, A., SUZUKI, M.: Effects of temperature and light on the translocation of photosynthetic products. Tohoku J. Agr. Res. **12**, 363–367 (1961).

GARDNER, D.C.J., PEEL, A.J.: The effect of low temperature on sucrose, ATP and potassium concentrations and fluxes in the sieve tubes of willow. Planta **102**, 348–356 (1972).

GAYLER, K.R., GLASZIOU, K.T.: Sugar accumulation in sugarcane. Carrier-mediated active transport of glucose. Plant Physiol. **49**, 563–568 (1972).

GEIGER, D.R.: Effect of sink cooling on translocation of photosynthate. Plant Physiol. **41**, 1667–1672 (1966).

GEIGER, D.R.: Chilling and translocation inhibition. Ohio J. Sci. **69**, 356–366 (1969).
GEIGER, D.R., CHRISTY, A.L.: Inhibition of sink tissue metabolism: effect on sucrose translocation and tissue impedance. Plant Physiol. **46** (Suppl.), 5 (1970).
GEIGER, D.R., CHRISTY, A.L.: Effect of sink region anoxia on translocation rate. Plant Physiol. **47**, 172–174 (1971).
GEIGER, D.R., GIAQUINTA, R.T., SOVONICK, S.A., FELLOWS, R.J.: Solute distribution in sugar beet leaves in relation to phloem loading and translocation. Plant Physiol. **52**, 585–589 (1973).
GEIGER, D.R., SOVONICK, S.A.: Temporary inhibition of translocation velocity and mass transfer rates by petiole cooling. Plant Physiol. **46**, 847–849 (1970).
GIAQUINTA, R.T.: Mechanism of low path-temperature inhibition of ^{14}C sucrose translocation. Ph.D. Dissertation. University of Dayton (1972).
GIAQUINTA, R.T., GEIGER, D.R.: Mechanism of inhibition of translocation by localized chilling. Plant Physiol. **51**, 372–377 (1973).
GIESE, A.C.: Cell physiology, 4th ed. Philadelphia: Saunders 1973.
GIFFORD, R.M., BREMNER, P.M., JONES, D.B.: Assessing photosynthetic limitation to grain yield in a field crop. Australian J. Agri. Res. **24**, 297–307 (1973).
GLINKA, Z., REINHOLD, L.: Induced changes in permeability of plant cell membranes to water. Plant Physiol. **49**, 602–606 (1972).
HAREL, S., REINHOLD, L.: The effect of 2,4-dinitrophenol on translocation in the phloem. Physiol. Plantarum **19**, 634–643 (1966).
HARTT, C.E.: The effect of temperature upon translocation of ^{14}C in sugar cane. Plant Physiol. **40**, 74–81 (1965).
HATRICK, A.A., BOWLING, D.J.F.: A study of the relationship between root and shoot metabolism. J. Exptl. Botany **24**, 607–613 (1973).
HEWITT, S.P., CURTIS, O.F.: The effect of temperature on loss of dry matter and carbohydrate from leaves by respiration and translocation. Am. J. Botany **35**, 746–755 (1948).
HIATT, A.J., LOWE, R.H.: Loss of organic acids, amino acids, K and Cl from barley roots treated anaerobically and with metabolic inhibitors. Plant Physiol. **42**, 1731–1736 (1967).
HILLIARD, J.H., WEST, S.H.: Starch accumulation associated with growth retardation at low temperatures in a tropical plant. Science **168**, 494–496 (1970).
HO, L.C., MORTIMER, D.C.: The site of cyanide inhibition of sugar translocation in sugar beet leaf. Can. J. Botany **49**, 1769–1775 (1971).
HULL, H.M.: Carbohydrate translocation in tomato and sugar beet with particular reference to temperature effect. Am. J. Botany **39**, 661–669 (1952).
HUSAIN, S.M., LINCK, A.J.: The effect of chilling of the physiological and stimulated apex of 2- and 3-leaf plants of *Pisum sativum* L. cv. Alaska on lateral shoot growth, C-14, IAA movement and P-32 accumulation. Plant Physiol. **20**, 48–56 (1967).
JONES, L.H.: The physiology of production in *Phaseolus*. Genet. Agraria **23**, 1–4 (1969).
KENDALL, W.A.: Effect of certain metabolic inhibitors on translocation of ^{32}P in bean plants. Plant Physiol. **30**, 347–350 (1955).
LANG, A.: The effect of petiolar temperature upon the translocation rate of ^{137}Cs in the phloem of *Nymphoides peltata*. J. Exptl. Botany **25**, 71–80 (1974).
LINCK, A.J., SWANSON, C.A.: A study of several factors affecting the distribution of phosphorus-32 from the leaves of *Pisum sativum*. Plant Soil **12**, 57–68 (1960).
LOOMIS, R.S., WILLIAMS, W.A., HALL, A.E.: Agricultural productivity. Ann. Rev. Plant Physiol. **22**, 431–468 (1971).
LOTT, J. R., ROSENE, H.F.: Effects of 4,6-dinitro-o-cresol on water influx and oxygen uptake of excised onion roots. Am. J. Botany **43**, 69–72 (1956).
LYONS, J.M.: Chilling injury in plants. Ann. Rev. Plant Physiol. **24**, 445–466 (1973).
LYONS, J.M., RAISON, J.K.: Oxidative activity of mitochondria isolated from plant tissues sensitive and resistant to chilling injury. Plant Physiol. **45**, 386–389 (1970a).
LYONS, J.M., RAISON, J.K.: A temperature-induced transition in mitochondrial oxidation: contrasts between cold- and warm-blooded animals. Comp. Biochem. Physiol. **37**, 405–411 (1970b).
LYONS, J.M., WHEATON, T.A., PRATT, H.K.: Relationship between physical nature of mitochondrial membranes and chilling sensitivity in plants. Plant Physiol. **39**, 262–268 (1964).
MAJUMDER, S.K., LEOPOLD, A.C.: Callose formation in response to low temperature. Plant and Cell Physiol. **8**, 775–778 (1967).

MASON, R.G., PHYLLIS, E.: Oxygen supply and the inactivation of diffusion. Ann. Botany **50**, 455–499 (1936).

MCNAIRN, R.B.: Phloem translocation and heat-induced callose formation in field grown *Gossypium hirsutum* L. Plant Physiol. **50**, 366–370 (1972).

MCNAIRN, R.B., CURRIER, H.B.: Translocation blockage by sieve-plate callose. Planta **82**, 369–380 (1968).

MILBURN, J.A., WEATHERLEY, P.E.: The influence of temperature on the process of water uptake by detached leaves and leaf discs. New Phytologist **70**, 929–938 (1971).

MÜLLER, K., LEOPOLD, A.C.: The mechanism of kinetin-induced transport in corn leaves. Planta **68**, 186–205 (1966).

NELSON, C.D.: The effect of climate on the distribution and translocation of assimilates. In: Environmental control of plant growth (ed. L.T. EVANS), ch. 10, p. 149–174. New York: Academic Press 1963.

NOBEL, P.S.: Temperature dependence of the permeability of chloroplasts from chilling-sensitive and chilling-resistant plants. Planta **115**, 369–372 (1974).

OWEN, P.C.: Effects of cool periods (15° C) at night on taichung (native). No. 1 rice. Exptl. Agric. **8**, 289–294 (1972).

QURESHI, F.A., SPANNER, D.C.: The effect of nitrogen on the movement of tracers down the stolon of *Saxifraga sarmentosa* L. with some observations on the influence of light. Planta **110**, 131–144 (1973a).

QURESHI, F.A., SPANNER, D.C.: The influence of dinitrophenol on phloem transport along the stolon of *Saxifraga sarmentosa* L. Planta **111**, 1–12 (1973b).

QURESHI, F.A., SPANNER, D.C.: Cyanide inhibition of phloem transport along the stolon of *Saxifraga sarmentosa* L. J. Exptl. Botany **24**, 751–762 (1973c).

RAISON, J.K.: The influence of temperature-induced phase changes on the kinetics of respiratory and other membrane-associated enzyme systems. Bioenergetics **4**, 559–583 (1972).

RAISON, J.K., LYONS, J.M., THOMPSON, W.W.: The influence of membranes on the temperature-induced changes in the kinetics of some respiratory enzymes of mitochondria. Arch. Biochem. Biophys. **142**, 83–90 (1971).

ROECKL, B.: Nachweis eines Konzentrationshubs zwischen Palisadenzellen und Siebröhren. Planta **36**, 530–550 (1949).

ROVIRA, A.D., BOWEN, G.D.: The influence of root temperature on ^{14}C assimilate profiles in wheat roots. Planta **114**, 101–107 (1973).

SHIH, C.Y., CURRIER, H.B.: Fine structure of phloem cells in relation to translocation in cotton seedlings. Am. J. Botany **56**, 464–472 (1969).

SIJ, J., SWANSON, C.A.: Effect of petiole anoxia on phloem transport in squash. Plant Physiol. **51**, 368–371 (1972).

SOVONICK, S.A., GEIGER, D.R., FELLOWS, R.J.: Evidence for active phloem loading in the minor veins of sugar beet. Plant Physiol. **54**, 886–891 (1974).

STUART, D.M.: Reduction of water permeability in potato tuber slices by cyanide, ammonia, 2,4-dinitrophenol, and oligomycin and its reversal by adenosine-5′-triphosphate and cytidine-5′-triphosphate. Plant Physiol. **51**, 485–488 (1973).

SWANSON, C.A.: Translocation of organic solutes. In: Plant physiology (ed. F.C. STEWARD), vol. II, p. 481–551. New York: Academic Press 1959.

SWANSON, C.A., BÖHNING, R.: Translocation of carbohydrates. Plant Physiol. **26**, 557–564 (1951).

SWANSON, C.A., GEIGER, D.R.: Time course of low temperature inhibition of sucrose translocation in sugar beets. Plant Physiol. **42**, 751–756 (1967).

SWANSON, C.A., WHITNEY, J.B., JR.: Studies on the translocation of foliar applied P^{32} and other radioisotopes in bean plants. Am. J. Botany **40**, 816–823 (1953).

TAMMES, P.M.L., VONK, C.R., VAN DIE, J.: Studies on phloem exudation from *Yucca flaccida* Haw. VII. The effect of cooling on exudation. Acta Botan. Neerl. **18**, 224–229 (1969).

TERRY, N.: Developmental physiology of sugar beet I. The influence of light and temperature on growth. J. Exptl. Botany **19**, 795–811 (1968).

THROWER, S.L.: Translocation of labeled assimilates in the soybean. IV. Some effects of low temperature on translocation. Australian J. Biol. Sci. **18**, 449–461 (1965).

TING, H.P., WILSON, D.F., CHANCE, B.: Effects of uncouplers of oxidative phosphorylation on specific conductance of bimolecular lipid membranes. Arch. Biochem. Biophys. **141**, 141–146 (1970).

Toia, R.E.: Effects of inhibition of sink leaf metabolism on accumulation of translocate in the sugar beet (*Beta vulgaris* L.). MS thesis, University of Dayton, Ohio 1971.

Ullrich, W.: Zur Sauerstoffabhängigkeit des Transportes in den Siebröhren. Planta **57**, 402–429 (1961).

Vernon, L.P., Aronoff, S.: Metabolism of soybean leaves. IV. Translocation from soybean leaves. Arch. Biochem. Biophys. **36**, 383–398 (1952).

Walding, H.F., Weatherley, P.E.: The effect of cooling on translocation in *Salix viminalis*. J. Exptl. Botany **23**, 338–345 (1972).

Waldron, J.D., Glasziou, K.T., Bull, T.A.: The physiology of sugar-cane. IX. Factors affecting photosynthesis and sugar storage. Australian J. Biol. Sci. **20**, 1043–1052 (1967).

Wardlaw, I.F.: The control and pattern of movement of carbohydrate in plants. Biol. Rev. **34**, 79–105 (1968).

Wardlaw, I.F.: Temperature and the translocation of photosynthate through the leaf of *Lolium temulentum*. Planta **104**, 18–34 (1972).

Watson, B.T.: The influence of low temperature on the rate of translocation in the phloem of *Salix viminalis*, L. Ann. Botany (1975).

Weatherley, P.E.: On the uptake of sucrose and water by floating leaf disks under aerobic and anaerobic conditions. New Phytologist **54**, 13–28 (1955).

Weatherley, P.E., Watson, B.T.: Some low-temperature effects on sieve-tube translocation in *Salix viminalis*. Ann. Botany **33**, 845–853 (1969).

Webb, J.A.: Translocation of sugars in *Cucurbita melopepo* IV. The effect of temperature change. Plant Physiol. **42**, 881–885 (1967).

Webb, J.A.: Translocation of sugars in *Cucurbita melopepo* V. The effect of leaf-blade temperature on assimilation and transport. Canad. J. Botany **48**, 935–942 (1970).

Webb, J.A.: Translocation of sugars in *Cucurbita melopepo*. VI. The reversible low-temperature inhibition of ^{14}C movement and the cold acclimation of phloem tissue. Canad. J. Botany **49**, 717–733 (1971).

Webb, J.A., Gorham, P.R.: The effect of node temperature on assimilation and translocation of C^{14} in squash. Canad. J. Botany **43**, 1009–1020 (1965).

Webster, D.H., Currier, H.B.: Heat-induced callose and lateral movement of assimilates from phloem. Canad. J. Botany **46**, 1215–1220 (1968).

Willenbrink, J.: Über die Hemmung des Stofftransports in den Siebröhren durch lokale Inaktivierung verschiedener Atmungsenzyme. Planta **48**, 269–342 (1957).

Willenbrink, J.: Zur lokalen Hemmung des Assimilattransports durch Blausäure. Z. Pflanzenphysiol. **55**, 119–130 (1967).

Willenbrink, J.: Einige Beziehungen zwischen Stoffwechsel und Ferntransport im Phloem. Vortr. Gesamtgebiet Botan. **2**, 42–49 (1968).

Wright, M., Simon, E.W.: Chilling injury in cucumber leaves. J. Exptl. Botany **24**, 400–411 (1973).

IV. Possible Mechanisms of Phloem Transport

12. Protoplasmic Streaming

M.J. CANNY

A. Introduction

After HARTIG'S discovery of the sieve tube in 1837 and his later researches (1858a, b) that established the importance of the phloem as the tissue containing a rich organic sap, plant physiologists were firmly convinced that this was the channel in which the "elaborated sap" formed by the leaves was exported throughout the plant. It seems that from 1860 to 1885 they were content to believe that the mechanism of movement of the nutrients in the phloem was by diffusion down a gradient of concentration. DE VRIES (1885) states: "Following the prevailing view, initiated and developed by SACHS about the movement of organic nutrients in plants, the most general cause of this movement was considered to be diffusion. Consumption of each substance by growth and metabolism, and a corresponding enrichment in particular cells and organs determine the direction in which the movement goes, while the transfer itself is generally a diffusive one." He firmly points out that this is quantitatively quite untenable, that diffusion would take two years and seven months to transfer a milligram of sugar through a distance of one meter of pure water from a 10% source solution, and that this cannot conceivably be the basis of long-distance transport. Even when the gradient of sugar concentration is established the transfer of a mg through a cm^2 would take six days. He argues instead in favor of the streaming motions observable in protoplasm as a more credible mechanism and studied fresh phloem to see to what extent such motions occurred there and whether the speeds of motion provided the necessary acceleration. He made careful hand sections in 5% sugar solution, and allowed several hours for them to recover before observing them. He records: "Fine examples for the observation of movement of the protoplasm are offered as is well known by the species of the genus *Tradescantia*. I studied mainly *T. rosea*, a species closely allied to *T. virginica*. In July I found in vigorous, freely-flowering specimens over 70 cm high the movements in question everywhere I looked. In the conducting cells (Leitzellen) of the phloem of the vascular bundles the contents showed typical rotation: on one long wall ascending, on the opposite one circulating back down again. The speed was on average 0.2–0.4 mm min^{-1}. I followed up the movement in these cells in the young, half-grown branches borne by the inflorescences, in the youngest full-grown, the medium-aged and oldest internodes of the stem, in the midribs of the leaves and in the leaf sheaths, and finally in the rhizome and roots." After an extensive survey of the motions in other cells and tissues in many plants, he concluded that the movements were a general property of plant cells, and that they were a far more likely transport mechanism than diffusion.

However other investigators argued that though such streaming might occur in young sieve tubes, and in the other cells of the phloem, mature sieve tubes with open sieve pores showed no such movement (LECOMTE, 1889; STRASBURGER,

1891) and that the transport was more likely to be by the flow of the nutrient-rich solution through the pores. The acceptance of such a view seems to have been widespread until about 1920 when a more basic problem occupied ATKINS, BIRCH-HIRSCHFELD, and DIXON, namely whether the phloem was after all the channel of transport. The experiments and arguments on which these doubts were based can now be seen to be ill-founded, though we are still troubled by the dilemma in which DIXON found himself when he calculated the flow rates necessary in sieve tubes to achieve specific mass transfers of the measured size as in Eq. (2) of Chapter 5.

As late as 1926 MASON and LEWIN could write about their yam measurements (Chapter 5, Fig. 1): "If now it be assumed that the carbohydrates moved at a concentration of 25 percent in the sieve tubes, a velocity of transport of ... 88 cm per hour would result. A movement at this rate is, of course, impossible through sieve tubes, even if their whole cross-section were available for transport. Thus, even when high concentrations are assumed, the phloem seems incapable of transmitting carbohydrates. That the phloem, in common with other living tissues, may transmit sugars at a limited rate is probably not in doubt, but that carbohydrates are *normally* transported through it seems impossible." By 1928 MASON had convinced himself that this apparent impossibility was a fact, and provided the proof that silenced all further argument (MASON and MASKELL, 1928a, b).

With this decided, the question of mechanism came once again sharply into focus, and CURTIS, who since 1920 had been championing the twin causes of the phloem *vs.* the xylem and protoplasmic streaming *vs.* passive flow, presented his most persuasive account of the possibilities of this hypothesis (1935). He pictured streaming motions stirring the contents of each sieve element and rapidly equalizing differences of concentration in them. Then, either there was diffusion across the short distance of wall and pore between consecutive sieve elements, or the streaming motion continued also through the pores, and effectively stirred the whole length of sieve tube, bringing the source concentration up to the sink. The advantages of such a mechanism were several: (1) it would allow simultaneous transport of different substances in opposite directions; (2) it would account for the apparent necessity for intact living cells; (3) it was free from a number of weaknesses that made the MÜNCH/CRAFTS passive-flow hypothesis unacceptable to many. He readily admitted that the hypothesis itself suffered from a number of weaknesses, and listed these at length. The principal two were (1) that with the streaming rates known from other cells it does not provide sufficient transport capacity; and (2) that streaming had not been certainly observed in mature sieve tubes. This balance of evidence might stand today as a summary of views on the matter, but there is now a good deal more evidence on all these counts to balance, some of which will be treated in this review. The problem of bi-directional movement is dealt with in Chapter 10; and some greater elaborations of streaming-type motions are discussed in Chapter 15.

B. The Phenomenon of Streaming

Detailed surveys of the phenomenon should be sought in recent reviews such as KAMIYA (1959, 1962), ALLEN and KAMIYA (1964), from which it is plain that the single appearance of visible motion of protoplasm covers a number of phenomena that are probably different. The motions seen in amoebae, slime moulds and giant algal cells like *Nitella* appear to represent three different sets of cytoplasmic organisations whose manifestation is visible motion. The amoebae are the center of a lively controversy and may be left to the zoologists as having little in common with sieve tubes. KAMIYA's studies of velocity profiles in *Physarum* and *Nitella* have shown that the motion is of two different kinds in these two organisms; that while the slime-mould flow shows the characteristics of a sol phase being forced through channels in a gel by local changes in pressure, in the alga, a stationary gel lining of protoplasm within the cell wall appears to generate a motive force where it is in contact with the interior sol phase driving the sol along in a helical path around the cell and sweeping the vacuole with it. This motion can survive in isolated drops of protoplasm wherever fragments of sol and gel are in contact. Most is known about these two systems because they are especially easy to study, and what has been learned from them is assumed to apply to other cells. Streaming in *Elodea* leaf cells, in hair cells and epidermal cells of many herbaceous species and the parenchyma of vascular tissues is assumed to have a good deal in common with *Nitella* and to be the result of similar sol-gel interactions.

One property of streaming protoplasm that is of especial relevance to its involvement in translocation is its speed. The two processes are commonly measured in quite different speed units, so here the streaming units of $\mu m\ sec^{-1}$ will be translated into the translocation units of $cm\ h^{-1}$. KAMIYA (1959, Table 1) lists 40 measurements of speeds in various plant materials. The fastest are in myxomycete plasmodia, about $4.5 \times 10^2\ cm\ h^{-1}$; the rapid algal motions of the Characeae have been timed at a maximum of about $27\ cm\ h^{-1}$, while the hair cells and epidermal cells of the higher plants, including *Elodea* yield values in the range 1 to $3.5\ cm\ h^{-1}$. These speeds may be compared with the speed of translocation. As has been argued elsewhere the concept of a speed associated with translocation is not clear in theory; it is difficult to devise satisfactory means of measuring it; and the results of such experiments provide answers ranging over 1,000-fold (Chapter 5 and CANNY, 1973). Nevertheless a majority of workers would probably agree in accepting a medium value of 50–100 $cm\ h^{-1}$. The plasmodial streaming speed exceeds nearly all values measured for translocation; the *Nitella* speed is rather less than most translocation values.

The reviews cited appeared just before a spate of reports that give hope of a new unity of these motions with those of many cells during morphogenesis and muscle myofibrils. This unity has a double basis in both structure and chemistry.

C. The Fine Structure of Streaming Protoplasm

It is becoming plain that these motions of protoplasm are all associated with microfilaments visible in the electron microscope, and filamentous structures (possibly aggregates of microfilaments) visible in the light microscope. KAMIYA (1959) described filamentous structures associated with motions in isolated drops of *Nitella* protoplasm, and these have been further described by KAMITSUBO (1966a, b) and KURODA (1964). The filaments may not themselves move, but the sol motion seems especially fast adjacent to them. Cytoplasmic fibers that may be of the same kind and share the same association with streaming have been pictured in the hair cells of *Heracleum* (O'BRIEN and MCCULLY, 1970), revealed by Nomarski optics. Their description suggests that the fibers are polarized to produce movement along their length in a particular direction.

In the electronmicroscope the regions of streaming protoplasm are found to contain close arrays of long microfilaments about 5–7.5 nm in diameter organised into bundles about 1 μm thick from which other cell organelles are excluded. These were shown in *Nitella* by NAGAI and REBHUN (1966), in *Avena* coleoptile transvacuolar strand and parietal protoplasm by O'BRIEN and THIMANN (1966), and in *Physarum* by WOHLFARTH-BOTTERMANN (1963). Similar microfilaments are known also from amoebae (POLLARD and ITO, 1968) and a number of animal cells. Since the visible fibrils can be seen to aggregate from and break up into much finer filaments, it seems reasonable to speculate that they are in fact formed from aggregates of the microfilament bundles. From their lack of motion themselves, it seems fair to locate them in the gel phase at the boundary with the moving sol.

D. Chemical Basis of Protoplasmic Streaming

It is becoming plain that the highly characteristic properties of the two proteins responsible for muscle contraction, actin and myosin, are to be found in many of these simpler systems. Myosin (HATANO and TAZAWA, 1968) and actin (HATANO and OOSAWA, 1966) have both been isolated from *Physarum* plasmodium, and each will cross-react with the other or with actin or myosin from muscle to form the actomyosin complex. Moreover each has its characteristic complex reactions: the myosin is an ATP-ase modulated by Ca^{2+} and Mg^{2+}; the G-actin polymerizes to F-actin and has a molecular weight and amino acid composition strikingly like that of muscle actin.

In addition a specific histochemical reaction has been used to identify the microfilaments of *Physarum* as actin. Not only are they the right size and shape, but they will form the so-called "arrowhead complexes" with the bridge-forming part of the myosin molecule, heavy meromyosin (HMM) by which it bonds to F-actin. These are rendered visible in the electronmicroscope by negative staining. Plasmodium microfilaments form the complex not only with HMM from plasmodium myosin, but even with HMM from rabbit myosin (POLLARD et al., 1970; NACHMIAS et al., 1970), and the reaction is blocked by Mg-ATP which dissociates the actomyosin complex of muscle. The directional orientation of the arrowheads shows that the filament has a polarity.

Though this technique has not yet been used to confirm the *Nitella* or higher-plant microfilaments as actin, there is a second test which implicates them with the streaming: the response to cytochalasin B. This compound has been shown to have a specific and reversible effect upon microfilaments in a variety of cells, disorganising the array of microfilaments, and suspending the contractile function with which they are associated (WESSELS et al., 1971; SPOONER, YAMADA, and WESSELS, 1971). These authors record that cytochalasin B stopped streaming in *Avena* epidermal cells and in *Nitella*, and the latter finding has since been documented by WILLIAMSON (1972a).

These important generalizations bring the known sliding-filament forces that can be generated by ATP between actin and myosin filaments into the streaming protoplasm as a likely generator of motion, and PRINGLE (1968) has focused attention on this possibility:

"At an even lower level of organisation, a protein resembling heavy meromyosin might exist without even the ability to associate into a dimer. An active change in the angle of attachment of such a molecule to the actin filaments when ATP is hydrolyzed could produce protoplasmic streaming past the filaments due to mobilization of the associate water molecules."

The rather different motion of the slime mould could be pictured as pressure flow of sol within the channels of the gel network where the actin filaments and myosin filaments would provide rhythmic contractions leading to local changes of volume. Such a view would place the highly-developed organization of muscle cells at the end of a long phylogenetic progression from a general property of primitive protoplasm based upon a single fundamental capability of this pair of proteins.

E. Translocation Models Using the Streaming Properties of Protoplasm

I. Rotation Streaming

The hypothesis, originated by DE VRIES and maintained by CURTIS in 1935, that the rotational streaming common in other cells would, if functioning in sieve elements, provide a vehicle for translocation, suited very closely the accelerated-diffusion ideas of MASON and MASKELL (see Chapter 5). These workers, however, did not favor it as a possible mechanism for three reasons: (1) despite careful observation, they were unable to find streaming motion in the sieve elements; (2) the mere circulation of protoplasm coupled with diffusion across sieve plates would not produce the acceleration of diffusion they had shown to exist; (3) the motions necessary to produce sufficient acceleration, namely streaming of protoplasm through sieve pores as well as around within sieve elements, would require too much energy. These objections are set out clearly in MASON et al. (1936), with a correction supplied by SPANNER (1962) who also straightens out some of the other loose thinking by myself and others. SPANNER's conclusion is that on the assumptions of MASON et al. such a mechanism would require an energy expenditure of 2.5 g sucrose per ml of sieve-tube sap per day, and his rejection of the possibility of this mechanism on these grounds has remained unquestioned.

II. Transcellular Strands

While not accepting the contemporary streaming hypothesis, MASON and his colleagues formulated no detailed mechanism of their own to account for their observations, but retained the name "accelerated diffusion" to express their faith in the genuineness of the analogy they had revealed. No other hypothesis with similar properties was put forward until the observations of THAINE (1961) suggested another similar (THAINE, 1962) and a more elaborate streaming mechanism (CANNY, 1962).

THAINE reported seeing and filming strands of protoplasm stretched across the lumen of sieve elements from sieve plate to sieve plate, in which particles could be seen moving in both directions. The particles did not stop at the sieve plate, but passed on through the sieve pores into the next consecutive element, and on through many plates. He timed the particles at 3 to 5 cm h^{-1}. Though others have contradicted THAINE's observations and interpretations (ESAU et al., 1963 and section G), THAINE continues to maintain the reality of what he sees (1964; THAINE et al., 1967), and several other workers report similar findings: PARKER (1964a, b; 1965a, b), FIELD and CLARK (1971).

This two-phase two-directional system of oppositely-moving protoplasmic strands lying in a sieve-tube sap had most interesting properties, and, as I pointed out, could be used to explain both qualitatively (CANNY, 1962) and quantitatively (CANNY and PHILLIPS, 1963) a great proportion of the known facts about translocation. The only additional requirements for this model were (1) a limited permeability of the strand-sap boundary to the translocated solute, and (2) some structural rigidity of the strands to resist osmotic swelling. The model had all the diffusion-analog properties needed to explain MASON and MASKELL's results, and also made testable predictions about the spread of radio-active tracer. These predictions were borne out by a large number of published records (CANNY, 1973; Chapter 16). The constant of proportionality between Specific Mass Transfer and gradient of sucrose (the slope of the line in Fig. 2 of Chapter 5 of this volume) could be expressed as a simple function of the speed of the strands and the ratio of their permeability and radius. It could also be measured in a different way from the steady-state relation just referred to, from the shape of the non-steady-state advancing profile of labeled translocate. Such measurements of it derived from a diversity of data are consistent with the value that MASON and MASKELL found (CANNY, 1973, Table 16.3). With the increasing certainty that structures of the size of THAINE's transcellular strands are not found in sieve tubes (Section G) this version of the model using streaming protoplasm of the classical kind has become less attractive. Its useful properties may be easily preserved at a smaller strand radius (comparable with that of the filamentous structures found in electron micrographs of sieve tubes) if the permeability is decreased in proportion, but at this point it ceases to have much in common with streaming protoplasm.

III. Peristaltic Pumping

THAINE has advanced (1969) another model using transcellular strand structures, but having more in common with slime-mould (pressure flow) streaming than Characean streaming—what he calls cytoplasmic pumping. This uses some contractile property of protoplasm acting circumferentially around tubules within the strands to generate waves of peristalsis travelling along the strands, and so propelling a fluid content which is the stream of translocate. Such peristaltic pumping has been further investigated in theory by AIKMAN and ANDERSON (1971) who conclude that it is energetically feasible. If the tubule surface is partially permeable to translocate and the peristalsis operates in both directions, this model becomes formally identical with the CANNY/PHILLIPS model. Further discussion of peristaltic models is contained in Chapter 15 of this volume.

F. The Occurrence of Streaming in Sieve-Element Protoplasm

From the time of DE VRIES's paper affirming the occurrence of visible streaming in sieve tubes a number of observers have published reports that they have seen it. These have been answered by denials from other workers criticizing the methods used and interpreting the results in some other way, and have sparked off a fresh review of the fragmentary evidence and an inconclusive skirmish, each side leaving the other unconvinced, and bystanders bewildered. Several of these sparring matches have been mentioned: DE VRIES *vs.* LECOMTE, CURTIS *vs.* MÜNCH/CRAFTS, THAINE *vs.* ESAU; and the most recent is continued in this volume. Rather than join these controversies, weighing again the possibilities of artefact and misinterpretation, it seems preferable to pose a neutral question: what can be seen in the functioning sieve tube? and record those observations that seem useful in trying to answer it. This has been attempted at some length in CANNY (1973), and only a short summary of the relevant records can be given here.

The first fact to be clear about is the very great difficulty of microscopic observations of sieve tubes that are "functioning". The extreme sensitivity of the translocation function to damage by cuts into sieve tubes was certainly not appreciated by DE VRIES, and indeed dawned rather slowly on the collective consciousness of translocation workers, and is less appreciated than it should be even today. Cut phloem has its translocating capacity destroyed for a distance which may extend many centimetres from the cut, and visible disruptions of sieve-tube organisation have been found 10 to 12 cm from the cut (LECOMTE, 1889). This sensitivity to damage almost certainly arises from the high turgor pressure of the sieve tubes (measured as 20 to 40 at by MITTLER, 1957) and the disruptive surges produced when this pressure is released, and it makes the observation of functioning phloem very awkward. Intact phloem must be observed, which means in practice that a dissected vascular strand must be arranged on the microscope stage while it is still attached to source and sink, or the microscope must be fixed to a tree trunk over a zone of exposed phloem (HUBER and ROUSCHAL, 1938) and viewed with incident light. Little can be seen unless the sieve tubes are isolated almost entirely from surrounding cells, and yet such interference is most likely to stop their function and alter their structure. To be sure that such alteration has not occurred, some confirmation is required that the observed sieve tubes are translocating: either a fluorescent dye which may be observed simultaneously with the structure, or a radioactive marker whose passage can be checked subsequently. With these constraints it is not surprising that trustworthy accounts of the appearances to be seen in active sieve tubes are few, and that many records need to be discounted as the products of damage.

Those who put the most determined effort into careful preparations of fresh phloem, fully conscious of the fragility of the system they were dealing with, were HUBER (1932), HUBER and ROUSCHAL (1938), SMALL (1939), and BAUER (1949).

Of these only BAUER observed material (dye) being translocated through the sieve tube he was watching and so checked that it was functioning; only SMALL records seeing motions that he believed were those of streaming protoplasm. THAINE's observations have already been mentioned. The recent work of FENSOM and his colleagues is treated separately in Chapter 9 of this volume. From consideration of these records several common generalisations can be made: (1) very few operations were successful, in the sense of providing an image that the author trusted (SCHUMACHER, 1930, quotes a 10% success rate; BAUER produced five satisfactory preparations out of some unspecified large number). (2) the more careful the preparation and the less damaged the sieve tube, the less structure there was to be seen in it. They speak of an empty, glassy appearance in contrast with neighboring parenchyma cells whose organelles would be plainly seen. (3) visible structures within sieve tubes were evidence of damage. The first sign of least damage was the appearance of fibrillar elements within the homogeneous lumen (Aufhängefäden "suspension threads"). On more serious trauma, starch grains appeared, released from parietal plastids, and could be seen executing rapid Brownian-type motions. FENSOM has analyzed the excursions of particles he calls 'marker particles' and which may be distinct from these grains as being in fact faster than Brownian (FENSOM et al., 1968, and Chapter 9 of this volume). More drastic injury showed the results of a pressure surge, with the starch grains clustered near a sieve plate and in Brownian motion. The final collapse of particles and fibrils forms a slime plug—the classical fixation-artefact by which sieve tubes are recognised in dead tissue. (4) movement will not be seen except as movement of some structure, and if the contents are optically homogeneous, i.e. the structures are beyond the limits of resolution, no movement will be seen, however vigorous. Moreover, if the movement is rapid and magnified in proportion to the magnification of the microscope, the persistence of vision will not allow its distinction. Only high-speed flash or cine techniques will reveal it.

The fairest answer to the question: "What can be seen in a functioning sieve tube?" seems on the evidence to be: "Nothing".

G. Structural Components of Sieve Elements that Might be Related to Streaming

The investigation of the structure of sieve elements by electronmicroscopy that was stimulated by THAINE'S reports of transcellular strands has yielded no evidence for the presence of components of such size, or fragments that might be derived from them. Rather, as will be seen from Chapter 1, the electron images suggest a sparse network of microfilaments of P-protein about 25 nm in diameter filling the lumen, while around the walls are a few organelles: plastids containing starch, stacks of cisternae of endoplasmic reticulum, mitochondria with weakly-developed membranes. There is no nucleus, no ribosomes, no dictyosomes. One might interpret these cell-biological appearances as signs of a cell still retaining a few vestigial metabolic activities, but specialized nearly to the point of death for some non-synthetic function, requiring to be supported by neighboring cells in the functions of energy supply, protein synthesis and nuclear control.

In terms of what was said in Section C, the structures that might be evidence of the capacity to generate motion would be microfilaments of actin, possibly organised into fibrils. Though the filaments of the sieve-tube lumen are rather larger than those found in streaming protoplasm or in the I-band of the sarcomere (7.5 nm), some have pointed to the similarity between them, and suggested that they may provide the motive power for translocation. MacRobbie (1971) calculates "that if P-protein filaments were capable of generating a shearing stress comparable with that generated by the microfilaments in *Nitella*, then at the density in which they are found in *Cucurbita* exudate they would provide adequate motive force to drive translocation". The polarity of the filaments would need to be ordered, and she suggests ways in which this might be controlled. The flows she envisages being produced by such shearing forces are not easily classifiable as being either protoplasmic streaming or as mass flow. They share a structural, chemical, and mechanical basis with the former, but could not be seen in the light microscope since there are no particles moving that are big enough to see; they have the simple hydrodynamics of the latter, but with pressure gradients generated internally, and with the possibility of reversal, since the filament polarity may be reversed. Here again the present review begins to overlap the discussion of Chapter 15.

A way to test whether the filaments of P-protein are indeed actin, is to use the specific histochemical test already mentioned—the formation of arrowhead complexes with heavy meromyosin, and the dissociation of the complexes with ATP—which has proved so useful in the slime mould and other organisms. Williamson (1972b) has made this test on filaments from the phloem exudates of *Ricinus* and *Cucurbita*, and reports a negative result. There was no binding of HMM. In the same paper he also reports a negative test with the filament-disorganizing substance: cytochalasin B failed to affect the movement of labeled translocate, and caused no apparent alteration of the fine structure of the sieve elements. It is possible that the technical difficulties of the HMM test have not been overcome for these preparations, and that problems of penetration and degradation of cytochalasin are responsible for the absence of any effect, since a positive result was reported by Thompson and Thompson (1973). Working with isolated phloem strands of *Heracleum* they showed that sucrose transport from a lanolin well on the strand was drastically reduced after 10 min of pretreatment at another site with 30 mg/l cytochalasin B. The inhibition of translocation was general throughout the strand even remote from the feeding well and began to wear off after about an hour. At the present time of active investigation of the properties of the filaments in phloem there is no clear decision as to whether they either generate a force to drive translocation or whether they are actin, or have properties in common with the filaments in streaming protoplasm.

H. Conclusion

From this survey of the evidence it is concluded that protoplasmic streaming of the kind observable in other plant cells does not occur in sieve elements. Their structure is too homogeneous and on too fine a scale to be visible even if motion occurs within them. The microfilaments they contain seem to have little in common with the microfilaments found in association with streaming protoplasm, structurally or chemically, and if they are a means of generating motion, then their organization is different from that of the actin/myosin systems that are found in other plant and animal cells.

References

AIKMAN, D.P., ANDERSON, W.P.: A quantitative investigation of a peristaltic model for phloem translocation. Ann. Botany N.S. **35**, 61–72 (1971).

ALLEN, R.D., KAMIYA, N. (eds.): Primitive motile systems in cell biology. New York-London: Academic Press 1964.

BAUER, L.: Über den Wanderungsweg fluoreszierender Farbstoffe in den Siebröhren. Planta **37**, 221–243 (1949).

BIRCH-HIRSCHFELD, L.: Untersuchungen über die Ausbreitungsgeschwindigkeit gelöster Stoffe in der Pflanze. Jahrb. Wiss. Bot. **59**, 171–262 (1920).

CANNY, M.J.: The mechanism of translocation. Ann. Botany N.S. **26**, 603–617 (1962).

CANNY, M.J.: Phloem translocation. London: Cambridge University Press 1973.

CANNY, M.J., PHILLIPS, O.M.: Quantitative aspects of a theory of translocation. Ann. Botany N.S. **27**, 379–402 (1963).

CURTIS, O.F.: The translocation of solutes in plants. New York-London: McGraw-Hill 1935.

DE VRIES, H.: Über die Bedeutung der Circulation und der Rotation des Protoplasma für den Stofftransport in der Pflanze. Botan. Z. **43**, 1–6, 17–26 (1885).

DIXON, H.H.: Transport of organic substances in plants. Nature **110**, 547–551 (1923).

ESAU, K., ENGLEMAN, E.M., BISALPUTRA, T.: What are transcellular strands? Planta **59**, 617–623 (1963).

FENSOM, D.S., CLATTENBURG, R., CHUNG, T., LEE, D.R., ARNOLD, D.C.: Moving particles in intact sieve tubes of *Heracleum mantegazzianum*. Nature **219**, 531–532 (1968).

FIELD, J.H., CLARK, C.H.: Rapid streaming in the sieve tubes of wheat. School Sci. Rev. **183**, 53, 339 (1971).

HARTIG, T.: Über die Bewegung des Saftes in den Holzpflanzen. Botan. Z. **16**, 329–355, 337–342 (1858a).

HARTIG, T.: Über den Herbstsaft der Holzpflanzen. Botan. Z. **16**, 369–370 (1858b).

HATANO, S., OOSAWA, F.: Isolation and characterization of plasmodium actin. Biochim. Biophys. Acta **127**, 488–498 (1966).

HATANO, S., TAZAWA, M.: Isolation, purification and characterization of myosin B from myxomycete plasmodium. Biochim. Biophys. Acta **154**, 507–519 (1968).

HUBER, B.: Beobachtung und Meßung pflanzlicher Saftströme. Ber. Deut. Botan. Ges. **50**, 89–109 (1932).

HUBER, B., ROUSCHAL, E.: Untersuchungen über die Protoplasmatik und Funktion der Siebröhren. Ber. Deut. Botan. Ges. **56**, 380–391 (1938).

KAMITSUBO, E.: Motile protoplasmic filaments in cells of Characeae. I. Movement of fibrillar loops. Proc. Japan Acad. **42**, 507–511 (1966).

KAMITSUBO, E.: Motile protoplasmic filaments in cells of Characeae. II. Linear fibrillar structure and its bearing on protoplasmic streaming. Proc. Japan Acad. **42**, 640–643 (1966).

KAMIYA, N.: Protoplasmic streaming. Protoplasmatologia, vol. VIII 3a. Wien: Springer 1959.

KAMIYA, N.: Protoplasmic streaming. In: Enc. Pl. Phys., vol. XVII/2, p. 979–1035 (1962).

KURODA, K.: Behavior of naked cytoplasmic drops isolated from plant cells. In: Primitive motile systems in cell biology (ed. R.D. ALLEN, N. KAMIYA), p. 31–40 (1964).

LECOMTE, H.: Contribution a l'étude du liber des angiospermes. Ann. Sci. Nat. Botan. Ser. **10**, 193–324 (1889).

LOEWY, A.G.: An actomyosin-like substance from the plasmodium of a myomycete. J. Cellular Comp. Physiol. **40**, 127–156 (1952).

MacRobbie, E.A.: Phloem translocation. Facts and mechanisms: a comparative survey. Biol. Rev. **46**, 429–481 (1971).
Mason, T.G., Lewin, C.T.: On the rate of carbohydrate transport in the greater yam, *Dioscorea alata*. Roy. Dublin Soc. Sci. Proc. **18**, 203–205 (1926).
Mason, T.G., Maskell, E.J.: Studies on the transport of carbohydrates in the cotton plant. I. A study of diurnal variation in the carbohydrates of leaf, bark and wood, and of the effects of ringing. Ann. Botany (London) **42**, 189–253 (1928a).
Mason, T.G., Maskell, E.J.: Studies on the transport of carbohydrates in the cotton plant. II. The factors determining the rate and the direction of movement of sugars. Ann. Botany (London) **42**, 571–636 (1928b).
Mason, T.G., Maskell, E.J., Phillis, E.: Further studies on transport in the cotton plant. III. Concerning the independence of solute movement in the phloem. Ann. Botany (London) **50**, 23–58 (1936).
Mittler, T.E.: Studies on the feeding and nutrition of *Tuberolachnus salignus* (Gmelin) (Homoptera, Aphididae). I. The uptake of phloem sap. J. Exptl. Biol. **34**, 334–341 (1957).
Nachmias, V.T., Huxley, H.E., Kessler, D.: Electronmicroscope observations on actomyosin and actin preparations from *Physarum polycephalum* and on their interactions with heavy meromyosin subfragments I from muscle myosin. J. Mol. Biol. **50**, 83–90 (1970).
Nagai, R., Rebhun, L.L.: Cytoplasmic microfilaments in streaming *Nitella* cells. J. Ultrastruct. Res. **14**, 571–589 (1966).
O'Brien, R.P., McCully, M.: Cytoplasmic fibers associated with streaming and saltatory-particle movement in *Heracleum mantegazzianum*. Planta **94**, 91–94 (1970).
O'Brien, T.P., Thimann, K.V.: Intracellular fibers in oat coleoptile cells and their possible significance in cytoplasmic streaming. Proc. Natl. Acad. Sci. U.S. **56**, 888–894 (1966).
Parker, J.: Transcellular strands and intercellular particle movement in sieve tubes of some common trees. Naturwissenschaften **11**, 273–274 (1964a).
Parker, J.: Sieve-tube strands in tree bark. Nature **202**, 926–927 (1964b).
Parker, J.: Strand characteristics in sieve tubes of some common tree species. Protoplasma **60**, 86–93 (1965a).
Parker, J.: Stains for strands in sieve tubes. Stain Technol. **40**, 223–225 (1965b).
Pollard, T.D., Ito, S.: The role of cytoplasmic filaments in viscosity changes and contraction in extracts of *Amoeba proteus*. J. Cell Biol. **39**, 106a (1968).
Pollard, T.D., Shelton, E., Weihung, R.R., Korn, E.D.: Ultrastructural characterization of F-actin isolated from *Acanthamoeba castellanii* and identification of cytoplasmic filaments as F-actin by reaction with rabbit heavy meromyosin. J. Mol. Biol. **50**, 91–97 (1970).
Pringle, J.W.S.: Mechano-chemical transformation in striated muscle. Symp. Soc. Exptl. Biol. **22**, 67–86 (1968).
Schumacher, W.: Untersuchungen über die Lokalisation der Stoffwanderung in den Leitbündeln höherer Pflanzen. Jahrb. Wiss. Bot. **73**, 770–823 (1930).
Small, J.: Technique for the observation of protoplasmic streaming in sieve tubes. New Phytologist **38**, 176–177 (1939).
Spanner, D.C.: A note on the velocity and the energy requirement of translocation. Ann. Botany N.S. **26**, 511–516 (1962).
Spooner, B.S., Yamada, K.M., Wessels, N.K.: Microfilaments and cell locomotion. J. Cell Biol. **49**, 595–613 (1971).
Strasburger, E.: Über den Bau und die Verichtungen der Leitungsbahnen in den Pflanzen. Histol. Beitr. **3** (1891).
Thaine, R.: Transcellular strands and particle movement in mature sieve tubes. Nature **192**, 772–773 (1961).
Thaine, R.: A translocation hypothesis based on the structure of plant cytoplasm. J. Exptl. Botany **13**, 152–160 (1962).
Thaine, R.: Protoplast structure in sieve-tube elements. New Phytologist **63**, 236–243 (1964).
Thaine, R.: Movement of sugar through plants by cytoplasmic pumping. Nature **222**, 873–875 (1969).
Thaine, R., Probine, M.C., Dyer, P.Y.: The existence of transcellular strands in mature sieve elements. J. Exptl. Botany **18**, 110–127 (1967).
Thompson, R.G., Thompson, A.D.: Inhibition by cytochalasin B of sucrose transport in isolated phloem strands of *Heracleum*. Can. J. Botany **51**, 933–936 (1973).

WESSELS, N.K., SPOONER, B.S., ASH, J.F., BRADLEY, M.O., LUDUENA, M.A., TAYLOR, E.L., WRENN, J.T., YAMADA, K.M.: Microfilaments in cellular and developmental processes. Science **171**, 135–143 (1971).

WILLIAMSON, R.E.: An investigation of the contractile protein hypothesis of phloem translocation. Planta **106**, 149–157 (1972a).

WILLIAMSON, R.E.: A light-microscope study of the action of cytochalasin-B on the cells and isolated cytoplasm of the Characeae. J. Cell Sci. **10**, 811–819 (1972b).

WOHLFARTH-BOTTERMANN, K.E.: Cell structures and their significance for amoeboid movement. Intern. Rev. Cytol. **16**, 61–131 (1963).

13. Electroosmotic Flow

D.C. SPANNER

A theory of sieve-tube mechanism based on the phenomenon of electroosmosis was first put forward by D.S. FENSOM in 1957. This suggested the diffusion of H^+ ions as the cause of the emf's required. The following year the present author (SPANNER, 1958) put forward a theory based on the K^+ ion and taking into account the newer knowledge of sieve-plate structure then becoming available. With modifications this theory is still current, and it is the one which will be discussed in the present chapter.

A. Presuppositions of the Potassium Theory

Besides taking it for granted that the sieve tubes are the actual conduits, the theory presupposes the following points:

1. Movement follows a mass-flow pattern in the sense in which chromatographic movement is mass-flow, i.e. all molecules in a sieve tube, of a given species, possess a velocity in common which may however differ from that of other species or of the solvent. In this it differs from diffusion-type theories.

2. The pores of at least a fair proportion of the sieve plates are occluded with P-protein or other material to an extent rendering the ultimate channels minute enough to make electroosmotic forces a dominating influence.

3. The occluding material is strongly and negatively charged at the pH of the sieve-tube sap.

4. Potassium dominates the mobile ions of the sap.

5. Arrangements exist in the phloem tissue to mediate energy to the translocation process through the active transport of the K^+ ion (and perhaps other ions) across the cell membranes of the sieve-tube complex.

These would seem to be the main presuppositions of the theory. The first it shares in common with the Münch hypothesis and certain other theories; the others are more or less peculiar to it. The second and fourth are well supported by the evidence, and the third and fifth are *a priori* very reasonable (YAPA and SPANNER, 1972; but see KOLLMANN, 1973; KLUGE and ZIEGLER, 1964). It is in quantitative relationships that the theory finds its severest test. Some miscellaneous points that tell in its favor (though they hardly rank as evidence) are the plausible suggestions it is able to offer for certain otherwise problematical features of the sieve tubes: the presence of P-protein, the abundant membrane aggregates, the alkalinity of the sap, and the peculiar nature of the sieve-tube wall. In addition it suggests a major role for a macronutrient, potassium, whose function has hitherto been inadequately explained.

B. Electroosmosis as a Phenomenon

Electroosmosis is one of four very common and influential phenomena collectively known as electrokinetic effects. The others are streaming and sedimentation potential, and electrophoresis. They depend upon the fact that at most interfaces in systems containing dissolved electrolytes a separation of ions by sign occurs forming what is called an electrical double layer. A typical instance is illustrated (Fig. 1). Here the material of a solid phase, either because it contains integral ionisable groups like —COOH or because it adsorbs from the liquid phase anions like OH^-, has become negatively charged on its surface. The fixed negative charges have attracted a preponderance of mobile cations into the layer of fluid immediately adjacent to the surface. The two thin sheets of electric charge, one firmly attached to the solid surface and the other occupying a narrow zone of fluid immediately adjacent to it, constitute the "electrical double layer". Depending on whether the solid or the liquid phase is free to move, and on whether movement is promoted by a potential gradient or non-electrically, so one or other of the four effects is realized. In electroosmosis the solid phase is fixed and relative movement is promoted by a potential gradient. The phenomenon is not difficult to understand, and its magnitude can be appreciated with the help of very simple theory.

Fig. 2 shows a typical situation. It represents a section of a thin membrane traversed by minute pores. The material of the membrane is such as to carry (in this case) fixed negative charges. The milieu contains a simple electrolyte, such as KCl. Adjacent to the charged surface of the membrane material the fluid phase contains a preponderance of mobile cations; in particular this will be true of the fluid columns within the pores. If these are sufficiently narrow their excess of cations over anions

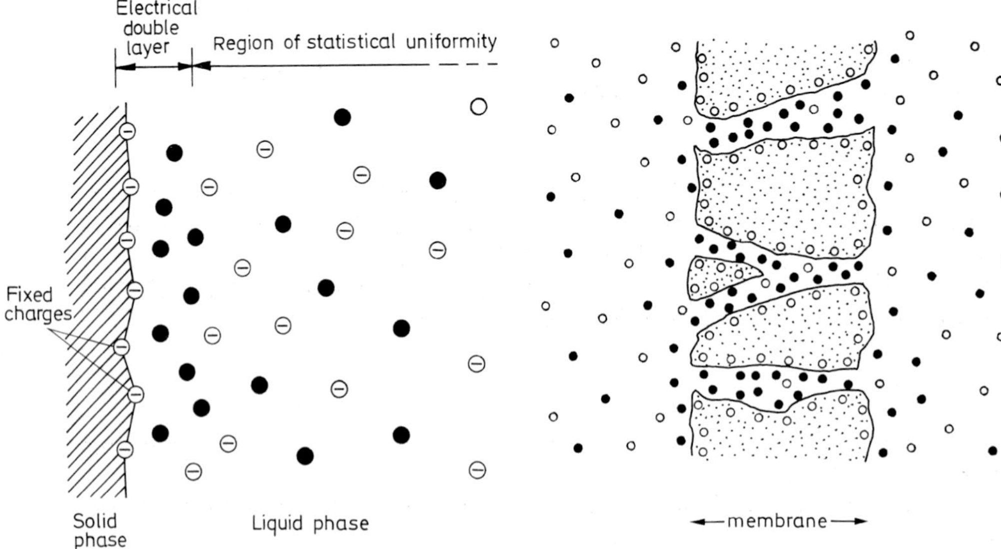

Fig. 1. Structure of the electrical double layer (● Cations, ⊖ Anions)

Fig. 2. Scheme for electroosmosis. Flow occurs when an electrical potential is applied across the membrane (○○ Anions, ●● Cations)

will be very marked; if they are wide it will be correspondingly less. What determines whether the pores have to be regarded as "wide" or "narrow" is the thickness of the electrical double layer, and this depends on the ionic strength of the solution. For a simple salt like KCl some typical figures are quoted as a guide (Table 1).

What causes electroosmosis in the situation shown is the imposition of a potential gradient across the membrane. Taking a simple viewpoint, the fluid columns in the pores are effectively charged; hence they move in the applied electric field. From a rather more adequate viewpoint, the cations in the pores move in one direction and the anions in the other. Since the cations outnumber the anions, and all the moving ions alike exert a frictional drag on the fluid (including any neutral molecules, such as sugars, that it contains; see, e.g. JARVIS and TYE, 1960), there will be a net drag in the direction taken by the cations. The movement resulting from this is the electroosmosis.

Table 1. Thickness of electrical double layer with a uni-univalent salt like KCl; with a di-divalent salt such as $MgSO_4$ the thicknesses would be halved

Concentration	Thickness
10^{-3} M	96 Å
10^{-2} M	30 Å
10^{-1} M	10 Å

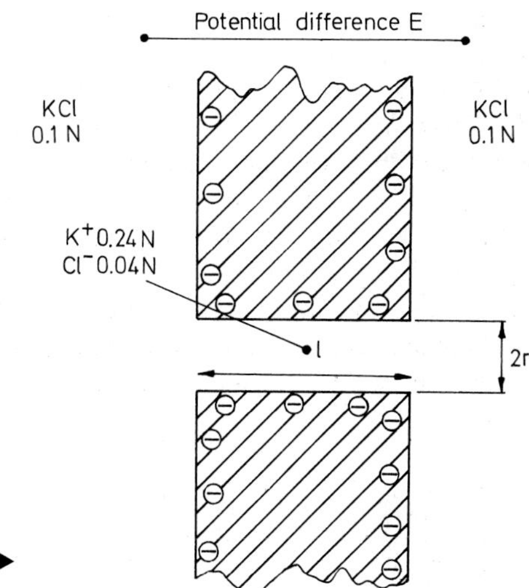

Fig. 3. Idealized pore in a charged membrane. ▶ Concentrations are expressed in normalities

Quantitatively, the effect is an important one. Consider for simplicity a straight pore (Fig. 3) of length l and radius r. The ionic situation within the pore represents a Donnan equilibrium. Suppose the concentrations of salt and ions are as indicated, corresponding to a bulk charge concentration in the membrane material of about 0.2N. The net charge on the fluid in the pore is

$$Q = \pi\, r^2\, l\, (c^+ - c^-)\, F$$

where F is the Faraday and c^+, c^- are the concentrations of the positive and negative ionic charges.

Under the influence of the electric field the column experiences a resultant force given by

$$\mathbf{F} = Q \cdot \frac{E}{l},$$

and this averaged over the cross sectional area represents a mean pressure of

$$P=\frac{\mathbf{F}}{\pi r^2}=EF\,(c^+-c^-).$$

Writing $E=0.05$ volt, $F=96{,}500$ coulombs, and $(c^+-c^-)=0.2\times 1{,}000$ equivs m^{-3} we get $P=965{,}000$ Pascals $=9.5$ atm. This result does not mean that the electroosmotic flow under these conditions would equal that produced by a pressure difference of this magnitude, for the point-to-point distribution of force over the cross-section (which is important) would not be quite the same. Nevertheless it serves to show that the effect is a powerful one, and experiment readily confirms this. It is worth noting that the thickness of the membrane does not appear in this formula.

I. Anomalous Osmosis

The special case of what is called anomalous osmosis is also of interest. When a suitable membrane separates two salt solutions differing in concentration, diffusion of the ions sets up a potential across the membrane. In the absence of any imposed potential difference this can itself cause strong electroosmosis. The direction may either help or hinder the ordinary osmosis. The situation is a little difficult to comprehend because unlike the state of affairs in the previous case there is an obvious movement of both cations and anions in equal amounts and in the same direction across the membrane, although the potential difference acts on them oppositely. The explanation requires a consideration of the detailed distribution of the ions within the system of pores. This probably results in the circulation of minute currents passing one way at points nearer the charged walls and the other way at points further from them. In particular, smaller pores may interact in this sense with larger ones (HÖBER, 1946). The phenomenon is of obvious importance in connection with the theory under discussion as will be apparent later. In anomalous osmosis the energy for transport comes from the free energy provided by the equalization of concentration. The fine scale of the circulating currents obviously involves a frictional element which lowers the rate of permeation, making the membrane more resistive than it otherwise would be; the currents can, in effect, be regarded as a sort of turbulence. Where the potential is of extraneous origin, and the membrane such that ions of only one sign can pass, this small-scale turbulence is of course avoided and with it a source of free energy loss; but the system loses its power of transporting the opposite ion. There is thus an inverse relationship between the power to transport ions of both signs, and thermodynamic economy. To what extent it is worthwhile to sacrifice the latter to attain the former is a point which will be raised later.

II. Design for an Electroosmotic Pump

It is appropriate here to consider a design for a simple electroosmotic pump. Fig. 4 outlines a trial scheme. A tube in the form of a ring is interrupted at one point by a membrane permeable only to cations. Close to the two sides of this are inserted suitable electrodes and the tube is filled with a solution of KCl. The action is as follows.

On applying a potential difference to the electrodes the K^+ ions in the membrane pores (from which Cl^- ions are excluded) move down the field dragging the water columns with them. Concurrently, Cl^- ions approach the lower side of the membrane and retreat from the upper side, fairly rapidly setting up an osmotic gradient which reinforces the electroosmosis, possibly by as much as ten times (BARRY and HOPE, 1969; WEDNER and DIAMOND, 1969; PRAISSMAN et al., 1973; compare KEDEM and KATCHALSKY, 1963). The potential difference therefore causes an electroosmotic water movement in the direction of K^+ transport reinforced almost at once, and perhaps very strongly, by an osmotic movement. This state of affairs however is not permanent, for the reasons which follow.

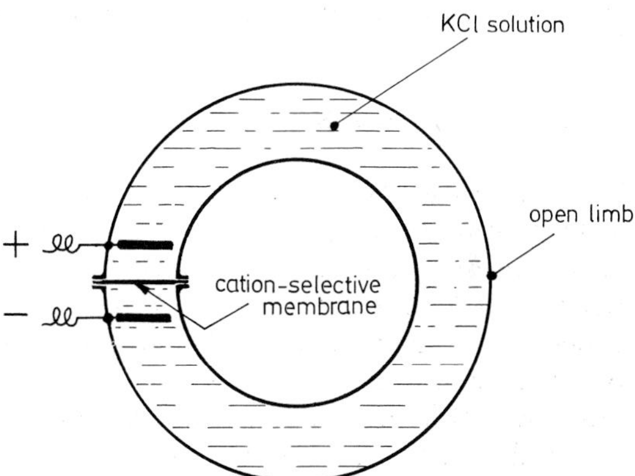

Fig. 4. Design for a closed-circuit electroosmotic pump

It is in principle permissible to imagine electrodes whose sole action is the supply, or removal, of cations; zinc electrodes in a solution of $ZnCl_2$ would act in this way. Assuming for simplicity that the electrodes are of this type in the present case (it is not being implied that such K^+ electrodes can be made) the further development of the system will be as follows. There will of course be a return flow of solution up the right-hand limb. This will carry KCl towards the upper electrode where it will accumulate; simultaneously it will drain away KCl from the lower. At the anode Cl^- will be discharged and will then attack the metal to produce KCl, which will dissociate at once to give K^+ and Cl^-. The result therefore of the arrival of a Cl^- is the provision by the anode of a K^+ to partner it. At the cathode K^+ is simply removed. The passage of current results therefore in the build-up of both ions in the region of the anode, and their removal from the region of the cathode. Eventually a state of affairs arrives in which the electroosmotic flow is working against a steady osmotic differential resulting from this transference of salt (Fig. 5). When this condition supervenes the concentrations of the two ions will naturally be everywhere the same; but whereas the Cl^- ion will be at rest under the combined influence of the diffusive, electrical and hydrodynamic forces, the K^+ ion will be moving. It is not difficult to see that in the right-hand limb the direction of its drift will be against the stream, i.e. from anode to cathode. This final steady condition will consequently be characterised by:

1. Continuous transport of K^+ from anode to cathode both through the membrane and in the open limb (the latter against the stream);

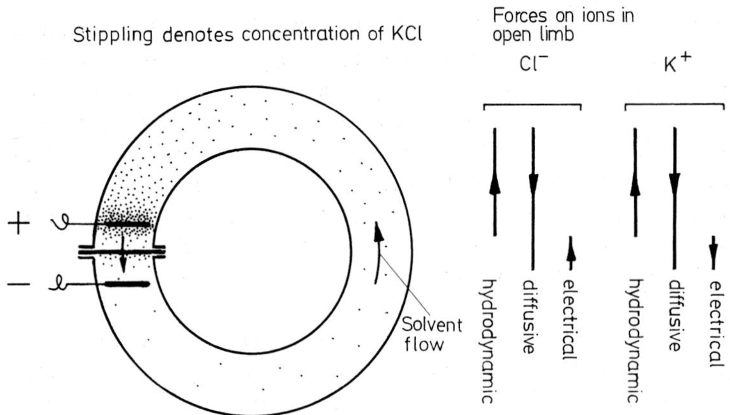

Fig. 5. Electroosmotic pump—final steady state and balance of forces

2. A circulation of water propelled by K^+ movement through the membrane, opposed by

3. A counter osmotic gradient from anode to cathode;

4. Zero transport of Cl^- throughout.

Altogether, the situation hardly looks promising for the present theory. All it contributes positively is a slow movement of water.

III. A Modified Design

It is however, possible to change the design in a very fundamental way. To do this we replace the Cl^- ion by another anion incapable of movement, say by being bound to a diffuse macromolecular structure filling the lumen; this structure must be thought of as open enough to make it incapable of inducing electroosmotic effects itself. With this change result (3) above would be avoided. The absence of the build-up and depletion effects around the electrodes would leave the flow permanently at a higher level (though its initial osmotic enhancement would be absent too). A second consequence would be that in the absence of concentration gradients the hydrodynamic forces on the K^+ ion in the limb would become dominant there; as a result this ion would be transported with the stream instead of against it.

Such a modified design of pump has features which are clearly subject to optimization, and the study of how its performance could be raised to the highest possible level might be suggestive and rewarding. One possible way in which it might be improved is by the incorporation in the solution of a bulky non-electrolyte (sucrose?). If the sensitive pores were fine enough this might be preferentially jostled through by the moving K^+ ions, setting up an osmotic gradient in a direction to assist flow. A related effect is already known in a complementary situation (BISHOP and RICHARDS, 1968). It amounts to securing a more effective coupling between the ions and the uncharged species present. Such an improved coupling might also be achieved by solutes which attached themselves, after the manner of a hydration shell, to the K^+ ions; amino acids are at least worth considering.

The introduction of a small amount of *mobile* anion would have little effect on its operation; the hydrodynamic forces, where these are strong, would sweep it up to the membrane when not only its concentration gradient but other factors would help it to enter and cross. Once across it would travel faster than equivalent cations owing to the favorable electrical gradient. It is arguable therefore that the system as envisaged would transport anions, and transport them possibly as fast as cations. Where the ionic strength in the pores is high such factors as ion-pairing (which renders the anion neutral) and unstable complex formation (e.g. MgX^+ cf. CdI^+, reversing its charge) might assist transport without impairing electroosmotic efficiency.

In the working model the flux of K^+ across the membrane is made up of two parts: the first represents ions moving between the electrodes; the second, ions moving on to circulate *via* the open limb. Both these components are electroosmotically effective, but the current and energy input to the system is connected with the first only. How small a proportion this important component represents of the total membrane flux will depend on hitherto unspecified characteristics of the system, and again a study of optimization for a minimum value might be suggestive for its physiological interest.

Finally, if the closed circuit were to be cut in the middle of the right-hand limb, straightened out and joined end to end with similar units pumping in the same direction, a linear sequence would be obtained which would function in the way already described. Such a linear sequence clearly need show no overall gradient of either pressure or electrical potential. Its motive power would be provided by the electrode currents at the periodically spaced membranes. A linear system like this would be analogous to a sieve tube.

We may sum up therefore by saying that it would seem possible, in practice, to construct an electroosmotic system which would transport water, non-electrolytes and ions of both signs in the way the sieve tube is believed to do. The main conduits would however need to contain enough diffuse immobile anionic material to leave the potassium ion (at least over an appreciable region near the plates) distinctly in the ascendant over the mobile anions; its purpose would be to prevent the development of obstructive concentration gradients across the electroosmotically-sensitive region. The system would appear to be amenable to optimization; and it would possess necessary features showing considerable resemblance to the actualities of the sieve tube.

C. Statement of the Theory

The description that has been given of the working of a model electroosmotic pump has already indicated the main lines of the theory. This supposes that at least a fair proportion of the sieve plates in a file of conducting elements have their pores fairly closely occluded with P-protein as indicated typically in Fig. 6, and in Fig. 20, Chapter 1. The filaments here lie parallel and at a separation from one another of the order of 10 nm more or less. The iso-electric point of the protein, it is postulated, lies on the acid side of neutrality; thus at the alkaline pH of the sap the

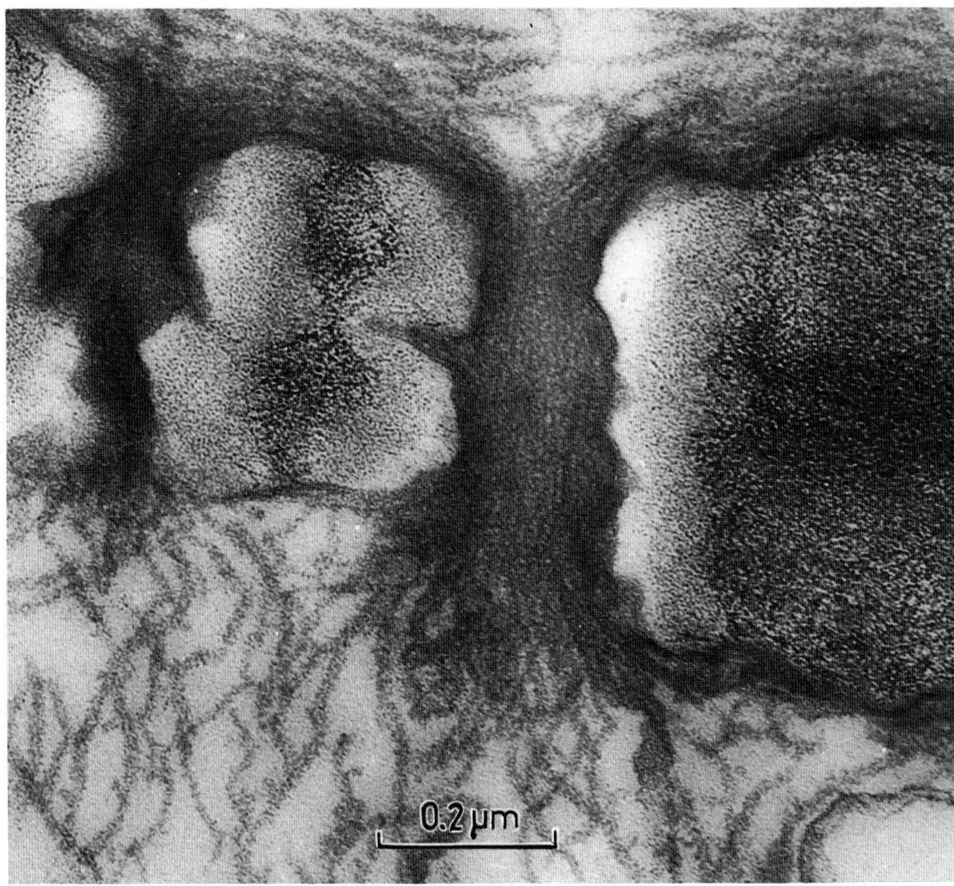

Fig. 6. Pores in a sieve plate from petiole of *Nymphoides peltatum.* Note the parallel and close distribution of the helical P-protein fibrils. By courtesy of R.L. JONES.

filaments bear negative charges. If these suppositions are true, it follows that the sieve plate constitutes a 'membrane' ideally suited, *prima facie*, for the development of electroosmotic forces. Compared with experimental membranes of ion-exchange material it appears to have certain striking advantages: it is extraordinarily thin (about 1 µm); and more important, it can be argued that its charge-bearing substance is arranged to make the maximum possible use of its charged centers and to offer the least possible resistance to solution flow. A comparison of Fig. 6 with the Stereoscan picture (Fig. 7) of the material of a cation-permeable membrane is enough to emphasize these points, the straight uniform channels in the former being in strong contrast to the tortuous irregular ones in the latter. It will be recalled that the "equivalent pressure" developed by a given potential difference is independent of the thickness of the membrane (Eq. 1); moreover it is clearly the case that with oblique pores inclined at an angle θ to the normal it is reduced by the factor cos θ. Both these considerations (as well as others) will clearly favor the sieve plate as a transducer of electrical forces into rapid solution flow.

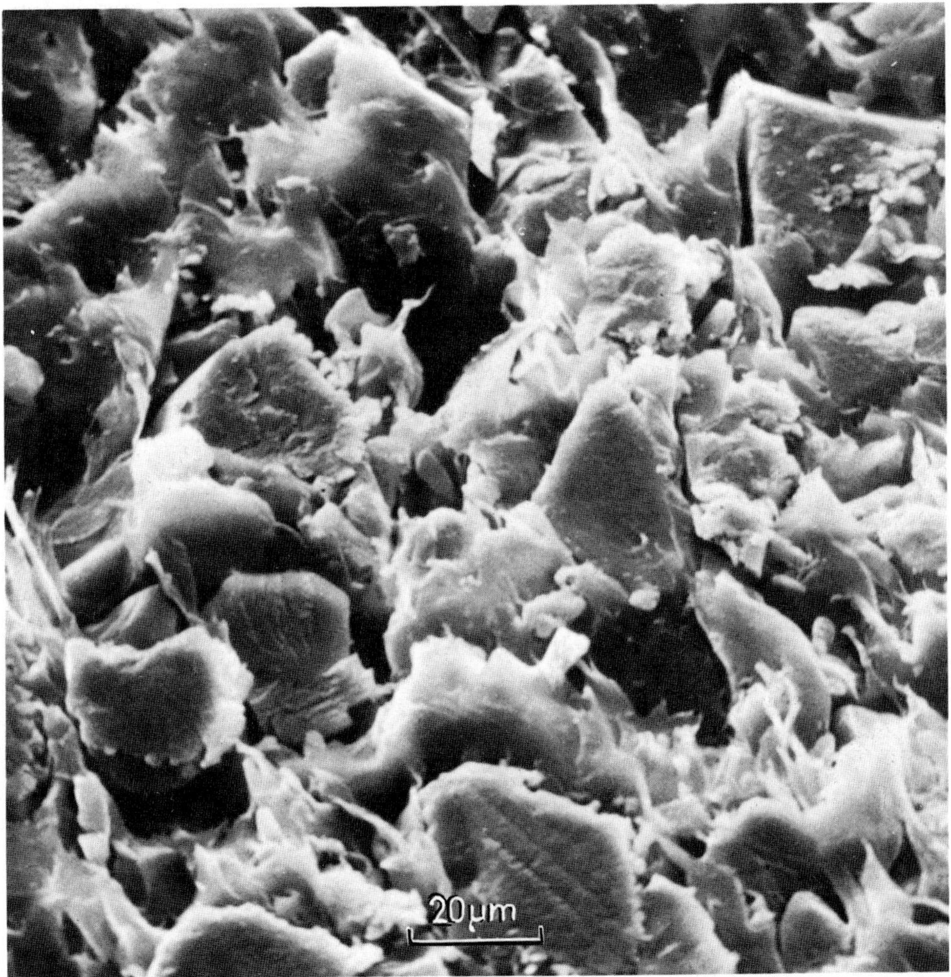

Fig. 7. Scanning electronmicrograph of cation-exchange resin membrane; plane of section normal to surface. By courtesy of Miss V. COWPER

A further supposition is that the P-protein in the lumen of the sieve tube—uniformly dispersed, aggregated near the wall or occupying principally the downstream end of the element—represents *in the region it occupies* the immobile anionic equivalent of at least a fair proportion of the K^+ present in the sap there. It is possible that other material also contributes to this role: the abundant membrane substance of *Metasequoia*, (KOLLMANN, 1964), the fibrillar material of the plastids of such genera as *Tetragonia* (FALK, 1964) or the dispersed protein of the flagellate bodies of Leguminosae (LAFLECHE, 1966) are possible cases. It is not difficult to believe that all of these would be negatively charged in the alkaline sap.

Finally, it is postulated that a difference of potential across the sieve plate is maintained by the active uptake of K^+ across the sieve-tube membrane above the plate, with its loss below. This movement corresponds to the electrode action in the

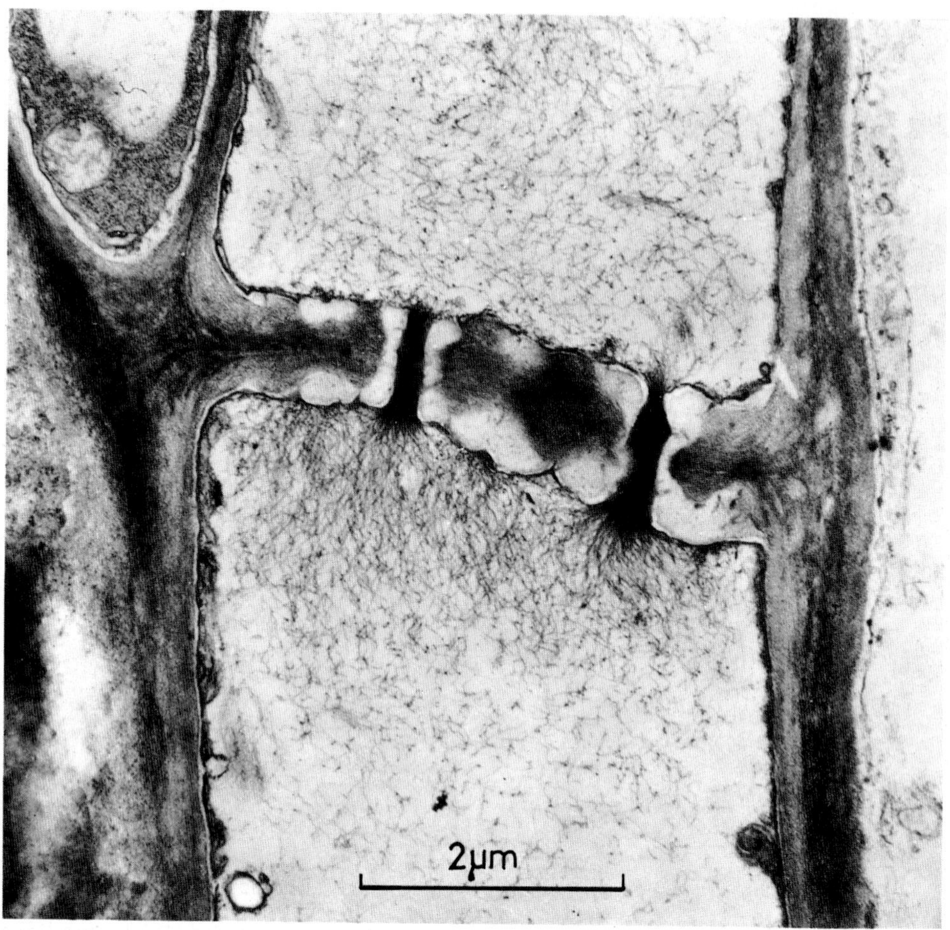

Fig. 8A. Longitudinal section of sieve tube from hypocotyl of *Helianthus* seedling. Note the disposition of P-protein; companion cells to left. By courtesy of Dr. A.W. SIDDIQUI

model discussed, and the most plausible suggestion is that it would be energized by ATP, of which the sieve tubes have both a high content and a high turnover rate (see Chapter 2). Polarization of the plate might reasonably be attributed to the action of the hydrodynamic forces in sweeping the strongly anionic ATP against the upper face of the sieve plate and draining it away from the lower (see Addendum 1). There is a possibility here of positive feedback amplifying the hydrodynamic effect: to the locus to which K^+ is transported electrogenically into the sieve tube ATP will be electrostatically attracted. Obviously, the polarization envisaged by these suggestions is not one morphologically defined; it is a consequence, not a cause, of the direction of flow. In this it seems to be consistent with the known facts.

The general scheme for the potassium theory is illustrated in Figs. 8A and 8B. The electrical potential follows longitudinally a more or less saw-tooth profile, with however local irregularities, particularly near the plates.

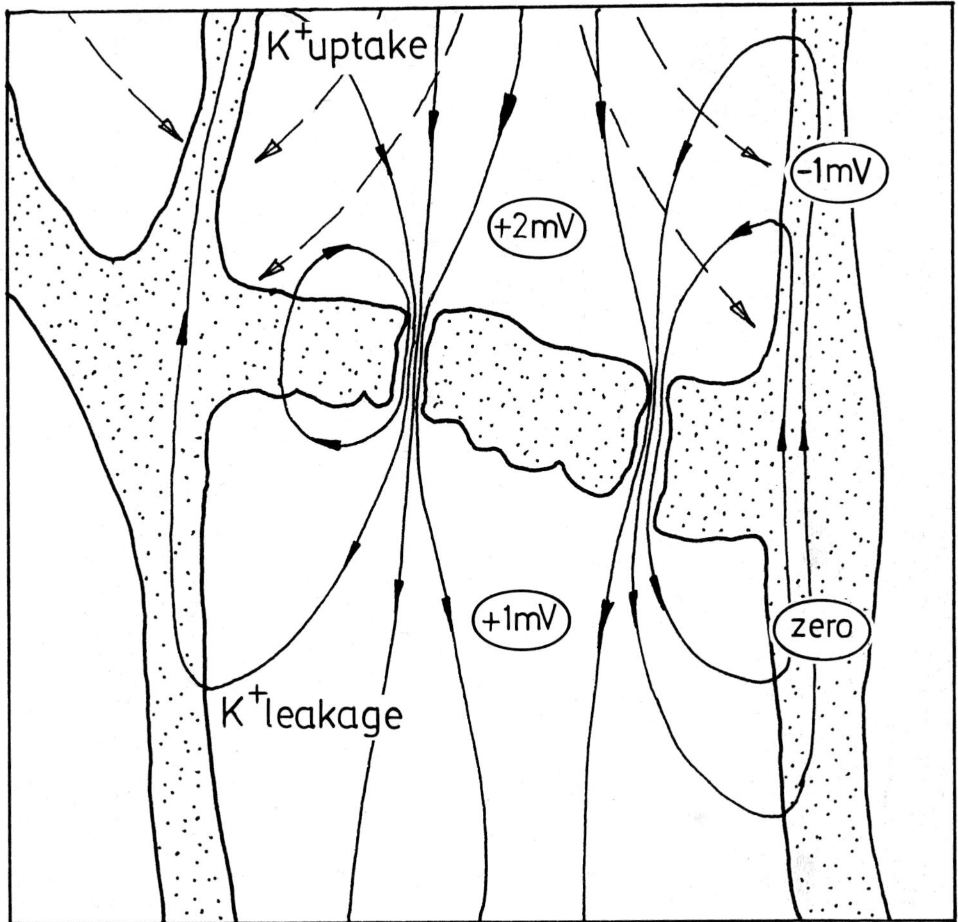

Fig. 8B. Scheme for electroosmosis based on circulation of K^+ ion (solid lines) and supply of high-energy compounds (dotted lines). Direction of assimilate flow downwards. The potentials are hypothetical. Cf. Fig. 8A

I. Further Comments

Before discussing the detailed working of the phloem system in terms of the theory it is worth making one or two comments which will not be further elaborated. The first concerns the possible occurrence of local osmotic irregularities due to the differential transport of cations and anions through the plates. The situation in the simple pump illustrated in Fig. 5 has already been discussed so far as it affects longitudinal movement. Clearly however it would be expected to result in local *lateral* uptake or loss of water where the channel walls are semi-permeable as in the sieve tubes. This lateral movement might in some circumstances be important, though at the moment how this could be so is not apparent.

The second comment concerns some of the less-noted constituents of the sieve-tube sap. The amino acids in particular may merit attention; it is not inconceivable that with their special physico-chemical properties their influence on such a process as electroosmosis might be unexpected. It is perhaps in less obvious considerations such as these that an alleviation of some of the problems the theory faces may be looked for.

II. Initiation of Transport

Sieve tubes are not of course conducting all the time; when they are only just mature, when mobile carbohydrate is exhausted and when the direction of movement is undergoing reversal are occasions when they are for the moment quiescent. How does the theory envisage the initiation of the transport process following such a moment?

We may start with the supposition that the P-protein is more or less dispersed in the lumens, or perhaps aggregated along the walls, the pores being open (see, for a possible illustration of this, EVERT et al., 1973). At such a time the sap may be considered low in sugar content; perhaps the potassium content is low too, though on both of these points there is not a great deal of evidence. Awakening of source activity in one part of the plant accompanied by loading of sugar into the adjacent sieve tubes will in these circumstances initiate at the source a Münch-type flow which will gradually extend down the columns. At first the rise of pressure creeping axially will cause lateral exosmosis of water lower down; but as sugar passes along the tubes a positive tendency to take in water will supervene. Thus reinforced, the longitudinal flow will extend to lower and lower reaches, till eventually it enters the sink region. Meanwhile changes in the distribution of the P-protein may be envisaged. Longitudinal movement will be first in evidence in the region of the column nearest the source. In this region therefore the P-protein dispersed in the lumen will tend to be borne downwards towards the sieve plates. Sooner or later *some* of these will begin to undergo occlusion; and wherever this reaches a sufficient degree mobile anions (in particular ATP) will build up above the plate and polarisation by metabolically-energized differential uptake of the K^+ ion will begin. Thus electroosmosis will reinforce the weak MÜNCH flow, and the occlusion of the plate in question will become more marked, perhaps in the process illustrating the property of self-optimization which is such an interesting feature of certain biological systems (ROSEN, 1967). It is clearly not necessary to assume that all plates become occluded, or that those which do become so never revert to the open condition. In fact, if the process proceeds on the lines suggested it seems reasonable to suppose that only a proportion of the plates would become electro-osmotically active; and that even in these the P-protein plugs would remain labile structures.

III. Insertion of P-Protein into the Pores

One interesting question concerns how the protein fibrils ever become so regularly and beautifully disposed within the sieve-plate pores as they often appear to be. It seems inconceivable that in the case illustrated in Fig. 20, Chapter I, the disposition could result from the trauma of sudden violent surge; and this micrograph is not exceptional by any means. The present theory regards the situation illustrated as natural, and explains it tentatively as follows. The slow MÜNCH movement is gentle enough to allow the dispersed fibrils to orientate themselves along the hydrodynamic flow lines. Thus the first-comers thread themselves easily through the pores. If they are numerous enough they initiate weak sieve-plate polarization in the way described and with it there arises an electric field whose direction (Fig. 8 B) while propelling the K^+ ion downwards urges the fibrils upwards. This field stabilizes the latter against the hydrodynamic forces, and they are able to adjust themselves axially into the "crystalline" pattern so often noticed (Fig. 20, Chapter 1). In this state their lateral separation is subject to a condition of minimum potential energy (ELLIOTT, 1968); consequently here and there fibrils move closer together and open up regions into which newcomers can be inserted by the hydrodynamic forces, which in these relatively open regions will be rather more influential than in the compacter ones. Finally the contents of the pore attain a steady configuration stabilized by the combined influences of the hydrodynamic forces, the electric field, and the 'crystallising' tendency of long, regular, charged molecules. It is in this condition that careful preparation finds them, though it seems possible that in cases such as Fig. 8 A wound callose has compressed them somewhat. It might be mentioned that the equilibrium separation of the fibrils depends on the ionic strength of the medium (ELLIOTT, 1968); so do the electroosmotic intensity and the degree of polarization of the plate. These factors being interlinked would seem to raise at least the possibility of self-optimization by the system.

Cessation of translocation would be followed by similar changes in the reverse order, molecular Brownian movement eventually distributing the fibrils uniformly throughout the lumens, and fall in ion concentration perhaps leading to condensation of the P-protein against the walls (EVERT et al., 1973).

These suggestions are no doubt speculative; but they offer a plausible account of phenomena otherwise hard to explain.

IV. The Active Uptake of Potassium

It is clear that one of the most exacting requirements of the theory concerns arrangements for the active uptake of potassium. That this is a difficult point can be seen by a simple calculation (FENSOM and SPANNER, 1969). If the mean linear velocity in the sieve tubes is 50 cm h^{-1}, and if the number of molecules of water conveyed by one mole of K^+ is 150 then it is easy to see that a current density in the conduits of about 0.5 amp cm^{-2} is involved. If 10% only of the potassium is recirculated at the sieve plate this reduces to 0.05 amp cm^{-2}; and for a sieve tube 30 μm in diameter where active uptake occurs over a length of 100 μm the membrane flux implied is 4×10^4 pmoles cm^{-2} s^{-1} based on the simple surface area of the plasmalemma. An attempt to justify the limitation of the potassium recirculation to 10% is made below; meanwhile it must be admitted that even so the potassium flux is very high. One of the most relevant comparisons is provided by the recent measurements on the potassium flux into stomatal guard cells. It is difficult to obtain a strictly comparable figure from these; but the data of HUMBLE und RASCHKE (1971) on *Vicia*, and RASCHKE and FELLOWS (1971) on *Zea* would seem to indicate a rate of about 100 pmoles

$cm^{-2}\,s^{-1}$. Far more striking are the data of ATKINSON et al. (1967) for the chloride secretion of the salt glands of the mangrove *Aegialitis*. The figure they arrive at is 5,000 (or even 25,000) pmoles $cm^{-2}\,s^{-1}$. In this situation vesicular transport seems to be involved (BAKER and HALL, 1973). Comparison of these reported figures with the above *very rough* estimates of what the electroosmotic theory requires is sufficiently promising to encourage further examination of the matter; certainly the difficulty faced by the theory is hardly, at this stage of the problem of mechanism, a decisive one. Several ways of meeting it are therefore worth consideration.

V. Membrane Expansion

The possibility of this was first raised (SPANNER and JONES, 1970) in a form to which subsequent work has not lent support. However, the fact remains that ordered membrane aggregates are not only conspicuous features of sieve tubes, often making an appearance early in ontogeny, but that they seem also to be associated with ATPase activity (see for instance, CATESSON, 1973). If it is a right principle to expect structure to appear commensurate with function then at least that principle is not violated by the suggestion, hard though it may be to support, that these membrane aggregates are somehow concerned with the postulated ion uptake. It has also been proposed (SIDDIQUI, JONES and SPANNER, 1974) that certain prominent invaginations of the plasmalemma may be involved, perhaps pinocytotically.

These two suggestions cannot be ruled out at this stage; but there are others.

VI. Limitation of the Potassium Circulation

Within small pores, moving solutes exert a marked interaction with each other (BISHOP and RICHARDS, 1968; the pores here were very small, about 0.8–1.3 nm). Especially if the P-protein packing in the pores is close this raises an interesting possibility. If the migrating K^+ ions confined in the minute channels move large solute molecules such as sucrose and glutamic acid preferentially to water, an osmotic differential will be set up over the plate assisting flow. The practical result will be that the electrical forces will be partly converted into osmotic ones, with interesting results.

Consider the circular electroosmotic pump of Fig. 5 with immobile anion. Let subscripts$_{1,2}$ refer to the open limb and to the membrane path respectively. Let I be the potassium current in terms of moles; v the stream velocity; c the molar concentration of the K^+ ion; l the path length; and A the cross-section of the stream.

Then if E is the applied potential difference and u the mobility of the ion, the current in the limb can be considered as composed of: (1) a component due to the solution flow, and of magnitude $v_1 A_1 c_1$; and (2) a component due to the potential gradient, and of magnitude $-\frac{uE}{l_1} \cdot A_1 c_1$. Thus we can write

$$I_1 = v_1 A_1 c_1 - \frac{uE}{l_1} \cdot A_1 c_1 . \tag{1}$$

Within the pores a similar analysis will hold with the addition of a term representing the opposition in the narrow channels to the movement of K^+ caused by the "osmotic loading", i.e. the tendency to diffuse back of the molecules of uncharged solute which are being preferentially "jostled forward" by the ion. This effect may be considered proportional to the stream velocity. Hence we may write

$$I_2 = v_2 A_2 c_2 + \frac{uE}{l_2} \cdot A_2 c_2 - \alpha v_2 A_2 c_2, \tag{2}$$

where α is the constant of proportionality. Finally we shall have the approximate relation

$$A_1 v_1 = A_2 v_2. \tag{3}$$

Combining these equations we derive the result

$$\frac{I_2 - I_1}{I_1} = \frac{\frac{c_2}{c_1}\left(1 - \alpha + \frac{uE}{l_2 v_2}\right) - \left(1 - \frac{uE}{l_1 v_1}\right)}{\left(1 - \frac{uE}{l_1 v_1}\right)}, \tag{4}$$

which if l_1 is large reduces to

$$\frac{i}{I_1} = \frac{c_2}{c_1}\left(1 - \alpha + \frac{uE}{l_2 v_2}\right) - 1 \tag{5}$$

where $i = I_2 - I_1$ is clearly the electrode current. The ratio i/I_1 may be regarded broadly as the proportion of the main K^+ current which undergoes recirculation at the sieve plate. Since c_2/c_1 depends on the relative concentrations of the P-protein in the pores and the lumen it is likely to be high; and Eq. (5) shows that the possibility of i/I_1 being low depends very much on a high value of α. In a typical sieve plate of thickness 1 µm we might suppose $l_2 = 5$ µm (possibly considerably greater), $v_2 = 200$ cm h^{-1}, $u = 7.6 \times 10^{-4}$ cm^2 volt^{-1} s^{-1} and E say 1 millivolt. This makes the term $\frac{uE}{l_2 v_2}$ small; consequently the sucrose "back pressure" on the ion would need to be of comparable magnitude to the hydrodynamic forces ($\alpha \approx 1$), if the effect is to reduce the circulation current considerably. It seems difficult to make an *a priori* judgement on this point. The potassium longitudinally translocated would of course need a long-distance return path; the logical suggestion for this is the xylem (GREENWAY and PITMAN, 1965).

VII. Sieve-Element Length

It would clearly relieve the problem of membrane area if the uptake of K^+ were to be spread over a greater length of sieve tube. Short elements thus pose the biggest difficulty. However it is quite unnecessary to assume that all sieve plates are involved (as pumps) at once; indeed the preceding discussion would suggest that this is unlikely. For if sieve plates too close together became simultaneously occluded the absence of sufficient lateral membrane area for K^+ exchange would prevent satisfactory polarization; and sooner or later, it can be argued, the less satisfactorily-involved plates would "give way" and lose their P-protein, the latter being swept away by the hydrodynamic forces in the absence of a stabilizing electrical gradient over the plate. Clearly, the more involved plates would benefit from the accession of further P-protein and become still more involved. Thus a state of affairs would be established in which functioning plates were interspersed with non-functioning ones. This conclusion is surely not difficult to accept, granted the premises of the theory. It implies that the system may automatically adjust itself to provide adequate lateral membrane area; and it suggests, incidentally, that some of the plates will not show the necessary degree of occlusion. That is not to say that they are valueless. If they help to prevent a too-complete drift of the anionic P-protein towards the functioning plates the preceding discussion of model systems has shown that they perform a vital purpose.

VIII. Function of Companion Cells

In general the theory regards the companion cells as concerned with the "care and maintenance" of the sieve tubes, and with the provision of high-energy compounds such as ATP for their machinery. It is not impossible, however, to think of the companion cells as themselves concerned with the circulation of potassium. They might absorb it from the apoplast and discharge it into the sieve tubes through their characteristic plasmodesmata. The suggestion does not seem very attractive in some ways; for instance, the companion cells do not always seem to have the right longitudinal position. Nevertheless it has some relevance to the question of membrane area.

D. Objections to the Potassium Theory

Until the thoughtful and comprehensive criticisms of MACROBBIE, very sporadic objections only had been raised against the electroosmotic theory. MACROBBIE'S criticisms may be summarized as follows (MACROBBIE, 1971):

1. The theory cannot provide for the transport of both anions and cations.

2. It faces the difficulty of explaining why the sieve tube is extremely leaky over that part of its length below the plate while managing a very active uptake of K^+ over the part above it, this differentiation being easily reversible.

3. The circulating current of K^+ is too large, both for the membrane involved and for the return path through the apoplast. MACROBBIE does not consider this the major difficulty; she makes the interesting suggestion that repetitive action potentials might meet it.

4. The mechanism would require too much energy for the recirculation of the potassium; "very long sieve elements" would mitigate it.

5. It fails to meet the evidence for bi-directional movement in a single sieve tube.

Other authors have raised additional objections:

6. Thus, FENSOM (1972) has objected that at the measured K^+ concentration of the sieve tubes, the transport per mole of K^+, of water (and by implication) of sugar, would be very low; that the potassium current "would vaporise the fluid transported" if the resistance were "reasonable"; and that measurements of the crucial electrokinetic cross-coefficient give extremely small values for phloem tissue. Electric currents applied to isolated phloem would cause an appreciable effect, which however is not found; also the theory suggests a long-distance transport of potassium with consequent build-up at the base of the plant.

7. Finally, it has been pointed out that P-protein is not invariably present in sieve elements (e.g. in gymnosperms, cereals and some palms); that phloem is able to transport virus particles (CRONSHAW and ESAU, 1967) and mycoplasmas (BOWYER and ATHERTON, 1970; WORLEY, 1973); and that sieve plates with open pores can be found with fair frequency.

None of these objections however appears insuperable, though all merit serious consideration. They will be dealt with in order.

1. Anions are certainly transported in the phloem, and at a rate which appears little different from that of cations (for Refs. see QURESHI and SPANNER, 1973d). However, as remarked earlier, in so-called "anomalous osmosis" we have a common phenomenon in which electroosmosis is associated with the transport of both species at identical rates. However different in magnitude the concomitant flow may be from that occurring in the sieve tubes, anomalous osmosis at least shows that concurrent transport is possible. Again, in closely-occluded sieve plate pores the ionic strength may well be appreciable, and ion-pairing (which effectively neutralizes the anion charge) and unstable complex formation (which may reverse it) may, as noted earlier, both be significant. Finally, where the flow is as rapid as it is in the sieve tubes hydrodynamic forces would be appreciable. These would act both to concentrate the anions and to force them through.

In an experimental system based on a cation-exchange membrane the efficiency of electroosmosis falls off as the concentration of the bathing solution is raised; high ionic strength tends to nullify the power of the membrane to discriminate cations from anions. In other words, raising the external concentration with such a salt as KCl tends to produce a ratio of equality in the numbers of mobile cations and anions in the membrane pores, and it is this tendency that causes the slackening in the transport phenomenon. However, the situation around the sieve plate, it is suggested, differs in a fundamental respect. The 'external solution' here contains a high proportion of *immobile* anion, the P-protein. Consequently the K^+ ion, which partners it, is assured of a continuing ascendancy over the *mobile* anions in the sieve-plate pores, up to an appreciably higher general ionic strength (see Addendum 2). It is this continuing ascendancy which holds the electroosmosis to a high level under conditions which, it can be argued, enable mobile anions to enter the pores and pass through.

2. This difficulty is provisionally met by noting two characteristics of the system. First, anions will to some extent at least be "piled up" by the hydrodynamic forces above the plate. This effect will be stronger with polyvalent anions, such as ATP at the alkaline pH of the sap, and will in itself polarize the plate. Second, as noted earlier,

where K^+ is actively taken up, a local potential situation will be created which will attract more ATP. This element of positive feedback will further strengthen the polarization. Below the plate the situation will of course be reversed.

3. This is certainly one of the weakest points in the theory. However at some risk of incurring the charge of special pleading it has been argued that the prominent membrane aggregates in the sieve tube may be involved in ion uptake; that the "physiological unit" of the sieve tube may be several times longer than the morphological element; that the companion cell may possibly function in ion-uptake; and that the percentage of the moving K^+ undergoing recirculation at the sieve plate may be drastically reduced by "osmotic loading" of the ion in the pores, or by some other unsuspected effect. Some of these suggestions mutually strengthen each other. Consider for instance n consecutive loosely-plugged sieve plates. Imagine the sequence changed into a consortium of $n-1$ unplugged plates and a final tightly-plugged one. Converted in this way into a single physiological unit the problem of lateral membrane area is reduced to $1/n$-th. Further, the effectiveness of any "osmotic loading" of the K^+ ion is increased by the denser plugging, bringing with it a reduction in the proportion of the K^+ ion recirculated at the plate; and this effect may well be a large one. True, the hydraulic resistance of the column will probably be raised, but so will be the power of the electroosmotic forces. It is not difficult to believe that the sieve-tube system is capable of optimizing itself in this way and automatically selects the most appropriate value of n.

Finally, it is possible to fall back on the argument that perhaps the sieve-tube membrane (bathed as it is in abundant sucrose) is quite exceptional, without equal among the membranes of other plant cells. Even this would hardly be a weaker position than the claim that the P-protein, in a milieu almost devoid of the apparatus and organisation of normal cytoplasm, nevertheless manages to exert a muscular effort on a scale and with an intensity without botanical parallel.

4. This objection is weakened by the realization that the necessary potential drop over the sieve plate may be much less than the values previously published. The original 25 mV (SPANNER, 1970) was never very securely based. The theory of Section B indicates that a potential difference of 50 mV is more or less equivalent to a pressure drop of 9.5 atm; the Appendix of an earlier paper (FENSOM and SPANNER, 1969) suggests that in a typical plugged pore no more than 0.12 atm across the plate is needed to produce a high velocity of flow. Combining these figures it would appear that the potential difference to be postulated is only of the order of a millivolt or two.

The problem of energy is also alleviated by the suggestion of "osmotic loading" of the K^+ ion since this would reduce, perhaps considerably, the circulation current; and by the suggestion of sieve elements functioning together as consortia. Incidentially the objection of inadequate apoplast path is also covered.

5. Bidirectional movement in one and the same sieve tube is a claim of which the present writer has never been convinced. The latest evidence (QURESHI and SPANNER, 1971; FRITZ, 1973) makes it even more unnecessary to concede. It must be remembered that the demonstration of such bidirectional movement would tell equally against the MÜNCH hypothesis and against one based on shearing-force generation by actin filaments; MACROBBIE'S suggestion that the latter mechanism is compatible with it is hardly admissible in view of the extreme narrowness of the sieve tubes in relation to the speed of lateral diffusive spread within them.

6. FENSOM's objections have in part been met already. Vaporization is a difficulty more apparent than real. It overlooks the minute length of the resistive path (a matter of microns through the sieve plate and back); the low volume fraction of the tissue which this represents; the fact that electroosmosis implies a reduction in resistivity since the solvent is moving in the same direction as the ions; and the cooling of the resistive sites not only by thermal conduction but by the stream itself.

Electrical measurements on excised or displaced phloem are difficult to evaluate. The tissue is no doubt highly disturbed; further, it is impossible to exclude irrelevant paths in parallel (and in series) with the sieve-plate pores. Thus the experimental electroosmotic system is hardly comparable with that postulated by the theory (SPANNER, 1970).

That potassium would build up in the basal part of the plant may in fact be an argument in favor rather than otherwise. There is a well-known connection between root-pressure and translocation; and this may well turn not only on the provision of carbohydrate to the roots, but also on the provision of potassium. If the latter is the case, the implication would be that the potassium transported to the roots in the phloem is transferred to the xylem. This suggestion, arising from the observed facts about root pressure, fits in readily enough with the consequence of the theory, and in turn relieves it of the problem of potassium build-up. The problem hardly arises with transport towards the *stem* apex, for there the leaves soon turn from phloem-import to phloem-export.

7. The remaining objections are not difficult to meet. Where P-protein is not present some sieve-plate pores at least are nevertheless found to be occluded with other material usually membranous (e.g. EVERT et al., 1971). Such material is also found in the sieve-tube lumens. It is not impossible to believe that it functions as a negatively-charged framework analogously to P-protein; it is probably harder to accept that it behaves like actomyosin. That virus particles and mycoplasmas can traverse the sieve plates is again no problem, for as discussed earlier the sieve-plate plugs are to be thought of as labile structures which form and reform as occasion requires, and as the translocation process waxes and wanes. Finally, the demonstration of some open or more or less open pores is in line with the suggestion made above, that sieve elements function as consortia. On the other hand the mere presence of substantial amounts of P-protein in the sieve-element lumens (let alone in the sieve-plate pores) considered in the case of trees with their quite low gradients of osmotic (ZIMMERMANN, 1960) or hydrostatic pressure (HAMMEL, 1968), constitutes an almost insuperable difficulty for the MÜNCH hypothesis.

E. Further Evidence for the Potassium Theory

Much of the more important evidence for the present theory has, by implication, already been presented. However certain potentially important matters have not so far been discussed and it is appropriate to mention them briefly.

First, there is considerable support for the idea that potassium has a direct effect on translocation. HARTT (1969) takes this view, and gives an impressive list of the earlier papers. AMIR and REINHOLD (1971), in a systematic investigation of the effect of omitting six major essential elements wrote that "only in the case of K-deficiency were clear effects noted *well before any visible symptoms* became apparent" (their italics). True, they inclined to the view that potassium plays its decisive role, not in the sieve tubes, but somewhere between the chloroplast and the "translocation pool" of sugar awaiting transport; nevertheless, like HARTT, they found that potassium deficiency was an influential factor. Even mild deficiency depressed translocation. The connection between potassium and transport challenges further study.

Second, there is the evidence of BOWLING (1969) for a sawtooth profile of electrical potential down the sieve-tube column. The evidence is not so cogent as could be wished, for the axis investigated was in short excised lengths in which transport was almost certainly at a standstill. Further, the potentials are large and could easily be DONNAN effects resulting from the accumulation of P-protein on corresponding sides of successive sieve plates. However, even if this were the right explanation, it would still have the positive implication that this material possessed an electrically-charged character, and this is one of the essential postulates of the theory.

F. Comparison with Other Theories

I. The Münch Hypothesis

The MÜNCH hypothesis probably has more supporters at the moment than any other. It has inspired, and continues to inspire, a splendid amount of active work. Nevertheless there are grave objections to it. It is probably unnecessary to stress the resistance implied by the presence of the P-protein, which even when disposed as shown in the electronmicrographs reproduced in the monograph of CRAFTS and CRISP (1971; Figs. 2.9, 2.10, 2.11) must be highly obstructive. What is almost equally an objection is its inability to give any reasonable explanation of the presence of P-protein at all. It is difficult to accept that this material is either a reserve food substance or a waste product; contrast its form and disposition with the neatly-sequestered reserve protein bodies of monocot plastids or waste oxalate crystals of *Salix* phloem parenchyma. It seems equally unrealistic to regard it as a plugging mechanism for damaged sieve tubes. Against any possible evolutionary advantage it may have in this connection one must set the substantial resistance it almost certainly offers to the normal functioning of the tubes; the "expensive" nature of the material; and the agreed availability of other methods of staunching the flow—the universal callose mechanism, gelling of the sap in *Cucurbita*, and clogging of the pores by starch grains. If the problem of damaged sieve tubes is so urgent that first-aid in milliseconds rather than minutes is required, why has the plant not utilized a mechanism like that exquisite device of the tracheids, the bordered pit? But indeed, the problem does not seem all that urgent; and the mere presence of P-protein remains a fact that counts strongly against the MÜNCH hypothesis.

On the physiological side there are similar weighty objections. The most recent work on inhibitors (QURESHI and SPANNER, 1973a, b, c) confirms the view, previously the majority one, that the sieve tubes are the locus of an active translocation mechanism. No longer does it seem possible to refer the effect of poisons exclusively to the source and sink regions, nor to blockage of the conduits or breakdown of their plasma membranes.

Low temperatures have complex effects; the claim often made that the evidence here favors the MÜNCH hypothesis is very precarious. Plants sensitive and insensitive to frost injury respond rather differently (Chapter 4); but the behavior of their transport rate at low temperatures is in important respects similar to that of their mitochondrial activity (GIAQUINTA and GEIGER, 1973; LYONS and RAISON, 1970), and to the rise and fall times of the action potential in *Nitella* (BLATT, 1974). Facts such as these make it look as if the electroosmotic theory can readily enough accommodate the evidence by reference merely to the rate of supply of energy. However, the theory offers a further very plausible suggestion. The labile P-protein plugs are held in the sieve-plate pores by two forces substantially in balance: the hydrodynamic drag, and the electrical upthrust on their negatively-charged structure. Interference with ion uptake by any sort of inhibition would threaten this balance, and expose the plugs to being swept out by the residual flow, which would hardly be reduced in proportion owing to the transport pressures developed outside the inhibited region. It is arguable therefore that after an initial fall in translocation rate the flow *might* recover as the inhibited plates had their pores blown clear of P-protein, and recover perhaps to a rate even higher than before. The latter phenomenon has in fact been reported in low temperature studies (e.g. SWANSON and GEIGER, 1967), and in work involving anoxia (SIJ and SWANSON, 1973).

It is often suggested that the common observation of positive gradients in the phloem (usually of osmotic potential) is evidence in favor of the MÜNCH hypothesis. Of course, it is consistent with it; but its impact is weakened when it is recalled that gradients in the correct direction are almost inevitable on any theory of mechanism. Two factors are involved: first, the progressive osmotic intake of water along the tubes; and second, the metabolic removal of nutrients for storage or cambial growth (see for instance LANG, 1973). The observation therefore is not critical.

Finally, there is the question of gradient and direction. As has been pointed out, the theory under discussion invokes a prior MÜNCH flow. The significance of gradient is thus common to both, and both account in almost identical terms for the initial dominating influence of sugar. But whereas one requires the *maintenance* of an adequate gradient, to the other it becomes eventually of little importance. It is here that the smallness of the gradients found in trees is relevant. Further, the functioning of the sieve-tube system becomes a problem for the MÜNCH hypothesis when (as in certain mangroves, SCHOLANDER, 1968) the xylem operates regularly at a *tension* of 30–60 atm. Unless the sieve tubes or their sap are quite unusual it is difficult to see how enough turgor can be generated in the phloem to allow the development of steep gradients, since sieve tubes, unlike vessels, are not constructed to withstand negative pressures. For the electroosmotic theory the problem is less acute.

II. The Contractile Protein Theories

An important and promising group of suggestions invokes in some way the idea that the P-protein is 'muscular' rather than 'skeletal', however its properties are believed to be exercised in detail. These ideas have been ably presented by MACROBBIE (1971). In some ways they are attractive; nevertheless they too have considerable weaknesses. Positively, they account adequately for the presence of P-protein; some forms draw a plausible parallel with the well-known and common phenomenon of protoplasmic streaming; all seem consistent with the evidence of inhibitor studies; and by invoking an initial MÜNCH flow they accommodate the facts linking gradient and direction. Negatively, however, there is the failure, almost complete at the moment, to demonstrate the postulated properties in the P-protein. For a material required, *ex hypothesi*, to possess extraordinary activity this is a very damaging thing. P-protein is abundant in the sap; surely, it may be asked, expressed sap should show some of the writhing movements of say *Nitella* cytoplasm? Or some of the reactions of actomyosin-like proteins? So far work on this aspect has shown little promise.

The microscopical evidence is equally against the suggestion. First, the clear milieu in which the filaments are supposed to act appears far different from the organised cytoplasm surrounding them in say *Nitella* or *Physarum*. Second, electronmicrographs offer little encouragement to the view that P-protein is organized either to provide peristaltic forces, or shearing ones. In general it appears to have a random dispersion in the lumens and a regular distribution only in the sieve-plate pores. Is it really possible to envisage shearing or peristaltic forces acting in the latter situation, let alone the former? It seems an inadequate reply to blame surge artefact disruption every time (for the filaments are required to form robust structures with a point of fixity somewhere). Surely there should be *some* indication, in preparations classified as good by the best standards we have, of P-protein organized in a suggestive way and on a realistic scale to do the task attributed to it? The criticism again is a damaging one. Third, it seems difficult to account for the ready reversibility of flow. Actin filaments are polarized; the bundles too must be anchored. If they operate in the lumen, the anchorage must presumably be a *point*, with reversal of flow accompanying a swinging about this point. The bundles would require to be considerably shorter than the sieve elements to allow this. But of all this there is hardly a trace of visual evidence. If anchorage is rather at the sieve plate this accords ill with the filaments extending, often symmetrically, right through and out at each side; how in this case, can one envisage reversal? And how can the packed fibrils act to promote flow through the interstices between them? The ideas here must be worked out much more plausibly before they can be convincing, for the more or less agreed implication of fibrils in protoplasmic streaming is in too different a context to be quoted as sufficient demonstration that the system is workable.

In fact the contractile protein theories imply a sophistication of organization in the sieve tubes for which there is almost no evidence. They fail too to take account of the rather different situation in cereals and gymnosperms; and it is difficult to fit into their scheme certain specialized features such as the flagellar body of the sieve tubes of Leguminosae, none of which pose too difficult a problem for the electro-osmotic theory. Future research may change the situation, but at the moment the electron-microscope evidence is sufficiently firm to render this unlikely. MACROBBIE makes the apt remark that "it would ... be surprising if a completely new mechanical system had evolved in phloem rather than an adaptation" of the common actomyosin mechanism. However, electroosmosis does not necessarily qualify for the former description; it is at least possible that plasmodesmata, with their complex structure, function by a less highly developed form of the present proposals. Active potassium transport is already well-documented.

Physiologically, some of the actomyosin theories imply that transport follows a diffusion pattern. There is no evidence for this that cannot be satisfactorily explained otherwise, and there is plenty of evidence against it (see for instance QURESHI and

SPANNER, 1971). Coupled with the foregoing arguments the case would seem to be fairly strong therefore against ideas embraced by the term "diffusion analogue."

G. Conclusion

The electroosmotic or potassium theory presents a fairly consistent and satisfactory account of the main phenomena of the translocation process. Its details are in many respects tentative; but there is no clear corpus of evidence against it, as exists against several other theories. Quantitatively, matters are difficult, but if self-optimization is a possibility this is not altogether unexpected, for "test" parameters are not likely to be optimized ones. The theory invokes a mechanism in which electroosmosis is only the king-pin; rather more central to it is the role of potassium. It operates like a servo-mechanism, a MÜNCH-type gradient providing the initial impulse. Energy-wise it is demanding, but it is not apparent that it is more so than theories invoking contractile protein. No doubt a simple (and slow) MÜNCH mechanism would be less so; but it is highly probable that in the evolutionary sense thermodynamic efficiency and energy economy are of less importance than the ability to grow fast, and a powerful translocation mechanism is an obvious requirement for this. It would be foolish to claim too much for the present theory; but fantastic as is the picture it presents of long-trunked trees (such as *Eucalyptus* or rattan palms) with a phloem stream driven by countless millions of ring-vortices of the potassium ion, the picture offered by the actomyosin theories is at least equally so; and many workers would consider the MÜNCH hypothesis, in such an extreme (but inescapable) situation, to be a non-starter. Plants, like animals, are "fearfully and wonderfully made". It remains to be seen whether any of the less satisfactory features of the present theory can be improved enough to enable it to fit the recognisedly astonishing facts of the translocation process.

Addendum 1. Hydrodynamic Polarization of the Sieve Plate

What happens to anions in the sieve tubes when the plates are *completely impermeable* to them can be shown as follows. Differentiation of the expression for the electrochemical potential of an ion with respect to distance shows that the force on the ion can be written

$$\text{Force per mole} = -\left(\frac{RT}{c}\cdot\frac{\mathrm{d}c}{\mathrm{d}x}+zF\boldsymbol{E}\right) \tag{1}$$

where c is the concentration, z the charge number, F the Faraday and $\boldsymbol{E}$ the electrical potential gradient. The hydrodynamic force, in the same direction, is $\frac{v}{u}\cdot zF$, where u is the electrical mobility of the ion and v the velocity of the stream. Thus in the steady condition we have

$$-\left(\frac{RT}{c}\cdot\frac{\mathrm{d}c}{\mathrm{d}x}+zF\boldsymbol{E}\right)+\frac{vzF}{u}=0 \tag{2}$$

In this, u is considered negative for anions. Making the simplifying assumption that $\boldsymbol{E}$ is constant we can integrate this to give

$$c=c_0\exp\left[\frac{zF}{RT}\left(\frac{v}{u}-\boldsymbol{E}\right)x\right], \tag{3}$$

c_0 being the concentration at $x=0$. Taking the origin of x as immediately below the sieve plate in an element of length l we get the interesting relations:

$$c_l/c_0=e^{\alpha l} \tag{4}$$

$$c_l/\bar{c}=\alpha l\left(\frac{e^{\alpha l}}{e^{\alpha l}-1}\right), \tag{5}$$

where

$$\alpha=\frac{zF}{RT}\left(\frac{v}{u}-\boldsymbol{E}\right).$$

For a univalent anion $z=-1$; and taking $u=-6.4\times10^{-4}\,\mathrm{cm}^2\ \mathrm{s}^{-1}\ \mathrm{volt}^{-1}$, $v=50\ \mathrm{cm\ h}^{-1}$, $l=500\ \mu\mathrm{m}$, $\boldsymbol{E}=25\ \mathrm{mV}$ over $500\ \mu\mathrm{m}$, $R=8.315$ joules deg^{-1} mole^{-1}, $F=96{,}500$ coulombs $\mathrm{equiv.}^{-1}$ and $T=293\ ^\circ\mathrm{K}$ we get $\alpha l=1.98\ (21.7+0.5)=44$, with $\boldsymbol{E}$ clearly unimportant relative to v/u. Introducing this value into (4) and (5) shows that the ratio c_l/c_0 (which in a serial system like the sieve tube represents the degree of polarization of the sieve plates) is virtually infinite; while the ratio $c_l/\bar{c}$ (which represents the concentration of the anion just above the sieve plate relative to its mean level) has the high value of 44. Where sieve elements function as consortia of several together, both these ratios will be correspondingly increased. Thus even if the plates are not fully anion-impermeable a considerably enhanced concentration immediately above them is to be expected, especially if the anion tends to polyvalency like ATP.

It should be noted that $\bar{c}$, the *average* concentration of the anion in the sieve tubes, may be larger than that obtained by analyzing exudate, since if the sieve plates have low anion permeability the exudate may to some extent be "desalted" as it is forced through them. Unless it contains an appreciable quantity of P-protein it will of course have a balanced content of mobile anions and cations (HALL and BAKER, 1972).

Eq. (2) can be alternatively derived by expressing the fact that the backward diffusion of the ion down its concentration gradient balances the movement due to the streaming and the potential gradient. Einstein's relation between the diffusion coefficient and the mobility $\left(D=\frac{RTu}{zF}\right)$ is needed.

Addendum 2. Donnan Equilibrium between Lumen and Pores

Consider the equilibrium between the lumen of the sieve tube and the sieve-plate pores. Both contain immobile anion, the P-protein (equivalent concentration X), together with potassium (concentration K) and a mobile anion (concentration A). Denoting the two phases by the subscripts$_{1,2}$ we can write the following equations:

$$K_1 = A_1 + X_1, \tag{1}$$

$$K_2 = A_2 + X_2, \tag{2}$$

expressing electroneutrality; and

$$K_1 A_1 = K_2 A_2 \tag{3}$$

expressing the Donnan equilibrium. What we wish to find is the ratio $\gamma = K_2/A_2$ which represents the preponderance of mobile cations over anions in the sieve-plate pores. Solving these equations for K_2, A_2 in terms of K_1, X_1 and X_2 we find

$$\gamma = K_2/A_2 = \frac{\sqrt{4K_1(K_1 - X_1)/X_2^2 + 1} + 1}{\sqrt{4K_1(K_1 - X_1)/X_2^2 + 1} - 1}. \tag{4}$$

This indicates that not only is γ high when X_2 (P-protein concentration in the sieve pores) is high, but also when X_1 (the concentration in the lumen) is high, both being reckoned in terms of K_1, the total content of mobile cation in the lumen.

To illustrate this consider the case in which $K_1 = \frac{1}{4} X_2$, $X_1 = 0.8\, K_1$. This gives $\gamma = 81$. If X_1 be reduced to zero (i.e. if the lumen be clear of P-protein) then γ falls to 18. Thus the presence of P-protein in the lumen at about one quarter of its concentration in the pores very greatly increases the cation selectivity of the latter. It need not, at this concentration, be electroosmotically very effective in the lumen.

Addendum 3

The question of the simultaneous transport of both anions and cations can be viewed in the following light. In a system without lateral leakage translocating under steady conditions the movement of a solute across any transverse section will be determined solely by the loading (or unloading) rate. If this be appreciably higher for cations (e.g. K^+) than for anions then the situation will be that while cations and anions are in balance everywhere their rates of movement across the sieve plates will be appreciably different. This is the state of affairs envisaged by the electroosmotic theory. Thus if K^+ is loaded into the sieve tubes at a higher rate than comparable anions (as it may well be) sieve-plate electroosmosis would be a distinct possibility, accompanied however by transport of both sorts of ions at their loading rates.

References

AMIR, S., REINHOLD, L.: Interaction between K-deficiency and light in ^{14}C- sucrose translocation in bean plants. Physiol. Plantarum **24**, 226–231 (1971).

ATKINSON, M.R., FINDLAY, G.P., HOPE, A.B., PITMAN, M.G., SADDLER, H.D.W., WEST, K.R.: Salt regulation in the mangroves *Rhizophora mucronata* LAM. and *Aegialitis annulata* R. BR. Australian J. Biol. Sci. **20**, 589–599 (1967).

BAKER, D.A., HALL, J.L.: Pinocytosis, ATP-ase and ion uptake by plant cells. New Phytologist **72**, 1281–1291 (1973).

BARRY, P.H., HOPE, A.B.: Electroosmosis in membranes: effects of unstirred layers and transport numbers. II. Experimental. Biophys. J. **9**, 729–757 (1969).

BISHOP, W.H., RICHARDS, F.M.: Properties of liquids in small pores. Rates of diffusion of some solutes in cross-linked crystals of β-lactoglobulin. J. Mol. Biol. **38**, 315–328 (1968).

BLATT, F.J.: Temperature dependence of the action potential in *Nitella flexilis*. Biochim. Biophys. Acta **339**, 382–389 (1974).

BOWLING, D.J.F.: Evidence for the electroosmotic theory of transport in the phloem. Biochim. Biophys. Acta **183**, 230–232 (1969).

BOWYER, J.W., ATHERTON, J.G.: Observations on the relationship between *mycoplasma*-like bodies and host cells of legume little-leaf diseased plants. Australian J. Biol. Sci. **23**, 115–125 (1970).

CATESSON, A-M.: Observations cytochimiques sur les tubes criblés de quelques angiospermes. J. de Microscopie **16**, 95–104 (1973).

CRAFTS, A.S., CRISP, C.E.: Phloem transport in plants. San Francisco: W.H. Freeman 1971.

CRONSHAW, J., ESAU, K.: Tubular and fibrillar components of mature and differentiating sieve elements. J. Cell Biol. **34**, 801–816 (1967).

ELLIOTT, G.F.: Force-balances and stability in hexagonally-packed polyelectrolyte systems. J. Theoret. Biol. **21**, 71–87 (1968).

EVERT, R.J., ESCHRICH, W., EICHHORN, S.E.: Sieve-plate pores in leaf veins of *Hordeum vulgare*. Planta **100**, 262–267 (1971).

EVERT, R.F., ESCHRICH, W., EICHHORN, S.E.: P-protein distribution in mature sieve elements of *Cucurbita maxima*. Planta **109**, 193–210 (1973).

FALK, H.: Zur Herkunft des Siebröhrenschleimes bei *Tetragonia expansa* Murr. Planta **60**, 558–567 (1964).

FENSOM, D.S.: The bioelectric potentials of plants and their functional significance I. An electrokinetic theory of transport. Can. J. Botany **35**, 573–582 (1957).

FENSOM, D.S.: A theory of translocation in phloem of *Heracleum* by contractile protein microfibrillar material. Can. J. Botany **50**, 479–497 (1972).

FENSOM, D.S., SPANNER, D.C.: Electroosmotic and biopotential measurements on phloem strands of *Nymphoides*. Planta **88**, 321–331 (1969).

FRITZ, E.: Microautoradiographic investigations on bidirectional translocation in the phloem of *Vicia faba*. Planta **112**, 169–179 (1973).

GIAQUINTA, R.T., GEIGER, D.R.: Mechanism of inhibition of translocation by localized chilling. Plant Physiol. **51**, 372–377 (1973).

GREENWAY, H., PITMAN, M.G.: Potassium retranslocation in seedlings of *Hordeum vulgare*. Australian J. Biol. Sci. **18**, 235–247 (1965).

HALL, S.M., BAKER, D.A.: The chemical composition of *Ricinus* phloem exudate. Planta **106**, 131–140 (1972).

HAMMEL, H.T.: Measurement of turgor pressure and its gradient in the phloem of oak. Plant Physiol. **43**, 1042–1048 (1968).

HARTT, C.E.: Effect of potassium deficiency upon translocation of ^{14}C in attached blades and entire plants of sugar cane. Plant Physiol. **44**, 1461–1469 (1969).

HÖBER, R.: Physical chemistry of cells and tissues. London: J. and A. Churchill 1946.

HUMBLE, G.D., RASCHKE, K.: Stomatal opening quantitatively related to potassium transport. Evidence from electron-probe analysis. Plant Physiol. **48**, 447–453 (1971).

JARVIS, J.W., TYE, F.L.: Transport of non-electrolytes through ion-selective membranes by electroosmosis. J. Chem. Soc. **127**, 620–624 (1960).

KEDEM, O., KATCHALSKY, A.: Permeability of composite membranes. Part 3, Series array of elements. Trans. Faraday Soc. **59**, 1941–1953 (1963).

KLUGE, M., ZIEGLER, H.: Der ATP-Gehalt der Siebröhrensäfte von Laubbäumen. Planta **61**, 167–177 (1964).

KOLLMANN, R.: On the fine structure of the sieve-element protoplast. Phytomorph. **14**, 247–264 (1964).

KOLLMANN, R.: Fine structural and biochemical characterization of the sieve-tube protein. Proc. Res. Instit. Pomology. Skierniewice, Series E, No. 3, 61–71 (1973).

LAFLECHE, D.: Ultrastructure et cytochimie des inclusions flagellées des cellules criblées de *Phaseolus vulgaris*. J. de Microscopie **5**, 493–510 (1966).

LANG, A.: A working model of a sieve tube. J. Exptl. Botany **24**, 896–904 (1973).

LYONS, J.M., RAISON, J.K.: Oxidative activity of mitochondria isolated from plant tissues sensitive and resistant to chilling injury. Plant Physiol. **45**, 386–389 (1970).

MACROBBIE, E.A.C.: Phloem Translocation. Facts and Mechanisms: a comparative survey. Biol. Rev. **46**, 429–481 (1971).

PRAISSMAN, M., MILLER, I.F., BERKOWITZ, J.M.: Ion-mediated water flow. I. Electroosmosis. J. Memb. Biol. **11**, 130–151 (1973).

QURESHI, F.A., SPANNER, D.C.: Unidirectional movement of tracers along the stolon of *Saxifraga sarmentosa*. Planta **101**, 133–146 (1971).

QURESHI, F.A., SPANNER, D.C.: The effect of nitrogen on the movement of tracers down the stolon of *Saxifraga sarmentosa*, with some observations on the influence of light. Planta **110**, 131–144 (1973a).

QURESHI, F.A., SPANNER, D.C.: The influence of dinitrophenol on phloem transport along the stolon of *Saxifraga sarmentosa*. Planta **111**, 1–12 (1973b).

QURESHI, F.A., SPANNER, D.C.: Cyanide inhibition of phloem transport along the stolon of *Saxifraga sarmentosa* L. J. Exptl. Botany **24**, 751–762 (1973c).

QURESHI, F.A., SPANNER, D.C.: The simultaneous movement of two ions in the phloem of the *Saxifraga* stolon. Planta **112**, 121–128 (1973d).

RASCHKE, K., FELLOWS, M.P.: Stomatal movement in *Zea mays*: Shuttle of potassium and chloride between guard cells and subsidiary cells. Planta **101**, 296–316 (1971).

ROSEN, R.: Optimality principles in biology. London: Butterworths 1967.

SCHOLANDER, P.F.: How mangroves desalinate seawater. Physiol Plantarum **21**, 251–261 (1968).

SIDDIQUI, A.W., JONES, R.L., SPANNER, D.C.: Translocation in the stolon of *Saxifraga sarmentosa*. The ultrastructural background. Ann. Botany (London) **38**, 145–149 (1974).

SIJ, J.W., SWANSON, C.A.: Effect of petiole anoxia on phloem transport in squash. Plant Physiol. **51**, 368–371 (1973).

SPANNER, D.C.: The translocation of sugar in sieve tubes. J. Exptl. Botany **9**, 332–342 (1958).

SPANNER, D.C.: The electroosmotic theory of phloem transport in the light of recent measurements on *Heracleum* phloem. J. Exptl. Botany **21**, 325–334 (1970).

SPANNER, D.C., JONES, R.L.: The sieve-tube wall and its relation to translocation. Planta **92**, 64–72 (1970).

SWANSON, C.A., GEIGER, D.R.: Time course of low temperature inhibition of sucrose translocation in sugar beets. Plant Physiol. **42**, 751–756 (1967).

WEDNER, H.J., DIAMOND, J.M.: Contributions of unstirred-layer effects to apparent electrokinetic phenomena in the gall-bladder. J. Memb. Biol. **1**, 92–108 (1969).

WORLEY, J.F.: Evidence in support of "open" sieve-tube pores. Protoplasma **76**, 129–132 (1973).

YAPA, P.A.J., SPANNER, D.C.: Isoelectric focusing of sieve-tube protein. Planta **106**, 369–373 (1972).

ZIMMERMANN, M.H.: Absorption and translocation: transport in the phloem. Ann. Rev. Plant Physiol. **11**, 167–190 (1960).

14. Pressure Flow

J.A. MILBURN

A. Introduction

Retrospectively it seems unfortunate that the discovery of blood circulation in animals (proved by HARVEY, 1628) coincided with studies in xylem- and not phloem-sap transport in plants, because the similarity between blood transport and sieve-tube transport has become increasingly apparent. Attempts to apply positive pressure circulation models proved abortive (HALES, 1733) because xylem-sap pressures are not positive when sap transport is most vigorous. Furthermore, the driving force for flow was established as solar evaporation, which induces negative-pressure gradients contrasting with the circulation of blood. Phloem transport studies developed slowly after the discovery of sieve tubes (HARTIG, 1837) and his proposal of positive pressure transport in 1860. The concept of circulation was renewed by MÜNCH (1930) who demonstrated that water could be collected from partially isolated sieve tubes by reverse osmosis. According to MÜNCH's scheme, pressure developed osmotically as a consequence of solute secretion into the sieve tubes and this provided the necessary driving mechanism for transport. Since water was transported along with solutes, its return *via* the xylem was proposed to complete a circulatory pathway.

Schemes for osmotic pressure flow have met with objections which continue to cause debate; some alternatives would replace pressure flow completely, others would merely augment the flow at the expense of metabolic energy. A key problem has been the extent to which the sieve plates, which occlude sieve tubes transversely at frequent intervals, are porous. For many years it has been known that sieve-plate pores are capable of plugging and it has been pointed out that some such mechanism is essential to plant survival to protect the nutrient transport system, at positive pressure, from excessive predation or injury. Several different sealing mechanisms are known to operate, being functionally analogous to the clotting of blood. Despite great efforts to counter these mechanisms, evidence is still conflicting regarding the condition of intact sieve-plate pores *in situ* during translocation.

Many excellent reviews of phloem transport have appeared in recent years (WEATHERLEY and JOHNSON, 1968; BIDDULPH, 1969; CRAFTS and CRISP, 1971; ZIMMERMANN and BROWN, 1971; MACROBBIE, 1971; CANNY, 1973) to which the reader is referred for more extensive coverage than is possible here, where the intention is to examine osmotic pressure flow so as to point out useful avenues for future research. Qualitative demonstrations are summarized, but this type of experimentation has to a great extent lost its value. Disappointingly, opposing schools in the great phloem controversy are apt to go their separate ways. This review attempts to bridge some of the more obvious chasms.

B. Pressure-Flow Systems

In principle, pressure may be generated in several ways to drive phloem sap through sieve tubes. Solute loading systems are known in animals, such as the gall bladder, which can generate positive hydrostatic pressures directly in iso-osmotic conditions (see e.g. DIAMOND, 1965). Systems are also known, such as that in *Physarum*, the slime mould studied by KAMIYA and others (see Chapter 12), in which high rates of mass flow have been observed. It takes place in a plasmodium and is driven by contractile proteins powered by ATP up to rates of 450 cm per h. This system and also the more conjectural systems such as electro-osmosis, peristalsis or flagellar beating, described in Chapters 12, 13 and 15, may be described as producing or augmenting pressure flow, i.e. a bulk or mass flow of solution along a pressure gradient. To avoid confusion it will be assumed in this chapter that pressure flow implies that pressure drives transport through essentially passive sieve tubes in the sense intended by WEATHERLEY and JOHNSON (1968). The main transport mechanism driving pressure flow is therefore due to osmosis, but active secretory processes at source and sink are not necessarily excluded.

I. Münch Osmotic Pressure-Flow Models

When, in 1930, ERNST MÜNCH described his osmotic-pressure hypothesis, he provided phloem physiology with its most successful hypothesis to date. It has been of great importance in influencing experimental designs and interpretations. Though his proposals are not universally accepted, favorable evidence has accumulated steadily. In essence, his model (Fig. 1a) consists of two osmometers acting in opposition with a common water supply. Water enters the "source" osmometer, equivalent to a photosynthesizing leaf etc., where the solutes are more concentrated. Solution then travels through the connecting tube (representing stem transport) until it reaches the "sink" osmometer, equivalent to a root, fruit, etc., where water is expelled by reverse osmosis. Flow ceases when the solutions in the osmometers become equal in concentration, but the positive internal hydrostatic pressure persists. It is important to appreciate that during flow the solute concentration can differ markedly between "source" and "sink" because equilibrium has not been reached; under these conditions the hydrostatic gradient is virtually uniform throughout. The hydrostatic pressure gradient is thereby less than the corresponding osmotic gradient across the source membranes, but greater than the osmotic gradient across the sink membranes. Thus the system overall produces water influx and efflux with a bulk flow of solution from "source" to "sink" which tends to balance solute concentrations in the enclosed system through the passive mediation of water. A working model of a sieve tube was described by LANG (1973), which demonstrated these and similar effects which are implicit also in a series of mathematical models which have appeared recently (e.g. CHRISTY and FERRIER, 1973, see Chapter 16).

II. Intact Plants: Elaboration on the Münch Model

Firstly, solutes must be secreted or absorbed across the osmotic membranes to induce flow. Secondly, the resistance to longitudinal flow, virtually zero in the

MÜNCH model, shown in Fig. 1a, becomes highly significant in sieve tubes. This fact was not apparently appreciated by ESCHRICH et al., 1972. This in turn produces a gradient of hydrostatic pressure between source and sink. Furthermore, the water potentials at source and sink are not necessarily equal; the pressure-gradient of the xylem sap is itself influenced both by transpiration and by gravity as discussed below.

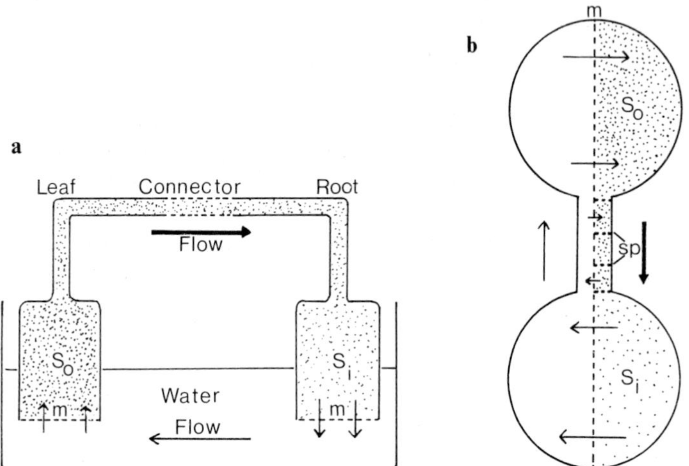

Fig. 1a and b. Osmotic flow models. Solute concentrations are indicated by the degree of stippling. Semipermeable membranes *m* maintain osmotic systems at the Source S_0 and the Sink S_i. Water movement is by osmosis whilst solution flow (phloem transport) is shown (a) Münch's osmometer model. Both osmometers tend to produce hydrostatic pressure, but since pressure S_0 exceeds S_i, water enters S_0 and is expelled by reverse osmosis at S_i. The internal hydrostatic pressure is the integrated resultant of both osmometers. Solute concentrations across the membranes are the controlling factors. (b) A more realistic osmotic flow model applicable to plants. A degree of semi-permeability is possessed by the whole system, but is presumed of greater importance at source S_0 and sink S_i. Solution flow is through one or more sieve tubes from S_0 to S_i with sieve plates *sp*. Water circulation could occur through the xylem or *via* a similar sieve-tube system acting in the opposite direction. S_0 could be leaves or storage organs, S_i represents roots, meristems, fruits or storage organs

From the standpoint of the MÜNCH model (Fig. 1b) it may be noted that providing the water balance of a plant is sufficiently high it should be possible to maintain exudation until exudate has been diluted osmotically until it is almost pure water. Seemingly this does not occur; possibly it is prevented by the swelling of callose in sieve-plate pores and plasmodesmata as the degree of hydration increases (see Chapter 4) and by continued secretion of solutes into the sieve tubes.

A further complication is that we know very little about the effective permeability of membranes and tissues surrounding the phloem. Unlike the model where two osmometers are connected by a single impermeable tube, the whole system is to some degree semi-permeable throughout, though this may vary, for example, between leaves in which xylem and phloem conduits are practically adjacent, and in secondarily thickened stems, where a cambium is interposed. Also, sieve tubes may become anastomosed towards their termini (ESAU, 1969, p. 154).

The location of the osmotically-active membrane system is critical, but in doubt. Many have assumed from the MÜNCH model that the sieve-tube plasmalemma is *the* location, but this is by no means certain. Whilst objections can be raised against the notion that bulk flow occurs from chloroplasts to sieve tubes, as MÜNCH originally thought, it is likely that cells adjoining sieve tubes may be directly involved, especially the companion cells (see Chapter 17). If loading: unloading processes occur *outside* the sieve tubes, a bulk flow of *solution* would take place between sieve tubes and adjoining cells. Unfortunately we know almost nothing about this part of the loading: unloading system or indeed its capacity to affect the hydrostatic pressure of sap directly. If this were to occur, pressure flow could be driven through "passive" sieve tubes at the expense of metabolic energy. Possibly the extrafloral nectaries provide a useful mechanism analogous to loading *via* plasmodesmata (LÜTTGE, 1971). Certainly the tissues lend themselves to experimentation more readily than the inaccessible companion-cell complex.

According to MÜNCH's model, an interruption which stops flow in the connecting tube (equivalent to the stem phloem) halts the entire pattern of flow. In stems

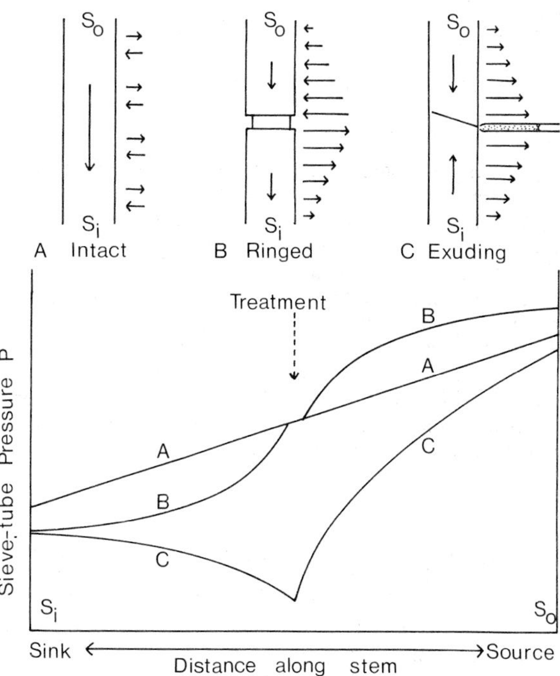

Fig. 2A–C. Diagrammatic representation of the source: sink responses of stems in different situations (top) and the corresponding hydrostatic pressure changes anticipated (below). Solid arrows represent relative flow rates for longitudinal or lateral flow on different scales (length $\propto$ flux). (A) Flow through an intact stem transporting assimilates (↓) from leaves S_0 towards the roots S_i. The role of the stem probably fluctuates between that of a source (→) and a sink (←). Storage and utilization usually predominate. (B) In a ringed stem the downward flow is curtailed, but does not stop. Above the ring the pressure increases and the stem assumes the role of a sink (←). Below the ring the stem becomes an emergency source (→) as the hydrostatic pressure is reduced. (C) During exudation (incision or stylet) the hydrostatic pressure is reduced locally causing storage cells to become sources (→) in the proximity of the wound however, the elastic and semi-permeable nature of sieve tubes would produce immediate changes so that some flow continues. When a stem is ringed between source and sink the severed sieve tubes normally plug near the ring but internal flow does not necessarily cease. Above the ring the secretion of solutes into sieve tubes may continue to raise the osmotic potential of the sap which induces a corresponding increase in hydrostatic pressure. Below the ring consumption by "sink" tissues causes a corresponding fall in hydrostatic pressure (in Fig. 2 compare A with B). Secondary effects would follow because sieve tubes are elastic and change their volume in response to pressure. Furthermore, changes in pressure and solute concentration would rapidly modify the solute influx and efflux patterns with cells adjoining the sieve tubes. It is a tacitly accepted part of the model that sources and sinks are to some extent interchangeable, depending on the relative availability of solutes.

When a sieve-tube system is tapped by an incision to initiate exudation there must be a local reduction in hydrostatic pressure (Fig. 2C). This change seemingly converts even a natural sink (e.g. *Cocos* inflorescence, *Cucurbita* fruit, or *Ricinus* root, see MILBURN 1974) into a source which can lose solutes through exudation. It is important to note that if the translocation stream is tapped by aphids, which are commonly assumed not to affect transport patterns, similar but more localized changes will be initiated to those produced by exudation from incisions. A similar disturbance may be expected if a pulse of radioactive carbon dioxide is applied to a leafy shoot at a concentration which alters the rate of assimilation. If the solute concentration changes the internal hydrostatic pressure within sieve tubes changes must be expected which modify previous translocation patterns.

III. The Effect of Gravity

Gravity has a somewhat paradoxical effect on translocation. At first sight gravity might be expected to promote flow 'down the bast'. However, the descent of phloem sap by mass flow requires the ascent of a corresponding amount of water *via* the xylem to maintain the flow. The system, therefore, operates like a siphon (Fig. 3). Such a siphon with equal limbs could only contribute to flow if air were allowed to enter the tube to displace the liquid and there is no evidence to suggest that

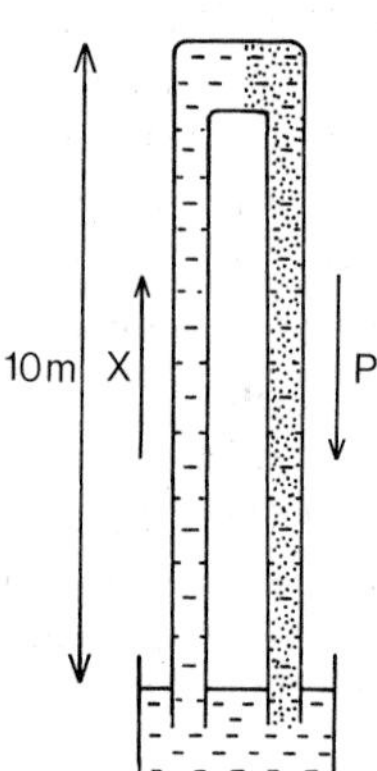

Fig. 3. Siphon model to illustrate the influence of gravity on sieve-tube transport from leaves to roots. When water occupies both tubes, the pressure in the water-filled tubes is −1 bar at the top and 0 bar (atmospheric pressure) below. If a 20% sucrose solution (stippled, density 1.08) fills the phloem limb *P*, a maximum driving pressure of 0.08 bar is established per 10 m

this happens in sieve tubes. However, gravity operates on the solutes secreted into sieve tubes enhancing flow marginally, depending on the density of the descending stream. The vertical driving pressure for a 20% sucrose solution would be about 0.008 bar m^{-1}.

The hydrostatic pressure in any liquid-filled tube standing vertically is affected by gravity (see Fig. 3), becoming more negative with elevation. When hydrostatic pressure measurements are performed on trees, such as the manometric determinations of HAMMEL (1968), it must be remembered that the measured differences in pressure are *not* the only driving forces operating. Thus pooling over 60 measurements from each elevation, HAMMEL's mean pressure differences over a vertical 4.8 m was 1.63 bars, giving an apparent pressure gradient which would include the density effect described above, of 0.34 bar m^{-1}. (This value, despite considerable variations between some values, is highly significant statistically; the figures cited by CRAFTS and CRISP, 1971 are not correct). However, in a static system the pressure decreases through elevation alone by 0.108 bar m^{-1} on account of gravity. Thus the true pressure differential driving phloem sap is 0.34 plus 0.108 equals 0.448 bar m^{-1}.

IV. Reverse-Osmosis Experiments

MÜNCH believed that the high internal pressure of sieve tubes, coupled with the fact that solutes would be removed, should cause water secretion at a "sink". His experimental justification was that water could be collected over periods of several months from tongues of bark, left attached to whole trees above but detached below. MOLOTOVSKY (1934) successfully repeated this work but others failed to do so (WEEVERS and WESTERNBERG, 1932; MASON et al., 1936). Unfortunately, the experimental design is weak because although evaporation was prevented by oiled-paper covers, there was no guarantee that the bark did not lose water simply by distillation under non-isothermal conditions. BROWN's (1964) observations are open to the same objection.

Recently similar, but more critical, experiments have been performed (MILBURN, in prep.). Evaporation and distillation were prevented by submerging attached bark tongues in tubes of inert and harmless mineral oil. Droplets of liquid water were produced under these conditions (Fig. 4) whilst callus tissues developed on the separated xylem and phloem tissues. Bark tongues, remaining attached below and separated above, also secreted water. The amount of water secreted tended to decrease despite continued callus growth. These experiments are interesting in that they demonstrate unequivocably the capacity of bark to transport liquid water longitudinally. The fall in secretion may well indicate that water can also be recycled in the phloem. Other observations also suggest circulation in phloem including bidirectional transport (see Chapter 10), a return capacity for hormones (see e.g. BIDWELL, 1973) and tracer experiments in which ^{14}C sap could be made to travel through an attached 'J' bark tongue (S.M. HALL unpublished). Similarly, it is interesting to note in this connection that whilst a ringed stem normally produces a heavy wound callus above the ring, suggesting an interruption of downward flow to roots, the development of callus has also been observed below the ring (see NOEL, 1970) suggesting assimilate ascent from the root "sink".

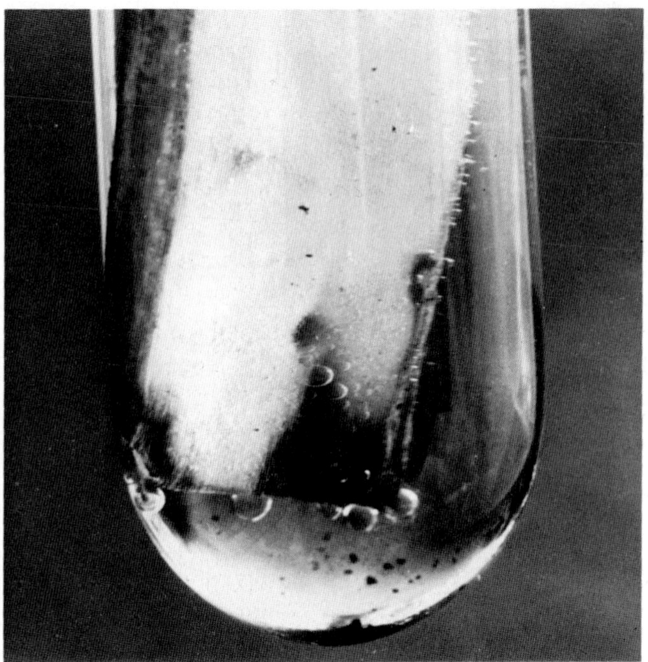

Fig. 4. Exudation of water droplets under mineral oil from a tongue of *Salix* bark attached above. Water droplets sink in the oil whilst gas bubbles rise. Distillation could not account for water collection in the glass tube filled with mineral oil and shows clearly the capacity of bark to transport water, probably through sieve tubes

V. The Role of Extra-Floral Nectaries

Many plants bear nectaries which do not seem to function like floral nectaries in attracting pollinating insects to flowers. These extra-floral nectaries tend to be widely distributed over rapidly growing plants such as *Hevea brasiliensis* (FREY-WYSSLING, 1935), *Impatiens balsamifera* and *Ricinus communis*, on stems, petioles, leaf surfaces and around leaf margins. Secretion is vigorous under strong illumination, especially during the rapid growth of leaves, but absent in shaded or slow-growing plants. These nectaries are supplied by sieve tubes (LÜTTGE, 1971), but the fluid secreted has a much lower nitrogen and phosphorus composition than corresponding phloem exudate (ZIEGLER, 1956). Nectaries seem closely analogous to aphids, which extract required solutes, but excrete unwanted sugars in the form of honeydew. If so extra-floral nectaries may function as complicated hydraulic bleed-valves in which living cells participate in extraction of required solutes and probably monitor the secretion process thus also enhancing a unidirectional supply of building materials to the developing organs. It is difficult to explain their evolution and widespread occurrence if they lack a functional role, or why they do function in this way unless nutrients are supplied as a bulk flow of solution.

C. Objections to Osmotic Pressure Flow

The search for alternative mechanisms to explain phloem transport other than osmotic pressure flow has arisen for two reasons. Firstly, the degree to which "normal" sieve plates are porous is questioned and secondly, certain observations have seemed to invalidate MÜNCH's model.

I. Structural Considerations

It has seemed contrary to any reasonable concept of efficiency that a simple bulk-flow pipeline should be obstructed at frequent intervals by structures like sieve plates. Furthermore, almost since their discovery, claims have been made that sieve-plate pores are plugged (VON MOHL, 1855, see ESAU, 1969) which would eliminate the question of simple bulk flow. However, the fact that sieve plates are altered in response to damage by sealing, and seal during periods of dormancy, is established beyond dispute. The idea that sieve plates may have a protective function which is their *raison d'être* in protecting the all-important nutrient supply (ZIMMERMANN, 1969b; MILBURN, 1972b) seems to account for these enigmas, but it has not been accepted universally. An efficient sealing action is not essential merely to prevent an excessive loss of assimilates; ecologically it may be more crucial to render the amounts of escaping sap inadequate to sustain a large predator. Nevertheless the sapsucker, a species of woodpecker and one of the largest predators on the phloem, not infrequently kills its host trees (TATE, 1973). Considerable efforts have improved the apparent degree to which sieve pores are found in an open condition using rapid-freezing techniques etc. There remain those who, considering that this may represent the normal functioning condition, find the resistance to flow excessive for osmotic pressure flow (see WEATHERLEY and JOHNSON, 1968; WEATHERLEY, 1972). However, it is equally possible that even the best fixation methods produce some fibrillar resistance and that if fixation techniques could be extrapolated to zero damage, there would be no significant plugging of sieve-plate pores. Electronmicroscopists use "rule of thumb" tests to check the degree to which artifacts have been produced during fixation. Asymmetry of materials on each side of a sieve plate thus indicates a physical pressure surge. However, artifacts due to chemical change, such as protein coagulation by oxidation as in *Cucurbita* sap, cannot be detected so easily, and other artifacts might be produced similarly.

Any theory which proposes naturally filled sieve-plate pores must explain how (and why) exudation phenomena can be demonstrated. One approach (e.g. SIDDIQUI and SPANNER, 1970) proposes pumping mechanisms situated in, and supported by, sieve plates during phloem sap exudation. The structures then must produce or permit turgor release and exudation. The difficulty with this proposal is that the flow rates and the volumes of exudate may be high. Furthermore, exudation results in flow from opposite directions. The requirements for such a high flow-rate, instantly polarizable, pumping mechanism considerably exceed known physical systems, even though they might just be feasible in an imagined steady-state system (AIKMAN and ANDERSON, 1971, see discussion in Chapter 16).

A more acceptable view (CANNY, 1973) proposes that exudation phenomena represent an abnormal condition in which a delicate pumping mechanism, stable under normal conditions, has been "blown out" by a rapid surge of sap when turgor is released on puncturing. However, it has been observed that *Ricinus* plants can be massaged frequently without detectable adverse effects (MILBURN, 1971) and similar pressure surges would be normal in field-grown plants subject to wind, or in bark-flap surgery, such as performed by MASON and MASKELL (1928). Significantly when specimens of *Fraxinus americana* phloem were examined by electronmicroscopy before and after exudation experiments, no difference in the sieve plates could be detected between treatments. They both appeared blocked (ZIMMERMANN and PARTHASARATHY, unpublished). CANNY (1973) distinguishes stylet exudation as being "gentle", hence equating with the undamaged condition and exudation from incisions, despite the fact that flow into the punctured sieve element induces it to refill 3 to 10 times s^{-1} (ZIMMERMANN, 1961). MITTLER (1957) calculated this rate at nearly 28 times s^{-1} and the mean velocity of flow around 500 cm h^{-1} (see also Chapter 6).

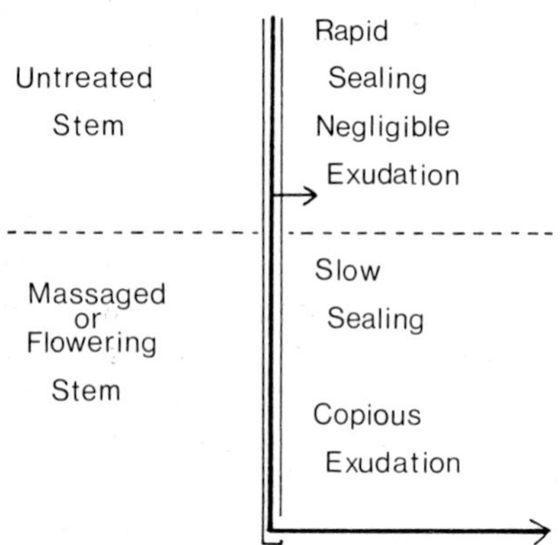

Fig. 5. If stems are massaged or affected by flowering, they exude copiously when cut. When untreated stems are cut, they exude very little, but exudation from the freely exuding distal stem is drastically reduced. This shows that the stem seals rapidly, but nevertheless supplies most of the exudate when the system is intact. The implication is that there may be similar solution transport in other plants which, when severed, also fail to exude

CANNY (1973) seems to propose that exudation occurs only when sieve tubes are damaged and abnormally conductive due to the removal of fragile structures which have a natural capacity to promote transport. This cannot be the case for several reasons. TAMMES (1933) observed that when an exuding *Arenga* inflorescence is excised, exudation is reduced to a small fraction. On examining the severed stalk, which *must* have been conducting practically all the exudate at a high rate, no exudate was produced. In similar experiments performed recently on *Cocos* inflorescences we found exactly the same results. MILBURN (1971) showed considerable exudation from locally-massaged *Ricinus* bark which must have been supplied through untreated bark above (see Fig. 5); yet when the latter was incised, exudation was practically nil. Furthermore, specific-mass transfer calculations (see below) show that, whatever the driving mechanism, sieve tubes *must* be capable of transport capacities of the order of magnitude indicated by exudation studies.

The phloem anatomy of gymnosperms has received a good deal of attention and seems to preclude a bulk flow of phloem sap. Thus KOLLMAN and SCHUMACHER (1963) found by electronmicroscopy that the sieve areas in *Metasequoia* had a median nodule in the perforated walls between adjacent sieve cells which was filled with dense stainable cytoplasmic material. However, it should be noted that aphids feed successfully on gymnosperms, indeed sap has been collected through isolated stylets from *Picea abies* by ZIEGLER and MITTLER (1959) and also from *Pinus strobus* and *P. resinosa* by G.P. HILL (unpublished data). Furthermore, phloem exudate from gymnosperms serves as a food supply for sapsuckers (*Sphyrapicus varius*), even in winter (TATE, 1973). The exudate seems more dilute than in comparable angiosperms (ca. 14% w/v MÜNCH, 1930). It seems from these exudation phenomena that phloem sap is transported in conifers in bulk by the same mechanisms as in other plants. How this can be reconciled with anatomical investigations remains to be seen.

The beauty of the osmotic pressure-flow system is that it can explain very easily how solutes appear to move from high concentrations to low ones. Each sieve tube behaves like a giant cell. Unloading of solutes reduces solute concentration and pressure which initiates solute loading at some distant source. It would explain how solutes are mobilized during exudation, even to the extent that a natural sink is converted instantly to assume the role of a source to meet a new low-pressure demand. We have hardly begun to investigate the structural mechanisms producing this response (but see KING and ZEEVART, 1974).

II. Bidirectional Transport

When sieve tubes are punctured, sap flows from opposite directions towards the wound. This "opposed" flow towards an artificial sink is not the critical issue. If the phloem behaves like MÜNCH'S simple model, it should be impossible for a simultaneous "bidirectional flow" of different solutes to occur (faster than diffusion) in opposite directions through the connecting tube. The fault here is that MÜNCH'S model has often been applied, somewhat naively, to the whole sieve-tube complex rather than each individual sieve tube. The notion that sieve tubes transport sap of identical composition in unison is not correct (ZIMMERMANN, 1960). Sieve-tube transport is normally reversed during leaf development when assimilates are first imported then exported, and at a certain stage flow through adjacent sieve tubes may be in opposite directions (see BIDDULPH, 1969, also Chapter 10). Bidirectional transport through different sieve tubes is probably part of normal growth. Such a device would greatly improve solute distribution, and possibly the evolution of bicollateral phloem may have been favored to this end.

If, however, bidirectional flow can be shown to occur simultaneously in a single sieve tube, MÜNCH'S pressure-flow hypothesis must be either abandoned or augmented by some additional mechanism.

III. Differential Transport

Some workers have assumed that since MÜNCH'S model should transmit solutions in bulk, the relationship between the concentration of components must be constant. In fact, labeled water and solutes may seem to move at different rates (e.g. CHOI and ARONOFF, 1966; PEEL et al., 1969; PEEL, 1970). There are three difficulties with the interpretation. Firstly, sieve tubes are not passive connecting tubes; they have the capacity to load and unload solutes along the pipeline as shown by numerous tracer experiments (see also Chapter 8). Secondly, sieve tubes are permeable to water and have a small diameter which allows the rapid exchange of tritiated water with water in surrounding tissues (CATALDO et al., 1972; ZIMMERMANN, 1974, Appendix II). Hence, the claim that solutes are transported whilst labeled water seems to remain stationary in no way conflicts with the osmotic model when it is correctly applied. Thirdly, there is no reason why all sieve tubes must transport in unison. The complex profiles of ANTOSZEWSKI et al. (1973) may be explained by this possibility.

IV. Polarized Flow

Palm inflorescences provide an example of tissues in which flow appears to be polarized, for if the inflorescence is detached the sliced tip exudes whereas the stalk does not (see TAMMES, 1933). An alternative explanation is that the sealing capacity of the tissues is different so that the wounded tip continues to bleed whereas the stalk becomes sealed instantly in response to cutting. The latter must be the correct explanation, because a middle section cut from the inflorescence exudes phloem sap from *both* ends. This shows a latent capability to transport in either longitudinal direction as would be supposed on the basis of pressure flow through sieve tubes.

D. Observations Supporting Osmotic Pressure Flow

A considerable number of experimental observations supply quantitative support for pressure flow in sieve tubes which could be driven by osmotic flow. These are summarized briefly in Table 1. Details may be found in the references listed. The list is by no means exhaustive and repetition of findings have not been included.

Of the demonstrations in Table 1, probably the simplest, most easily performed and highly convincing is that of exudation (HARTIG, 1860). Bark of a large *Quercus* tree, when punctured with a stout needle, exudes up to 100 μl of sap almost instantaneously. This demonstration should be performed by all students of phloem physiology in the knowledge that each sieve element has a volume of about 0.001 μl and only a few are punctured by the needle tip.

DIXON and GIBBON (1932) and DIXON (1933) performed pertinent work which has been sadly neglected. They found evidence of considerable pressure gradients in a young tree from the phloem exudate which had "unexpectedly high" osmotic pressures (13–35 atm). Also tracer solutions (Indian ink and potassium ferrocyanide) could be injected through sieve tubes under quite moderate pressure (3 atm). They considered that their experiments supported the Münch hypothesis in showing convincingly that hydrostatic pressure can drive solutions through sieve tubes. This observation is supported by the recent microcannulation work of BARCLAY and FENSOM (see Chapter 9).

It is not commonly understood that even quite simple exudation experiments, in which incisions are made across phloem at frequent intervals can give very useful information about the behavior of the material used and also the sap-flow mechanism

Table 1. Summarized observations supporting osmotic pressure flow (additional to text)

1. Marco Polo, 12th Cent., noted profuse flow of sugary sap from palms. Flow was enhanced by watering the roots. (See HODGE, 1963)
2. Rapid exudation of small quantities of sap when tree-bark sieve tubes were punctured. (HARTIG, 1860).
3. Phloem translocation in *Gossypium* bark seemed always to flow from high to low solute concentrations. (MASON and MASKELL, 1928)
4. Ferric chloride soln., pressure injected (3atm) moved 3.5 cm through *Fraxinus* sieve tubes in 30 min. (DIXON and GIBBON, 1932)
5. Solute gradients in trees indicate an osmotic flow from source (leaves) to sink (roots). (HUBER et al., 1937)
6. Rapid transport of curlytop virus in *Nicotiana* and *Beta* correlated with phloem transport. (BENNETT, 1937)
7. Palm phloem exudation is maximal by night and minimal by day. (BOSE, 1947)
8. Aphid stylets inserted in *Salix* sieve tubes exude phloem sap by positive pressure (incisions fail). (KENNEDY and MITTLER, 1953)
9. Pressure on *Salix* bark can reversibly induce flow from excised stylets; pressures very high. (MITTLER, 1957)
10. Enhanced xylem-sap pressure increases the rate of flow from excised stylets in *Salix* phloem. (WEATHERLEY et al., 1959)
11. Transmission of heat pulse suggests solution flow through *Heracleum* displaced phloem. (ZIEGLER and VIEWEG, 1961)
12. Measurement of high sieve-tube turgor pressures in *Quercus* sieve tubes. (HAMMEL, 1968)
13. Sieve plates of *Nicotiana* fixed in open condition by wilting before fixation: no plugging. (ANDERSON and CRONSHAW, 1970)
14. Exudation from *Ricinus* stems enhanced by massage pretreatment. Growth unaffected. (MILBURN, 1970, 71)
15. Passage of carbon black particles through sieve-plate pores of *Yucca* by E.M. (TAMMES and IE, 1971)
16. Protracted translocation through *Cucurbita* petiole despite 15 cm anaerobic section. (SIJ and SWANSON, 1973)
17. Inhibition of translocation partial by chilling: due to blockage not metabolic pumps. (GIAQUINTA and GEIGER, 1973)
18. Passage of carbon black through *Heracleum* sieve plates by microinjection. (BARCLAY and FENSOM, 1973)
19. In small plants (*Ricinus*) a steep concentration gradient in phloem is concealed in leaves and roots. (MILBURN, 1974)

itself. If the sealing process occurs rapidly only a little exudate escapes from the initial cut, collecting from two directions. Similar successive cuts collect from only one direction and produce about half the initial amount of sap, especially if the cuts are not made too rapidly so that the slight loss in turgor can be restored. If however the sealing processes are quite sluggish, the initial cut seems to drain the entire system. Only trivial amounts of sap can be collected from successive cuts, especially if they are made in rapid succession. In this latter case it is apparent that the turgor of the sieve-tube system has been drained by the initial cut because slight pressure applied some distance from an incision will induce further exudation, showing that exudation has been curtailed by loss of turgor and not the operation of a sealing system. *Fraxinus americana, Ricinus communis* and *Cucurbita* spp. can all provide ideal material for the latter type of experiment, also *Macrocystis pyrifera* in which conduction occurs through trumpet hyphae. This latter experiment shows directly that exudation must occur by pressure flow and that turgor pressure can provide the driving force.

Despite the fact that the above demonstrations contribute a considerable body of circumstantial evidence supporting the pressure-flow mechanism, objections can still legitimately be made on the basis of quantitative experimentation. This will be examined below.

E. Quantitative Studies on Phloem Transport

From the preceding section, it is apparent that the stage has been reached when simple demonstrations and experiments, which may be open to differing interpretations, are insufficient to settle the debate on mechanism. Instead, we must try to quantify the parameters to test the model more exhaustively. Unfortunately, we are not in a position to measure all of the parameters precisely and must utilize what information we have from scattered sources.

Ideally, we should be able to collate information on sieve-tube transport in much the same way as xylem transport (DAINTY, 1969). This simple approach is complicated by the fact that sieve tubes apparently lose their capacity to conduct, due to plugging, when they are severed or disturbed. The fact that sieve plates are the accepted site of plugging has lead to extensive speculation regarding the capacity of sieve-plate pores to transmit the necessary amounts of phloem sap (see WEATHERLEY and JOHNSON, 1968, and CRAFTS and CRISP, 1971 for somewhat divergent viewpoints). At the microscopic and submicroscopic scale, the uncertainty concerning sieve-plate pore dimensions, their statistical frequency and the legitimacy of the Poiseuille equation, which is normally used to calculate flow rates, all add uncertainty to any conclusions derived. Instead of this treatment, it is proposed to concentrate on conductivity of whole sieve tubes.

According to the pressure-flow model, transport through the phloem sieve tubes can be described completely if the hydraulic conductivity is measured and compared with the known performance of sieve tubes, expressed by dry weight increase in terms of specific mass transfer data. Thus for flow through the sieve tubes:

$$L \quad = \quad J_V \quad \div \quad \Delta P/l$$

Hydraulic conductivity $cm^2\,s^{-1}\,bar^{-1}$	=	Rate of Volume flow $cm^3\,cm^{-2}\,s^{-1}$	÷	Pressure gradient per cm $bar\,cm^{-1}$

where J_V is the volume flow of sap V through channels of known crossection A in time t and the pressure gradient is expressed cm^{-1}. This formula is closely analogous to Ohm's law expressed as $1/R = I/E$ and has been simplified by omitting the effect of sap viscosity, here assumed to be unity. Using this formula, we can attempt to measure L from J_V and $\Delta P/l$ Measurements of the known increase in dry matter of a sink in unit time through sieve tubes of known crossection, thus

	SMT	=	J_V	$\times$	c
	Specific mass transfer	=	Rate of volume flow	$\times$	Sap concentration
	$\mathrm{g\,cm^{-2}\,s^{-1}}$	=	$\mathrm{cm^3\,cm^{-2}\,s^{-1}}$	$\times$	$\mathrm{g\,cm^{-3}}$
Hence:	L	=	SMT	$\div$	$(c \times \Delta P/l)$

giving an independent check. Though we cannot be certain of some parameters, such as $\Delta P/l$, it is fortunately common to both equations and so does not significantly alter the comparison.

I. The Influence of Water Potential

Clear responses to changes in water balance were obtained in studies of aphid stylet exudations from *Salix* phloem (WEATHERLEY et al., 1959). Positive xylem-sap pressure enhanced flow and osmotic solutions in the xylem depressed the rate of exudation. Similar studies on exudation from *Ricinus* shoots (HALL and MILBURN, 1973) showed that exudation rates could be controlled markedly by regulating the supply attributable to the availability of water and for this reason many 'toddy tappers' collect only at night. Recently a *Phoenix* palm used for phloem-sap collection by night continued to drip sap until the late morning when flow stopped (11 a.m. November 1972, Calcutta), apparently due to a reduction in turgor pressure from an adverse water balance rather than phloem sealing (personal observation). These experimental observations illustrate an osmotic response in phloem transport.

However, it is well documented that many plants can exude sap after wilting (Fig. 6). Also aphids, which depend to some extent on favorable phloem-sap pressures to feed, do so but at a reduced rate when their host plants wilt. Exudate is usually more concentrated during water stress, occasionally extremely so (50%, WEATHERLEY et al., 1959). These changes may be secondary through continued solute loading after sink uptake is reduced by water stress.

It is unfortunate that xylem water potentials have not been measured in more studies of phloem transport. In excised tissues e.g. *Yucca* inflorescences, standing in water, the water potential is probably almost zero. In small plants e.g. *Ricinus*, xylem tensions are normally 5 ± 2 bars when plants are well watered and it is unlikely that the water potential gradient is critical under constant laboratory conditions. However, in plants under changing diurnal conditions or in tall trees, the xylem-sap tensions and hence the water potential which must be overcome by an osmotic system, may become significant. The real situation seems even more complex, however, for where it might be expected that a reduced xylem-sap tension at night should dilute the phloem exudate, HUBER et al. (1937) and ZIEGLER (1956) found that at night the solute concentration increases. The explanation seems likely to be connected with water stress effects on "source and sink" (see Concentration Gradients below). Further work on this phenomenon is urgently needed to find out why the water potential apparently exerts so little effect.

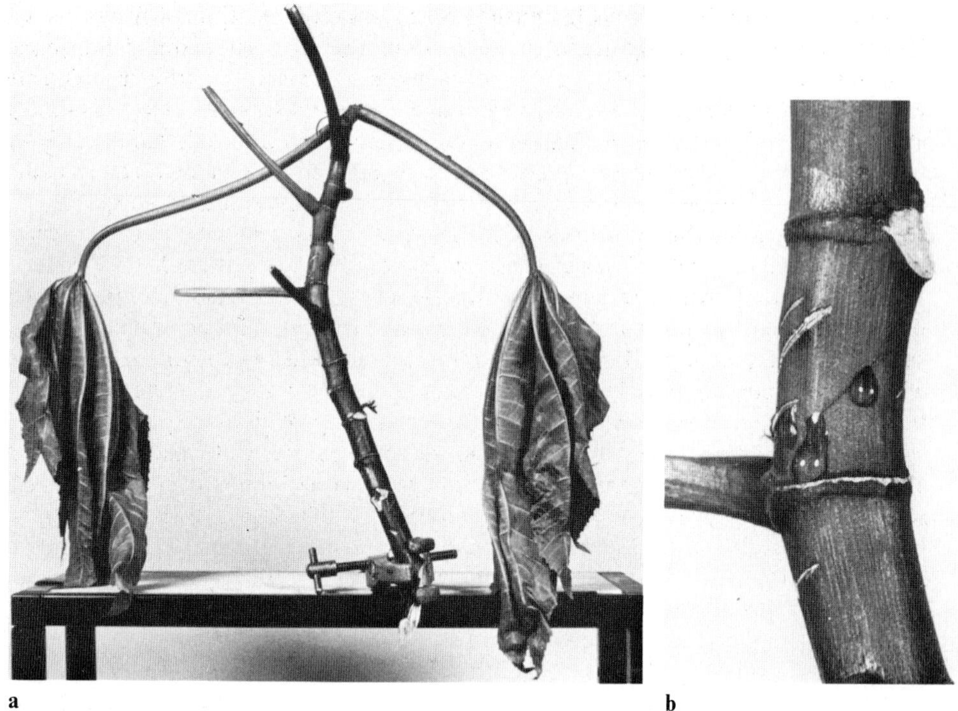

Fig. 6a and b. A *Ricinus* shoot severed from the roots has lost water until wilting is severe (a). Nevertheless if incisions are made in the stem, they exude freely showing that the phloem sieve tubes have not lost their turgor and are still pressurized to a remarkable extent (b)

Theoretically, if the xylem-sap tension could be increased to the point at which sieve-tube turgor reached incipient wilting (exudation zero) it should be possible to measure the opposing xylem-sap tension so that under normal water regimes the phloem turgor could be calculated by subtraction thus:
Sieve-tube Turgor-pressure P=Sap Osmotic potential π−Xylem water potential Ψ bars. Unfortunately, at least in *Ricinus*, exudation continues beyond wilting point when xylem sap has cavitated extensively (MILBURN, 1975). Pressure bomb measurements of xylem-sap tensions become less valid under such conditions.

II. Determination of Sieve-Tube Turgor Pressure *P* and Gradients $\Delta P/l$

1. Direct Measurement of Turgor *P*

MITTLER (1957) applied the Poiseuille equation to sap flow through a severed aphid stylet (1–2 μl h^{-1}) which tapers from 2 μm diameter down to 1 μm at the tip. He calculated that 20–40 atm would be required to produce such flow in *Salix*. Unfortunately, the technique has not been extended. Aphid stylets are not ideal tubes and wider artificial tubes would allow turgor reduction through exudation to a significant extent.

Ordinary hypodermic needles pushed into bark become choked immediately. HAMMEL (1968) ingeniously modified the tip to reduce blockage and fitted a simple compressed-bubble manometer. Sieve-tube turgor of *Quercus rubra* measurements were somewhat variable. The highest value recorded was 20.4 bars. Hammel attempted to measure the pressure gradient and his readings indicate a value of 0.44 bar m^{-1} (see above) in reasonable agreement with those indicated from the concentration gradient (see below). However, it should be noted that the experiments were conducted late in the season (Oct., Nov.) and might well have been greater in summer and especially at night as a single set of readings indicated.

Similar experiments with a modification of HAMMEL's technique were performed recently (1973, 1974 unpublished) on *Fraxinus americana*. Turgor pressures up to 19.4 bars were measured. It was difficult to decide the extent of invisible leakage with the technique, visible leakage was more serious in younger tissues higher up the tree. Leakage was indicated also by the tendency of liquid to recede in the capillary after reaching peak compression. Similar attempts were made by TAMMES (1952) on *Arenga* inflorescence stalks and by MILBURN (unpublished) in *Ricinus* stems. Leakage proved a problem after pressures of a few bars had developed in both cases.

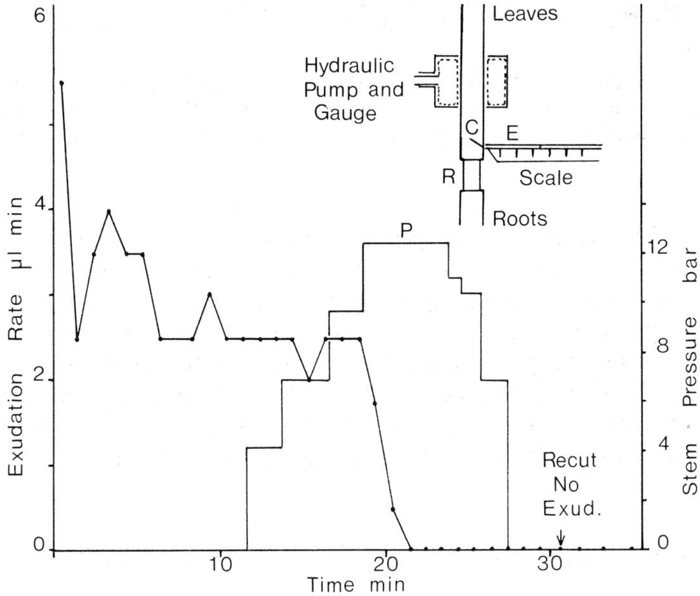

Fig. 7. An experiment to measure the surface pressure applied to a newly ringed *R* stem to curtail exudation *E* from cut *C*. The pressure-cuff (inset) consists of a rubber sleeve inside a metal jacket connected to a pump and gauge. When the exudation rate is approximately constant, the pressure *P* is increased in stages until flow stops. Since exudation rate could have stopped by sealing, it is necessary to recut above *C* to show that the pressure cuff has indeed stopped the flow. Xylem tension 3 bars. Exudate osmotic potential was −13 bars. Flow recovers and exudation occurs after a few hours if recut. The following day the pressure *P* required to stop flow in the same ringed stem had increased. Over 12 bars were needed to reduce flow and even 17 bars did not stop flow completely.

A new technique under test for direct sap-pressure measurements is the hydraulic pressure-cuff. A similar, more delicate, system is used to measure human blood-pressure (c. 0.1 bars). Its application to plants is difficult because a sleeve round the phloem must be capable of pressurization until the sieve-tube turgor is overcome (c. 10–25 bars) and the sieve tubes are compressed. It can be applied only to plants without extensive fibrous protection round the sieve tubes. A typical result is shown in Fig. 7. Exudation from a cut in a *Ricinus* stem was monitored as compression was increased. Pressures required to stop exudation were of the order 10–20 bar showing that similar pressures must be applied manually during massage experiments to be effective (MILBURN, 1971). Apparently exudation cannot be stopped sharply by a slow steady increase in pressure. The effect is often progressive as if conducting sieve tubes differ in turgor pressure as suggested by HAMMEL (1968). These preliminary experiments support sap concentration studies which indicate that high pressure gradients may well operate in plants around 0.5 m tall. This view contrasts with the concentration data for trees indicating physiological dissimilarity (MILBURN, 1974).

Regrettably HAMMEL's experiments (1968), which represent the most comprehensive of their type, with an admirably direct approach, reveal inconsistencies which must demand caution in interpreting his results. (For example, on October 28 the osmotic pressure of sieve-tube sap was c. 25 bars, xylem tension in leaves nearby was 25.3 bars, yet sieve-tube turgor pressures ranged from 12 to 16.9 bars!). We need more extensive documentation of this type, possibly with systems which have been simplified by removal of superfluous organs by surgery, before we can be sure how turgor pressure gradients really operate under natural conditions.

2. Concentration Gradients in Sieve Tubes

Indirect measurements of pressure gradients $\Delta P/l$ can be obtained by studying sap concentration in sieve tubes which generally decrease from leaves towards the root "sink". However, the assumption must be made that water is freely available to sieve tubes across the semi-permeable membrane system. This assumption is at least partially justified by experiments demonstrating the effect of water potential changes on sieve-tube transport. It would appear that xylem tensions may be subtracted from the osmotic pressure to give turgor pressure readings and hence gradients. ZIMMERMANN (1961) showed for *Fraxinus* trees that during exudation the sap becomes diluted until the rate of water influx matches the loading rate for solutes. Severe difficulties arise in the case of *Ricinus,* an herbaceous plant, in which solute loading and unloading appear to be more vigorous (MILBURN, 1974). Thus instead of a dilution curve, a source has the capacity to increase both sap concentration and exudation rate to a high steady plateau. The assumption that solute concentrations correspond to the development of hydrostatic pressure only if the water flux exceeds that of solutes seems inapplicable in this case.

On the grounds outlined above, solute-concentration gradients in trees have been considered as providing a reasonable indication of pressure gradients. Few have calibrated the refractometers used in some determinations with actual osmotic pressure measurements on sap. There are more serious problems, however, because it was found that the sap concentration increases at night when xylem-sap tensions fall, but falls by day when increasing xylem sap tensions should increase the concentration. Additionally, the concentration gradients steepen by night (HUBER et al., 1937; ZIEGLER, 1956). An increase in pressure by night would not be surprising, but the concentration of solutes should decrease. There seem two main possibilities: (1) loading from storage may increase by night and (2) the demands of the root-growth sink increase by night as an enhanced water supply promotes growth which increases the flow rate in the sieve tubes. The net effect is a concentration wave, transported through the phloem faster than it can be removed, which passes down the trunk.

The refractometry determinations of HUBER et al. (1937) indicated a solute gradient of 0.2 bar m^{-1} by day and 0.3 bar m^{-1} by night which corresponds with ZIMMERMANN's (1971) figure of 0.25 bar m^{-1} for tall trees. HAMMEL (1968) from 49 remarkably consistent cryoscopic determinations on exudate from a large *Quercus* tree found a gradient of 0.35 bar m^{-1} both night and day. However, DIXON (1933) found much steeper gradients in a young *Fraxinus* tree. Nine cryoscopic determinations gave gradients averaging 5.5 bar m^{-1}. Possibly the gradients are different within large and small trees, but the discrepancies are too great to be ignored. In calculations below a figure of 0.5 bar m^{-1} will be adopted based on the likelihood that underestimation is quite probable due to local dilution and the role of the tree trunk as a sink.

In smaller plants like *Ricinus*, stem concentration gradients seem to be much steeper than in trees (see also CRAFTS, 1932) and the sap is more concentrated than might be expected. Using ring-massage or bark-ringing, MILBURN (1974) showed that sieve tubes in stems could be sampled quite locally at intervals from roots to leaves. Solute gradients in the stem were only slight. In contrast, exudation from stem tissues near roots or leaves changed as sap was drawn from them during

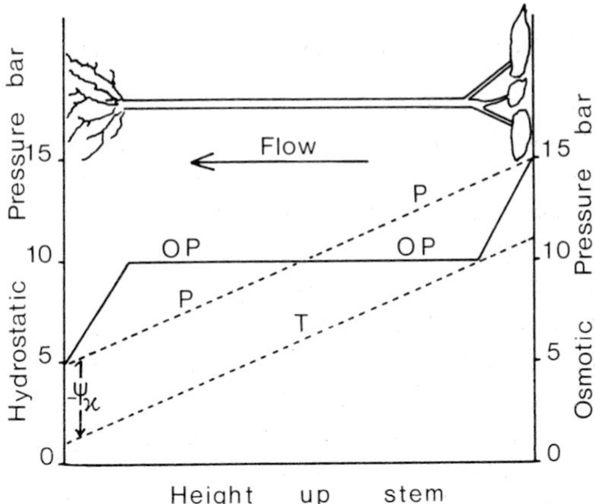

Fig. 8. Diagram to illustrate the apparent pressure gradient in *Ricinus* measurements of the osmotic potential *OP* of exudate samples. Solute concentrations seem to change more rapidly in leaves (source) and roots (sink) than in the intervening stem. The hydrostatic pressure is probably governed by solute concentration differences in source and sink to give the conjectured gradient of hydrostatic pressure *P*. Since xylem sap is under tension (water potential $-\Psi_x$) the turgor gradient *T* in the sieve tubes parallels but is lower than *P*. Though sap samples from the stem would indicate a negligible value, the overall driving gradient *P* is probably around 10 bars when the resistance to flow is very considerable. When the longitudinal hydraulic conductivity of phloem increases, flow increases and the gradients of *P* and *T* become much flatter. Thus during rapid flow the osmotic pressure exceeds the turgor pressure at the source and conversely the turgor pressure exceeds the osmotic pressure at the sink

exudation. Exudate samples drawn from roots rapidly became diluted, whilst sap drawn from leaves increased in concentration to a plateau and exudation continued at a high rate for a long time. Events in these plants seem to be dominated by changes at source and sink (see Fig. 8). The non-linear concentration gradients imply that high pressures of the order of 10 bars are involved for a small plant 0.5 m tall; further evidence for this finding is indicated by the pressure-cuff studies described above. It remains to be seen to what extent the problems in interpreting tree concentration gradients are related to those in *Ricinus*.

Ultimately, the only way to be sure that solute concentrations correspond to hydrostatic pressures is to measure the pressure directly. Any readings would have to be corrected for the xylem water-potential differences at source and sink. In a dynamic flow system the hydraulic conductivity for water through the semi-permeable membrane system must also be taken into account.

III. Sieve-Tube Hydraulic Conductivity (*L*) from Specific Mass Transfer (SMT)

The capacity of phloem to transfer dry matter can be measured accurately from the increase in dry weight of plant organs (fruits, stems, roots) within a known time. To find the specific mass transfer, it is necessary to know in addition the area of cross section of the pathway. This latter measurement is a weak link in the determination of specific mass transfer (SMT). The common assumption that sieve tubes occupy 20% of the phloem has been rightly questioned by LAWTON (1972), CANNY (1973) and others and it will be assumed for simplicity that the figure is 50%. Nevertheless, the indications are that the method, initiated by DIXON and BALL (1922), is reliable and can provide a useful reference standard for other measurements. SMT data for whole phloem have been compiled by CANNY (1973 and Chapter 15) from which the highest values have been taken as a basis for sieve-tube performance using the equation above. Additional assumptions made are that pressure gradients in small plants are around 10 bars ($\Delta P/l = 0.2$ bar cm^{-1}) as indicated for *Ricinus* seedlings (MILBURN, 1972b, 1974) whereas in trees the pressure gradient is assumed to be 0.5 bars per m ($\Delta P/l = 0.005$ bar cm^{-1}), values range from 0.2–8.9 bar m^{-1} (see MILBURN, 1974). It is also necessary to assume that the sieve-tube pathway is roughly uniform between source and sink (c. the plant stature), a measurement seldom recorded. The value for $\Delta P/l$ is somewhat greater than that (0.002 bar cm^{-1}) proposed by ZIMMERMANN (1969b), but it seems possible that pressure gradients may have been underestimated by taking diurnal rather than nocturnal measurements of sap concentrations (see above).

It may be observed in Table 2 that the hydraulic conductivity requirements are halved if the sap concentrations, or the pressure gradients, are doubled. If, however, sieve tubes occupy 25% of the "total phloem" the estimated hydraulic conductivity must be doubled. It goes without saying that in the future, we must make measurements to replace the tentative assumed values. Nevertheless, since the same assumptions apply to the comparative data, the importance of very accurate estimates is reduced. It will be observed that the pressure gradients believed to apply to small plants is much greater than those accepted for trees, a point which needs further substantiation.

Table 2. Longitudinal hydraulic conductivity L of sieve tubes necessary to account for mass-transfer measurements in (i) herbaceous plants and (ii) trees. *Assumptions*: sieve tubes occupy 50% of phloem in cross-section*, solution transported is 20% (0.2 g cm^{-3}) in trees and 10% (0.1 g cm^{-3}) in herbs under an overall pressure gradient of 10 bars. Trees are assumed 20 m tall: herbaceous plants 0.5 m. (*Except for *Beta* where 29% was measured)

Worker(s) and Year	Test Species	Mass Transfer (g day^{-1})	Phloem Trans. Sect. ($cm^2 \times 10^{-2}$)	SMT (Sieve tubes) (g h^{-1} cm^{-2})	Pressure Gradient $\Delta P/l$ (bar cm^{-1})	Hydraulic Conductivity L (cm^2 bar^{-1} s^{-1})
Herbaceous plants						
DIXON and BALL (1922)	*Solanum tub.*	0.50	0.422	9.87	0.200	0.137
CRAFTS (1933)	*Solanum tub.*	0.89 (max)	1.76	4.20	0.200	0.058
MASON and LEWIN (1926)	*Dioscorea al.*	6.10	5.7	8.91	0.200	0.123
GEIGER et. al. (1969)	*Beta vulg.*	—	—	4.80	0.200	0.067
Trees						
MÜNCH (1930)	*Acer pseudopl.*	39.91	26.3	12.64	0.005	3.514
MÜNCH (1930)	*Quercus rub.*	72.75	67.4	8.99	0.005	2.500
MÜNCH (1930)	*Tilia parvifl.*	31.91	45.5	5.84	0.005	1.622

IV. Sieve-Tube Hydraulic Conductivity (L) from Sap Velocity

According to MÜNCH's model, the velocity of phloem-sap transport is an important parameter which should be easy to determine. In practice, it becomes meaningless rather easily (see ZIMMERMANN, 1971). Sieve tubes behave independently and a velocity measurement in one tube is no indication of flow rates in adjacent tubes. Workers have tended to measure the more spectacular "approximate peak velocity" i.e. the time an applied tracer front can first be detected some distance from the point of application. This parameter, on account of the paraboloid flow profile, is useless for quantitative studies. Values are tabulated by CRAFTS and CRISP (1971) which commonly range 70–100 cm h^{-1}, but may be considerably greater, especially for short durations.

The preferred parameter is therefore the "average velocity" i.e. the mean flow rate of a column of sap through the sieve tubes concerned. Unfortunately, any solute, labeled or unlabeled, is liable to be exchanged or removed *en route* as commonly indicated by autoradiography so that the use of solute detection can be very misleading. An alternative promising method depends on timing the transmission of warmed phloem sap. ZIEGLER and VIEWIG (1961) used this heat-pulse technique on displaced *Heracleum* phloem and obtained average velocities of $50 \pm 20\,\mathrm{cm\,h^{-1}}$. Bidirectional flow would produce an underestimation.

Another method is to follow a "ratio wave" of phloem sugars, which is produced during loading as sap passes down the phloem (ZIMMERMANN, 1969a). These are probably the most accurate determinations to date and ranged 30–70 cm h^{-1}. Normally, the study of flow rates requires anatomical studies to determine the sieve-tube cross-sectional area. This method is admirably free from this requirement for determination of SMT thus:

SMT	=	c	×	$\bar{v}$
Specific mass transfer $\mathrm{g\,h^{-1}\,cm^{-2}}$	=	Sap concentration $\mathrm{g\,cm^{-3}}$	×	Average velocity $\mathrm{cm\,h^{-1}}$

Then, since the Volume flux J_v is numerically equal to Average velocity $\bar{v}$, for sieve tubes

L	=	$\bar{v}$	÷	ΔP
$\mathrm{cm^2\,s^{-1}\,bar^{-1}}$		$\mathrm{cm\,s^{-1}}$		$\mathrm{bar\,cm^{-1}}$

These equations have been used in Table 3 using data from the experiments described above. In the case of ZIMMERMANN's (1969a) data, his own assumptions for maximum and minimum values of SMT are compared with the assumptions applied in the previous section and his mean average velocity. It is quite clear that L hydraulic conductivity of sieve tubes measured by this method is very close to the required figures for herbaceous plants and trees shown in Table 2.

Table 3. Longitudinal hydraulic conductivity L of sieve tubes derived from measurements of sap movement as mean velocity using heat pulse and ratio wave detection. The same assumptions are applied as in Table 2 except where actual measurements are indicated*

Plant Type	Test Species	Worker(s) and Year	Mean Velocity ($\mathrm{cm\,h^{-3}}$)	Sap Conc. ($\mathrm{g\,cm^{-3}}$)	SMT Sieve tubes ($\mathrm{g\,cm^{-2}\,h^{-1}}$)	Pressure Gradient $\Delta P/l$ ($\mathrm{bar\,cm^{-1}}$)	Hydraulic Conductivity L ($\mathrm{cm^2\,bar^{-1}\,sec^{-1}}$)
Herbaceous plant	*Heracleum mant.*	ZIEGLER and VIEWEG (1961)	50(±20) mean	0.10	5.0	0.20	0.069
Tree	*Fraxinus amer.*	ZIMMERMANN (1969a)	30 min.	0.20*	6.0	0.002*	4.17
	Fraxinus amer.	ZIMMERMANN (1969a)	70 max.	0.25*	17.5	0.002*	9.72
(Standard assumptions)	*Fraxinus amer.*	ZIMMERMANN (1969a)	50 mean	0.20	10.0	0.005	2.78

V. Sieve-Tube Hydraulic Conductivity (L) by Volume Transfer V

TYREE and FENSOM (1970) describe attempts to measure L of isolated strands of phloem from *Heracleum* petioles in an electro-osmometer. The highest value they found (see Table 4) is very low, which is hardly surprising considering the strands were isolated over an hour for the measurement and plugging seems inevitable, a danger they freely admit. There is also a serious danger of flow through leakage rather than longitudinal transmission.

Table 4. Longitudinal hydraulic conductivity L for sieve tubes by volume transfer through severed phloem of herbaceous plants and an arborescent monocotyledon. Assumptions used are the same as in Table 2 (sieve tubes occupy 50% phloem, sap transported is 10% w/v, overall pressure gradient is 10 bars). *Arenga* is assumed to be 10 m *Yucca* 2 m, and *Heracleum* and *Ricinus* 0.5 m between "source" and "sink"

Plant Type	Test Species	Worker(s) and Year	Volume flow (μl)	Duration flow (sec)	Phloem Trans. Sect. ($cm^2 \times 10^{-2}$)	SMT Sieve tubes ($g\ cm^{-2}\ h^{-1}$)	Hydraulic Conductivity L ($cm^2\ bar^{-1}\ sec^{-1}$)
Herbaceous plants	*Heracleum mant.*	TYREE and FENSON (1970)	—	—	Est. 20%	—	0.016(max)
	Ricinus comm.	MILBURN (1972a)	12	60	0.4	15.3	0.25
	Yucca flacc. (infl.)	VAN DIE and TAMMES (1966)	11×10^2	3,600	2.5	6.9	0.12
Trees	*Arenga pinn. (infl.)*	TAMMES (1952)	24×10^4	3,600	34	98.8	19.61

A direct measurement of volume transfer has been made on *Arenga* palm inflorescence by TAMMES (1952). Exudation was steady and prolonged providing the inflorescence was sliced daily and the cross-sectional area of sieve tubes was measured directly. The system is probably somewhat artificial in that it is unlikely that a natural "sink" could utilize 240 ml of sap per hour and the phloem may well have become abnormally conductive. Unfortunately, we have not measured the pressure gradient in palms (it is estimated as for a tree) and the vascular system may change in conducting capacity in the trunk where anastomoses occur. But this experiment, however interpreted, gives a remarkable quantitative demonstration of the capacity of sieve tubes to translocate by hydraulic conduction. Calculations for *Arenga* and also *Yucca* hydraulic conductivity are included in Table 4.

A somewhat different technique can be used to determine the hydraulic conductivity of phloem from exudation for a relatively short duration. When sieve tubes are incised, the internal turgor pressure is released and sealing processes begin. If however, sufficiently accurate readings can be obtained one can extrapolate back to zero time when the full turgor pressure provides the driving force and sealing of the wound is zero. Such an experiment (described by MILBURN, 1972a) is analyzed in this way. The bark had been subjected to massage pretreatment, but very similar results have been obtained subsequently with unmassaged *Ricinus* stems also. The phloem cross-section was measured and the proportion of sieve tubes was estimated from separate experiments. The turgor pressure was around 10 bars from micro-manometer pressure-cuff studies (unpublished) and concentration gradient studies (Milburn, 1974) so that the hydraulic conductivity for unidirectional transport could be measured (Table 4).

It can be seen that using the same assumption in Table 4, the L for sieve tubes is remarkably close to the necessary magnitudes as in Table 2, and those found independently by velocity measurements in Table 3. There seems no reason to believe that sieve tubes exude abnormally due to "blowing clear" the sieve-plate pores during exudation as some have suggested. *Arenga* is a possible exception but it will be recalled that the conduction of sap is not due to a catastrophic release, but built-up progressively by skillful slicing. Clearly within the terms of present experimental error, there is no necessity to invoke special metabolic pumping devices to enhance translocation through sieve tubes. In short, sieve plates are probably porous, as glimpsed by scanning electron-microscopy (Milburn and Sprent, in prep.).

F. Summary

The common assumption that Münch's osmotic pressure-flow model can be applied to the whole of the phloem, seems, except under special circumstances, unsatisfactory. Since sieve tubes can behave independently, the model can be applied quite ligitimately on an individual basis only. However, under certain circumstances, it is most likely that they act in unison e.g. when supplying a powerful sink or during exudation. In the intact condition, it is quite likely that bidirectional transport may operate so that phloem has a capacity to circulate materials, like blood flow in animals. A large number of experimental demonstrations give massive support for the operation of a pressure-flow mechanism in sieve tubes: these have been summarized. Many apparent discrepancies cited against the osmotic mechanism originate from an oversimplified application of Münch's model to whole plants.

Osmotic pressure flow requires open sieve-plate pores for normal operation; it is supposed that their sealing is a complex protective device. We are unlikely to prove the extent to which the pores are open *in vivo* until we can control the sealing mechanisms. It is proposed, therefore, that the best way forward is to attempt to quantify the parameters of the transport system as comprehensively as possible. Only then will it be possible to say the extent to which an additional driving mechanism utilizing metabolic energy, must be postulated. From the scanty information we possess, it seems unlikely that active pumping through sieve-elements is necessary for the known translocation requirements.

Experimental data need to be comprehensive so that we can determine the hydraulic conductivity of phloem as a whole tissue and then relate this to the conditions within the sieve tubes concerned. Control over environmental fluctuations and a reduction of plant complexity by surgery may well be necessary to improve the accuracy of measurements. In the field, the ideal time to study phloem transport is probably at night. Our techniques for measurement of such parameters as pressure can be refined considerably. The use of data on sap concentration as synonymous with the development of hydrostatic pressure by osmosis must be avoided unless water potentials and fluxes are known.

Calculations are presented, not because they are exact or even the best possible estimates, but rather to indicate approximately the values we may expect when further measurements, so urgently needed, are made. We are fortunate in having differing techniques at our disposal to check experimental measurements. Only when the systems which can be investigated readily are understood can the situation in more difficult plants be fully appreciated. This review points the way to resolving wide divergences of opinion by concentrating on physiological measurements where there seems to be no deadlock.

References

AIKMAN, D.P., ANDERSON, W.P.: A quantitative investigation of a peristaltic model for phloem translocation. Ann. Botany N.S. **35**, 761–772 (1971).

ANDERSON, R., CRONSHAW, J.: Sieve-element pores in *Nicotiana*. J. Ultrastruct. Res. **32**, 458–471 (1970).

ANTOSZEWSKI, R., KAMINSKA, M.K., DZIECIOL, U.: Translocation profile of assimilates in the strawberry petiole. Trans. 3rd Symp. Accumulation and Translocation: Series E No. 3, Warsaw 31–40 (1973).

BARCLAY, G.F., FENSOM, D.S.: Passage of carbon black through sieve plates of unexcised *Heracleum sphondylium* after microinjection. Acta Botan. Neerl. **22**, 228–232 (1973).

BENNETT, C.W.: Correlation between movement of the curly-top virus and translocation of food in tobacco and sugar beet. J. Agr. Res. **54**, 479–502 (1937).

BIDDULPH, O.: Mechanisms of translocation of plant metabolites, p. 143–164 (1969).

BIDWELL, R.G.S.: A possible mechanism for the control of photoassimilate translocation. Trans. 3rd Symp. Accumulation and Translocation. Series E No. 3, Warsaw 77–89 (1973).

BOSE, J.C.: Plants and their autographs. London: Longmans, Green and Co. 1947.

BROWN, C.L.: Discussion: Phloem transport and its relation to growth. In: The formation of wood in forest trees. p. 300 (ed. M.H. ZIMMERMANN). New York: Academic Press 1964.

CANNY, M.J.: Phloem translocation. London: Cambridge Univ. Press 1973.

CATALDO, D.A., CHRISTY, A.L., COULSON, C.L., FERRIER, J.M.: Phloem transport of THO in *Beta vulgaris*. Plant Physiol. **49**, 690–695 (1972).

CHOI, I.C., ARONOFF, S.: Photosynthate transport using tritiated water. Plant Physiol. **41**, 1119–1129 (1966).

CHRISTY, A.L., FERRIER, J.M.: A mathematical treatment of MÜNCH's pressure-flow hypothesis of phloem transport. Plant Physiol. **52**, 531–538 (1973).

CRAFTS, A.S.: Phloem anatomy, exudation, and transport of organic nutrients in cucurbits. Plant Physiol. **7**, 183–225 (1932).

CRAFTS, A.S.: Sieve-tube structure and translocation in the potato. Plant Physiol. **8**, 81–104 (1933).

CRAFTS, A.S., CRISP, C.E.: Phloem transport in plants. San Francisco: Freeman 1971.

DAINTY, J.: The water relations of plants. In: physiology of plant growth and development (ed. M.B. WILKINS). Maidenhead, England: McGraw Hill 1969.

DIAMOND, J.M.: The mechanism of isotonic water absorption and secretion. Symp. Soc. Exptl. Biol. Cambridge 329–347 (1965)

DIXON, H.H.: Bast Sap. Scient. Proc. Roy. Dublin Soc. **20**, 487–494 (1933).

DIXON, H.H., BALL, N.G.: Transport of organic substances in plants. Nature **109**, 236–237 (1922).

DIXON, H.H., GIBBON, M.W.: Bast-sap in plants. Nature **130**, 661 (1932).

ESAU, K: The phloem. Encyclopedia of plant anatomy, vol. 2. Berlin-Stuttgart: Gebrüder Borntraeger 1969.
ESCHRICH, W., EVERT, R.F., YOUNG, J.H.: Solution flow in tubular semipermeable membranes. Planta **107**, 279–300 (1972).
FREY-WYSSLING, A.: Die Stoffausscheidungen der höheren Pflanzen. 378 p. Berlin: Springer 1935.
GEIGER, D.R., SAUNDERS, M.A., CATALDO, D.A.: Translocation and accumulation of translocate in the sugar beet petiole. Plant Physiol. **44**, 1657–1665 (1969).
GIAQUINTA, R.T., GEIGER, D.R.: Mechanism of inhibition of translocation by localized chilling. Plant Physiol. **51**, 372–377 (1973).
HALES, S.: Vegetable staticks. Oldbourne Bk. London (1727), reprinted 1967.
HALL, S.M., MILBURN, J.A.: Phloem transport in *Ricinus*. Its dependence on the water balance of the tissues. Planta **109**, 1–10 (1973).
HAMMEL, H.T.: Measurement of turgor pressure and its gradient in the phloem of oak. Plant Physiol. **43**, 1042–1048 (1968).
HARTIG, T.: Vergleichende Untersuchungen über die Organisation des Stammes der einheimischen Waldbäume. Jahresber. Fortschr. Forstwiss. u. forstl. Naturk. **1**, 125–168 (1837).
HARTIG, T.: Beiträge zur physiologischen Forstbotanik. Allgem. Forst- u. Jagdztg. **36**, 257–261 (1860).
HARVEY, W.: Exercitatis de motu cordis et sanguinis. Frankfort-on-Main (1628).
HODGE, W.H.: Toddy collection in Ceylon. Principes. J. Palm Soc. (Miami) **7**, 70–79 (1963).
HUBER, B., SCHMIDT, E., JAHNEL, H.: Untersuchungen über den Assimilatstrom. Tharandt. Forstl. Jahrb. **88**, 1017–1050 (1937).
KENNEDY, J.S., MITTLER, T.E.: A method of obtaining phloem sap *via* the mouth parts of aphids. Nature **171**, 528 (1953).
KING, R.W., ZEEVART, J.A.D.: Enhancement of phloem exudation from cut petioles by chelating agents. Plant Physiol. **53**, 96–103 (1974).
LANG, A.: A working model of a sieve tube. J. Exptl. Botany **24**, 896–904 (1973).
LAWTON, J.R.: Seasonal variation in the secondary phloem of some forest trees from Nigeria. New Phytol. **71**, 335–348 (1972).
LÜTTGE, U.: Structure and function of plant glands. Ann. Rev. Plant Physiol. **22**, 23–44 (1971).
MACROBBIE, E.A.: Phloem translocation. Biol. Rev. **46**, 429–481 (1971).
MASON, T.G., LEWIN, C.T.: On the rate of carbohydrate transport in the greater yam *Dioscorea alata*. Proc. Roy. Irish Acad. **18**, 203–205 (1926).
MASON, T.G., MASKELL, E.J.: Studies on the transport of carbohydrates in the cotton plant. I. A study of diurnal variation in the carbohydrates of leaf, bark and wood, and of the effects of ringing. Ann. Botany (London) **42**, 189–253 (1928).
MASON, T.G., MASKELL, E.J., PHYLLIS, E.: Further studies in transport in the cotton plant. III. Concerning the independence of solute movement in the phloem. Ann. Botany (London) **50**, 23–58 (1936).
MILBURN, J.A.: Phloem exudation from castor bean: induction by massage. Planta **95**, 272–276 (1970).
MILBURN, J.A.: An analysis of the response in phloem exudation on application of massage to *Ricinus*. Planta **100**, 143–154 (1971).
MILBURN, J.A.: Phloem transport in *Ricinus*. Pestic. Sci. **3**, 653–665 (1972a).
MILBURN, J.A.: Phloem physiology and protective sealing mechanism. Nature **236**, 82 (1972b).
MILBURN, J.A.: Phloem transport in *Ricinus*: Concentration gradients between source and sink. Planta **117**, 303–319 (1974).
MILBURN, J.A.: Xylem and phloem transport in *Ricinus*. Johri Commemoration volume. Meerut, U.P., India: Sarita Prakashan (1975).
MILBURN, J.A., SPRENT, J.I.: Observations on conducting tissues of *Ricinus* by Scanning Electron-microscopy (SEM). (In prep.)
MITTLER, T.E.: Studies on the feeding and nutrition of *Tuberolachnus salignus* (Gmelin) *(Homoptera Aphididae)*. J. Exptl. Biol. **34**, 334–341 (1957).
MOHL, H. VON: Einige Andeutungen über den Bau des Bastes. Botan. Z. **13**, 873–881, 889–897 (1855). (Referred to in ESAU (1969) p. 12).
MOLOTOVSKY, G.K.: O pyty po proverke teorü Miunkha. Botan. J. U.S.S.R. **19**, 225–230 (1934).
MÜNCH, E.: Die Stoffbewegungen in der Pflanze. Jena: Fischer 1930.

NOEL, A.R.A.: The girdled tree. Botan. Rev. **36**, 162–195 (1970).

PEEL, A.J.: Further evidence for the relative immobility of water in sieve tubes of willow. Physiol. Plantarum **23**, 667–672 (1970).

PEEL, A.J., FIELD, R.J., COULSON, C.L., GARDNER, D.C.J.: Movement of water and solutes in sieve tubes of willow in response to puncture by aphid stylets. Physiol. Plantarum **22**, 768–775 (1969).

SIDDIQUI, A.W., SPANNER, D.C.: The state of the pores in functioning sieve plates. Planta **91**, 181–189 (1970).

SIJ, J.W., SWANSON, C.A.: Effect of petiole anoxia on phloem transport in squash. Plant Physiol. **51**, 368–371 (1973).

TAMMES, P.M.L.: Observations on the bleeding of palm trees. Extr. Rec. Trav. Neerl. **30**, 514–536 (1933).

TAMMES, P.M.L.: On the rate of translocation of the bleeding-sap in the fruit stalk of *Arenga*. Proc. Sect. Sci. Koninkl. Ned. Acad. Wetenschap. **55**, 141–143 (1952).

TAMMES, P.M.L., IE, T.S.: Studies on phloem exudation from *Yucca flaccida* flow. IX Passage of carbon black particles through sieve-plate pores of *Yucca*. Acta Botan. Neerl. **20**, 309–317 (1971).

TATE, J.: Methods and annual sequence of foraging by the sap sucker. The Auk. **90**, 840–856 (1973).

TYREE, M.T., FENSOM, D.S.: Some experimental and theoretical observations concerning mass flow in the vascular bundles of *Heracleum*. J. Exptl. Botany **21**, 304–324 (1970).

TYREE, M.T., ZIMMERMANN, M.H.: The theory and practice of measuring transport coefficients and sap flow in the xylem of red maple stems (*Acer rubrum*). J. Exptl. Botany **22**, 1–18 (1971).

VAN DIE, J., TAMMES, P.M.L.: Studies of phloem exudation from *Yucca flaccida* flow III Prolonged bleeding from isolated parts of the young inflorescence. Koninkl. Ned. Acad. Wetenschap. Proc., Ser. C **69**, 648–654 (1966).

WEATHERLEY, P.E.: Translocation in sieve tubes. Some thoughts on structure and mechanism. Physiol. Veget. **10**, 731–742 (1972).

WEATHERLEY, P.E., JOHNSON, R.P.C.: The form and function of the sieve tube: A problem in reconciliation. Int. Rev. Cytol. **24**, 149–192 (1968).

WEATHERLEY, P.E., PEEL, A.J., HILL, G.P.: The physiology of the sieve tube. Preliminary experiments using aphid mouth parts. J. Exptl. Botany **10**, 1–16 (1959).

WEEVERS, T., WESTERNBERG, J.: Versuche zur Prüfung der Münchschen Theorie der Stoffbewegungen in der Pflanze. Proc. Sec. Sci. Koninkl. Ned. Acad. Wetenschap. **34**, 1173–1178 (1931).

ZIEGLER, H.: Untersuchungen über die Leitung und Sekretion der Assimilate. Planta **47**, 447–500 (1956).

ZIEGLER, H., MITTLER, T.: Über den Zuckergehalt der Siebröhren- bzw. Siebzellensäfte von *Heracleum mantegazzianum* und *Picea abies* (L) Karst. Z. Naturforsch. **14**b, 278–281 (1959).

ZIEGLER, H., VIEWEG, G.H.: Der experimentelle Nachweis einer Massenströmung in Phloem von *Heracleum mantegazzianum* Somm. et Lev. Planta **56**, 402–415 (1961).

ZIMMERMANN, M.H.: Longitudinal and tangential movement within the sieve-tube system of white ash (*Fraxinus americana* L). Beih. Z. Schweiz. Forst. **30**, 289–300 (1960).

ZIMMERMANN, M.H.: Movement of organic substances in trees. Science **133**, 73–79 (1961).

ZIMMERMANN, M.H.: Translocation velocity and specific mass transfer in the sieve tubes of *Fraxinus americana* L. Planta **84**, 272–278 (1969a).

ZIMMERMANN, M.H.: Translocation of nutrients. In: Physiology of plant growth and development (ed. M.B. WILKINS). New York: McGraw Hill 1969b.

ZIMMERMANN, M.H.: Transport in the phloem. In: Trees, structure and function by ZIMMERMANN, M.H., and BROWN, C.L., p. 221–279. Berlin-Heidelberg-New York: Springer 1971.

ZIMMERMANN, M.H.: Long-distance transport (Conceptual developments in plant physiology, 1924–1974). Plant Physiol. **54**, 472–479 (1974).

15. Other Possible Mechanisms

D.S. FENSOM

A. Introduction

In this chapter three assumptions will be made. The first will be that we do not yet know everything about the structural details of living phloem, and that there are therefore conditions of fine structure which exist in the living, functioning state which are yet to be discovered. The second is that the knowledge about the actual movement of translocate, the shape of its front, the profile of its concentration pattern with time and tracer selection or distribution, all within a single sieve tube, are not fully elucidated. The third assumption is that each of the chief mechanisms advanced to account for translocation presents formidable difficulties (WEATHERLEY and JOHNSON, 1969; MACROBBIE, 1971; FENSOM, 1972; CANNY, 1973): the doubtful evidence of two-way trans-plate streaming at adequate rates in the case of the protoplasmic streaming hypothesis; the theoretical and experimental objections to electroosmosis; the problems of adequate pressure-driven flow in the presence of plasmatic filaments in plate pores and the difficulties over apparent metabolic control of movement in the case of pressure flow. These assumptions suggest that further study of the problem is desirable and further speculation about mechanism is quite proper. Indeed the results obtained on isolated phloem strands and by micro-injection of single sieve tubes (see Chapter 9) are so difficult to explain by any of these three mechanisms alone, that alternatives must be explored if this evidence is to be taken seriously.

Historically it is interesting to note that HALES in his Vegetable Statics (1738) thought that a circulatory arrangement existed in plants remotely similar to that in animals, perhaps operated by root or leaf pressure. This analogy has not been very useful. BOSE in his studies on plants (1923) had in mind peristaltic waves up the xylem tubes and by suggestion he also implied that a similar system operated in the phloem. The waves that he contemplated seem to have been contractions along the whole of the vessel and not through narrow tubules within the sieve tubes. MANGHAM (1917) proposed that the sucrose was carried in the sieve tubes along the internal active surfaces of the tube by a surface active matrix. He was unable to "see" such surfaces in his day, but there has recently been evidence that it may exist in the form of the plasmatic filaments (p.f.) or P-protein.

A number of more recent proposals will now be considered.

B. Peristalsis of Cell Walls

The possibility that a type of peristaltic movement did in fact occur in the cell walls of phloem has recently been considered in a tentative fashion by JONES (private communication). This reflection probably resulted from difficulties encountered with other mechanisms. But the cine-film of LEE et al. (1970) and other careful observations on living phloem (D.C. WILDON, 1971) seem to make such a mechanism highly unlikely. Nonetheless, rhythmic changes in diameter of roots through the day have been recorded by M.G. HUCK using time-lapse photography, therefore the speculation is certainly warranted.

C. Micro-Electro-Kinesis

Variations of the electro-osmotic theme have been proposed. For instance HEJNOWICZ (1970) suggested that charged groups moving in parallel direction down the walls of a reticulum could carry between them ions or particles of opposite charge. These counter ions would also drag solution along with them and thus produce a translocation flow. This proposal suffers from many of the objections of electro-osmotic theory (MACROBBIE, 1971): the efficiency of flow is less than a pressure-driven mechanism, and the current density would probably be unduly high. In addition, a series of channels must exist axially in the sieve elements. With the exception of papers by THAINE (1962; 1969) and JARVIS and THAINE (1971) there is almost no evidence that membrane-bound channels exist between 0.5 and 5 μ diameter in sieve elements. But the possibility must not be ruled out that channels loosely delineated by strands of plasmatic fibres are present, and that these could act in part through micro-electro-kinesis to change their shape as well as to carry waves of charge along their inner surface. Also, it should be noted in passing that any contractile protein mechanism would almost certainly involve charge displacement and spatial redistribution. In this sense micro-electro-kinesis and contractile protein waves might ultimately be hard to tell apart.

D. Surface Active Movement Mechanism

1. The movement of surface active molecules over a liquid interface in monolayers is known to occur wherever the molecular interaction between the surface phase and the "active" molecule is appropriate (cf. BULL, 1951). Moreover the rate at which a monolayer can spread over a surface is much higher than ordinary diffusion in liquids. The force of spreading is the difference in surface tension between the original surface and the monolayer, and its rate approaches that of diffusion in a gas. Thus very fast movements of ^{14}C label in plants (NELSON et al., 1958) have been attributed either to gas diffusion in aerenchyma channels, or to surface active movements in the vascular system (WHITTLE, 1970).

MANGHAM (1917) proposed that sucrose in solution could adsorb onto the internal surface of sieve tubes and could thereby move rapidly within the system. In order to move the large quantities of sucrose which are translocated in the sieve elements, a relatively large *continuous* surface must exist axially through the system, sucrose must itself adsorb onto the surface with a substantially lowered surface tension than the "clean" surface, and sink areas must exist to remove the adsorbed sugar. The sink areas are thought to exist, but the only surfaces of continuity running through the sieve-tube system are the plasmalemma of the sieve elements and (according to FENSOM, 1972; LEE, 1972, JOHNSON, 1968 and 1973) the p.f. or P-protein. The surface of the plasmalemma was found to be too small to carry all the sucrose moved, but LEE (1972) has proposed that the reticulum of plasmatic filaments (p.f.) could do so, for its surface was estimated as probably 10 times as great. (LEE (1972) calculated the area of the p.f. to be 100 times that of the plasmalemma, but unlike FENSOM (1972) he assumed 3×10^5 filaments per sieve element, and diameter of 120×10^{-8} cm, as well as a smaller area for sucrose molecules). Consider a sieve element 20×10^{-4}cm diam., 200×10^{-4}cm long (hence volume $\approx 6.4 \times 10^{-8}$ cm^3) containing 0.3 M (i.e. 10%) sucrose. It would hold 1.9×10^{-11} moles. Suppose each molecule occupied 100 A^2—10^{-14} cm^2. Then 1.9×10^{-11} moles$=6 \times 10^{23} \times 1.9 \times 10^{-11} = 12 \times 10^{12}$ molecules which would occupy $12 \times 10^{12} \times 10^{-14} = 12 \times 10^{-2}$ cm^2. But the area of 40,000 p.f., each 60×10^{-8} cm diam. strands running through one sieve element (supposing they do so) is $6\pi \times 10^{-7} \times 4 \times 10^4 \times 2 \times 10^{-2} = 15 \times 10^{-4}$ cm^2, which is two orders of magnitude too small.

We may conclude that the entire sucrose present cannot travel on the surface of p.f., and its chemical structure would seem to make direct adsorption on p-protein (a lipo-protein?) unlikely.

2. There is another possibility. A carrier molecule such as a sterol glucoside (FISHER, 1970), a sucrose phosphate or an amino acid moiety (KNIGHT et al., 1974) might adsorb onto the P-protein surface and move rapidly along it. This situation would lead to the appearance of a small proportion of fast flow dragging a larger mass flow after it. Evidence that these two types of flow occur exists in the work of NELSON et al. (1958; 1959) WHITTLE (1971), FISHER (1970), and above all in recent work on detached phloem strands (see Chapter 9).

A somewhat similar model was first postulated and described experimentally by VAN DEN HONERT (1932). In its new form it would require a considerable continuous surface within the sieve elements (e.g. the P-protein or p.f. reticulum); it requires carrier molecules to adsorb on the surface with appropriate lowering of surface tension; it might require loading mechanisms to attach sucrose or other solute to the carrier molecule (say ATP-ATP-ase) at sites in the system and unloading sites.

There exists some experimental evidence for all these possibilities at the moment. If such a mechanism were operating, it would appear bimodal in front, i.e. a small fast portion would precede an apparent mass flow; it would probably act to vibrate the plasmatic filaments (p.f.) as reported by FENSOM et al. (1968) and LEE et al. (1970); it would appear bi-directional, in the sense that sucrose would spread out from a loading centre in both directions in a sieve tube; it conceivably could allow for bypassing bi-directional transport in a single sieve element under certain conditions; the sieve plates would no longer be pressure barriers; poisons or conditions which altered the loading-unloading or the surface structure would affect it greatly.

There are remaining difficulties: are the energy requirements reasonable? Can it account for apparent pulses (do they move?); can it account for apparent gaps in tracer continuity in single strand experiments? Why should the rate of translocation be so dependent (apparently) on sucrose and on K^+ concentrations?

Evidence concerning the fine structure of p.f. reported in the last decade suggests that it exists in the state of a high order helix in the sieve elements (PARTHASARATHY and MÜHLETHALER 1969; SIDDIQUI and SPANNER, 1970; BEHNKE, 1971; ROBIDOUX et al., 1973). It is possible to envisage a carrier molecule moving on the proteinaceous (or lipoidal) surface of the microfibrillar helix from loading site to unloading site (transfer cells, marker particles). The drag on surrounding solution would conceivably cause the spiral to vibrate (even to coil and uncoil), to aid mixing of solution in the lumina and to add some active drag of sucrose solution through plate pores wherever the pore callose is minimal. Exchange between the surface-held tracer and bulk solution would probably occur in the case of ^{3}H label and some ^{14}C. Though no such carrier molecule is known with precision, all of these possibilities have at least some support in existing experimental evidence and this model in its revised form must not be disregarded.

3. A variation of the surface-active hypothesis is that special molecules line sieve pores and p.f. to reduce the frictional forces of flow, by anomalous viscosity as it were. This proposal has been invoked by proponents of Pressure Flow in order to reduce the pressure loss across sieve plates (ZIMMERMANN and BROWN, 1971 p. 269). While some claim that this type of molecule exists, the claims are currently suspect. Therefore other forms of the surface active hypothesis look far more promising.

E. Reciprocating Flow Hypothesis

Recently MILLER (1973) proposed that phloem transport could result as readily from a reciprocating movement of sieve-tube sap as from a mass flow in one direction. He points out that a kinetic analysis of such a system would give profiles similar to those reported in the literature. He proposes oscillations with a displacement of one cm. and a period of the order of a minute; similar to those found during streaming of cytoplasm in the slime mould *Physarum polycephalum*. His mechanism therefore includes a reciprocating protoplasmic streaming (presumably by a contractile protein of unknown action) together with some osmotically driven mass flow.

This proposal, while ingenious, has almost no experimental evidence to support it. Indeed, the microscopic studies of living phloem systems show no indication of such a phenomenon (LEE et al., 1970; THAINE, 1962). Nor do the tracer experiments of FENSOM and DAVIDSON (see KNIGHT et al., 1974), quoted by MILLER, really support such a hypothesis, for all the pulses detected in their work seem to be moving unidirectionally. Finally, the problems which beset the pressure-flow theory are here doubled so that both from experiment and energy considerations the proposal seems highly unlikely.

F. Contractile Proteins

Various proposals involving the action of contractile proteins in sieve tubes have been considered in recent years. For a wider discussion of the possible part played by contractile proteins in plant cells, particularly microfilamentous material, the reader is referred to MACROBBIE (1971). This present section will be confined to various types of contractile protein mechanisms possible in sieve tubes other than those proposed specifically in CANNY or THAINE's (1962) model of Protoplasmic Streaming (see also Chapter 12 in this volume, and CANNY, 1973).

1. Long-distance linear movement of P-protein, travelling as an "endless belt" down one side of a sieve element, through many plates and back in the other direction, has been mooted by CANNY (1962) and LEVITT (1969) since it seemed to account for certain observations. However, the scarcity of direct microscopical evidence to support this motion, the relative immobility of "marker particles" which are known to be attached to P-protein and which have been observed in living strands to exhibit saltatory, but not translatory movements, and the difficulties of crossing-over and return, all make this proposal improbable.

2. When living sieve tubes are examined by ordinary light microscopy, liquid near the sieve plates often appears to shimmer in a manner similar to the flagella in flame cells of tubellarians (FENSOM et al., 1968; FENSOM, p. 275 in ZIMMERMANN and BROWN, 1971). This has suggested that fibrils of p.f. attached to sieve plates, might propagate contractile waves along them which would project a stream of liquid through the sieve-plate pores. But this postulate also suffers from the lack of any direct evidence in its favor. Moreover the shape of the sieve tubes, the apparent attachment and extent of P-protein (ROBIDOUX et al., 1973; JOHNSON, 1973), the slowness of liquid flow resulting and the impossibility of accounting for pulses or bidirectional flow, all discount its possibility.

3. JAROSCH (1964) suggested that since the plasmatic filaments of P-protein exists in the form of a high order helix, its high speed rotation about its longitudinal axis could account for longitudinal flow through sieve-plate pores. Thus he proposes that the contractile nature of the P-protein operates by spinning of its helical form, so that liquid near its surface is propelled as water would be by an Archimedes screw. To permit such an operation the rotating helix must be inside a channel—presumably of unrotating p.f. Also the spinning molecules must be held by bearings, as it were, both to control their spinning and to prevent their own linear propulsion. Once again, there does not seem to be direct evidence available in sieve tubes which would support this postulate, but disproof may be difficult. This type of mechanism could permit a bidirectional movement and also pulses in the same sieve element, supposing these phenomena to be real.

4. Of more importance is the suggestion recently advanced by MACROBBIE (1971) that the p.f. is composed of actin filaments and that myosin dimers in solution may be activated to move along their surface dragging sucrose solution with them. This is envisaged as producing a mass type of flow, capable of change in direction once the actin-myosin orientations are reversed by, say, a prior pressure flow. The contractile part of this model would be the molecular bridges running along the surface of the actin filaments. This would certainly seem to account for and explain many of the flow profiles observed in phloem, but would neither explain bi-directional by-pass movement within a single sieve element, nor apparent pulse flow of tracer nor bimodal flow in any one direction, if these observations are valid.

The initial orientation suggested by MACROBBIE (1971) requires a small prior pressure-flow to orient the molecules which would then enhance the flow by interaction and produce a flow force inside the sieve elements. This poses difficulties associated with pressure flow. On the other hand if the initial orientation could be effected by a surface-active carrier molecule, running from source to sink along the P-protein reticulum, or by a kind of action potential, or by microperistaltic wave along parts of the same material, some of the difficulties remaining with it might be overcome.

Certainly there is good evidence that the p.f. is implicated, though it now seems unlikely that it is actin-myosin KLEINIG et al., 1971; WILLIAMSON, 1972; SABNIS and HART, 1974. It is in surprising quantity in the sieve tubes; it coexists with ATP and the ATP-ase reported along it (SAUTER and BRAUN, 1968; GILDER and CRONSHAW, 1973); it is reduced in translocation upon the addition of cytochalasin-B (THOMPSON and THOMPSON, 1973; AIKMAN, personal communication; KNIGHT et al., 1974); its vibrations clearly cease when cooled to 1 °C (LEE et al., 1970) as shown by the cessation of dancing movement of discrete ribbons of marker particles in living sieve tubes in cine studies. MACROBBIE (1971) calculated from energy considerations arising from KAMIYA'S work in *Nitella* that energy dissipation and specific mass transfer would conform reasonably with the reported surface area of the p.f. (her area calculations based on KOLLMANN'S weight volume figures are in agreement with observations made by electron-micrograph studies and optical measurements of number of fibrilla strands per pore and pores per plate in *Heracleum* (FENSOM, 1972; LEE, 1972), where the p.f. in the pores are assumed to run axially through the lumen).

5. While BARCLAY and FENSOM (1973) have very clear evidence from microinjection that carbon black moves by a mass flow, other similar experiments using ^{14}C sucrose have indicated that the mass flow is accompanied by another type of movement. Indeed FENSOM (1972) has proposed that the basic mechanism is a contractile protein one, but that it operates at the level of small aggregates of p.f., possibly operating as tubular-like arrangements which can expand up to 60 nm diameter and contract to perhaps 6 nm diameter. This system could load and transport concentrated sucrose solution in small series of apparent vesicles which themselves aggregate into larger pulse trains about 3–5 cm apart. The speed of sucrose movement within each pulse train is suggested to be about 10^{-1} cm sec^{-1}, to agree with measurements made on isolated phloem strands. But these wave trains are also thought to induce a mass flow of solution outside them, but at a lower speed. Thus the resulting system is bimodal in the sense that two main flows are detectable: the mass flow mode in which the bulk of solution moves; the pulse-flow mode which is linked to metabolic activity and is often the chief driving force to the system unless the sieve pores are large and free from p.f. The postulates for this model are given as follows (ZIMMERMANN, 1971, p. 275; FENSOM, 1972).

(A) Phloem translocation occurs in two key modes, "mass flow" and microfibrillar flow and a number of subsidiary modes.

(B) The microfibrillar flow is a loading and translocation of sucrose in or onto plasmatic filaments possibly by a type of microperistalsis. Its amount and efficacy depends on the integrity of microfibrillar continuum stretching through lumina and plates of the sieve tubes. Loading can take place in each cell. Microfibrillar flow is prevented by cold blocks, cytochalasin-B, and desiccation, as well as by mechanical disruption (it is very easily damaged). It can be by-passingly bidirectional in the same sieve element.

(C) The mass flow can move like a pressure flow under loading pressures at the plasmalemma. But more frequently it is moved outwards by the microfibrillar flow mechanism in which waves in phase may be passing through sieve plates to act as peristaltic pumps. Mass flow is prevented by callose restriction of sieve-plate pores and also by cessation of the microfibrillar flow mechanism. The mass flow will have the flow profile of an "activated diffusion".

(D) A small, very fast surface-layer component of translocation also seems to be present. Pressure flow and electroosmotic components have also been detected and it is thought that they may all contribute to the movement and control of movement of sucrose solution.

(E) Sieve plates, when not constricted with callose, act as pumps, not barriers. They are also important points of safety to a plant whenever the phloem system is damaged. They act as anchors for some of the transcellular fibrils. Companion cells are thought to provide energy for ATP reservoirs and for loading and unloading of sucrose. Acid phosphatase and K^+ Mg^{++} are thought to be necessary for contractility of protein, although the ATP-ase would seem to differ from that common in actin-myosin systems (MATILE, personal communication).

(F) The different modes of translocation are thought of as being complimentary to one another: one may augment another or it may also operate under conditions which would prevent another mode from functioning.

These postulates are illustrated in diagrammatic form in Figs. 1 and 2.

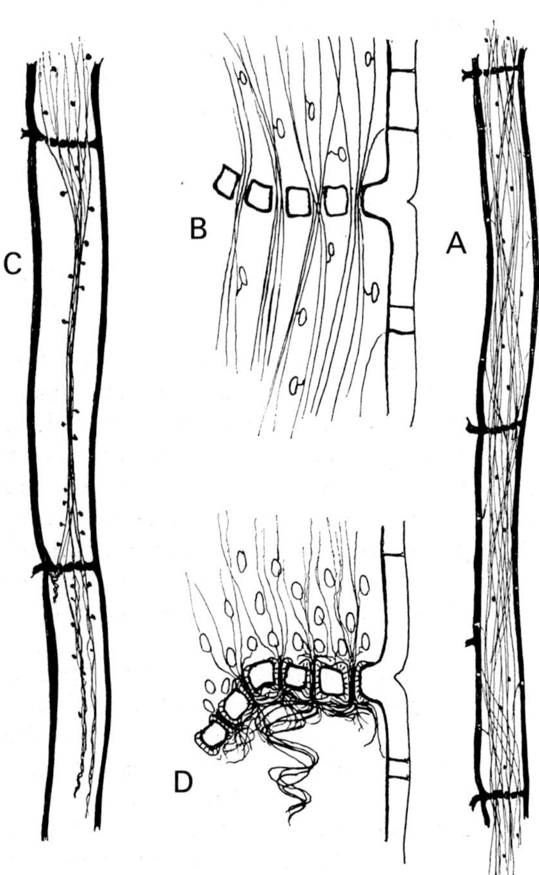

Fig. 1. Diagram of m.f.m. (microfilamentous material or P-protein) in sieve tubes as deduced from work with isolated phloem strands (Chapter 9).
(A) intact sieve tube; (B) enlargement of undamaged sieve plate to show fibrils and filaments with attached marker particles; (C) partly-damaged sieve tube; (D) enlargement of sieve plate from (C) to show both callose constrictions of pores and m.f.m. aggregations

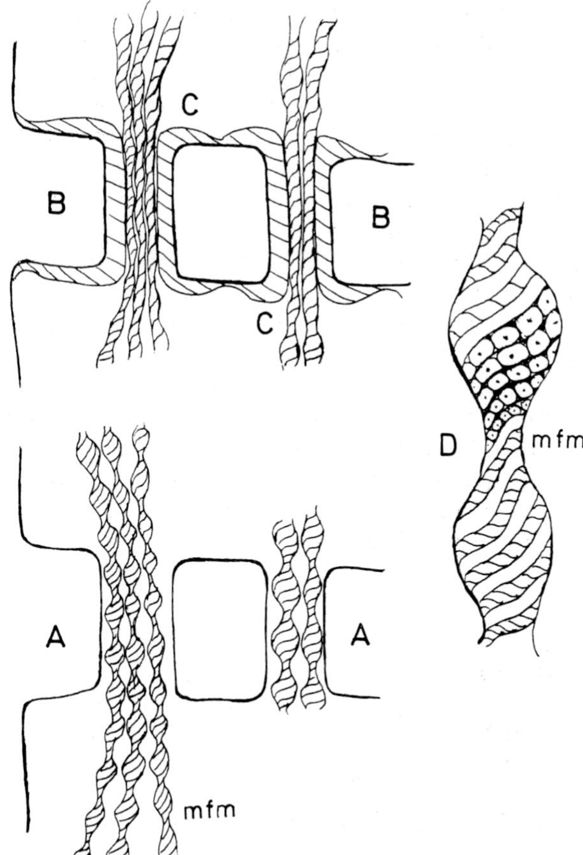

Fig. 2. Diagram of possible arrangement of m.f.m. passing through sieve plates as postulated by FENSOM (1972) for a microperistaltic model. (A–A) microperistaltic waves in phase allowing mass flow outside microfibrils. No callose. (B–B), callose deposits (C–C) constricting sieve-tube pores in a cut strand, preventing mass flow and restricting pulse flow. (D) enlargement of a possible structure for the m.f.m. to allow a contractile protein mechanism to operate, left by adjacent sliding of filamentous spirals, or right, by beaded units which enlarge by flattening and contract by thickening

Supposing the work reported on isolated phloem strands to be valid, the objections to this proposal are chiefly three: 1) only a few studies with the electronmicroscope have evidence of vesicle trains of the size (60 nM × 100 nM) postulated (ROBIDOUX et al., 1973, JOHNSON, 1973 and possibly IE et al., 1966); the small waves of constriction and expansion postulated would require a frequency of about 10^4 sec^{-1} ($v=10^{-1}$ cm sec^{-1}; $\lambda=10^{-5}$ cm) which is rather high for known contractile proteins—although molecular bridges must make and break at much higher frequencies. The number of vesicle trains or fibril aggregates running axially through the sieve elements seems to be much smaller than the measured filament frequency.

6. A further proposal has recently been made by N.S. ALLEN for protoplasmic streaming in *Nitella* (ALLEN, 1974). She finds that the microfibrillar material in this giant alga cell is arranged in two forms, bundles of fibrils axially stretched close to the stationary chloroplast layer, and filamentous branches of these bundles, attached at one end to the axial aggregates but free to undulate sinusoidally along their length. Waves of contractility along this semi-attached protein across the filaments causes the fluid nearby to move with a slight sinusoidal motion, which can be detected by lazer-light, Nomarski, cine-photography. A similar system might

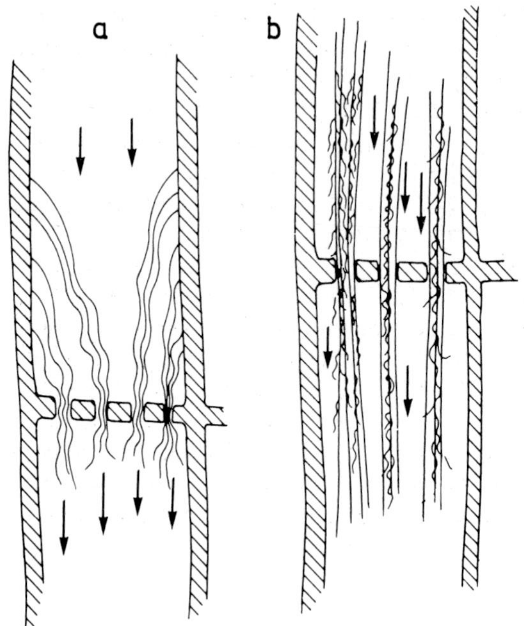

Fig. 3a and b. Diagram of sieve tube and plate illustrating mass flow activated by swishing microfilamentous material (m.f.m.) attached (a) to the sieve-tube wall, (b) to axial fibrils as postulated by ALLEN (1974)

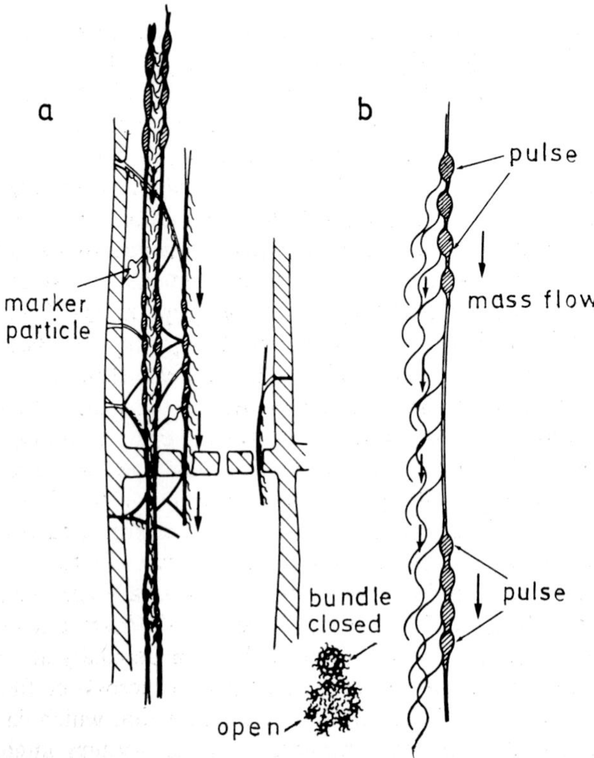

Fig. 4a and b. Diagram of sieve tube and plate illustrating a bimodel system (FENSOM and WILLIAMS, 1974) in which the swishing microfilaments (m.f.m.) are anchored to axial fibrillar bundles capable of microperistaltic action. (a) shows the sieve tube and (b) the individual axial fibril with attached filaments

be operating in phloem (Fig. 3.) for it would fit most of the observations made on *Heracleum*, and if the large "anchor" bundles of fibrils were of the size observed by ROBIDOUX et al. (1973), these bundles could conduct internally the so-called pulses which precede the mass flow. The model might then look somewhat as indicated in Fig. 4. This model would seem to be closer to current electronmicroscope findings than model (E) and at the moment of writing, to fit more recent evidence than any other: a bimodal profile, channels through the sieve-tube lumen unbounded by membranes, a few anchored axial fibrils or aggregates of microfilaments and many loose filaments, (JOHNSON, 1973) apparently at random when fixed under glutaraldehyde. Energy consumption would also seem to be adequate—better than a microperistaltic system by about two orders of magnitude. FENSOM and WILLIAMS (1974) have discussed this in more detail in an article where they calculate that at a specific mass transfer of around 10 $g\,h^{-1}\,cm^{-2}$ sieve tubes, the energy dissipation expressed as sucrose consumption would be of the order of $^{1}/_{2000}$ g sucrose cm^{-2} h^{-1}. If this proposal is sustained, the contractile protein mechanism will become a special modification of the protoplasmic-streaming hypothesis, discussed previously, and would supply its motive force along channels more or less continuously through channels traversing both the lumina and the plates.

G. Concluding Considerations

If the difficulties which are reported with the three older flow mechanisms are valid, as many workers think, other mechanisms must be explored. Of these, the four which seem most likely to fit known observations are (a) a modification of the surface active theory, in which some carrier molecule moves along a continuous reticulum of p.f., dragging bulk solution of sucrose behind it. (b) A contractile protein mechanism which operates at the level of p.f. aggregates, possibly as very small tubular bodies or swellings which drag bulk solution behind them. (c) A contractile protein mechanism which operates between axially oriented p.f. and the nearby solution, assuming protein interaction such as actin filaments operating against myosin fragments with some prior orienting mechanism superimposed on the system. (d) A contractile protein mechanism which operates by the wave motions of microfilament material, free at one end, attached to fibrils and in channels through the sieve-tube gel reticulum. All these mechanisms postulate that at least some strands of microfilamentous material extend longitudinally through pores and lumen of sieve elements. All these mechanisms could produce a bimodal type of flow: a small amount of fast movement followed by a slower mass flow. All these mechanisms would seem to require ATP, ATP-ase and K ions for their loading and unloading within the sieve element. All could conceivably cause vibrational effects to appear on the p.f. reticulum and all might operate in two directions at the same time within the same element. All meet requirements of energy usage and specific mass transfer as far as can be told, and all will make the mass-flow components appear as an "activated diffusion". In each case the sieve plates become pumps rather than barriers so long as callose deposits are minimal. Figs. 1, 3, and 4 would illustrate all these models if the microperistaltic waves were suitably replaced by (a) a surface-active carrier molecule, (c) a series of contractile protein waves or linkages with the moving solution.

There is no particular reason *a priori* why one single mechanism should act alone in sieve tubes or in all plants. Multi-modal action is well known in other instances, for example blood clotting in mammals or, in plants, the phloem sealing mechanism at sieve plates (callose formation and slime plugging). The evidence for a type of mass flow as one of the modes continues to be strong; indeed with the visual records of the mass flow of carbon particles in isolated phloem strands by micro-injection, the existence of a mass flow seems strengthened. But so too are pieces of evidence accumulating that other modes of flow also act in sieve tubes, surface active in nature or otherwise.

Suppose a contractile protein mechanism operates of the type postulated in (F) above. What might be the expected contributions of the various modes to the driving force? A rough estimate based on isolated strand and short time leaf feeding experiments may be hazarded:

(i) Pressure-driven mass flow (MÜNCH flow) will be present and may require between 100% and 1% of the energy dissipation, depending on the relative sizes of the sieve-tube channels, the pressure differences operating and the density of P-protein, (p.f.) in them. Plants with large plate pores and minimal or no p.f. would drive their sucrose solution mainly by this mechanism. On the other hand through plasmadesmata-like pores or those containing many plasmatic filaments the pressure-flow components may be very small.

(ii) Mass flow driven by the swishing of contractile protein filaments, anchored to axial fibrils, might represent up to 95% of the energy dissipation.

(iii) Pulse or "package" flow, driven by a kind of microperistaltic action, normally contributing less than 5% of the total quantity of sucrose flow, but up to 50% of the energy dissipation. Where the sieve tube is callosed, the percentage may be greater. However, since this mode may initiate and sustain the lashing of the filaments, its importance is thought to be paramount.

(iv) Surface active and electroosmotic components may be present but are thought to contribute below 0.1% of the total sucrose movement, but capable of contributing to feed-back control mechanisms.

What key points remain then to be discovered or still to be elucidated to help discriminate between these and the various other mechanisms? They would seem to include the following questions.

Does the P-protein, as fibrils, really extend axially and in a partial continuum through lumina and plate pores of the sieve elements in undamaged, mature, conducting phloem? Has it filamentous branches which are free to twist or undulate?

Is some form of contractile protein really implicated in the sucrose transport system rather than merely in the sucrose-loading system (i.e. into the sieve tube itself)? What is its chemical make-up? What is its physical fine structure *in situ?*

Does a bimodal profile of flow truly occur in individual sieve tubes?

Is by-passing bi-directional flow really possible within a single sieve tube?

Do *pulses* of sucrose truly exist and do they *move* out of an area of sucrose loading ahead of a mass flow? (If they do, then the surface-active mechanism is not as probable as some form of microperistalsis).

When these questions are clearly answered, it should be possible to discount certain mechanisms and to discriminate between others. At the moment, the use of single isolated phloem strands seems to offer an important new way to approach the problem, just as the use of aphid stylets has done. But there is one final consideration. We do not yet know for certain the mechanisms which cause the various types of protoplasmic streaming found in plant cells (But see HEPLER and PALEVITZ, 1974). It may still prove to be that the actual mechanism is novel to our conception and that molecular propulsive forces occur in plants which are as yet unknown at the macroscopic level at which we presently operate. If so, the future holds much of interest in store: in the meantime it is possible that we have put a finger on the key.

References

AIKMAN, D.: The reduction of translocation by cytochalasin B. (Personal communication).

ALLEN, N.S.: Endoplasmic filaments generate the motive force for rotational streaming in *Nitella*: J. Cell Biol **63**, 270–287 (1974).

BARCLAY, G.F.; FENSOM, D.S.: Passage of carbon black through sieve plates of unexcised *Heracleum sphondylium* after microinjection. Acta Botan. Neerl. **22**, 228–232 (1973).

BEHNKE, H.D.: The contents of the sieve-plate pores in *Aristolochia*. J. Ultrastruct. Res. **36**, 493–498 (1971).

BOSE, J.C.: Physiology of the ascent of sap. Bose Research Institute, Calcutta: Trans. S. Longmans, Green and Co. 1923.

BULL, H.D.: Physical biochemistry, p. 191–234. New York: John Wiley and Sons 1951.

CANNY, M.J.: The mechanism of translocation. Ann. Botany (London) **26**, 603-17 (1962).

CANNY, M.J.: Phloem translocation. London: Cambridge Univ. Press 1973.

FENSOM, D.S.: A theory of translocation in phloem of *Heracleum* by contractile protein microfibrillar material. Can. J. Botany **50**, 479–497 (1972).

FENSOM, D.S., CLATTENBURG, R., CHUNG, T., LEE, D.R., ARNOLD, D.C.: Moving particles in intact sieve tubes of *Heracleum mantegazzianum*. Nature **219**, 531–532 (1968).

FENSOM, D.S., WILLIAMS, E.J.: A note on Allen's suggestion for long-distance translocation in the phloem of plants. Nature **250**, 490–492 (1974).

FISHER, D.B.: Kinetics of C-14 translocation in soybean. 1. Kinetics in stem. Plant Physiol. **45**, 107–113 (1970).

GILDER, J., CRONSHAW, J.: ATP-ase in the phloem of *Cucurbita*. Planta **110**, 189–204 (1973).

HALES, S.: Vegetable staticks, 3rd ed. London 1738.

HEJNOWICZ, Z.: Propagated disturbances of transverse potential gradient in intracellular fibrils as the source of motive forces for longitudinal transport in cells. Protoplasma **71**, 343–364 (1970).

HEPLER, P.K., PALEVITZ, B.A.: Microtubules and microfilaments. Ann. Rev. Plant Physiol. **25**, 309–362 (1974).

HUCK, M.G.: Cine film: Time lapse photography of roots. U.S. Dept. of Agric., Alabama Ag. Exp. Stat., Auburn, Ala., U.S.A.

IE, T.S., TAMMES, P.M.L., VAN DIE, J.: Studies on phloem exudation from *Yucca flaccida* Haw. V. Electron microscopy of sieve plate pores. Proc. Koninkl. Ned. Akad. Wetenschap. **C 69**, 660–663 (1966).

JAROSCH, R.: Screw-mechanical basis of protoplasmic movement. In: Primitive motile systems in cell biology (ed. R.D. ALLEN and N. KAMIYA), p. 599–620. New York and London: Academic Press 1964.

JARVIS, P., THAINE, R.: Strands in sections of sieve elements cut in a cryostat. Nature New Biol. **232**, 236–237 (1971).

JOHNSON, R.P.C.: Microfilaments in pores between frozen etched sieve elements. Planta **81**, 314–332 (1968).

JOHNSON, R.P.C.: Filaments but no membranous transcellular strands in sieve pores in freeze-etched, translocating phloem. Nature **244**, 464 (1973).

JONES, R.L.: Personal communication.

KLEINIG, H., DÖRR, I., WEBER, C., KOLLMANN, R.: Filamentous proteins from plant sieve tubes. Nature New Biol. **229**, 152–153 (1971).

KNIGHT, B.K., MITTON, G.D., DAVIDSON, H.R., FENSOM, D.S.: Micro-injection of ^{14}C sucrose and other tracers into isolated phloem strands of *Heracleum*. Can. J. Botany **52**, 1491–1499 (1974).

LEE, D.R.: The possible significance of filaments in sieve elements. Nature 235:266 (1972).

LEE, D.R., FENSOM, D.S., COSTERTON, J.W.: Particle movement in intact phloem of *Heracleum*. Ottawa, Canada: Canad. Natl. Film Library 1970.

LEVITT, J.: Introduction to plant physiology, p. 104. St. Louis: Mosby Co. 1969.

MACROBBIE, E.A.C.: Phloem translocation, facts and mechanisms: A comparative survey. Biol. Rev. **46**, 429–481 (1971).

MANGHAM, S.: On the mechanism of translocation in plant tissue. An hypothesis with special reference to sugar conduction in sieve tubes. Ann. Botany (London) **31**, 293–311 (1917).

MATILE, P.: Personal communication.

MILLER, D.M.: The reciprocating flow hypothesis of translocation in plants. Can. J. Botany **51**, 1623–1628 (1973)

NELSON, C.D., PERKINS, H.J., GORHAM, P.R.: Note on a rapid translocation of the photosynthetically assimilated ^{14}C out of the primary leaf of the young soybean plant. Can. J. Biochem. Physiol. **36**, 1277–1279 (1958).

NELSON, C.D., PERKINS, H.J., GORHAM, P.R.: Evidence for different kinds of concurrent translocation of photosynthetically assimilated ^{14}C in the soybean. Can. J. Botany **37**, 1181–1189 (1959).

PARTHASARATHY, M.V., MÜHLETHALER, K.: Ultrastructure of protein tubules in differentiating sieve elements. Cytobiologie **1**, 17–36 (1969).

ROBIDOUX, J., SANDBORN, E.B., FENSOM, D.S., CAMERON, M.L.: Plasmatic filaments and particles in mature sieve elements of *Heracleum sphondylium* under the electronmicroscope. J. Exptl. Botany **24**, 349–359 (1973).

SABNIS, D.D., HART, J.W.: Studies on the possible occurence of actomyosin—like proteins in phloem. Planta **118**, 271–278 (1974).

SAUTER, J.J., BRAUN, H.J.: Histologische und cytochemische Untersuchungen zur Function der Baststrahlen von *Larix decidera* Mill. unter besonderer Berücksichtigung der Strasburger-Zellen. Z. Pflanzenphysiol. **59**, 420–438 (1968).

SIDDIQUI, A.W., SPANNER, D.C.: The state of the pores in functioning sieve plates. Planta **91**, 181–189 (1970).

THAINE, R.: A translocation hypothesis based on the structure of plant cytoplasm. J. Exptl. Botany **13**, 152–160 (1962).

THAINE, R.: Movement of sugars through plants by cytoplasmic pumping. Nature **222**, 873–875 (1969).

THOMPSON, R.G., THOMPSON, A.D.: Inhibition by cytochalasin B of sucrose transport in isolated phloem strands of *Heracleum*. Can. J. Botany **51**, 933–936 (1973).

VAN DEN HONERT, T.H.: On the mechanism of the transport of organic materials in plants. Proc. Koninkl. Ned. Akad. Wetenschap. Ser. C Biol. Med. Sci. **35**, 1104–1111 (1932).

WEATHERLEY, P.E., JOHNSON, P.R.C.: The form and function of the sieve tube: a problem in reconciliation. Intern. Rev. Cytol. **24**, 149–192 (1968).

WHITTLE, C.M.: The behavior of ^{14}C profiles in *Helianthus* seedlings. Planta **98**, 136–49 (1971).

WILDON, D.C.: Cine film. School of Biol. Sciences, Univ. of East Anglia, Norwich, U.K. (1971).

WILLIAMSON, R.E.: An investigation of the contractile protein hypothesis of phloem translocation. Planta **106**, 149–157 (1972).

ZIMMERMANN, M.H., BROWN, C.L.: Trees: Structure and function, p. 268 and 275. Berlin-Heidelberg-New York: Springer 1971.

16. Theoretical Considerations

M.T. TYREE and J. DAINTY

A. The Basic Transport Equations

Many physiologists have lamented the fact that there has been far too much theorizing and far too little definitive experimentation into the translocation of assimilates in the phloem. The lack of definitive experimentation can in part be explained by the complexity and the delicacy of the system being studied. But definitive experiments cannot be devised without first erecting well-defined models. We feel that the volume of theorizing would be far less lamentable if it were based on clearly stated premises and developed by the application of sound transport theory. With only a relatively few exceptions most of the "theorizing" has been qualitative, *ad hoc*, and more akin to imaginative pipe-dreaming. There is no doubt that the slow development of definitive and quantitative models is in large part a result of the complexity of the system and the large number of unknowns involved. To a lesser extent the development of quantitative theories is hindered by a failure to recognize the interdependence and the relative importance of the basic transport processes that may be simultaneously occurring at the same place, e.g. net diffusion down a sieve-tube lumen, bulk fluid flow down a sieve-tube lumen, and the transport of solute and solvent into and out of the sieve-tube lumen.

The quantitative literature on translocation is difficult to follow and difficult to build upon because of the multiplicity of symbols used for identical quantities and because there is often more than one way to solve the mathematical equations invoked to quantify a particular model; if the solution is not sufficiently general it may be difficult to incorporate into a more involved model.

By using a standardized symbolism and a more or less complete set of transport equations, we hope to present a unified (albeit incomplete) theoretical frame-work that can be built upon by others.

In most quantitative models of translocation the concentration of the translocate within a sieve tube (or microtubule within a sieve tube) is assumed to be radially uniform, i.e. the same everywhere within a plane perpendicular to the central axis of the tube. Clearly many physical conditions mitigate radially uniform concentrations, as, for instance, the loading and unloading of translocate across the periphery of the tube. If fluid flow is laminar within the tube then the higher fluid velocities towards the center would tend to disrupt radial uniformity if there is a concentration gradient along the length of the tube.

However the assumption of radially uniform concentrations is well founded as can be seen from the following simple considerations. There is a simple relation between the mean displacement, $\bar{x}$, of a diffusing solute and the time, t, it takes to diffuse the mean distance (GLASSTONE, 1951).

The relation is,

$$\bar{x}^2 = 2Dt, \tag{1}$$

where D is the coefficient of diffusion (about 10^{-5} cm^2 s^{-1} for most solutes). From Eq. (1) we can calculate the time it would take for a high concentration of solute to travel from the center to the periphery (or *vice versa*) of a cylindrical sieve tube 20 μm ($=2 \times 10^{-3}$ cm) in diameter. The time is $(10^{-3})^2/2 \times 10^{-5} = 0.05$ sec. If the solute is travelling down the cylindrical sieve tube by laminar fluid flow at a mean velocity of 50 cm h the mean down-stream displacement of the fluid in 0.05 s is only 7 μm. Thus radial diffusion of solutes is sufficient to give radially uniform concentrations within the length of typical sieve cells (=100 to 500 μm long). The assumption of radially uniform concentration will be adopted in all subsequent considerations.

I. Fick's Equations

Under some restricted circumstances FICK's equations may be applied to translocation models; for example, if sieve cells are loaded or unloaded *via* companion cells through plasmodesmata, then FICK's equations may apply to diffusion of solutes through the pores. Strictly, FICK's equations apply to transport within the sieve-tube lumen only when the fluid is stationary. When the fluid moves it is still possible to have diffusion of solutes with respect to the moving fluid and simultaneous fluid flow. In this case FICK's equations need to be modified.

When long distances are involved, FICK's first equation applies only to the steady state, i.e., only when the concentration profile is time-independent. FICK's first equation is,

$$J = -D\frac{dC}{ds}, \tag{2}$$

where s (cm) is the distance in the direction of diffusion, C (mole cm^{-3} or gm cm^{-3}) is the solute concentration, D (cm^2 s^{-1}) is the solute diffusion coefficient, and J (mole cm^{-2} s^{-1} or gm cm^{-2} s^{-1}) is the flux rate of solute due to diffusion.

FICK's first equation also applies in the non-steady state; in this case it gives the instantaneous flux at any given point in terms of dC/ds at that point. FICK's second equation is more general because it applies to non-steady state conditions. The second equation can be derived from the first by the application of the principle of matter conservation to Eq. (2) in a vanishingly small region; the relation is, in one dimension

$$\frac{\partial C}{\partial t} = D\frac{\partial^2 C}{\partial s^2}. \tag{3}$$

More complicated forms of Eq. (3) can be written for two or three dimensional diffusion in rectilinear, cylindrical or spherical coordinates.

FICK's equations are rarely used in translocation problems because it is recognized that there must be bulk fluid flow (either unidirectional or bidirectional). Basically, whenever the concentration times the mean velocity of the fluid flow is more than, say, 100 times $-D\frac{dC}{ds}$, diffusion can be ignored. For example, suppose there is a concentration gradient of 10^{-5} mole cm^{-3}/cm (=1 molar/m) at a point where the concentration is 10^{-4} mole cm^{-3} (=0.1 molar) the mean velocity need be only

10^{-4} cm s^{-1} (=0.36 cm h^{-1}) to affect a flux rate 100 times the diffusional flux when $D = 10^{-5}$ cm^2 s^{-1}.

CANNY and PHILLIPS (1963) demonstrated that an equation of the form of Eq. (3) applies to their bidirectional transport model (cf. Section C.II.b.). Although the mathematics of their system is analogous to the mathematics of diffusional problems, they are not proposing that translocation is a diffusion process.

II. Localized Membrane Permeation

One of the biggest handicaps to successful theorizing is that we know very little about how water and solutes are loaded onto or unloaded from sieve tubes. The mechanism of loading may be symplasmic and the pathway may be *via* the plasmodesmata from the site of synthesis to the sieve cell. Alternatively the pathway may be apoplasmic in which case two or more plasmalemma membranes need to be permeated either by passive or active mechanisms (cf. Chapter 17). Recent results on sugar beet indicate that both symplasmic and apoplasmic transport may be involved in the loading and unloading process; on the basis of cryoscopic studies GEIGER et al. (1974) suggest the possibility of symplasmic transport from the site of synthesis up to the sieve-element companion-cell complex. From here the sugars must first enter the apoplast before being actively taken up by the transport system.

Although membrane permeation into or out of the sieve-element companion-cell complex may be involved we do not know whether the process is active or passive for water and the solutes. Below we give some of the transport equations governing active and passive membrane permeation.

1. Passive Permeation of Non-Electrolytes

Passive permeation of neutral solutes across cell membranes is given by

$$J^* = -P^*(C^i - C^0), \tag{4}$$

where J^* (mole cm^{-2} s^{-1} or gm cm^{-2} s^{-1}) is the membrane flux rate (influx positive), P^* (cm s^{-1}) is the solute permeability coefficient, and C^i and C^0 (mole cm^{-3} or g cm^{-3}) are the solute concentrations inside the sieve cell and outside the sieve cell respectively.

The transport equation for water flux is better given in terms of the water-volume flux, J^*_w (cm^3 s^{-1} cm^{-2}), and depends on the difference in water potential between the inside, Ψ^i (bar), and the outside, Ψ^0 (bar), solutions,

$$J^*_w = -L_p(\Psi^i - \Psi^0), \tag{5}$$

where L_p (cm^3 s^{-1} cm^{-2} bar^{-1} or cm s^{-1} bar^{-1}) is the hydraulic conductivity of the membrane. In some models it is useful to relate both the water flux and the solute flux to the solute concentration and the hydrostatic pressure in the cell. This can be done because Ψ^i is given by,

$$\Psi^i = P - \pi = P - RT \sum C^i, \tag{6}$$

where π is the osmotic pressure of the fluid in the sieve element (which nearly equals the gas constant, R, times the absolute temperature, T, times the sum of the concentrations of all the solutes inside the sieve-element fluid) and where P (bar) is the hydrostatic pressure in the cell. The right side of Eq. (6) is only approximately correct because the equivalence between π and $RT\sum C^i$ holds exactly only if the solution is ideal and dilute and because the equation assumes that the membrane is much less permeable to solutes than it is to water.

Ultimately it is not possible to discuss transport in the phloem without bringing ion transport into the picture. If uni-directional mass flow occurs then ions must be unloading down-stream and ions travelling up in the xylem might also have to be loaded on to the phloem. However we know very little about ion transport in the phloem. We will not complicate the picture at this stage by consideration of ion transport.

2. Enzyme Mediated Permeation

If the mechanism of membrane permeation is enzyme mediated, i.e. either by active transport or by "facilitated" diffusion (STEIN, 1967), then other transport equations are necessary. The transport equation used depends solely on the model invoked. For example, if transport is by "facilitated" diffusion with Michaelis-Menton-type kinetics and with the same Michaelis-Menton constant for influx and efflux, then the net flux, J^*, will be

$$J^* = \frac{C^0 J_{\max}}{K_m + C^0} - \frac{C^i J_{\max}}{K_m + C^i}, \tag{7}$$

where K_m is the Michaelis-Menton constant and $J_{\max}$ is the maximum reaction rate (expressed in terms of a flux rate). If the K_m's for influx and efflux are allowed to be unequal then Eq. (7) would describe one of the many possible active transport equations.

III. Laminar Flow Equations

Most people assume laminar fluid flow occurs within sieve tubes; and in most cases sieve tubes are approximated by cylindrical pipes. Poiseuille's law is commonly applied even though it is recognized not to be an accurate description of fluid flow through sieve-plate pores which are scarcely longer than they are wide. This is unfortunate because the sieve-plate pores collectively offer a greater resistance to water flow than the lumen for all but the narrowest cells (CHRISTY and FERRIER, 1973). The application of Poiseuille's law to sieve-plate pores will lead to an underestimate of the required pressure gradients because edge effects are ignored.

Poiseuille's law relating the volume flow rate, dV/dt ($\mathrm{cm^3\,s^{-1}}$) through a pipe to the pressure gradient, dP/ds (bar $\mathrm{cm^{-1}}$), down the pipe is given by,

$$\frac{dV}{dt} = -10^6 \frac{\pi r^4}{8\eta} \frac{dP}{ds}, \tag{8}$$

where r is the radius of the pipe and η is the viscosity of the fluid. In some cases it is useful to express the pressure gradient, dP/ds, in terms of the solute concentrations and apoplasmic water potentials. To do this we need to solve Eq. (6) for P, relate Ψ^i to Ψ^0 through Eq. (5), and differentiate the result; when this is done the answer is,

$$\frac{dP}{ds}=RT\sum\frac{dC^i}{ds}+\frac{d\Psi^0}{ds}-\frac{1}{L_p}\frac{dJ_w^*}{ds}. \tag{9}$$

If the volume flux from the outside into the sieve element changes little with distance or if the membrane hydraulic conductivity is high, then the last term in Eq. (9) can be ignored; under these conditions the pressure gradient in the sieve tube equals the osmotic pressure gradient plus the apoplasmic water potential gradient (which is usually of opposite sign).

IV. Equations Expressing Conservation of Matter

Many useful relations can be derived and several of the elementary transport equations presented above can be connected by relations which basically incorporate the principle of matter conservation. The simplest and most common relation gives the dependence of the solute flux rate (J = specific mass transfer) upon the average fluid velocity in the sieve tube and the solute concentration;

$$J=C^i\bar{v}=C^i\bar{J}_v \tag{10}$$

where $\bar{v}$ (cm s^{-1}), is the average fluid velocity in the sieve cell and $\bar{J}_v$ is the volume flux rate down the tube (averaged radially).

Another relation important to tracer kinetics gives the rate of change of solute concentration, $\partial C/\partial t$, at any point in the translocation path in terms of the solute flux rate, J^*, across the membrane bounding the tube of radius r and the rate of change of solute flux with distance, $\partial J/\partial s$,

$$\frac{\partial C}{\partial t}=\frac{2}{r}J^*-\frac{\partial J}{\partial s}. \tag{11}$$

In Eq. (11) we have ignored the solute concentration changes associated with sap dilution during osmotic water entry, and the volume contribution of the sugar. At steady state $J^*=\frac{r}{2}\frac{dJ}{ds}$. Other conservation statements that apply to the Münch pressure flow model are presented in Section B.I.1.

V. Phenomenological Equations from Irreversible Thermodynamics

The phenomenological equations of irreversible thermodynamics have been used a great deal recently, (SPANNER, 1970; TYREE and FENSOM, 1970; MACROBBIE, 1971; AIKMAN, 1972). Unfortunately these exercises tell us very little that is new because the theory is too general. They do tell us something about possible interactions between "forces" and fluxes which are probably second-order effects. According to the formalism of irreversible thermodynamics, each flux is a linear sum of the products of coefficients and all the thermodynamic forces,

$$J_i = \sum_{j=1}^{n} L_{ij} X_j, \qquad i = 1, 2, \ldots, n, \tag{12}$$

where X_j is the thermodynamic driving force on the jth flux and L_{ij} are the phenomenological coefficients bearing a reciprocity relationship, $L_{ij} = L_{ji}$ for all $i \neq j$.

The theory tells us little that is new because the values of the coefficients, L_{ij}, are unknown and frequently even the magnitude of the forces, X_j, are unknown. The phenomenological equations have been most frequently invoked in electro-osmotic models of translation. By guessing the values of the relevant parameters in electroosmosis, authors have been led to diametrically opposite conclusions regarding the possibility of electroosmotic transport systems (SPANNER, 1970; MACROBBIE, 1971). Attempts at measuring the relevant parameters have only led to equivocal results (BOWLING, 1968 and 1969; TYREE and FENSOM, 1970; TYREE, 1971).

B. Mathematical Models for Mass Flow: Energetics and Forces

In this section we will discuss some of the theoretical aspects of models involving unidirectional mass flow within sieve cells. These are the MÜNCH pressure-flow model, the peristaltic pumping model, the transcellular cyclosis model, and the electroosmotic model.

I. The Münch Model Treated Quantitatively

MÜNCH proposed his qualitative model of how unidirectional mass flow could arise in sieve tubes over 40 years ago (MÜNCH, 1927 and 1930). Several attempts have been made to calculate or measure the driving force (the pressure gradient) required to motivate MÜNCH pressure flow; some recent attempts are those by WEATHERLEY and JOHNSON (1968), CRAFTS and CRISP (1971), HAMMEL (1968), TAMMES et al. (1971), and TYREE and FENSOM (1970). Only recently has anyone attempted to erect a comprehensive mathematical model.

Credit for the first attempt at deriving a complete mathematical description of MÜNCH pressure flow must go to ESCHRICH et al. (1972); in this paper the authors describe some interesting experiments using tubular semi-permeable membranes as a model system of the sieve tube which they interpret in terms of the mechanism put forward by MÜNCH. They arrived at some rather unrealistic conclusions and suggestions for new terminology for which they were speedily and justifiably criticized (WEATHERLEY, 1972). The tubular semi-permeable membranes used by ESCHRICH et al. (1972) were very large in diameter (7 mm) and only 20 cm long. They were held vertically in a water bath and a sugar-dye solution was carefully injected at the lower end of the tube at the onset of the experiment; this caused an osmotic movement of water into the lower part of the tube containing the sugar solution and so the front of the dye-sugar solution moved up the tube. The authors rightly pointed out that the gradient of hydrostatic pressure along their tube, calculated from Poiseuille's equation, was so small as to be negligible, but they incorrectly asserted that the direction of mass flow opposed the hydrokinetic pressure gradients in their system because they incorrectly interpreted the effect of gravitational potential gradients.

The model system of ESCHRICH et al. is not very representative of mass flow in phloem for two important reasons: (1) in sieve tubes the pressure gradient along the tube cannot be ignored and (2) in phloem there may be a large gradient of water potential outside the sieve tube which must be taken into account. Fortunately a more thorough model of Münch pressure flow in a real system (sugar beet) has been reported by CHRISTY and FERRIER (1973); their results and theoretical approach will be presented below in a different format.

CHRISTY and FERRIER (1973) presented a system of equations that described the temporal and spatial dependence of the sugar concentration, the turgor pressure, the sap velocity and the peripheral water influx (or efflux) for each element in a long sieve tube. The system of equations (some of them differential equations) had no simple solution, but the equations completely defined the Münch model in the non-steady state. By specifying the sugar-loading rate ($=3.4\times10^{-6}$ µgm s^{-1} per sieve element), the hydraulic conductivity of the sieve tube (from Poiseuille's law), and by guessing the hydraulic conductivity of the semi-permeable sieve cell membranes, they were able to obtain a steady-state solution by a laborious and costly numerical (iterative) computer calculation. Recently one of us (TYREE) has obtained a simpler steady-state solution of the same problem. The simpler steady-state solution still requires an iterative solution but it can be executed more rapidly and cheaply on a programmable desk calculator. The simpler solution is presented below.

In order to obtain an iterative solution, equations are sought which give the gradients of concentration and pressure at a point in terms of known quantities (including the concentration and the pressure) at the point. The iterative equation allows us to calculate new known quantities at adjacent points by multiplying their known rate of change with distance by a sufficiently small interval of distance, Δs.

The solution requires three statements of the conservation of matter and two transport equations: Poiseuille's law and an equation for passive water permeation across the sieve-cell membrane.

1. The Statements of Conservation of Matter

Fig. 1 illustrates a cylindrical sieve tube starting in the source region and transporting water and sucrose from left to right for positive fluxes. For simplicity the sieve tube is assumed to have a uniform radius; CHRISTY and FERRIER (1973) allowed their tubes to taper in the source and sink regions. For simplicity the sieve element is assumed to contain only water plus one sugar. If other sugars or ions are included a much more complex mathematical model results. ψ^0 is the outside water potential, J^* the sugar loading flux rate, J_w^* the passive water volume influx (or efflux), J the specific mass transfer, $\bar{J}_v$ the average volume flux, C^i the sucrose concentration inside and P the turgor pressure, are all functions of s the distance down the tube.

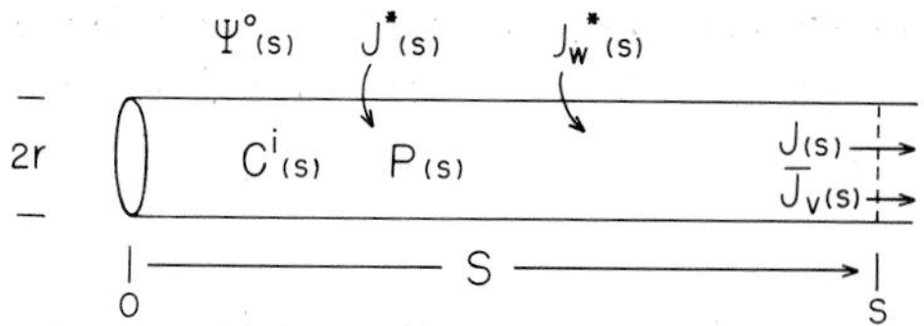

Fig. 1. A diagram showing the upper end of a cylindrical sieve tube of radius r. The sieve plates are not shown. All the parameters indicated are functions of distance s only in the steady state; $s=0$ at the top of the tube. The outside (apoplastic) water potential, Ψ^0 (bar), depends on the environmental water-stress conditions imposed on the plant; the sucrose loading rate, J^* (mole s^{-1} cm^{-2} of peripheral membrane), is fixed at a value to yield the appropriate specific mass-transfer rate, J (mole s^{-1} cm^{-2} of lumen cross-section); J_w^* (ml s^{-1} cm^{-2} of peripheral membrane) is the passive water influx or efflux rate; C^i (mole cm^{-3}) is the sucrose concentration in the lumen and P (bar) is the hydrostatic pressure in the lumen; $\bar{J}_v$ (cm s^{-1} or ml s^{-1} cm^{-2} of lumen cross-section) is the average fluid velocity or average volume flux rate through the lumen

The first conservation equation concerns specific mass transfer (SMT), i.e., Eq. 10;

$$J = C^i \bar{J}_v. \tag{10}$$

The second conservation statement is that in the steady state the sugar transport rate at point s must equal the total loading rate from $s=0$ to s, i.e.

$$\pi r^2 J = \pi r^2 (J^*)_{s=0} + 2\pi r \int_0^s J^* \, ds,$$

from which we obtain

$$J = \frac{2}{r} \int_0^s J^* \, ds + (J^*)_{s=0}, \tag{13}$$

where r is the radius of the tube. The third conservation statement is that in the steady state the volume flow rate at point s must equal the total volume loading rate from $s=0$ to s, i.e.

$$\pi r^2 (J_w^*)_{s=0} + \pi r^2 \bar{V}_s (J^*)_{s=0} + 2\pi r \int_0^s J_w^* \, ds + 2\pi r \bar{V}_s \int_0^s J^* \, ds = \pi r^2 \bar{J}_v$$

from which we obtain,

$$\bar{J}_v = \frac{2}{r} \int_0^s J_w^* \, ds + \frac{2}{r} \bar{V}_s \int_0^s J^* \, ds + (J_w^*)_{s=0} + \bar{V}_s (J^*)_{s=0}, \tag{14}$$

where $\bar{V}_s$ is the partial molar volume of sucrose ($=205$ cm^3 $mole^{-1}$). In our model we need to know the rate of change of the average volume flux with distance, i.e.

$$\frac{d\bar{J}_v}{ds} = \frac{2}{r} J_w^* + \frac{2}{r} \bar{V}_s J^*. \tag{15}$$

If any of the conservation equations are violated then the concentrations and volume of the system would change with time which violates the steady-state condition.

2. The Transport Equations

In this model we do not need a transport equation for the sucrose influx rate, J^*, because this is specified on the basis of experimental measurements. We do need to apply Poiseuille's law to the sieve-element lumen and the sieve plate separately. The sieve plate offers the greatest resistance to water flow, therefore the turgor pressure will drop more or less step-wise across each sieve plate. It is best to even out the step-wise turgor pressure gradient over a long distance by assigning a hydraulic conductivity, L, to the tube which averages the hydraulic conductivity of the lumen and plate over the length of each sieve element. If the lumen is of radius r and length l and if the sieve pores are of radius r^* and length l^* and occupy a relative area of $\alpha = 1/2$ (ESAU and CHEADLE, 1959), the averaging can be done by defining

$$\frac{dP}{dl} = \frac{\Delta P_{\text{lumen}} + \Delta P_{\text{plate}}}{l + l^*} \text{ (bar)}, \tag{16}$$

and by defining an average hydraulic conductivity, L, from Poiseuille's law by,

$$L = 10^{-6} \frac{(l + l^*) r^2 r^{*2}}{8 \eta (r^{*2} l + 2 r^2 l^*)} \text{ (cm}^2\, s^{-1} \text{ bar}^{-1}), \tag{17}$$

where η is the viscosity of the flowing sap and the factor of 10^{-6} converts from pressure in cgs units to bars. If sucrose is the only solute, we can then write from Eq. (9) that

$$\bar{J}_v = -L \frac{dP}{ds} = -L \left(RT \frac{dC^i}{ds} + \frac{d\Psi^0}{ds} - \frac{l}{L_p} \frac{dJ_w^*}{ds} \right). \tag{18}$$

The equation for passive water permeation comes directly from Eqs. (5 and 6):

$$J_w^* = -L_p(\Psi^i - \Psi^0) = -L_p(P - RTC^i - \Psi^0). \tag{19}$$

3. The Equations for Iteration

We need to use Eqs. (10, 13, 15, 18, and 19) to obtain equations relating $\bar{J}_v$, P, and J_w^* in terms of C^i and J^*, and we need iterative equations to obtain new values of P and C^i. First by equating Eqs. (10 and 13) we obtain,

$$\bar{J}_v = \frac{1}{C^i} \frac{2}{r} \int_0^s J^*\, ds + \frac{(J^*)_{s=0}}{C^i}, \tag{20}$$

and after dividing through by L we obtain,

$$\frac{dP}{ds} = -\frac{1}{C^i} \frac{2}{rL} \int_0^s J^*\, ds - \frac{(J^*)_s}{LC^i}. \tag{21}$$

Eq. (21) is an iterative equation for P provided we can determine P at $s=0$. Differentiating Eq. (20) with respect to s and equating the result to the right side of Eq. (15) yields a formula for dC^i/ds in terms of C^i, J^*, and J_v^* which can be used to calculate new C^i's by iteration:

$$\frac{dC^i}{ds}=\frac{(C^i-C^{i2}\bar{V}_s)J^*-C^{i2}J_w^*}{\int_0^s J^*\,ds+\frac{r}{2}(J^*)_{s=0}} \tag{22}$$

Since Ψ^0 is assumed to be known as a function of s, J_w^* is a function only of two unknowns; these are C^i and P (Eq. 19). We need only determine the boundary conditions on C^i, P and J_w^* at $s=0$ in order to iterate new values of C^i, P, J_w^* and $\bar{J}_v$. From Eqs. (13 and 14) it is clear that at $s=0$ $J=(J^*)_{s=0}$ and $\bar{J}_v=(J_w^*)_{s=0}+\bar{V}_s(J^*)_{s=0}$. Applying Eq. (10) yields

$$C^i=(J/\bar{J}_v)_{s=0}=\frac{J^*}{J_w^*+\bar{V}_s J^*} \quad \text{at } s=0 \text{ or} \tag{23}$$

$$J_w^*=(1/C^i-\bar{V}_s)\,J^* \quad \text{at } s=0. \tag{24}$$

It is worth noting here that substitution of Eq. (24) into Eq. (22) yields the result that $dC^i/ds=0$ at $s=0$ regardless of the values of C^i and J^* at $s=0$. Putting Eq. (24) into Eq. (19) we can solve for P at $s=0$.

$$P=\frac{\bar{V}_s-1/C^i}{L_p}J^*+RTC^i+\Psi^0 \quad \text{at } s=0. \tag{25}$$

The only other restriction that can be applied to the system is in the form of an inequality: $P>0$ for all s; we could also say that $C>0$ for all s but this is less restrictive since it could allow negative P's. Our choice of C^i at $s=0$ is arbitrary beyond the restrictions on P; therefore we are forced to conclude that several steady-state solutions are possible which will give the same net transport rate for sucrose depending on the choice of C^i at $s=0$. This point was overlooked by CHRISTY and FERRIER (1973). They considered their steady-state solution unique, but the exact solution is not unique; it depends on the previous history of the system and how the steady-state transport is approached. Our contention can be proved by examining Eq. (13); J does not depend on C^i, but as C^i drops $\bar{J}_v$ increases to keep J constant (see Eq. (20)).

To solve for $\bar{J}_v$, P, J_w^* and C^i by iteration we need only choose C^i at $s=0$ and the physical parameters of the system ($\Psi^0(s)$, $J^*(s)$, L, L_p, and r). The value of J_w^* at $s=0$ is determined by Eq. (24); Eqs. (21 and 22) can then be used to find dP/ds and dC^i/ds respectively. Multiplying dP/ds and dC^i/ds by the iteration interval Δs and adding the results to the previous values of P and C^i leads to new values of C and P at $s+\Delta s$. These new values of P and C^i can then be used to calculate new dP/ds and dC^i/ds values by the use of Eqs. (19, 21, 22).

A more detailed discussion of the iterative solution has been published (TYREE et al., 1974) in *Plant Physiology* together with several sample calculations. In Fig. 2

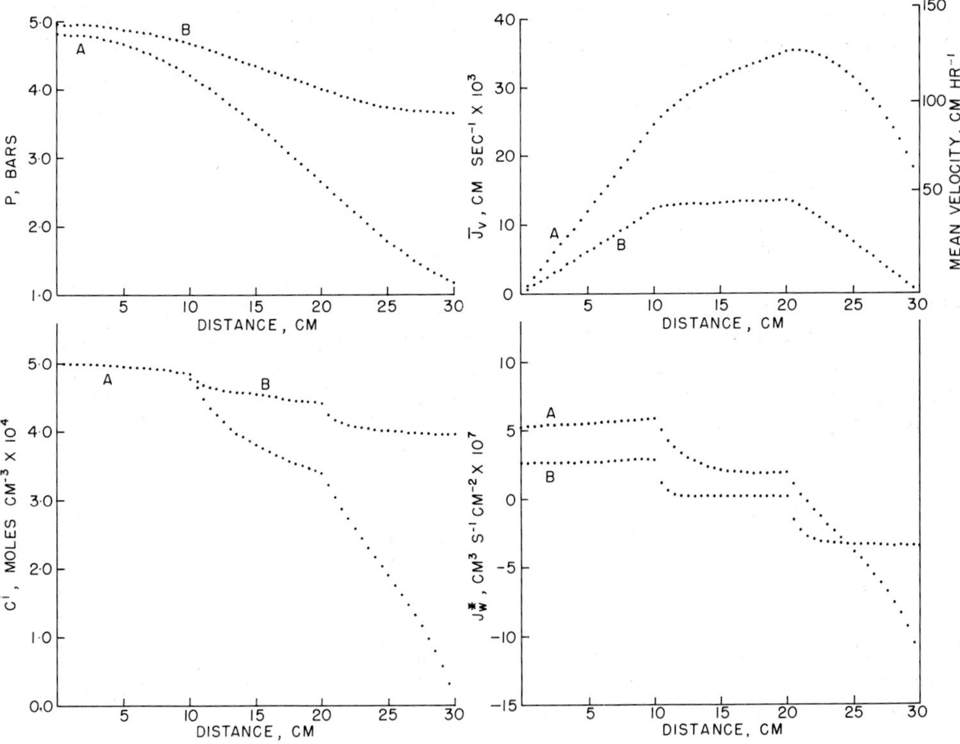

Fig. 2. Two steady state solutions of the translocation parameters in sugar beet. In both curves the hydraulic conductivity of the lumen, L, is 0.2 cm^2 s^{-1} bar^{-1}; the lumen radius, r, in 5×10^{-4} cm; and the sucrose concentration at the top of the tube ($s=0$) is 5×10^{-4} mole cm^{-3}. In curve A the hydraulic conductivity of the peripheral membrane, Lp, is 2×10^{-7} cm s^{-1} bar^{-1}, the water potential at $s=0$, Ψ^0 is -5 bar and the water potential gradient, $d\Psi^0/ds$ is 3×10^{-3} bar cm^{-1}; the sucrose loading rate J^* is 3×10^{-10} mole s^{-1} cm^{-2} in the first 10 cm of the path; J^* is zero in the middle 10 cm and the specific mass transfer is 12×10^{-6} mole s^{-1} cm^{-2} (=14.8 gm h^{-1} cm^{-2}) from $s=10$ to $s=20$ cm; in the last 10 cm the sucrose unloading rate J^* is -3×10^{-10} mole s^{-1} cm^{-2}. In curve B $Lp=5 \times 10^{-7}$; $\Psi^0(s=0)=-7$; $d\Psi^0/ds=1 \times 10^{-3}$; $J^*=1.5 \times 10^{-10}$ ($s=0$ to 10 cm); $J^*=0$ ($s=10$ to 20 cm) and the specific mass transfer rate is 6×10^{-6} mole s^{-1} cm^{-2} (7.4 gm h^{-1} cm^{-2}); and $J^*=-1.5 \times 10^{-10}$ for the last 10 cm ($s=20$ to 30 cm). Distance from the top of the sieve tube is plotted on the abscissa; on the ordinates are plotted the lumen pressure (P), the sucrose concentration in the lumen (c^i), the average sap velocity in the lumen ($\bar{J}_v$), and the passive water influx or efflux rate across the peripheral lumen membrane (J_w^*)

we present two solutions of the problem using some of the parameters of sugar beet given by Christy and Ferrier (1973) except that r is held constant over the path length. The caption to Fig. 2 gives the details regarding the choice of parameters.

Two of the biggest unknowns of this system are the values of the hydraulic conductivity of the sieve tube, L, and the sieve-element membrane hydraulic conductivity, L_p. The qualitative effect of raising the value of L is to decrease the magnitudes of the pressure gradient and concentration gradient everywhere in the path; the qualitative effect of increasing L_p is to increase the magnitude of the pressure gradient and to decrease the magnitude of the concentration gradient in the path region of sugar beet (Christy and Ferrier, 1973).

From the theoretical analysis of steady-state Münch pressure-flow systems over long distances TYREE et al. (1974) have put acceptable limits on the values of L_p and L if Münch pressure-flow is to succeed in trees. If a means could be devised to measure L_p and L in addition to concentration and pressure gradients, definitive conclusions regarding this mechanism of translocation could be arrived at.

II. The Peristaltic Pumping Model

There is little doubt that the basic translocation process is the bulk flow of a solution of sucrose and other solutes. Bulk flow is the only mechanism by which sucrose fluxes of the observed magnitude can be conducted over the distances found in phloem translocation. There is no way to "facilitate" diffusion of sucrose through a stationary liquid medium that will produce the observed fluxes. Even selective activated sucrose flux across sieve plates will be of no avail without substantial mixing of the sap in the sieve-element lumen.

The main point of disagreement is about how bulk fluid flow is motivated. In 1923 the Indian physiologist, J.C. BOSE, suggested that the bulk fluid flow is driven by peristaltic contractions in the phloem pathway. This concept was later refined by THAINE (1969) who proposed that peristaltic contractions occur in small membrane bounded tubules ("transcellular strands") which he claimed to observe traversing many sieve elements *via* the sieve-plate pores (THAINE, 1962). These ideas have been translated into a firm quantitative model in the imaginative article by AIKMAN and ANDERSON (1971); their treatment of the peristaltic model will be given below.

AIKMAN and ANDERSON (1971) reasoned that it would be profitable to examine the physical implications of a model for peristaltic pumping down transcellular strands 1 µm in radius in order to determine whether the quantitative predictions for flow-rates, pressure gradients, and energy-dissipation rates are physically acceptable. They proposed a detailed set of quantitative assumptions about the system and derived the physical consequences. Should it prove impossible to obtain an acceptable set of predicted values from an acceptable set of assumed values, then this would have constituted evidence for rejecting the model. Their conclusion is that their model is physically reasonable, but they of course recognize that this exercise in mathematical modeling does not prove it to be the real mechanism of translocation.

They argue that the peristaltic model has several qualitatively attractive features: (a) contractile systems are common in biology at the cellular level, e.g. muscle, cilia, flagella, and mitotic spindles, so that one is sure that the biochemical mechanisms have evolved for transducing chemical energy to mechanical work. (b) in peristaltic contractions bulk flow is pressure-driven, and thermodynamically, pressure is the force which most effectively drives a volume flow, and (c) the metabolic energy input for driving translocation is continuously distributed along the tubule.

For simplicity, AIKMAN and ANDERSON (1971) assumed the sieve elements were traversed by many tubules imagined to be circular in cross-section 1 µm in mean radius, each tubule being bounded by a wall containing circumferential elements which contract and relax rhythmically. The walls move only radially; the waves of contraction passing along the tubule drive an axial flow of solution within the tubule. The motion in the wall can be characterized by the mean radius of the tubule, $\bar{r}$ (cm), the amplitude of the contraction wave, b (cm), the velocity of propagation of the contraction wave, v (cm s^{-1}), the frequency of contractions, f (s^{-1}), and the wave length λ (cm). If sinusodial waves of contraction occur in the s direction then the tubule surface can be defined by,

$$R(s,t)=\bar{r}+b\sin\frac{2\pi}{\lambda}(s-vt) \tag{26}$$

where t is the time (seconds) and $R(s,t)$ is the tube radius as a function of time and distance. In a moving frame of reference travelling at velocity v with the wave, the radius r is independent of time,

$$r(s)=\bar{r}+b\sin\frac{2\pi s}{\lambda}. \tag{27}$$

The motion of solution within the tubule requires the use of additional parameters; these are: the viscosity of the solution, η (poise), the pressure, P (bar $=10^6$ dyne cm^{-2}), the axial volume flow rate in the tubule, dV/dt ($cm^3\,s^{-1}$), the time averaged axial volume flow rate of solution, $d\bar{V}/dt$, the solute concentration C (mole cm^{-3}), and the time averaged flux of solute within the tubule, $\bar{J}$ (mole $cm^{-2}\,s^{-1}$ = the specific mass transfer of sucrose averaged over time). If the fluid is incompressible, if the wave-length is long compared to the mean radius, if the flow is laminar, and if no volume flow occurs across the wall of the tube, then the pressure in the moving frame of reference is a function of s only:

$$\frac{dP}{ds}=-10^{-6}(8\eta q/r^4+8\eta v/r^2) \tag{28}$$

where q is the flow-rate in the moving frame of reference and the factor of 10^{-6} converts dyne cm^{-2} to bars.

In the stationary frame, the flow will vary as the wave passes, but the time-averaged flow, $d\bar{V}/dt$, will be q plus the wave velocity v times the average area of the tubule, i.e.

$$d\bar{V}/dt=q+\pi v(\bar{r}^2+b^2/2). \tag{29}$$

The beauty of the peristaltic model is that there need be no net pressure difference over a wave-length of contraction, under these conditions it can be shown that:

$$d\bar{V}/dt=\frac{\pi v b^2}{2}\,\frac{16\bar{r}^2-b^2}{2\bar{r}^2+3b^2}. \tag{30}$$

By equating Eqs. (29 and 30) q can be found in terms of v, $\bar{r}$ and b, and the pressure can then be found by integration of Eq. (28). From this the rate at which work is performed by the wall on the fluid can also be calculated from the product of the pressure, the perimeter of the wall and the radial velocity, $\partial R(s,t)/\partial t$, integrated with respect to the axial distance. If W (watt = Joule s^{-1}) is the rate of work, then

$$W=10^{-1}\int_{\text{path length}} P\,2\pi R(s,t)\frac{\partial R(s,t)}{\partial t}\,ds. \tag{31}$$

where the factor of 10^{-1} converts work in bar $cm^3\,s^{-1}$ to Joule s^{-1}.

The key parameters calculated by AIKMAN and ANDERSON are the maximum pressure, P_{max}, generated in a wave length of contraction, the maximum tension in the peristaltic wall, $T_{max} = P_{max}\, r$ and the rate of work performed, W. Values of $\bar{r}, b, v, \lambda$, and the number of tubules per square cm were chosen to give the experimentally observed rate of specific mass transfer ($J = C\bar{J}_v = C\, d\bar{V}/dt = 7 \times 10^{-6}$ mole s^{-1} cm^{-2} = 9 g sucrose cm^{-2} h^{-1}). To do this the mean square radius ($= \bar{r}^2 + 1/2\, b^2$) is taken to be 1 μm, the relative amplitude of contraction ($= b/\bar{r}$ is taken to be 0.4, the wave velocity (v) is taken to be 5×10^{-2} cm s^{-1}, the wave length (λ) is assigned a value of 100 μm, the sucrose concentration is 3×10^{-4} mole cm^{-3} and the viscosity is taken to be 2×10^{-2} poise (an overestimate). Using these values AIKMAN and ANDERSON calculated the maximum pressure to be only 1.13×10^{-3} bar, and the power consumption equaled 3.3 J s^{-1} per m of tubule.

The proof that these values are reasonable lies in comparing them to known values for biological contractile systems. In order to maintain the flow, a unit area of tubule wall must perform work at the rate of 5×10^{-8} Joule cm^{-2} s^{-1}. For comparison Brookshaw (1965) found that sea urchin sperm tails, 30 μm long and 0.2 μm in diameter, could do work against viscous water at a rate of 5×10^{-7} Joule cm^{-2} s^{-1}, i.e. 10 times the calculated required work rate. Another important energetic question can be asked. Is the reported metabolic rate of phloem sufficient to supply the required mechanical power? Assuming an efficiency of only 1/8 in converting sucrose to useful contractile work, AIKMAN and ANDERSON (1971), showed that the required sucrose consumption rate compares favorably with the observed consumption rate.

The calculated tension that the muscular walls would have to develop to produce the maximum calculated pressure is easily two orders of magnitude less than the tensions that vertebrate muscle is capable of sustaining (AIKMAN and ANDERSON, 1971). The only point of doubt arises from the fact that the maximum rate of relative circumferential contraction is about 50% faster than frog sartorius smooth muscle and 100 times faster than invertebrate smooth muscle. Be this as it may, the mathematical model proposed by AIKMAN and ANDERSON possesses many interesting advantages and internal consistencies. We hope that their model will stimulate future research.

The only other point that remains to be mentioned is that the peristaltic model is capable of either unidirectional or bidirectional transport. If the transport is bidirectional then the mathematical treatment of the temporal and spatial distribution of ^{14}C-sucrose in the translocation system will conform exactly to the models worked out by CANNY and PHILLIPS (1963). These models will be discussed in Section C of this chapter.

III. Electroosmosis and Transcellular Cyclosis

We cannot complete a section on models of how mass flow arises without reference to two other proposed models.

Some workers propose that mass flow is activated by a kind of transcellular cyclosis within tubules strung through sieve-plate pores. Alternatively, others believe the fluid in the lumen is directly activated by contractile protein filaments strung through the lumen and sieve-plate pores. This model cannot be properly evaluated to yield driving forces and energy requirements because we do not understand the mechanism of cyclosis. We will not treat this model here, but refer the reader to the best discussion we have seen (MACROBBIE, 1971).

In the electroosmotic model the sap is thought to be driven by the frictional interaction between the sap and the unidirectional flow of potassium ions across the sieve plate; the potassium is set into motion by an electrical potential difference generated across the sieve plate. We do not propose to discuss this model at all for three reasons: (a) an entire chapter in this volume (Chapter 13) is devoted to the model. (b) several experimental and theoretical treatments have appeared in the past (FENSOM, 1957; SPANNER, 1958 and 1970; DAINTY et al., 1963; TYREE and FENSOM, 1970; MACROBBIE, 1971; BOWLING, 1968, 1969), and (c) we are personally so convinced that electroosmosis cannot be the mechanism of translocation that we do not wish to belabor the point any further.

C. Mathematical Models Treating the Kinetics of Spatial and Temporal Distribution of Labeled Translocate

Many researchers have administered $^{14}CO_2$ and followed the spatial and temporal distribution of photosynthetically fixed tracer. Unfortunately the use of radioactive tracers has not solved the problem of translocation in spite of many optimistic hopes. The lack of success can be attributed largely to the complexity of the overall transport system comprising a photosynthetic system, a short-distance transport system for loading assimilates, a long-distance transport system in the vascular tissue, and another short-distance transport system for consumption, storage and retrieval. The tracer distribution is determined not only by the transport process within the sieve tubes, but also by the processes of loading into the sieve tubes and unloading to the sink. The sink may be a major terminal sink such as a developing fruit, or a minor sink amounting only to a minor unloading by lateral leakage along the path. To interpret tracer kinetics we need to develop mathematical models which incorporate these component factors.

No attempt will be made to review or synthesize all the tracer kinetics studies carried out to date. Examples from the literature will be drawn upon when they illustrate various facets of the as yet unresolved mathematical problems.

We will first examine what is known about the kinetics of loading of sieve tubes in the photosynthetic sites; later we will examine the kinetics of the tracer distribution in the translocation path when there are varying degrees of lateral unloading.

I. The Kinetics of Loading

In most experiments a photosynthesizing leaf is exposed to $^{14}CO_2$ either for a short pulse labelling period (e.g. about 10 min or less) or for a long period until steady-state translocation of radioactive assimilate occurs. The kinetics of loading can be complicated for at least two reasons:

(1) The photosynthetically fixed ^{14}C-sucrose could mix with one or more pools of unlabeled sucrose before being loaded, and these pools could be growing or shrinking with time. (2) the loading of ^{14}C-sucrose on to the transport path (e.g., petiole and stem) could be affected by the kinetic size of the leaf which is a measure

of the time delay in reaching the base of the leaf during the transport of label from the farthest point in the leaf.

One of the first quantitative studies was carried out by GEIGER and SWANSON (1965a, b) on 6-week-old sugar beet (*Beta vulgaris*) plants trimmed to a single source leaf and a sink consisting of a growing leaf and roots. In their first experiments GEIGER and SWANSON (1965a) pulse-labeled the source leaf with a large amount of $^{14}CO_2$ (50 μCi) for 7 to 10 min; before and after the pulse labeling, photosynthesis continued in normal air. The time-course of accumulation of ^{14}C in the total sinks was followed by direct analysis of plants harvested at various intervals as well as by monitoring the accumulation of translocated activity with a Geiger tube positioned against the sink leaf.

By kinetic and biochemical analysis they determined that sucrose was the major substance translocated and they determined that there was a rapid turn-over of label in the sucrose pool of the source leaf. Label began reaching the sink leaf after a 12- to 15-min-time lag; the rate of delivery peaked within about 30 min; and the rate of delivery diminished to near zero within an additional 50 min. In later steady-state labeling experiments GEIGER and SWANSON (1965b) were able to demonstrate steady-state translocation within 100 min after first exposing the source leaf to $^{14}CO_2$. They were also able to evaluate enough parameters to construct a mathematical model of phloem loading in sugar beet. These important parameters are the rate of photosynthesis, F (μgm sucrose min^{-1} dm^{-2} of leaf surface), the size of the sucrose pool in the leaf, S (μgm dm^{-2}), the rate at which the sucrose pool grows, A (μgm min^{-1} dm^{-2}). By assuming only one pool of sucrose, by assuming negligible time delay between the first application of $^{14}CO_2$ and the appearance of ^{14}C-sucrose in the pool, and by neglecting the kinetic size of the source leaf, they were able to derive an equation describing the accumulation of ^{14}C-sucrose in the source pool and its transport.

If L^* is the amount of ^{14}C-sucrose in the source pool (μgm dm^{-2}), then at time $t=0$ $L^*=0$ and as the steady state is approached L^* approaches $S+\text{A}t$. We can apply a conservation statement describing the time dependence of L^*; namely,

$$dL^*/dt = (dL^*/dt)_{\text{input}} - (dL^*/dt)_{\text{output}}, \quad \text{where} \tag{32a}$$

$$(dL^*/dt)_{\text{input}} = F, \quad \text{and} \tag{32b}$$

$$(dL^*/dt)_{\text{output}} = \left(\frac{L^*}{S+At}\right) T. \tag{32c}$$

Combining Eqs. (32a, b, c) leads to a non-linear differential equation (Eq. 33) which can be solved by the method of separation of variables to yield Eq. (34)

$$dL^*/dt = F - T\left(\frac{L^*}{S+At}\right) \tag{33}$$

$$L^* = S + At - S\left(\frac{S}{S+At}\right)^{T/A} \tag{34}$$

If there is a time delay t_D (min) between the first appearance of the label at the top of the transport path and its first appearance in the sink leaf then the rate of appearance of ^{14}C-sucrose in the sink leaf should be given by

$$\frac{\alpha T L^*}{S+A(t-t_D)} = \frac{\alpha T}{S+A(t-t_D)}\left(S+At-S\left(\frac{S}{S+A(t-t_D)}\right)^{T/A}\right) \quad \text{for } t>t_D. \tag{35}$$

where α is the fraction of the total exported ^{14}C-sucrose going to the sink leaf. (The rest is transported to the roots.) Eqs. 34 and 35 fit the experimental results quite well (GEIGER and SWANSON, 1965b). Had the source pool of sucrose not been growing then the kinetics of the pool would be given by a simple exponential function,

$$L^* = S - S\exp\left(-\frac{T}{S}t\right), \qquad A=0. \tag{36}$$

In the experiments carried out by GEIGER and SWANSON (1965b) the rate of growth of the pool ($A=7.8$ μgm min^{-1} dm^{-2}) was a little too large compared to the pool size ($S=3{,}900$ μgm dm^{-2}) for Eq. (36) to fit their results exactly.

A more thorough investigation of the kinetics of ^{14}C-sucrose loading has been carried out by FISHER (1970a, b, c) in his studies on soybean (*Glycine max*, var. Hawkeye). The kinetics of loading of ^{14}C-sucrose onto soybean petioles appears to be rather more complicated than it is in sugar beet. In part this could be explained by differences in leaf anatomy, but the loading kinetics in soybean is better understood than it is in sugar beet.

In his first paper, FISHER (1970a) looked at ^{14}C-photosynthate transport through soybean stems and petioles following pulse and steady-state labeling. He concluded that translocation proceeded with only slight peripheral loss of ^{14}C-sucrose to the stem or petiole. The peripheral loss amounted to less than 3% of the total radioactivity in the first two hours. He concluded that the kinetics of ^{14}C-translocation must be determined primarily by factors operating within the leaf, i.e. the kinetics of loading is translated into a spatial distribution of ^{14}C-sucrose in the translocation path.

FISHER also studied the kinetics of appearance of ^{14}C-labeled sucrose in the leaf and compared this to the kinetics of appearance of other ^{14}C-labeled compounds synthesized in the leaf and petiole after a 3-min-pulse-labeling period. The only compound in the leaf with kinetics at all similar to the export of sucrose was a sterol glucoside, a correspondence which held in both pulse labeling and steady-state labeling. FISHER suggests that the sterol glucoside may be involved in the transfer of sucrose into the phloem as a membrane carrier, but it is not clear to us why this should follow from the similarity of kinetics. Presumably an abundant supply of unlabeled sterol glucoside existed before the pulse-labeling period which could have contributed to the loading of ^{14}C-sucrose.

By comparing the specific activity of the sucrose in the source leaf to the specific activity of the $^{14}CO_2$ supplied during steady-state labeling, FISHER (1970b) concluded that only about 62% of the leaf sucrose is in the loading pools; the rest of the sucrose resides in a slowly exchanging compartment in the epidermal cells.

After a 3 min pulse label the relative activity of ^{14}C in soybean petioles did not peak until 20 min had passed. In a later paper, FISHER (1970c), pursued mathematical modeling in order to determine the kinetic size of leaves of different shape. In order to obtain relatively simple solutions he had to make several assumptions including a uniform translocation velocity at all points in the sieve cells in the source leaf. Clearly this assumption is not valid in a MÜNCH model if the sieve tubes are of uniform diameter and loaded equally everywhere (see Fig. 2), but the assumption is not too far wrong if the loading rate per cell is the same and if the cells taper towards the top of the loading zone (see CHRISTY and FERRIER, 1973). In soybean a figure of 2–3 min is given as a reasonable value for the kinetic size of the leaf. Since this time is still short compared to the time for the build-up of peak activity in the petiole, FISHER (1970c) appealed to the kinetics of sucrose exchange in the source pools for the explanation. FISHER referred to the peculiar anatomy of soybean leaves for his model; he assumed that there were two pools of sucrose, one located in a photosynthetic compartment (the palisade and spongy parenchyma) and the other in a non-photosynthetic compartment (paraveinal mesophyll, border parenchyma, and phloem parenchyma) (FISHER, 1967).

Since the pulse labeling time is short (3 min) FISHER presumed that the photosynthetic compartment rapidly reached a peak activity, L_0^* (dpm), and decayed exponentially,

$$L_1^* = L_0^* \exp(-kt/S_1), \tag{37}$$

where k is the transport rate from the photosynthetic compartment (μgm min^{-1}), L_1^* is the amount of radioactive sucrose in the photosynthetic compartment, and S_1 is the compartment size (μg). The exponential decay of radioactive sucrose in the first pool occurs because after the initial labeling period the transport rate of unlabeled sucrose into the pool (from photosynthesis) equals the transport rate of labeled and unlabeled sucrose out of the pool. An exponential dilution of tracer results. The differential equation for the non-photosynthetic compartment is

$$\frac{dL_2^*}{dt} = k\left(\frac{L_1^*}{S_1} - \frac{L_2^*}{S_2}\right) \tag{38}$$

where L_2^* is the activity of the second compartment (dpm) and S_2 is the size (μg) of the second compartment. The transport rate from the second compartment is assumed to equal the transport rate to it in the steady state. The solution of Eqs. (37 and 38) is

$$L_2^* = \frac{L_0^* S_2}{S_1 - S_2}\left(\exp\left(-\frac{kt}{S_1}\right) - \exp\left(-\frac{kt}{S_2}\right)\right). \tag{39}$$

FISHER (1970c) assumed that the turn-over rates of the two compartments, S_1/k and S_2/k, are proportional to their volumes. He demonstrated that assigning times of 77 min for S_1/k and 11 min for S_2/k yielded a kinetics for L_2^* (the activity of the ultimate source pool) that closely matched the activity in the petiole during translocation after a pulse label.

II. The Kinetics of the Through-Put Component

The work of GEIGER and SWANSON (1965a, b) and of FISHER (1970a, b, c) indicates that the temporal and spatial distribution of ^{14}C-assimilate in the translocation path reflects the kinetics of loading, but this is not generally true. For example, if the mechanism of translocation is MÜNCH pressure flow, the spatial profiles of ^{14}C-assimilate will be distorted within the translocation path by the inevitable passive water entry, J_v^*, into the sieve tube along the path length. The effect of water entry is to increase the translocation velocity down the path and simultaneously to dilute the translocated sap (see Fig. 2).

In some species significant lateral loss and simultaneous lateral accumulation of labeled assimilate can occur; this is almost surely the case in trees where the translocation path is long compared to the length of the loading zone and where carbohydrates are known to be stored in the stem (ZIMMERMANN and BROWN, 1971).

Many mathematical models have been derived attempting to explain the spatial and temporal distribution of labeled translocate in the transport path in terms of the lateral loss of label. The models fall into two classes: (1) those that envisage a unidirectional transport within the sieve tube and (2) those that envisage bidirectional transport through tubules within the same sieve tube. These models will be briefly reviewed below, but it is necessary to bear in mind that the models are ultimately independent of the mechanism by which bulk flow is assumed to occur.

1. Unidirectional Transport with Lateral Loss

The mathematics of unidirectional transport with lateral loss has been worked out by HORWITZ (1958). Only two examples will be given below.

The models are aimed at interpreting a specific kind of experiment. The experimental procedure consists of applying $^{14}CO_2$ to a leaf for a period and translocation is allowed to proceed down the stem. At various times after the start of the labeling, experimental plants are removed and the stems are cut up into segments of known length. The total ^{14}C-activity is extracted and measured in each segment; in some cases the chemical composition of the radioactive material is determined. The log of the ^{14}C-activity is usually plotted as a function of distance down the stem. By repeating the experiment for various translocation times a spatial and temporal picture of the kinetics of tracer distribution is built up. In most cases the semilogarithmic profiles are linear during the early stages of translocation; later the semilogarithmic profile either proceeds down the stem as an undistorted straight line or it develops into a convex curvilinear function of distance.

Let the point $s=0$ represent the point where the bottom of the loading zone and the top of the translocation path meet. At this point the concentration inside the tube will be a function of time only due to the kinetics of loading, i.e. $C^i(0,t)=f(t)$ only. Let us imagine that the slug of sap entering the tube at $s=0$ proceeds down the stem at a uniform velocity, v (cm s^{-1}) and that osmotic dilution due to passive water entry is negligible. If the efflux of sucrose is purely passive then we can use Eq. (4) to describe the C^i as a function of distance and time.

$$J^* = -P^*(C^i - C^0). \tag{4}$$

If the pipe is of radius r, then J^* equals $\frac{r}{2}\frac{dC^i}{dt}$, and if the outside sucrose concentrations are small compared to C^i then,

$$\frac{r}{2}\frac{dC^i}{dt} = -P^* C^i. \tag{40}$$

The outside concentration would remain small in the early stages of reversible leakage of sucrose to the outside; C^0 would always be small if the sucrose were rapidly converted to some non-translocated substance such as starch. If an imaginary slug of sap has been travelling in the pipe for time t^* then it has travelled to position $s = vt^*$ and the concentration as a function of position and time can be obtained by integrating Eq. (40) over the time of the experiment.

$$C^i(s, t) = C^i(O, t') \exp\left(-\frac{2P^*}{r} t^*\right), \tag{41}$$

where t' is the time at which the slug of sap entered the pipe at $s = 0$ ($t' = t - s/v$), and t^* is the time the slug of sap has been in the pipe ($t^* = s/v$). Therefore,

$$C^i(s, t) = C^i(0, t - s/v) \exp\left(-\frac{2P^*}{r}\frac{s}{v}\right), \quad s < vt. \tag{42}$$

In Eq. (42) C^i is to be interpreted as the concentration of radioactivity in the tube (dpm/cm^3) for tracer flux experiments. What is measured however is $Q = Q^i + Q^0 =$ the sum of the quantity of material in a small segment of pipe, Q^i, and the quantity outside the pipe, Q^0, in the same segment. If V_p is the volume of a short segment of pipe Δs long ($V_p = \pi r^2 \Delta s$) then Q^i in the segment is,

$$Q^i = V_p C^i(s, t). \tag{43}$$

We can evaluate Q^0 by starting with a conservation statement: $dQ^0/dt = -dQ^i/dt$, and noting that $J^* = \frac{1}{A_p}\frac{dQ^i}{dt}$, where A_p is the peripheral membrane area in the segment of pipe Δs long ($A_p = 2\pi r \Delta s$). Applying Eq. (4), the solution for C^i in Eq. (42) and remembering that C^0 is much less than C^i, we get

$$\frac{dQ^0}{dt} = P^* A_p C^i = P^* A_p C^i(0, t - s/v) \exp\left(-\frac{2P^*}{r}\frac{s}{v}\right). \tag{44}$$

Integrating Eq. (44) with time yields the value of Q^0 which can be added to Q^i to yield,

$$Q^i + Q^0 = V_p C^i(0, t - s/v) \exp\left(-\frac{2P^*}{r}\frac{s}{v}\right) + A_p P^* \exp\left(-\frac{2P^*}{r}\frac{s}{v}\right) \times \int_{s/v}^{t} C^i(0, t - s/v)\, dt \tag{45}$$

The interesting consequence that follows from Eq. (45) has been pointed out by HORWITZ (1958); the factor $\exp\left(-\frac{2P^*}{r}\frac{s}{v}\right)$ which multiplies the right-hand side of Eq. (45) so dominates the situation (except near the advancing front where $(t-s/v)$ is small) that it imposes the well-known exponential fall-off on the longitudinal pattern of tracer activity. Provided we work well behind the tracer front the exact form of the input function, $C^i(0,t)$ does not in practice matter, and the slope of the line obtained by plotting $\ln(Q^i+Q^0)$ versus s is fairly closely $-2P^*/rv$.

HORWITZ (1958) has shown that if the sucrose loss is passive and reversible (i.e. if Eq. (4) applies and C^0 is not much smaller than C^i), then the plot of $\ln(Q^i+Q^0)$ versus s is no longer log-linear, but after a time the plot again becomes approximately linear for intermediate times. Eq. (45) is also non-linear for very short times but it becomes nearly log-linear much more quickly than when reversible leakage occurs.

One last point is worthy of note here. Some investigators (e.g. CANNY) have tried to deduce the velocity of translocation ($\bar{J}_v$) from the family of curves of $\ln(Q^i+Q^0)$ versus s obtained by allowing translocation to proceed for different times in different plants before measuring Q^i+Q^0. $\bar{J}_v$ has been equated with $\Delta d/\Delta t$ where Δd is the distance between two plots of $\ln(Q^i+Q^0)$ separated by time Δt. SPANNER and PREBBLE (1962) have pointed out that this procedure is erroneous. The procedure is valid only if Q^0 is always zero (that is if there is no lateral leakage); only then would a spacial shift of the profile reflect the velocity of movement through the sieve tube. If there is no lateral leakage the log-linear behavior of Q^i would reflect an exponential increase of $C^i(0,t)$ with time.

2. Bidirectional Transport

CANNY and PHILLIPS (1963) developed another model which yielded specific answers for the spatial and temporal distribution of tracer in the non-steady state and which yielded specific values for the specific mass transfer (J) in the steady state. In the CANNY-PHILLIPS model the sieve tubes are traversed by smaller tubules (or cytoplasmic strands) running from cell to cell *via* the sieve pores. Half of the strands, termed positive strands, are moving sap inside the strands downstream at a velocity v and the sap is at concentration $C_1(s,t)$; the other half of the strands, termed negative strands, are moving sap inside the strands at a velocity $-v$ and the sap is at concentration $C_2(s,t)$. The positive and negative strands are surrounded by a stationary reservoir that exchanges sucrose passively and reversibly with both the positive and negative strands; the concentration of the reservoir is $C_0(s,t)$. At the top and bottom of the translocation path the positive and negative strands link up and sucrose is either loaded or unloaded. The CANNY-PHILLIPS model applies equally well to the slightly different model in which the positive and negative strands are in fact different sieve tubes and the stationary reservoir is the rest of the tissue surrounding the sieve tubes.

Looking at the positive strands in a frame of reference travelling at velocity v we can write an equation for $C_1(t)$ much like Eq. (40); that is,

$$\frac{dC_1}{dt} = -\frac{2P^*}{r}(C_1 - C_0), \tag{46}$$

where r is the radius of the strand and P^* is the permeability to sucrose of the membrane surrounding the positive strand. In a stationary frame of reference we can write,

$$\frac{dC_1}{dt}=\frac{\partial C_1}{\partial t}+v\frac{\partial C_1}{\partial s}. \tag{47}$$

Therefore the differential equation governing the concentration in the positive strand is,

$$\frac{\partial C_1}{\partial t}+v\frac{\partial C_1}{\partial s}=-\frac{2P^*}{r}(C_1-C_0). \tag{48}$$

If the negative strand has the same radius and permeability we can write,

$$\frac{\partial C_2}{\partial t}-v\frac{\partial C_2}{\partial s}=-\frac{2P^*}{r}(C_2-C_0). \tag{49}$$

By applying a conservation statement on sucrose we can also write an equation governing the reservoir,

$$\frac{\partial C_0}{\partial t}=\alpha\frac{P^*}{r}(C_1+C_2-2C_0), \tag{50}$$

where α = the cross-sectional area of all the strands divided by the cross-sectional area of the reservoir. CANNY and PHILLIPS (1963) have shown that when t is large compared to $r/2P^*$, the system of differential equations (48, 49 and 50) reduce to an equation much like FICK's second law; that is,

$$\frac{\partial S}{\partial t}=\frac{v^2 r}{4P^*}\frac{\partial^2 S}{\partial s^2}, \tag{51}$$

where $S=C_1+C_2$ at corresponding place and time. MACROBBIE (1971) pointed out that a similar diffusion type equation ought to apply to each strand and the reservoir separately.

CANNY and PHILLIPS (1963) solved Eq. (51) under the restricted condition when C_1 at $s=0$ is time-independent and equal to C^*. For a tracer experiment this is equivalent to assuming that the loading on the positive strands reaches a maximum steady-state value instantaneously after $^{14}CO_2$ is supplied to a leaf. Initially the tracer concentrations C_1, C_2, and C_0 are zero everywhere. The solution for each strand and the reservoir when $\alpha=1$ is

$$C_1(s,t)=C^*\,\mathrm{erfc}\frac{s}{2(Kt)^{1/2}} \tag{52}$$

$$C_2(s,t)=C^*\left(\mathrm{erfc}\left(\frac{s}{2(Kt)^{1/2}}\right)-2\left(\frac{r}{\pi P^* t}\right)^{1/2}\exp\left(-\frac{s^2}{4Kt}\right)\right) \tag{53}$$

and

$$C_0(s,t)=C^*\left(\mathrm{erfc}\left(\frac{s}{2(Kt)^{1/2}}\right)-\left(\frac{r}{\pi P^* t}\right)^{1/2}\exp\left(-\frac{s^2}{4Kt}\right)\right) \tag{54}$$

where $K = v^2 r/4P^*$ and where erfc is the "error function compliment" defined by

$$\operatorname{erfc}(x) = 1 - \frac{1}{2\pi^{1/2}} \int_0^x \exp(-y^2)\, dy.$$

When a stem is cut up into sections and assayed for ^{14}C-sucrose what is measured is a quantity proportional to $C_T = C_1 + C_0 + C_2$ which from Eqs. (52, 53 and 54) equals

$$C_T = 3\,C^* \left(\operatorname{erfc}\left(\frac{s}{2(Kt)^{1/2}}\right) - \left(\frac{r}{\pi P^* t}\right)^{1/2} \exp\left(-\frac{s^2}{4Kt}\right)\right). \tag{55}$$

It is frequently observed (MacRobbie, 1971) that for times in excess of about 1/2 h the concentration profile, C_T versus s, fits an equation of the form

$$C_T(s) = C_T(s=0)\operatorname{erfc}(s/a). \tag{56}$$

This behavior is predicted by Eq. (55) because for large values of time, t, the exponential term in the right-hand side of Eq. (55) is negligible. This kind of observation on the functional dependence of C_T on s, has been taken as evidence strongly supporting the Canny-Phillips model of translocation. A point may well be introduced here which has perhaps been overlooked by plant physiologists. Canny and Phillips (1963) state that their solution Eqs. (52 through 55) does not apply when the front of radioactivity approaches the sink because *the solution is valid only for an infinitely long translocation path.* This can be proved by noting that the limits of Eqs. (52 through 55) as t approaches infinity is C^* for all finite s in each case. This is the steady-state solution when the pipe is finite in length and the unloading rate is zero. Furthermore, it must be clearly understood that the solutions (Eqs. 52 through 55) do not apply to the transport path if there is ever any irreversible loss of ^{14}C-sucrose along the transport path; irreversible loss *would* occur if the sucrose were stored away in the form of some other carbohydrate (such as starch).

It would be far more reasonable to obtain a general solution of Eqs. (48, 49 and 50) when the loading and unloading rates at the top and bottom of the transport path are specified as the boundary condition. To our knowledge this has never been done. But the solution of this problem would not be an erfc profile (i.e. a diffusion profile).

It is frequently said that the Canny-Phillips-type transport system is incapable of maintaining a high specific mass transfer rate over long distances. From Eq. (10) we can calculate the specific mass transfer in the positive and negative strands separately. The specific mass transfer J (gs sucrose per sec per cm^2 of sieve tube) is then

$$J = \frac{A_s}{2A_t} v(C_1 - C_2) \tag{57}$$

if the positive and negative strands each have area $A_s/2$ and where A_t = the total cross-sectional area of the sieve tube. Since $A_s/2A_t$ is less than one and since C_2 is always greater than zero the transport efficiency of a bidirectional transport system is always less than a unidirectional system.

Canny and Phillips (1963) obtained a steady-state solution of Eqs. (48, 49, and 50), and demonstrated that the maximum distance over which a bidirectional transport system can transport at a given rate J is limited. The steady-state solution is obtained by setting $\partial C_1/\partial t$, $\partial C_2/\partial t$ and $\partial C_0/\partial t$ to zero in Eqs. (48, 49 and 50). When this is done it is evident that the solution of C_1, C_2, and C_0 as a function of s is a family of three straight lines of equal slope ($= -\sigma P^*/v r$) separated by a constant concentration difference, $\sigma/2$. The concentration of the negative strand, C_2, is always smaller than C_1 and C_0 at corresponding distances. By applying the limiting condition that C_2 can never be less than zero CANNY and PHILLIPS (1963) were able to calculate the maximum distance, 1_{max}, over which a specified specific mass transfer rate, J, can be maintained in the steady state; the relation in our symbols is

$$1_{max} = \frac{\alpha v C^* - 2J(\alpha+1)}{2P^* J(\alpha+1)} v r. \tag{58}$$

Clearly from Eq. (58) values of α, v, C^* and J must be restricted such that

$$\alpha v C^* > 2J(\alpha+1).$$

Unfortunately when CANNY and PHILLIPS (1963) calculated values for 1_{max} they chose values which violated this requirement. Let $\alpha=1$ (i.e. the combined cross-sectional area of the strands equals the cross-sectional area of the reservoir), then $v C^* > 4J$ and $v > 4J/C^*$. In order to maintain a specific mass-transfer rate of $J = 1.39 \times 10^{-3}$ g cm^{-2} s^{-1} ($= 5$ g cm^{-2} h^{-1}, one figure used by CANNY and PHILLIPS) when $C^* = 0.25$ g cm^{-3} the value of v must be greater than 2.23×10^{-2} cm s^{-1} ($= 80$ cm h^{-1}). CANNY and PHILLIPS incorrectly used $v = 20$ cm h^{-1} when $C^* =$ 0.25 g cm^{-3}. If we recalculate their curve for $v = 100$ cm h^{-1} ($= 2.78 \times 10^{-2}$ cm s^{-1}) we obtain a value for 1_{max} inversely proportional to P^* (the permeability of the strand membrane to sucrose). In other words $(1_{max})P^*$ is a constant; if $r = 10^{-4}$ cm and if $\alpha = 1$ then $(1_{max}) P^* = 6.95 \times 10^{-7}$ cm^2 s^{-1}. So if $P^* = 10^{-7}$ cm s^{-1} $1_{max} = 6.95$ cm and if $P^* = 10^{-8}$ cm s^{-1} $1_{max} = 69.5$ cm etc. Clearly P^* must be less than 10^{-8} cm s^{-1} in order for a bidirectional transport system to function over a reasonable distance. A value between 10^{-9} and 10^{-10} cm s^{-1} is almost certainly necessary.

To our knowledge no one has discussed another awkward consequence of the CANNY-PHILLIPS model. In the steady state the sucrose concentration is greater in the positive strands than in the reservoir, and the sucrose concentration is less in the negative strands than in the reservoir. Under these conditions the hydrostatic pressure in the positive strands should exceed the pressure in the reservoir and the pressure in the negative strands is less than in the reservoir. Thus the positive strands should tend to swell (or burst) and the negative strands should tend to collapse; if they do not, how are they rigid enough to overcome large pressure differences between the strands and the reservoir?

D. Summary

In order to develop complete mathematical and theoretical descriptions of the translocation process, we need three things: (1) A complete set of transport equations relating localized fluxes of solute and solvent to localized forces. (2) A basis for separating the first-order transport effects from second-order effects, i.e. a basis for deciding which forces are the most important. (3) A collection of conservation statements which tie the system of transport equations into a solvable set of equations.

Several mathematical models of the translocation process are reviewed, and some implications of the models are discussed.

References

AIKMAN, D.P.: A kinetic analysis of an interaction model of phloem translocation. Pestic. Sci. **3**, 643–651 (1972).

AIKMAN, D.P., ANDERSON, W.P.: A quantitative investigation of a peristaltic model for phloem translocation. Ann. Botany (London) **35**, 761–772 (1971).

BOSE, J.C.: Physiology of the ascent of sap. Bose Research Institute, Calcutta. Transact. 5. Longmans, Green and Co. 1923.

BOWLING, D.J.F.: Measurement of the potential across the sieve plates in *Vitis vinifera*. Planta **80**, 21–26 (1968).

BOWLING, D.J.F.: Evidence for the electroosmosis theory of transport in the phloem. Biochim. Biophys. Acta **183**, 230–232 (1969).

BROOKSHAW, C.J.: Non-sinusoidal bending waves of sperm flagella. J. Exptl. Biol. **43**, 155–169 (1965).

CANNY, M.J., PHILLIPS, O.M.: Quantitative aspects of a theory of translocation. Ann. Botany (N.S.) **27**, 379–402 (1963).

CHRISTY, A.L., FERRIER, J.M.: A mathematical treatment of Münch's Pressure-flow hypothesis of phloem translocation. Plant Physiol. (Lancaster) **52**, 531–538 (1973).

CRAFTS, A.S., CRISP, E.C.: Phloem transport in plants. San Francisco: W.H. Freeman Co. 1971.

DAINTY, J., CROGHAN, P.C., FENSOM, D.C.: Electroosmosis, with some applications to plant physiology. Can. J. Botany **41**, 953–966 (1963).

ESAU, K., CHEADLE, V.I.: Size of pores and their contents in sieve elements of dicotyledons. Proc. Nat. Acad. Sci. U.S. **45**, 156–162 (1959).

ESCHRICH, W., EVERT, R.F., YOUNG, J.H.: Solution flow in tubular semipermeable membranes. Planta **107**, 279–300 (1972).

FENSOM, D.S.: The bio-electric potentials of plants and their functional significance. I. An electrokinetic theory of transport. Can. J. Botany **35**, 573–582 (1957).

FISHER, D.B.: An unusual layer of cells in the mesophyll of soybean leaf. Botan. Gaz. **128**, 215–218 (1967).

FISHER, D.B.: Kinetics of C-14 translocation in soybean. I. Kinetics of the stem. Plant Physiol. (Lancaster) **45**, 107–113 (1970a).

FISHER, D.B.: Kinetics of C-14 translocation in soybean. II. Kinetics in the leaf. Plant Physiol. (Lancaster) **45**, 114–118 (1970b).

FISHER, D.B.: Kinetics of C-14 translocation in soybean. III. Theoretical considerations. Plant Physiol. (Lancaster) **45**, 119–125 (1970c).

GEIGER, D.R., GIAQUINTA, R.T., SOVONICK, S.A., FELLOWS, R.J.: Solute distribution in sugar beet leaves in relation to phloem loading and translocation. Plant Physiol. (Lancaster) (1974).

GEIGER, D.R., SWANSON, C.A.: Sucrose translocation in the sugar beet. Plant Physiol. (Lancaster) **40**, 685–690 (1965a).

GEIGER, D.R., SWANSON, C.A.: Evaluation of selected parameters in a sugar beet translocation system. Plant Physiol. (Lancaster) **40**, 942–947 (1965b).

GLASSTONE, S.: Textbook of physical chemistry, p. 259–260. London: MacMillan and Co. 1951.

HAMMEL, H.T.: Measurement of turgor pressure and its gradient in the phloem of oak. Plant Physiol. (Lancaster) **43**, 1042–1048 (1968).

HORWITZ, L.: Some simplified mathematical treatment of translocation in plants. Plant Physiol. (Lancaster) **33**, 81–93 (1958).

MACROBBIE, E.A.C.: Phloem translocation facts and mechanisms: A comparative survey. Biol. Rev. **46**, 429–481 (1971).

MÜNCH, E.: Dynamik der Saftströmungen. Ber. Deut. Botan. Ges. **44**, 68–71 (1927).

MÜNCH, E.: Die Stoffbewegungen in der Pflanze. Jena: Fischer 1930.

SPANNER, D.C.: The translocation of sugar in sieve tubes. J. Exptl. Botany **9**, 332–342 (1958).

SPANNER, D.C.: The electroosmotic theory of phloem transport in the light of recent measurements on *Heracleum* phloem. J. Exptl. Botany **21**, 325–335 (1970).

SPANNER, D.C., PREBBLE, J.N.: The movement of tracers along the petiole of *Nymphoides peltatum*. J. Exptl. Botany **13**, 294–306 (1962).

STEIN, W.D.: The movement of molecules across cell membranes, p. 127. New York-London: Academic Press 1967.

TAMMES, P.M.L., VAN DIE, J., IE, T.S.: Studies on phloem exudation from *Yucca flaccida* Haw. VIII. Fluid mechanics and exudation. Acta Botan. Neerl. **20**, 245–252 (1971).

THAINE, R.: A translocation hypothesis based on the structure of plant cytoplasm. J. Exptl. Botany **13**, 152–160 (1962).

THAINE, R.: Movement of sugars through plants by cytoplasmic pumping. Nature **222**, 873–875 (1969).

TYREE, M.T.: The steady-state thermodynamics of translocation in plants. In: ZIMMERMANN, M.H., BROWN, C.L., Trees. Berlin-Heidelberg-New York: Springer 1971.

TYREE, M.T., CHRISTY, A.L., FERRIER, J.M.: A simpler iterative steady-state solution of Münch pressure-flow systems applied to long and short translocation paths. Plant Physiol. **54**, 589–600 (1974).

TYREE, M.T., FENSOM, D.S.: Some experimental and theoretical observations concerning mass flow in the vascular bundles *Heracleum*. J. Exptl. Botany **21**, 304–324 (1970).

WEATHERLEY, P.E.: Solution flow in tubular semi-permeable membranes. Planta **110**, 181–187 (1972).

WEATHERLEY, P.E., JOHNSON, R.P.C.: The form and function of the sieve tube: A problem in reconciliation. Intern. Rev. Cytol. **24**, 149–192 (1968).

ZIMMERMANN, M.H., BROWN, C.L.: Trees; Structure and function. Berlin-Heidelberg-New York: Springer 1971.

V. Phloem Loading: Storage and Circulation

17. Phloem Loading

D.R. GEIGER

A. Introduction

I. Description of the Concept of Phloem Loading

In this article the term "phloem loading" is applied to the process by which the major translocated substances are selectively and actively delivered to the sieve tubes in the source region prior to translocation. Thus, substances which undergo phloem loading can be accumulated in the phloem cells to a level above their concentration outside the sieve tubes. Substances considered to undergo phloem loading include one or more major translocate sugars and perhaps some inorganic ions and certain amino acids. Phloem loading as used here does not necessarily imply that the process is the driving mechanism powering translocation although this seems likely.

For purposes of analysis this study of phloem loading will be subdivided into three aspects: the cell-to-cell transport preceding phloem loading; the mechanism of phloem loading; and finally the relation of the latter to long-distance transport in the phloem.

II. Development of the Münch Hypothesis and the Role of Phloem Loading in Translocation of Organic Solutes

In the area of phloem physiology the MÜNCH hypothesis (MÜNCH, 1930) has served to stimulate much work over the last four decades. In the original pressure-flow theory the concept of phloem loading was not developed. It was proposed that the sugar moved from the chloroplast to the phloem in the leaf by diffusion. CURTIS and ASAI (1939), ROECKL (1949) and other critics of this aspect of MÜNCH's original hypothesis point out that the sugar gradient in a leaf is not favorable to diffusion of assimilates into the phloem. A number of researchers including CRAFTS (1951), WANNER (1952) and BAUER (1953) suggested a modification of the pressure-flow mechanism in which sucrose or other transport sugars are actively loaded into the sieve tubes of the minor veins. As a result of phloem loading, assimilates are moved from the mesophyll into the sieve tubes where they accumulate at a high concentration. Central to these more recent refinements of the MÜNCH hypothesis is a vectorized movement of solute which actively establishes a high concentration of the major translocate species in the sieve tubes and which may also give rise to pressure flow of translocate.

Three lines of evidence support the existence of phloem loading as an integral part of the translocation process: autoradiographic and plasmolytic studies showing accumulation in the minor veins, experimental data indicating selective uptake of translocate species or their immediate precursors and demonstration of the key involvement of energy metabolism in translocation.

III. Experimental Verification of Phloem Loading

1. Demonstration of Phloem Loading by High-Resolution Autoradiography

High-resolution, whole-leaf autoradiography (Fig. 1A) has provided evidence of accumulation of labeled assimilate in the minor veins of exporting leaves of sugar beet (TURKINA, 1961; HO and MORTIMER, 1971; FELLOWS and GEIGER, 1974; GEIGER *et al.*, 1974) and of bean (KÖCHER and LEONARD, 1971). In all cases the mesophyll had considerably lower content of label than the minor veins, whether $^{14}CO_2$ or

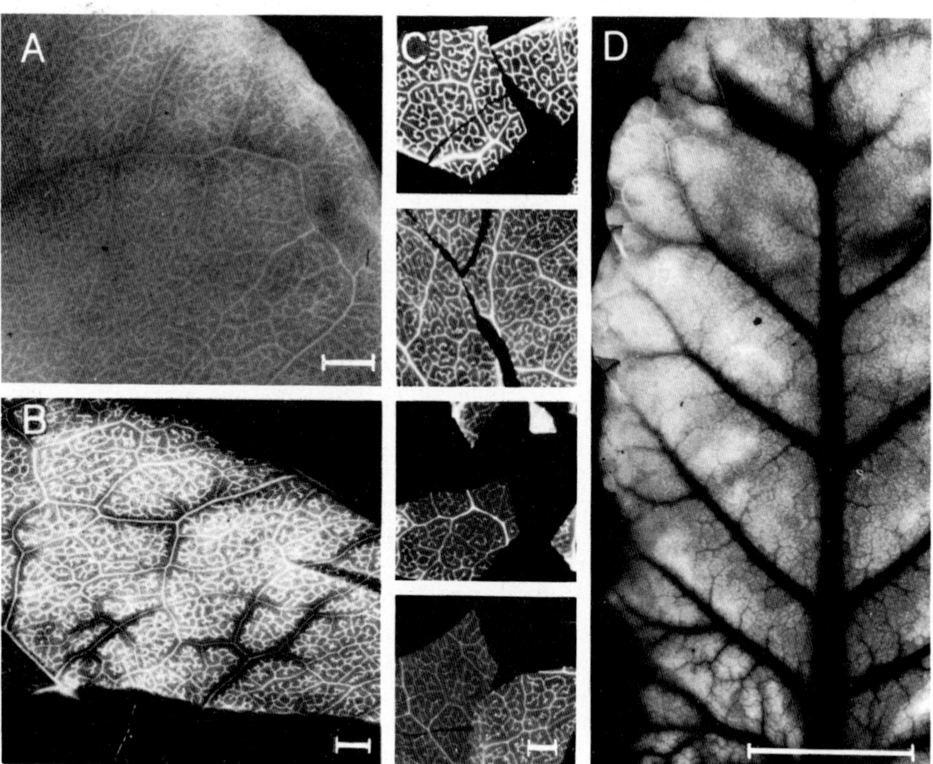

Fig. 1A–D. Autoradiographic studies of phloem loading. Markers indicate 1 mm (A, B, C) or 1 cm (D). (A) Sugar beet leaf presented $^{14}CO_2$ showing accumulation of label (white) in minor veins. (B) Region of a sugar beet leaf supplied exogenously with 20 mM ^{14}C-sucrose. Upper epidermis was abraded. (C) Sugar beet leaf pieces supplied with ^{14}C-sucrose at concentrations of 10 (top), 25, 100, and 200 (bottom) mM. Tissue exposed to labeled sugar for 30 min after upper epidermis was abraded. Free space was cleared by exodiffusion prior to drying. (D) Developing sugar beet leaf (30% FLL) presented $^{14}CO_2$. Tip region shows phloem loading. The bottom 60% of the leaf does not show loading and is presumably importing assimilate

exogenous ^{14}C-sucrose was supplied. The resolution was not sufficient to determine whether accumulation was in the companion cells, the sieve tubes or in both.

Evidence for phloem loading was also shown by histoautoradiography of leaf-blade tissue. Because phloem loading is preceded by transport from the site of carbon assimilation to the minor veins, label from $^{14}CO_2$ first appears in the cells most active in carbon fixation. In a C-4 plant such as maize the majority of the label appeared over the bundle sheath cells, even in periods as short as 10 sec, indicating that bundle sheath cells were capable of fixing CO_2 more rapidly than the mesophyll (BEDNARZ and RASMUSSEN, 1972). In C-3 plants such as oat and sugar beet, after 1 min of labeling the radioactivity in assimilate was generally distributed over the mesophyll (MOSS and RASMUSSEN, 1969). Label progressively moved from the chloroplasts to the minor veins where ^{14}C accumulated to a much higher level than in the surrounding mesophyll. A 5-min lag period before a significant level of label from $^{14}CO_2$ appears in the minor veins is common (TRIP, 1969; HO and MORTIMER, 1971). After a 6-h exposure of a sugar beet leaf to ^{14}C-sucrose solution, PRISTUPA (1964) found the greatest amount of label in the minor veins, with lesser amounts in the mesophyll around these veins and least in the remaining cells. The long exposure to the labeling solution presumably revealed the distribution pattern which is present under steady-state conditions.

Pulse labeling of translocate with ^{3}H-glucose (TRIP, 1969) and steady-state labeling with $^{14}CO_2$ (GEIGER and CATALDO, 1969) were used to locate cells involved in export of translocate. The companion cells of minor veins had the highest level of label while the adjacent sieve tubes had less label. TRIP postulated a transport as well as a loading function for the companion cells but the limitations in resolution of freeze-drying methods dictates caution in making too detailed conclusions from the data. Without notable exception, the evidence from autoradiography strongly supports the view that assimilate moves from the site of fixation to cells of the minor veins where it is taken up and accumulates to a level significantly higher than in the mesophyll.

2. Demonstration of Solute Accumulation in Minor Veins by Plasmolysis Studies

Additional evidence for phloem loading was provided by plasmolytic measurements of the osmotic pressure of various tissues of the source leaf blade. The results of these studies revealed a concentrating of solutes in the minor vein companion cells and sieve elements to a level above that in the mesophyll cells. ROECKL (1949) used plasmolysis, refractometry and cryoscopic techniques to measure the osmotic pressure of mesophyll cells and sieve sap of *Robinia pseudoacacia*. She found that the palisade mesophyll had an average osmotic pressure of 17.9 atm as measured by plasmolysis, while the sieve sap had an osmotic pressure of 31 atm, as shown by refractometric analysis. Because the osmotic pressure of the sieve sap was higher than that of the mesophyll, ROECKL concluded that diffusion of assimilate from the mesophyll to the sieve elements cannot occur as MÜNCH postulated but that a secretory mechanism raises the concentration of the assimilate between the mesophyll and the sieve sap. GEIGER et al. (1973) used electronmicroscopy to examine rapidly-frozen sugar beet leaf tissue which had been equilibrated with various concentrations of mannitol, to map solute concentration in various cells of the source leaf. The mesophyll was estimated to have an osmotic pressure of 13 bars compared to 30 bars for the sieve element-companion cell (se-cc) complex. The adjacent phloem parenchyma cells had an osmotic pressure of 8 bars with an abrupt concentration increase at the membrane of the se-cc complex. Sieve elements and companion cells generally showed the same osmotic pressure. Because nearly 80% of the sieve-tube solute is sucrose (FIFE et al., 1962), a high sucrose gradient is indicated by these data. At least one active loading step is required, probably at the membrane of the se-cc complex. Plasmolysis studies clearly demonstrate a concentrating of solute in the minor vein phloem, an integral part of the phloem loading process.

3. Demonstration of Selective and Active Uptake by Minor Veins

Other aspects of translocation which indicate the existence of phloem loading are the high degree of selectivity and the involvement of energy metabolism during uptake of solutes into the phloem. Selectivity will be discussed in Section C.II and the involvement of energy metabolism in Section C.III.2.

B. Structural Aspects of Phloem Loading

I. Extent and Distribution of Minor Veins in the Source Leaves

The vascular system of the angiosperm leaf is highly specialized for phloem loading and translocation. In a dicotyledon leaf such as that of the sugar beet the major veins undergo three or four branchings, ending in minor veins which branch and anastomose. ESAU (1967) applied the designation I to III for the major vein branches which serve chiefly for conduction of water and assimilates. The next branches, IV and V in the sugar beet leaf constitute the minor veins which are closely associated with the mesophyll and are specialized for exchange. Repeated branching of the veins brings the mesophyll to within about 65 μm (2 to 3 cells) on either side of the minor veins (WYLIE, 1939, average for 66 species of dicotyledons). SMITH and EPSTEIN (1964) observed that small solute molecules became limited in their uptake into leaf tissue when the distance to the free edge was greater than 150 μm. ESAU (1967) pointed out that this is close to the maximum distance between veins and mesophyll cells in the leaf blade of dicotyledons.

GEIGER and CATALDO (1969) analyzed the structure of 10-cm sugar beet leaves which were about 60% expanded and were translocating about 22% of the net carbon assimilated during steady-state photosynthesis. In these leaves, the combined length of minor veins (IV, V) was 70 cm/cm^2 blade compared to only 5.5 cm/cm^2 for I- to III-order veins. A length of minor vein equal to one mesophyll cell diameter received translocate from approximately 30 cells situated an average of 2 to 3 cell diameters away (75 μm). While the sieve elements and companion cells of the minor veins constituted only 0.6% of the blade volume, they had a combined membrane surface of approximately 90 mm^2/cm^2 leaf blade (Table 1 and SOVONICK et al., 1974). Most of this surface ($\sim$75%) is on the companion cells which are considerably larger in diameter in the minor veins than in the path.

Table 1. Phloem loading performance parameters for a 10-cm source leaf from a sugar beet plant photosynthesizing in light with an intensity of 21,500 lux (SOVONICK et al., 1974)

Parameter	Value
1. Volume se-cc complex in minor veins of 1 cm^2 source leaf	0.15 mm^3/cm^2 blade
2. Proportion of leaf-blade volume occupied by se-cc complex	0.6%
3. Surface area of se-cc complex in minor veins of 1 cm^2 source leaf	88 mm^2/cm^2 blade
4. Sucrose concentration in se-cc complex	0.8 M
5. Amount of sucrose present in se-cc complex of minor veins	45 $\mu g/cm^2$ blade
6. Proportion of source-leaf sucrose in se-cc complex	80%
7. Turnover time for sucrose in se-cc complex of minor veins: tr. rt. = 0.95 µg sucrose/min cm^2 blade	48 min
8. Half time for sucrose in se-cc complex of minor veins: tr. rt. = 0.95 µg sucrose/min cm^2 blade	33 min
9. Sucrose flux through membrane of se-cc complex of minor veins: tr. rate as above	3.2×10^{-9} moles/min cm^2 membrane
10. ATP required to maintain flux of sucrose 1:1 stoichiometry	2.8 n moles ATP/min cm^2 blade
11. Proportion of photosynthate carbon which would be required to supply ATP (glucose equivalent) at photosynthesis rate of 1.6 µgC/min cm^2	0.3% of C fixed
12. Ratio of sucrose required as a source of ATP to sucrose translocated	1.4% of transloc. sucr.
13. Flux of water into se-cc complex required to produce the sucrose: water ratio observed in the sieve sap	1.5×10^{-7} moles/min cm^2 membrane

II. Structural Features of Intermediary and Transfer Cells

The companion cells and sieve elements found in the minor veins contain a number of structural specializations. FISCHER (1885) observed the large size and deeply staining cytoplasm of the companion cells in minor veins during the course of his survey of dicotyledon leaves. FISCHER (1885) designated these specialized cells as "Übergangszellen" ("transition cells") and HABERLANDT (1914) developed the concept that these specially adapted cells have a role in transferring assimilates from the mesophyll to the sieve tubes. From the structural standpoint, this early work sparked a great volume of literature on the development of phloem and the structural nature of the functional sieve tube (ESAU, 1961, 1967, 1972).

It is now known that the straining arises from the high content of ribosomes and other organelles in the companion cells. The presence of many mitochondria and high "phosphatase" activity suggest high metabolic activity as is expected of cells active in solute transfer (WANNER, 1952). The companion cells are about twice the diameter of sieve tubes in the V-order veins, just the reverse of the size relationship in the path phloem (ESAU, 1967; GEIGER and CATALDO, 1969). Partly because the ontogeny of minor vein companion cells is obscure and partly to emphasize their physiological role, ESAU (1967) proposed that the term "transition cells", coined by FISCHER, be replaced by the term "intermediary cells". These cells appear to be ideally adapted to phloem loading.

In addition to these structural features of the se-cc complex which are common to dicotyledons, the leaves of about $^1/_3$ of the herbaceous dicotyledon species have specialized cells called "transfer cells" (GUNNING et al., 1968; GUNNING and PATE, 1969; PATE and GUNNING, 1972; see also Chapter 19). BRIARTY (1973) showed the presence of regular patterns of particles on the plasmalemma of transfer cells by freeze-etching of unfixed root nodule cells. The hexagonal arrays were associated with the wall ingrowths, on the outside of the inner layer of the plasmalemma. The wall protuberances characteristic of transfer cells were found to be formed in *Pisum* during a period of a day or so when the leaf lamina was expanding from 50 to 75% of its final size (GUNNING and PATE, 1969). This stage corresponds to the time when the leaf passes from the condition of being an importer of solutes to the state of exporter (WEBB and GORHAM, 1964; TURGEON and WEBB, 1973; FELLOWS and GEIGER, 1974).

III. Close Functional and Structural Association of Sieve Elements and Companion Cells

The close functional relationship between the companion cells and their associated sieve elements is suggested by the presence of special plasmodesmata between them and by the transfer of virus particles between these cells. The large plasmodesmata in the common wall are branched on the companion cell side (ESAU, 1967, 1972; GEIGER et al., 1971). Beet yellows virus, a rod-shaped, phloem-limited virus was found to have a pattern of distribution and a rate of transport similar to translocated assimilate (ESAU et al., 1967; ESAU and HOEFERT, 1971). The particles were transported from the site of their multiplication in the companion cell cytoplasm into the sieve elements *via* compound plasmodesmata. The virus appeared to move into and out of the sieve-tube lumen, along the sieve tubes and into the companion cells, depending on the source/sink relationship. The latter in turn was based on sugar concentration in a locale. The finding of GEIGER et al. (1973) that the osmotic pressures of sieve elements and associated companion cells were generally similar is also consistent with the concept of a close physiological relationship and ease of communication between the cells. It appears that uptake into sieve tubes from associated companion cells is not a rate-limiting step.

C. Physiological Aspects of Phloem Loading

I. Involvement of Free Space in the Path from Mesophyll to Minor Vein Phloem

One of the first steps in the export of assimilate from a photosynthesizing leaf is transport from the mesophyll chloroplasts to the minor veins, an event known to occur within a period of several minutes (TRIP, 1969). One possible model has sugar transport taking place entirely within the symplast or metablic space of the intervening cells, with intercellular transport occurring through the plasmodesmal connections. In this case the necessary concentrating mechanism conceivably may be located in the plasmodesms of the se-cc complex. An alternative possibility is that the photosynthate enters a "transport pool" inside the endoplasmic reticulum of the mesophyll cells, through which it is transported to the vascular tissue. This theory places the site of build-up of osmotic pressure in the mesophyll cells. Loading of sugar through the ER surface provides a continuous path into the sieve elements or the companion cells through the plasmodesmata. The fact that translocated sugars are rather inert metabolically presumably offers some protection from extensive conversion in transit.

A second type of model is based on the proposition that at some point in the pathway, the sugar to be translocated enters the apoplast, or free space of the tissue. The point at which the sugar re-enters the symplast is the loading site, probably at the surface of the se-cc complex. It is not likely that sugar exits from all of the mesophyll and parenchyma surface in view of the transpirational flow of water. More likely, outflow into the free space is limited to a more confined region such as the phloem parenchyma making the translocated sugar accessible to the loading site. Data discussed by KURSANOV et al. (1970) generally support loading of translocated sugar from the free space following exit from the symplast. Studies relating to this type of model will be discussed in the following section.

1. Loading and Translocation of Exogenously Supplied Sugars

If the free space is involved in transport to the phloem it should be possible to introduce ^{14}C-sucrose into the free space and produce labeling of the sugar undergoing phloem loading. Uptake into leaf tissue of sugar supplied to the free space has been reported (PENNELL and WEATHERLEY, 1958; VICKERY and MERCER, 1964, 1967; WEATHERLEY, 1955; KRIEDEMANN and BEEVERS, 1967a). Recently it was shown that exogenous ^{14}C-sucrose taken up by sugar beet leaf tissue was loaded into the phloem (FELLOWS and GEIGER, 1974; SOVONICK et al. 1974). Fig. 1B and 1C show phloem loading of ^{14}C-sucrose supplied to an intact sugar beet leaf (B) and to leaf disks (C). The sugars appear to be loaded more rapidly into the phloem than into the mesophyll. These studies suggest that phloem loading occurs directly into the phloem from the free space. A recent study compared sugar uptake by mesophyll cells and by minor veins isolated from tobacco leaf tissue (CATALDO, 1974). From analysis of sugar-loading kinetics he inferred that mesophyll cells took up sucrose faster than the minor vein phloem and concluded that phloem loading occurs from the mesophyll *via* a symplastic route. PEEL and FORD (1968) and GARDNER and PEEL (1971) applied exogenous ^{14}C-sugars to bark strips of willow and studied the composition of stylet exudate. The earlier work indicated the existence of a direct path of uptake into the sieve elements and companion cells and an indirect one *via* storage parenchyma. The indirect path seemed to be the usual one. The later work indicated a common uptake step suggesting uptake from the free space in both instances.

A critical test of whether sugar usually enters the free space prior to phloem loading and translocation is to determine if the rates obtained with exogenously applied sugar approximate those from photosynthesis. SOVONICK et al. (1974) studied rates of phloem loading and translocation in sugar beet plants and leaf disks (Fig. 2).

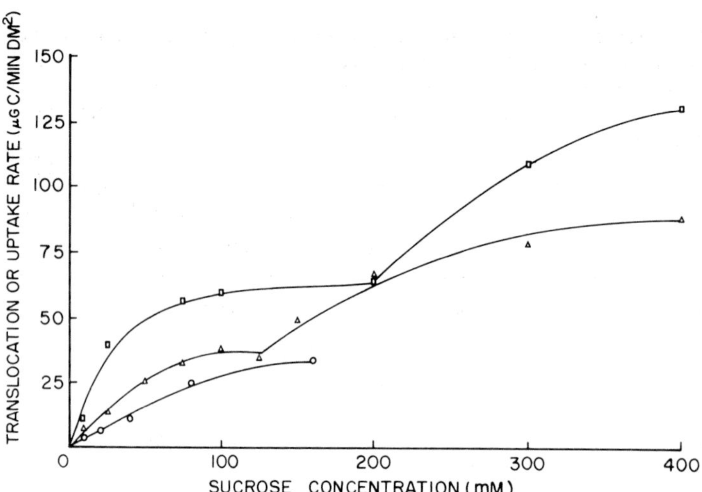

Fig. 2. Sucrose uptake rate for the sugar beet source leaf. Sugar supplied to abraded surface of leaf disks (△), to abraded upper surface of intact leaf (□) or by capillary using reverse flap method (○). SOVONICK et al., 1974

Allowing for differences in the penetration of sucrose solutions supplied by the various techniques, the rates obtained were comparable. The uptake and translocation rates from a number of studies are summarized in Table 2. Again, considering the differences in method, the parameters for translocation of photosynthate and of exogenous sugar as well as for sugar uptake by leaf discs show similarities, indicating that phloem loading of free space sugar may be involved in the various processes. To compare further the relative availability of photosynthetically derived translocated sugar and exogenous ^{14}C-sucrose GEIGER et al. (1974) used alternate methods of supplying ^{14}C to a sugar beet leaf. Translocation was studied by presenting labeled ^{14}C-sucrose at 20 mM concentration or $^{14}CO_2$ at 400 μl/l at 22,500 lux light intensity or both. The data are summarized in Table 3. The various experiments show that sugar at 20 to 25 mM is equivalent to photosynthate as a source of translocated sugar. In general, the data indicate that sugar supplied to the free space at concentrations in the physiological range is loaded and translocated at rates of the same order as found with photosynthetically derived translocated sugar.

2. Passage of Translocated Solute through the Free Space Prior to Phloem Loading

These findings do not rule out symplastic transport. In fact it is likely that sugars move from mesophyll to the minor veins *via* the symplast although experimental evidence is meager. Anatomical observations bear on the question. Measurements by WYLIE (1943) indicated that the mesophyll cells have diminished contact with each other because of the intercellular air spaces. The contact was only one-fourth of that between epidermal cells. Studies of the migration of virus particles between cells indicate that there are functional plasmodesmal connections in sugar beet between mesophyll cells, as well as between sieve elements and parenchyma

Table 2. Comparison of kinetic data for translocation or phloem loading in sugar beet obtained by various methods of supplying material to be translocated

Method of supplying material to be translocated	Plant material	Rate	K_j (mM)	Rate[b] or V_{max} (n moles sucrose/hr cm^2)	Concentration giving rate equal to translocation at 13,000 lux (mM)
A. $^{14}CO_2$/photosynthesis[1]	Sugar beet leaf	translocation rate			
13,000 lux			—	121[b]	—
21,500 lux			—	167[b]	—
54,000 lux			—	265[b]	—
B. ^{14}C-sucrose/abraded[2] leaf surface	Sugar beet leaf	translocation	16	294	20
C. ^{14}C-sucrose/leaf disks[2]	Sugar beet leaf	sucrose uptake[a]	88	277	27
D. ^{14}C-sucrose/cotyledon[3] immersion	Castor bean cotyledon	translocation	62	—	—
E. Sucrose/scutellum[4] slices	Maize scutellum	sucrose uptake	20	—	—
F. Sucrose/leaf pieces[5]	Bean leaf	sucrose uptake	10	—	—
G. Sucrose/vascular[6] bundles	Sugar beet leaf	sucrose uptake	12.5	—	—

1. SERVAITES and GEIGER (1974).
2. SOVONICK et al. (1974).
3. KRIEDEMANN and BEEVERS (1967a).
4. WHITESELL and HUMPHREYS (1972).
5. VICKERY and MERCER (1967).
6. TURKINA and SOKOLOVA (1972).

[a] Mesophyll accumulation constituted a portion of the accumulation which was estimated to be less than 1/3 of the accumulation by phloem loading.

[b] Not V_{max} but rate observed. Translocation did not show hyperbolic curve in response to increasing photosynthesis.

Table 3. Comparison of the availability of free space sugar and photosynthate for translocation. Translocation was measured by labeling the free space sugar, the $^{14}CO_2$ and both together during steady state photosynthesis at 22,500 lux. Data are averages from 4 experiments (GEIGER et al., 1974)

Method of labeling translocate	Translocation rate due to labeled component (μg C/min dm^2)	Percent of translocation from labeled component
1. ^{14}C-sucrose applied to upper leaf surface	29	55
2. $^{14}CO_2$ supplied to same site	22	45
3. ^{14}C-sucrose plus $^{14}CO_2$	51	100

cells, and between adjacent parenchyma cells (ESAU and HOEFERT, 1972). No mention was made of the connections between mesophyll cells and phloem parenchyma, the point at which translocate could be entering the free space.

Using the concepts of irreversible thermodynamics TYREE (1970) showed that the pathway of least resistance for the intercellular diffusion of small solutes is often the symplastic route, in contrast to the pathway involving both cell walls and cytoplasm. Evidence for interchange *via* plasmodesmata was presented by SPITZER (1970) based on electrical resistance measurements. Movement of solute in the symplastic system envisioned by TYREE is diffusional, requiring a source and a sink. The chloroplasts of the mesophyll cells and the free space in the immediate vicinity of the active membrane may constitute source and sink respectively.

Disruption of plasmodesmata by plasmolysis of the tissue was used as a means to study whether symplastic connections promote the movement of translocate from the mesophyll to the minor vein phloem. JARVIS and HOUSE (1970) studied the flow of ions from cortex to stele in corn roots which were untreated and in those plasmolyzed to disrupt cytoplasmic connections and found that the treatment inhibited the flow of ions. To determine whether translocation can still occur when the symplastic connections between mesophyll cells and between mesophyll and phloem cells are broken by plasmolysis, GEIGER et al. (1974) treated sugar beet leaves with a 0.8 M mannitol solution to see if translocation of ^{14}C-labeled photosynthate would continue. Translocation of label fell to near zero, but photosynthesis rate was similarly inhibited making the cause of inhibiton ambiguous. Microscopic examination of the tissue revealed collapse of cell walls which gave incomplete breakage of the symplastic connections. The effect of osmotic treatment on photosynthesis (BOYER, 1971) and probable effects of water stress on translocation (PLAUT and REINHOLD, 1967) make application of this method difficult. Although the results were not satisfactory when $^{14}CO_2$ supplied the source, addition of 20 mM ^{14}C-sucrose to the free space always restored translocation to pretreatment rates (GEIGER et al., 1974). The authors concluded that the major block to translocation in the plasmolyzed leaf was prior to the entry of translocate into the free space.

If the translocate species pass through the free space *en route* to the minor vein phloem, some of the molecules should pass into a bathing solution prior to phloem loading. A number of studies done at the Timiriazev Institute support this expectation. KURSANOV and BROVCHENKO (1970) measured the ability of bundles and of mesophyll-rich leaf pieces to leak sugar into the surrounding medium following a labeling with ^{14}C-glucose. Following leaching, free-space sugar appeared to be replenished repeatedly only in the mesophyll-rich pieces. KURSANOV and his coworkers interpret this result and the relatively greater capacity of the bundles to absorb sugar as pointing to a transport pathway which involves a free space component. As part of the method, the leaf pieces were washed for a relatively long time in water, which may have altered the tissue. Also, the fact that KURSANOV's mesophyll samples contained vascular tissue raises the question of which tissue type actually released the sugars in his leakage experiments.

HUMPHREYS and GARRARD (1971a, 1971b) observed sucrose leakage into water by corn scutellum by what appeared to be mass flow. They concluded that the leakage occurred from cut phloem endings. Leakage from whole scutella did not occur until the embryonic axis was removed. This leakage declined rapidly under normal conditions and seemed to point to a separate leakable sucrose pool in the tissue, presumably in the phloem. HUMPHREYS (1972) suggested that the sugar moves along the mesophyll and into the sieve tubes *via* the symplast in the maize embryo. He did not address the question of phloem loading nor the nature of the concentrating step, though the ER model is consistent with his conclusions.

Using sugar cane leaf discs, SCHOOLAR and EDELMAN (1971) found a similar leakage of sucrose in C_4 plants, but only under certain conditions. This leakage was limited by the cut surface of the vascular tissue. However, SCHOOLAR and EDELMAN did not feel that the phloem was the site of the secretion, since the flow still occurred under conditions in which callose was readily formed on the sieve plates. In this study secretion occurred only into solutions of iodoacetate (IOA) and was dependent on a concurrent supply of photosynthetic products. Basing their conclusions on these observations, the authors stated that IOA probably blocked normal flow of carbon to the vascular tissue and that the leakage ultimately involved diffusion from the cell walls of the exposed bundles. These studies demonstrate the variety of interpretation which can be placed on a similar observation of leakage.

Another method of evaluating the role of free space is to measure the rate of entry of a compound into a solution in contact with the free space or to measure the equilibrium concentration in this solution. HAWKER (1965), and GLASZIOU and GAYLER (1972) applied this method to estimation of the free space sugar concentration in intact sugar-cane sink tissue. By altering environmental conditions for the plants, it was shown that the sucrose concentration in the tissue and in the free space solution changed together, indicating a link between them. HAWKER inferred from the data that the free space is part of the transport pathway from the phloem into the sink tissue. A similar conclusion was arrived at by GLASZIOU and GAYLER (1972) working with the same tissue. A sucrose solution was circulated through a stalk section by means of a small pump. Solutions of different concentrations were curculated in the tissue until one was found that remained at the original level for one hour. Both of these studies indicated sucrose concentrations in the free space of up to 15% (w/v), values of the same order as in the tissue itself. Since the transpiration stream is in parallel with the free-space sugar movement in sink tissue, it may be that such massive flow *via* the free space is feasible in this tissue.

Using a similar method, GEIGER et al. (1974) attempted to intercept the translocate molecules if they entered the free space prior to phloem loading. They used unlabeled sucrose or glucose as trapping agents in a solution circulating over the abraded surface of a leaf photosynthesizing in $^{14}CO_2$. The rate of trapping of a component was considered to be a measure of turnover of the compound in the free space. When the light intensity was increased the rate of trapping by sucrose increased to the same extent as the translocation rate (Fig. 3). If glucose was used, no increase in the trapping rate was noted. Application of ATP to the leaf increased translocation rate by approximately 75% and the trapping of sucrose by approximately 66%. Glucose trapping was stopped or reversed by ATP addition. The authors concluded that the turnover rate of the translocate in the free space increased with the increase in the translocation rate. The data from isotope trapping, from supplying exogenous sugar with or without plasmolysis and from leakage studies appear to be consistent. The data support the view that sucrose moves by way of the symplast from the chloroplast to a point near the minor vein phloem. Here the sugar exits into the free space from which it is taken up into the phloem by an active uptake process.

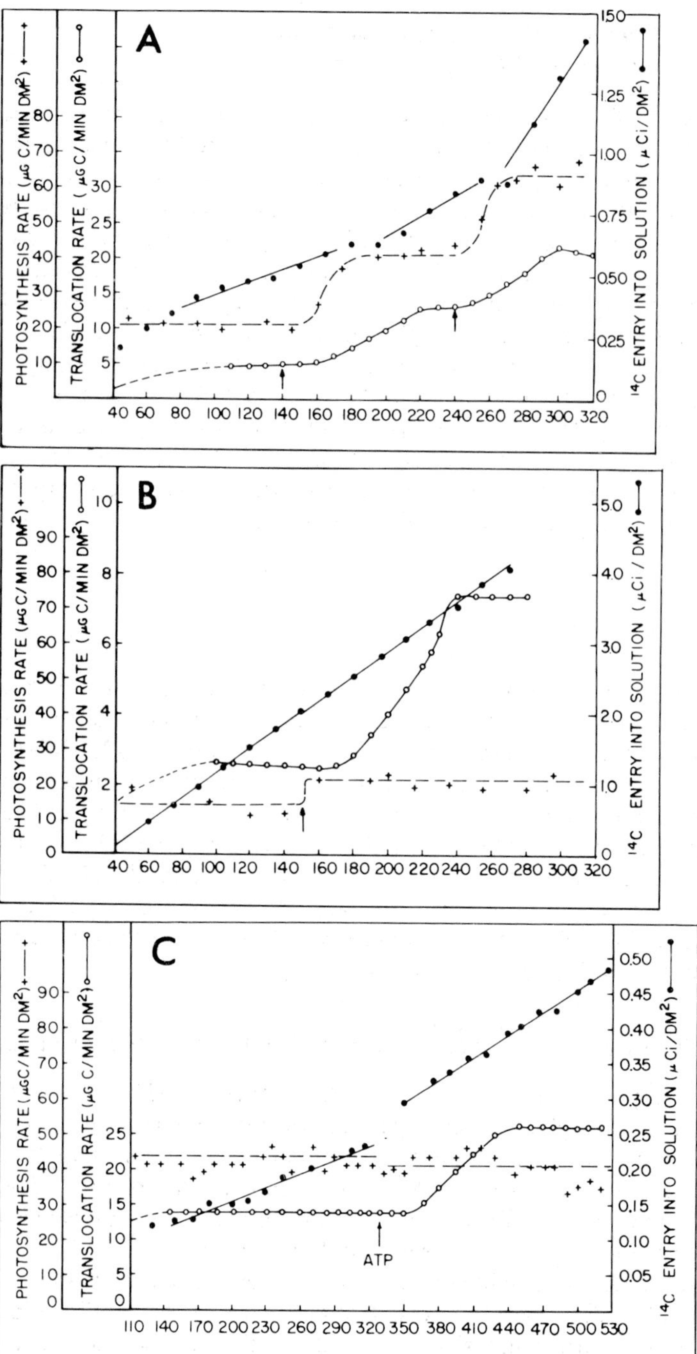

Fig. 3A–C. Isotope trapping of sucrose (A, C) or glucose (B) during photosynthesis in $^{14}CO_2$-containing atmosphere by a translocating sugar beet leaf. Leaf treated (↑) as indicated by increasing light intensity (A, B) or by application of 4 mM ATP in the circulating trapping solution. Sugar concentration in solution was 20 mM. Photosynthesis rate (+), total ^{14}C trapped by circulating solution (●) and translocation rate (○). GEIGER et al., 1974

3. Existence of a Sharp Concentration Change at the Membrane of the Sieve Element-Companion Cell Complex

If phloem loading occurs from the free space there should be a sharp increase in concentration at the site of loading. By contrast, symplastic movement from the mesophyll into the se-cc complex by diffusion should be accompanied by a noticeable gradient with the concentration highest at the mesophyll end unless the plasmodesmata can carry out a concentrating step at some point. No mechanism of this type has been reported to our knowledge. If the endoplasmic reticulum (ER) of the mesophyll is the site of the active sugar-loading step and the channel of conduction to the minor vein phloem, it should be visible in freeze-substituted material. Sucrose is presumed to serve as a cryoprotectant and is thought to be responsible for preservation of structure in the se-cc complex (GEIGER et al., 1973). No ER was observed in the mesophyll or phloem parenchyma cells in sugar beet tissue prepared by the freeze-substitution method. As discussed above, a sharp change in concentration was observed at the membrane of the se-cc complex supporting the belief that loading occurs at this membrane.

II. Selectivity of Phloem Loading

Phloem loading is a selective process. For many years it has been known that the composition of sieve-tube sap does not correspond to the composition of solutes in the leaf blade, nor in the tissue surrounding the sieve tubes (KÖCHER and LEONARD, 1971). The composition of sieve-tube sap appears to be the result of at least two different selective processes. One, carrier-mediated loading, may be either active or passive but is highly selective because of binding specificities; the other, non-mediated passive permeation selects only on the basis of the permeability of the membrane to the species in question. Superimposed on these mechanisms is compartmentalization of metabolites within cells or tissues which adds a further process that helps to determine the composition of sieve-tube sap.

1. Carrier-Mediated Transport and Molecular Structure in Relation to Selective Uptake

On the basis of the major sugars translocated, ZIMMERMANN (1957, 1960) distinguished three categories of plants. One type translocates sucrose as the chief component and only sugar, another contains large amounts of the raffinose type of oligosaccharides in addition to sucrose, whilst a third type contains mainly sucrose with variable smaller amounts of raffinose-type oligosaccharides. Some plants also have mannitol or sorbitol in the sieve-tube sap (see Appendix III).

Several methods have been used to identify the major sugars translocated, including analysis of the path phloem tissue (SWANSON and EL-SHISHINY, 1958). The validity of the methods requires that sugars should be distinguished in transit from those derived from translocated sugars and stored. Analysis of exudate obtained by aphid stylets (KENNEDY and MITTLER, 1953) or by incisions (ZIMMERMANN, 1957) obviate this difficulty. Review of the data from careful studies leads to the conclusion that sucrose and related galactose-containing oligosaccharides are the principal sugars translocated.

Table 4. Summary of data for experiments on the selectivity of phloem loading

Method of supplying labeled substance	Material sampled	Labeled substance supplied	Major labeled compounds recovered, in decreasing abundance	Reference
1. Into xylem at base of *Yucca* influorescence. 1% solution supplied	Bleeding sap at top of inflorescence stalk	a) glucose	sucrose	TAMMES et al. (1973)
		b) fructose	sucrose	
		c) galactose	sucrose	
		d) maltose	sucrose	
		e) lactose	sucrose, raffinose(?)	
		f) sorbitol	sorbitol, some sucrose	
		g) K glycerate	glyceric acid	
		h) K glycolate	glycollic acid	
		i) glycerol	glycerol	
		j) glutamine	glutamine	
2. Reverse-flap leaf feeding in *Fraxinus americana* for 24 h	Path and sink	a) verbascose	sucrose, verb-stachy, raffinose	TRIP et al. (1965)
		b) stachyose	verb-stachy, sucrose, raffinose	
		c) raffinose	verb-stachy, sucrose, raffinose	
		d) sucrose	sucrose, verb-stachy, raffinose	
		e) mannitol	mannitol, stachyose	
		f) galactose	verb-stachy, raffinose, sucrose	
		g) fructose	sucrose, verb-stachy, raffinose	
		h) sorbitol	sorbitol	
3. Application of sugar solutions to veins of leaf blade of tobacco	Successively larger branches of the leaf blade veins	a) sucrose	sucrose	YAMAMOTO et al. (1970)
		b) glucose or fructose	hexoses decrease, sucrose increases with distance from supply	
4. Reverse-flap feeding of squash leaves	Petiole	a) sucrose	sucrose, stachyose	HENDRIX (1973)

Table 4 (continued)

Method of supplying labeled substance	Material sampled	Labeled substance supplied	Major labeled compounds recovered, in decreasing abundance	Reference
5. Application of amino acid solutions to endosperm of castor bean seedlings	Hypocotyl	a) glutamate b) aspartate c) alanine d) valine	sucrose sucrose sucrose valine	STEWART and BEEVERS (1967)
6. Application of solution to surface of sunflower leaves	Petiole	a) alanine	sucrose	CHOPOWICK and FORWARD (1974)

The results of experiments with a variety of applied substances indicate selectivity associated with uptake during phloem loading (Table 4). The patterns observed can be explained by selective uptake of each of the major species found. Alternatively, the composition of the sieve sap could be the result of uptake of one or a few major solutes from which the characteristic pattern is derived by directed metabolism. For instance sucrose might be actively loaded, while glucose might only enter by passive permeation. On the other hand, both glucose and sucrose might be taken up actively with the glucose being changed to sucrose once it is inside. To date, the data relating to this problem have been sparse and not conclusive, with little or no work specifically addressing this question. In general these observations indicate the presence of a carrier or other highly selective mechanism capable of distinguishing molecular structure as part of the phloem-loading process.

TRIP et al. (1965) concluded from their studies that plants selectively translocate certain non-reducing species and within this group preferentially translocate some to a greater extent than others. HENDRIX (1973) showed that squash translocates ^{14}C-sucrose fed to attached leaves, indicating that the predominance of stachyose in the translocate does not arise from inability to load sucrose. BEITLER and HENDRIX (1974) established that stachyose is synthesized very early after CO_2-fixation. They concluded that the nature of the sugar supplied to the site of phloem loading controls the chemical nature of the solute translocated. In support of this view WEBB and GORHAM (1964) observed that the beginning of export from squash leaves coincided with the beginning of stachyose synthesis. Studies are still needed to determine to what extent selective translocation is controlled by the sugar species available, the carriers present and the directed nature of metabolism favoring production of certain sugars either before or after loading.

The selective active loading of non-reducing sugars for translocation apparently is an adaptation protecting these sugars from extensive metabolic conversion until they arrive in sink tissue where enzymes for their metabolism are present. ARNOLD (1968) discussed the probable basis for the selective translocation of sucrose and concluded that sucrose is an easily hydrolyzed, protected derivative of glucose.

In addition to the requirement that sugars be of the non-reducing type, there may be a need for the plant to possess enzymes for metabolism of the sugar to be translocated before it can be loaded into the phloem. Perhaps these enzymes are part of a binding-recognition mechanism of the carrier system. DOWNTON and HAWKER (1973) recently postulated that sucrose synthetase, which they found associated with the bundle sheath of corn leaves and with the vascular bundles of sugar cane may be involved in translocation. WOLOSIUK and PONTIS (1971) observed two forms of sucrose synthetase in Jerusalem artichoke tubers with K_m's of 56 mM and 200 mM respectively; these are close to the K_j values for the dual isotherms observed for phloem loading and translocation of sucrose by sugar beet (Fig. 2, and SOVONICK et al., 1974). AMAR and REINHOLD (1973) recently demonstrated that a carrier for amino acid transport could be readily removed from membranes with osmotic shock or EDTA, a treatment which removed only a small portion of the membrane protein. Recent concepts of membrane structure indicate that the incorporation of enzyme protein for a carrier function is feasible and that studies in this area may be successful.

In addition to certain sugars which constitute the principal osmotic constituents of sieve-tube sap, it is thought that protein amino acids and certain ions are selectively, and probably actively loaded into the se-cc complex. JOY and ANTCLIFF (1966) observed that protein amino acids such as glutamate and glycine were translocated out of a leaf when applied to the leaf surface, while non-protein amino acids such as D-alanine and amino-isobutyric acid were taken up by the leaf but not translocated. However, the pattern is not simple (Table 4). With an endogenous source of solute, HOFSTRA and NELSON (1969b) observed that although aspartate is a major product of photosynthesis in corn, only labeled sucrose was exported. Clear-cut evidence supporting active loading of amino acids into the phloem is lacking. Amino acids may be loaded into the phloem of certain plants or under certain conditions but the process apparently is not as widespread as one might assume.

2. Membrane Permeability as a Factor in Selective Uptake

Compounds, both naturally occurring metabolites as well as other materials such as agricultural chemicals, are sometimes translocated in the phloem in considerable quantity. A review of the large number of compounds which are phloem-mobile supports the view that any compound which is water-soluble and is able to penetrate the membranes of the sieve element-companion cell complex will be translocated to some extent. CRAFTS and CRISP (1971) list over 100 materials considered phloem-mobile, including non-biological materials such as herbicides, in addition to many classes of biological materials. The large number of synthetic materials entering the phloem and the relatively simple structural requirements for entry indicate that transport into the se-cc complex is non-mediated for most of the substances listed. The transport of permeant species is certainly consistent with a mechanism of phloem transport with a mass-flow component.

3. Compartmentalization of Separate Storage and Translocate Pools

Both for those materials which are actively loaded into the sieve elements and for those which can enter passively, compartmentation could conceivably result in "transport pools" and "storage pools" of potential translocate species. On the basis of data from pulse-labeling experiments carried out both with and without a $^{12}CO_2$ "chase", NELSON (1962) postulated the existence of separate storage and translocate pools for sucrose, the former being made available for translocation only under certain conditions such as darkness or low CO_2 concentration. From studies on the leakage from corn scutellum tissue, GARRARD and HUMPHREYS (1971) proposed the existence of two sucrose pools.

Storage sucrose, postulated to be in the vacuoles of mesophyll cells (HUMPHREYS and GARRARD, 1971a, 1971b) leaked only slightly. The transport pool, postulated to be in the vascular tissue, leaked readily into water. Sugar from the storage pool was made available only slowly to the transport pool, while newly synthesized sucrose was readily and continuously delivered to the transport pool. When scutellum slices were incubated in fructose in Tris buffer, sucrose was synthesized and continued to leak into the medium while the sucrose in the tissue remained constant. This latter sucrose leaked when the fructose medium was replaced with Tris alone and probably represented sucrose in the synthesis and transport compartments to a considerable extent.

Accepting the authors' assignment of location there is still a question of the relative size and importance of the storage sucrose pool in the mesophyll vacuoles. Although the data are provocative, considerable evidence will be needed to confirm the proposed compartmentation, its role, and the cytological location of these pools.

Some studies indicate that the compartmentation may not be very strict or that the storage compartment may contain rather small amounts of the specific sugar translocated. The kinetic analysis of GEIGER and SWANSON (1965) indicated that most if not all of the leaf sucrose was available for translocation. SOVONICK et al. (1974) calculated that approximately 80% of the sucrose in a sugar beet source leaf was in the se-cc complex of the minor vein phloem, with the remainder in the major veins and in cells outside the phloem. Presumably the sucrose present in the companion cells along the translocation system can become a source of translocate under certain conditions and in some sense can be considered a "storage sucrose" pool.

Another means of compartmentalization was reported by ESCHRICH (1970) who found that the D-isomers of amino acids such as D-phenylalanine were converted enzymatically in the leaf to malonyl derivatives such as N malonyl-D phenylalanine. These derivatives were phloem-immobile while the unaltered L-isomers entered the sieve elements and were translocated.

4. The Question of Sucrose Hydrolysis

A point of considerable disagreement centers around the need for hydrolysis or splitting of sucrose during phloem loading. A critical review of the literature supports the generalization that sucrose, when taken up by source leaves, does not undergo splitting, but that accumulated by sink tissue is split into hexoses. Results of studies of sucrose uptake by mature source leaves are given in Table 5. The first 5 entries indicate evidence for entry without splitting of sucrose. Entries 6 and 7, representing the work of BROVCHENKO and co-workers, indicate the presence of high invertase activity and considerable splitting of sucrose prior to uptake. Perhaps the invertase activity results from the dissection needed to separate the small veins used and the subsequent long washing process. Their "mesophyll" samples, which contain the minor veins that are most active in phloem loading, show considerably less splitting of sucrose as indicated by less asymmetry of sucrose labeling (BROVCHENKO, 1970). Part of the tissue supplied in entry 8 represents a translocation sink and as such may show splitting of sucrose prior to uptake because of the presence

Table 5. Summaries of studies on sucrose hydrolysis during uptake by source leaf tissue

Hydrolysis	Experimental material	Evidence	Reference
1. No	Maize scutellum	Rates of extracellular inversion too low	HUMPHREYS and GARRARD (1968)
		Increased sucrose uptake at optimal hexose concentration	
2. No	Castor bean cotyledon	Fructosyl ^{14}C-sucrose taken up intact	KRIEDEMANN and BEEVERS (1967a)
		Different response of hydrolysis and uptake of sucrose to pH	
		Supply ^{14}C hexose – only ^{14}C-sucrose found in cotyledon	
3. No	Tobacco leaf disks	Asymmetry of labeled sucrose supplied was maintained	PORTER and MAY (1955)
4. No	Sugar-cane leaves	Fructosyl ^{14}C-sucrose was loaded intact while a mixture of ^{14}C-fructose and unlabeled glucose resulted in uniformly-labeled sucrose in phloem	HATCH and GLASZIOU (1964)
5. No	Sugar beet petiole vascular tissue	^{14}C-sucrose + unlabeled glucose presented; sucrose retains ^{14}C-G/^{14}C-F = 1	TURKINA and SOKOLOVA (1967)
6. Yes	Sugar beet leaf veins washed 20 h	Rapid hydrolysis of supplied ^{14}C-sucrose by tissue piece	BROVCHENKO (1965)
		U-^{14}C-sucrose supplied; asymmetrically-labeled sucrose found in tissues	BROVCHENKO (1967)
		"Sucrose" absorption decreased by inhibiting invertase with Tris	BROVCHENKO (1970)
7. Yes	Sugar beet leaf veins washed 18–20 h	^{14}C-G/^{14}C-F = 2 to 3 in tissue when presented with U-^{14}C-sucrose	KURSANOV et al. (1967)
8. Yes	Bark strips of willow	Glucose mocity contained more activity than fructose in sucrose from early samples indicating inversion and more rapid entry by glucose than by fructose	FORD and PEEL (1967)
		Labeling patterns of organic phosphates	PEEL and FORD (1968)
9. Yes	Sugarcane stem	Sucrose, labeled in fructose was presented. Label in sucrose found in sinks was randomized	HATCH and GLASZIOU (1964)

of cell-wall invertase. Entry 9, as well as the work of HAWKER and HATCH (1965) and SACHER et al. (1963) present evidence that sucrose hydrolysis by invertase, in the tissue free space, is obligatory and rate-limiting for sucrose uptake and storage in sugar-cane storage tissue. In general the data on sucrose uptake appear to support the need for hydrolysis during uptake by sink tissue but not during phloem loading in the source.

III. Mechanism of Phloem Loading

1. Vectorizing Process: Capable of High Flux Rates and of Maintaining a Steep Gradient

The quantitatively important translocated sugars such as sucrose and stachyose are presumably in considerably higher concentration in the se-cc complex than in the surrounding mesophyll. If free space concentration of sucrose is approximately 20 mM as discussed above, and sucrose concentration is 800 mM in the se-cc complex (Table 1) the vectorizing step maintains a concentration ratio of at least 40:1. The necessity of a vectorizing process can be inferred from the data of CURTIS and SCOFIELD (1933). Their osmotic concentration studies indicated that in several sink tissues the average level of solute concentration exceeded that of source regions of the same plant. FISHER (1970) showed that the kinetic characteristics measured in soybean originated mainly in the source leaf. Presumably active uptake into the minor vein phloem plays an important role in determining the kinetics of translocation, especially if the vectorizing process supplies the energy which drives translocation.

Phloem loading thus must be capable of high flux rates and of maintaining a steep gradient. The concept of specific mass transfer (SMT), reviewed recently by ZIMMERMANN (1969), and ZIMMERMANN and BROWN (1971) cites a range of rates of flux through sieve tubes of from 6 to 18 g/h cm^2 sieve-tube cross section. Similarly, it is possible to determine the flux through the se-cc complex membrane during phloem loading for the range of observed translocation rates. From measurements and several assumptions SOVONICK et al. (1974) calculated parameters for the phloem-loading process (Table 1). They found that 3×10^{-9} moles of sucrose pass through a cm^2 of membrane per min (6×10^{-5} g sucrose/h cm^2 membrane). This flux rate is approximately 3 orders of magnitude greater than the rate cited by EDELMAN et al. (1971) for passive non-mediated permeation of sucrose with a 1 M difference in sucrose concentration. This high flux rate and the estimated 1:40 concentrating step from the outside to the inside of the se-cc complex membrane are highly significant and indicate an energy requirement for phloem loading.

2. Energy Supply: Coupling of Phloem Loading to Energy Metabolism

Inhibitor and promoter studies link energy metabolism to phloem loading. Several workers have found that ATP applied to a leaf seems to enhance loading (Table 6). COULSON et al. (1972) found no stoichiometric relationship between ATP turnover or respiration in the petiole and translocation rate and concluded that the major source of energy input energizing transport is in the source or sink or both.

Table 6. Effect of supplying exogenous ATP on the rate of translocation

Method of application	Effect noted	Reference
1. 5-min treatment with 6 mM ATP applied to sugar beet leaf following 2-min pulse of $^{14}CO_2$	70% increase in ^{14}C assimilates in veins 7- to 8-fold increase in younger plants	KURSANOV and BROVCHENKO (1961)
2. Infiltration of sunflower with 20 mM ATP Labeling with: a) $^{14}CO_2$ b) exogenous ^{14}C sucrose	 Promotion of export 100% increase in export	SHIROYA (1968)
3. Application of 1 to 5 mM ATP to phloem of *Pelargonium:* a) at site of dye application b) at separate site	 Promotion of Na-fluorescein movement No promotion	ULLRICH (1962)
4. Application of 4 mM ATP with 20 mM sucrose to leaf of sugar beet	60- to 75%-promotion of export of translocated sugar Increased turnover of free space sucrose in leaf blade	SOVONICK et al. (1974) GEIGER et al. (1974)

It is necessary to consider at which point and in what manner ATP acted in the systems discussed. Although the role of ATP as a compound with high phosphate transfer potential is usually emphasized, it may be that ATP was effective in an entirely different way. A number of suggested mechanisms have been proposed in the literature (Table 7). The specific means of coupling the potential energy of ATP to phloem loading awaits further elucidation of the carrier mechanism involved.

Table 7. Modes of action posited for ATP in sugar uptake and translocation studies

Experimental method and results	Proposed mechanism	Reference
1. ATP applied to leaf surface promotes export	Phosphorylation of hexoses for exit from mesophyll and entry into phloem. Part of carrier mechanism	KURSANOV and BROVCHENKO (1961) KURSANOV (1963)
2. Increased leakage of sucrose in maize scutellum. Reversal by divalent cations	ATP increases membrane permeability	HUMPHREYS and GARRARD (1971b)
3. ATP applied to sugar beet leaf causes increased sucrose export and increased turnover of free space sucrose	Promotion of phloem loading and possibly promotion of leakage in vicinity of minor vein phloem	GEIGER et al. (1974)

Studies of the effects of metabolic inhibitors on phloem loading are potentially helpful in the study of translocation mechanisms. A number of these studies are listed in Table 8 along with the results observed. With the exception of the failure of cyanide to inhibit phloem loading in sugar beet, the inhibitors significantly decreased translocation, exudation or sugar uptake when source tissue was treated. The failure of cyanide to inhibit phloem loading may be the result of a terminal oxidase which is resistant to cyanide inhibition (BONNER and VARNER, 1965). Treatment of older sugar beet leaves with 1-mM potassium cyanide was found to produce no decrease in oxygen consumption or carbon dioxide production (R.E. TOIA, University of Dayton, Dayton, Ohio M.S. Thesis). The work of FINKELMANN and REINHOLD (1963a, 1963b) elucidate the dual effect of 2,4-dinitrophenol (DNP). At 5×10^{-5} M concentration, the inhibitor lowered fructose uptake, but the uptake *vs.* concentration plot retained its normal hyperbolic shape. At a concentration of 10^{-3} M,

Table 8. Summary of results of respiratory inhibitors on phloem loading

Inhibitor	Parameter measured	Results	Reference
1. Dinitrophenol	Translocation of capillary-fed sucrose	60% inhibition; prevented by concomitant application of ATP	SOVONICK et al. (1974)
2. Dinitrophenol or oligomycin	Stylet exudation rate	Sudden stoppage of exudation; restarted when DNP replaced with water or ATP solution	GARDNER and PEEL (1972)
3. Dinitrophenol	Phosphate accumulation in celery vascular bundles	Inhibited uptake to about 15% of control	BIELESKI (1966)
4. Dinitrophenol, anoxia, uranyl ion, phloridzin	Sucrose uptake by maize scutellum slices	Inhibited significantly and to a greater extent than hexose uptake	WHITESELL and HUMPHREYS (1972)
5. Dinitrophenol, azide, cyanide	Sucrose uptake by bean leaf tissue	Nearly complete inhibition of sucrose uptake	VICKERY and MERCER (1964)
6. Cyanide	Phloem loading by sugar beet leaf	Failed to inhibit phloem loading	HO and MORTIMER (1971)
7. Anoxia	Translocation of capillary-fed sucrose	Complete inhibition of translocation	SOVONICK et al. (1974)
8. Anoxia	Sucrose uptake by sugar beet leaf pieces	50% inhibition of sucrose uptake	SOVONICK et al. (1974)
9. Anoxia	Sucrose uptake by *Atropa belladonna* leaf pieces	Inhibited uptake by 75%	WEATHERLEY (1955)
10. Fluoride	Stylet exudation rate	Gradual and variable inhibition of exudation	GARDNER and PEEL (1972)

DNP transformed the concentration time course into a straight line and seemed to increase the "apparent free space" of the tissue, presumably by greatly increasing the permeability of the plasmalemma by a direct physical effect on the membrane. HAREL and REINHOLD (1966) applied DNP to a leaf of soybean by reverse flap injection along with ^{14}C-sucrose. Translocation was inhibited by 80 to 90%. If the DNP was applied to a petiole stump along the path while the fed leaf was still present, translocation was inhibited. However, if the DNP was supplied after the fed leaf was allowed to load and translocate for 60 min and after the leaf was removed, the pattern of distribution was changed, but translocation was not inhibited. The results suggest that DNP inhibits translocation by inhibiting loading rather than the movement along the path.

Nectar glands, and also contact cells which release sucrose into vessel water of sugar maple, have been compared to the se-cc complex of the minor veins with respect to their ability to produce high sucrose fluxes. SHUEL (1959) observed that treating nectar glands with 10^{-5} M DNP increased oxygen uptake, presumably by uncoupling aerobic respiration, while 10^{-4} M DNP decreased oxygen uptake. Both treatments slowed nectar secretion considerably. In a study of the contact cells of *Acer saccharum*, Marsh. SAUTER et al. (1973) found the release of sucrose to be temperature dependent decreasing with temperature above and below 28° C. Treatment with p-chloromercuribenzoate inhibited release of sugar. High levels of respiratory enzyme activity were restricted to times when sucrose appeared in the vessels. Uptake of 100 mM sucrose into castor bean cotyledons was decreased by 10^{-4} M DNP and distribution of the ^{14}C-sucrose from the cotyledons was shown to be inhibited by 10^{-3} M DNP (KRIEDEMANN and BEEVERS, 1967a). KRIEDEMANN and BEEVERS concluded that inhibition resulted from an effect on loading of sugar into the cotyledons rather than on the translocation system itself. However, the effect of the inhibitor on respiratory metabolism was not determined. DNP at concentrations known to uncouple in the system used inhibited sucrose uptake into conducting bundles of sugar beet, as shown by TURKINA (1961) and TURKINA and SOKOLOVA (1972).

Attempts to study the energy requirement for loading of sucrose in source areas suffer from uncertainty as to whether the primary effects are on the translocation through the sieve tubes or on loading in the source. Work by QURESHI and SPANNER (1973) on *Saxifraga* stolon indicated that DNP at concentrations above 10^{-4} M stopped translocation when applied to a length of path, apparently without affecting the source. Concentrations of DNP too low to inhibit translocation through the path did cause a significant decrease of translocation when label and DNP were applied simultaneously to the source leaf.

The energy requirement of translocation provides a means of evaluating the various proposed mechanisms of translocation. WARDLAW (1974) reviewed the estimated energy requirements for several translocation models in the literature. A comparison of demand with available energy supply indicates that a number of theories seem feasible from this standpoint. WARDLAW concluded that the data favor mechanisms which do not require direct intervention of energy metabolism along the translocation path.

3. Saturation Kinetics

From the high level of solute accumulation in the se-cc complex of the minor veins there seems to be good reason to believe that phloem loading involves active, mediated uptake of the translocate species. All mediated transport processes share a number of characteristics; additional criteria exist for the distinction of active and passive carriers. The first group of criteria is specificity for the substance transported, the presence of saturation kinetics indicative of binding and specific inhibition, either by competing substances or by agents which block functional groups of proteins. Active carriers are further defined by transport against a chemical or electrochemical gradient, dependence on a source of metabolic energy and vectorial or unidirectional movement (LEHNINGER, 1970). The term "carrier" as used here does not specify a particular mechanism but includes the concept of binding to a recognition site on a molecule which mediates transfer across a membrane. Presumably some but not all uptake into the phloem occurs by a specific carrier mediated process.

Specificity for translocate sugars, the first criterion, has been discussed above (see C.II). A second criterion for participation of a carrier is the saturation of transport with increasing concentration of substrate. Data which show saturation kinetics for phloem loading and for translocation are presented in Fig. 2 and Table 2. A biphasic saturation curve was shown for translocation from castor bean cotyledons supplied with exogenous sucrose solution (KRIEDEMANN and BEEVERS, 1967a, 1967b). Similar biphasic curves were obtained for sucrose uptake in leaves by VICKERY and MERCER (1967), and TURKINA and SOKOLOVA (1972) using small vascular bundles isolated from sugar beet leaves and by FELLOWS and GEIGER (1974) and SOVONICK et al. (1974) using isolated leaf pieces. Autoradiography of leaves in the latter two studies revealed that most of the exogenously-supplied sugar was taken up by the minor veins (Fig. 1).

Data from studies in which saturation kinetics were observed are given in Table 9. The parameter of solute concentration required to produce half-maximum velocity (K_j) is sometimes used in solute-uptake studies (NOBEL, 1970). The presence of saturation kinetics absorption curves for uptake systems is generally considered to point to the existence of a relatively limited number of carrier molecules, which bind the permeant species. The significance of curves which saturate more than once, as substrate concentration is progressively increased, is not clear. Dual uptake curves have been reported previously in plants for sugar uptake (FINKELMAN and REINHOLD, 1963a; VICKERY and MERCER, 1967 and MARETZKI and THOM, 1972) for ion uptake (HIGINBOTHAM, 1973) and for amino acids (REINHOLD et al., 1970). A second saturation was not seen in the first two studies but in most other cases second (or higher) saturation curves were observed and were concluded to be evidence for a second uptake mechanism, or for a different phase of the same mechanism, induced by high substrate concentrations.

Most of the attempts to discover the mechanisms of multiple isotherms have been studies of ion uptake. Some workers believe that both mechanisms are located in the plasmalemma, while others believe that the high affinity system is in the plasmalemma, while the low affinity system resides in the tonoplast (see review in HIGINBOTHAM, 1973). Evidence exists in support of both theories. A study by LINASK and LATIES (1973) on glucose absorption by aged potato slices revealed

Table 9. Summary of the K_j's found for sucrose and glucose in various types of tissue

Author	Tissue used	Sugar studied	K_j* I (mM)	K_j* II (mM)
MARETZKI and THOM (1972)	Cultured sugar-cane cells	glucose	0.02	1.40
LINASK and LATIES (1973)	Potato slices	glucose	0.027–0.040 3.0–7.7	0.52–0.53 24–54
TURKINA and SOKOLOVA (1972)	Isolated sugar beet petiole bundles	sucrose	13	
CATALDO (1974)	Tobacco leaf discs	sucrose glucose	34 19	
	Isolated tobacco mesophyll	sucrose glucose	35 19	
	Isolated tobacco bundles	sucrose glucose	15 53	
WOLOSIUK and PONTIS (1971)	Sucrose synthetase isolated from Jerusalem artichoke tubers	sucrose (reverse reaction)	56	200

* More than one K_j is listed for multiphasic systems.

a multiple isotherm, with four distinguishable phases. These were interpreted to be independent systems, triggered in turn by the external glucose concentration, possibly involving both the plasmalemma and the tonoplast. Recently LEONARD and HODGES (1973) observed a multi-phasic uptake curve for potassium with increasing concentration. The data did not fit a typical Lineweaver-Burk plot. These authors interpreted the phases to be the result of negative cooperativity, a change in binding characteristics brought about by the presence of the bound substrate. A survey of the literature on multiphasic uptake dictates caution in applying simple interpretations. Uptake studies in which translocation rates are used as a measure of sugar uptake must be interpreted with a separate set of precautions because the material being transported into the vascular tissue is rapidly transported away from the site of initial uptake. The effect of this removal can be seen in the data of KRIEDEMANN and BEEVERS (1967a) who found a second phase of sucrose uptake into the endosperm of castor bean after the initial hyperbolic saturation curve, only when the seedling axis was intact. The second uptake phase did not appear to saturate and was abolished when the seedling was removed. Since the sucrose concentration of the phloem exudate was approximately 70 mM, uptake from solutions more concentrated than this may have been due to facilitated diffusion promoted by the rapid removal of the substrate, once inside the cells.

SOVONICK et al. (1974) observed biphasic saturation curves for translocation rate with increasing exogenous sucrose concentration, whether the sugar was supplied by reverse capillary-feeding or through the abraded leaf surface. All of the methods produced a dual isotherm for sucrose absorption with the second phase becoming prominant above approximately 100 mM concentration. When studying uptake in whole leaves the determination of K_j is further complicated by the presence of a large unstirred layer around the area of uptake. When such an unstirred layer is present, the K_j found is likely to be too high. Differences in the K_j values obtained by different methods (Fig. 2) are presumably a result of this effect. The highest rates reported by SERVAITES and GEIGER (1974) for translocation of photosynthate are below the V_{max} found for the first phase of sucrose loading of exogenous ^{14}C-sucrose (Table 2). If higher translocation rates are necessary it appears that the second system which TURKINA and SOKOLOVA (1972) interpret as operating by facilitated diffusion could conceivably function. However, the K_j of 600 mM by SOVONICK et al. (1974) is below the estimated sucrose concentration of se-cc complex of the minor veins (Table 1). Although biphasic curves have been reported for phloem loading and translocation, neither their mechanism nor their significance in translocation is clear. It seems that the kinetic studies support the presence of a recognition site which shows saturation.

A third evidence for carrier-mediated phloem loading is the demonstration of competitive or specific binding inhibition but to date little or no work of this type has been reported.

D. Control Aspects of Phloem Loading

I. Production of Osmotic Pressure in Sieve Elements and Companion Cells Generates Motive Force for Translocation

In addition to selecting the major translocate species, phloem loading is considered by some to be the source of at least part of the motive force for translocation. The results of studies in which energy metabolism is inhibited locally point to the source and sink as the point of origin of the driving force for translocation (see Section D, Chapter 11). For a proposed mechanism to be feasible it must be able to generate the required pressures. ZIMMERMANN and BROWN (1971) noted that sieve-tube sap concentration gradients reported in the literature range from 0.1 to 1.4 bars/m with most values from 0.2 to 0.4 bars/m. Using a direct measuring technique, HAMMEL (1968) found turgor pressures of from 10 to 20 bars and gradients of 0.2 to 0.4 bars/m in red oak sieve tubes. He determined that the pressures observed were being generated by a somewhat undefined "leaf-cell sap" with an osmotic pressure of 20 to 30 bars.

The osmotic pressure of 28 to 32 bars found in the sieve element-companion cell complex by GEIGER et al. (1973) seems adequate to produce the pressures generally reported or posited for the sieve-tube sap. The fact that the overall osmotic pressure of the leaf is lower than that of the sieve sap is not evidence against the production of the driving pressure by the se-cc complex, because the latter is a small proportion of the blade. Water, entering from a free space solution with an osmotic pressure of a few bars, is capable of generating a maximum hydrostatic pressure on the order of 25 to 30 bars, depending on the tension in the xylem.

Observations on the effect of leaf-water status on solute export also support the role of water influx into the phloem in driving translocation. PLAUT and REINHOLD

(1967) observed that water stress, which presumably decreased the osmotic gradient across the sieve-element membranes, exerted an inhibitory effect on movement within the sieve tubes rather than on uptake or secretion into the sieve elements; the effect was reversed by irrigating the plants. WARDLAW (1974) recently reviewed the topic of water relations of sieve tubes. Relatively rapid translocation from leaves with a water deficit of 20 to 30 atm indicates an osmotic pressure of more than 20 to 30 atm in the sieve elements. Data presented by BREVEDAN and HODGES (1973) show that low water potential in the exporting leaf inhibits translocation more strongly than photosynthesis, consistent with the involvement of water flux in driving translocation.

If water enters the same minor vein membranes as the sugar is thought to enter and in the ratio that is found for the sieve-tube sap, water would enter at 1.5×10^{-7} moles min^{-1} cm^{-2}, membrane. This calculated rate falls within the range of 1×10^{-7} to 1.5×10^{-5} moles min^{-1} cm^{-2} for a 1 atm pressure difference as reported in GIESE (1973). Active phloem loading of sugar appears to be able to account for the observed flux rates and pressures.

Critics of mass flow question whether pressure generated in the source can be transmitted down the translocation system. Recent reports which have provided evidence for unobstructed sieve plates and a clear sieve-element lumen with P-protein and organelles lining the walls (FISHER, 1971; EVERT et al., 1973; GIAQUINTA and GEIGER, 1973) support the feasibility of this mechanism. BARCLAY AND FENSOM (1973) have demonstrated that suspended carbon black particles injected into a relatively slightly damaged sieve element were carried through the sieve plate by mass flow (see p. 233). Recent experiments with labeled water and sucrose led to the conclusion that water and sucrose move *via* solution flow in the sieve tubes (CATALDO et al., 1972a, 1972b). The effectiveness of an osmotic gradient in altering the pressure in sieve tubes was demonstrated by WEATHERLEY et al. (1959). These workers found that decreasing the osmotic gradient across the sieve-element membrane by perfusing the xylem with 15% mannitol caused the rate of exudation from aphid styles to fall to less than 10% of the original rate; the concentration of sucrose in the exudate increased from 20% sucrose to nearly 40% sucrose.

An even more direct demonstration of the ability of a gradient of osmotic pressure in the source phloem to produce flow is found in studies by HUMPHREYS and GARRARD (1971a; 1971b) and HUMPHREYS (1972). ^{14}C-sucrose, synthesized from exogenous ^{14}C-fructose, leaked from the cut phloem of maize scutellum tissue if it was sliced or if the embryo axis was removed. The amount of leakage was proportional to the osmotic pressure difference between the initial fructose concentration and the subsequent osmoticum. The leakage was quite slow in 1.0 M sorbitol. From their data it can be inferred that the source of the pressure flow had an osmotic pressure somewhat in excess of 1 M (30 bars). Their studies support the conclusion that the pressure flow is being generated in the small veins of the leaf and is consistent with the hypothesis that mass flow is driven by water flux across the plasma membrane down a water-potential gradient generated by active phloem loading of the se-cc complex, particularly in the minor veins of the source.

CHRISTY and FERRIER (1973) recently developed a mathematical model to generate pressure profiles based on parameters observed in the sugar beet. The calculated profiles and fluxes generally demonstrate the feasibility of mass flow generated by osmotic pressure differences between the solution in the se-cc complex of the source and its surroundings. The osmotic status of sink tissue also enters into the driving force which moves the translocate (FELLOWS and GEIGER, 1974).

It appears likely that under many conditions neither source nor sink exert an overriding control over assimilate translocation. The modeling studies of GIFFORD et al. (1973) indicate that for the barley crop, studied under field conditions, neither source nor sink dominated in limiting crop yield. As discussed above, active loading of source-region minor vein phloem probably serves to establish the "push" which helps determine the distribution of translocate. Considerable data are accumulating which indicate that the "pull" provided by the sinks is of equal or greater importance than the "push" from the source in determining the direction of translocation and its rate (KRIEDEMANN and BEEVERS, 1967a; KING et al., 1967; GAYLER and GLAZIOU, 1972; WARDLAW, 1974; FELLOWS and GEIGER, 1974). WU and THROWER (1973) demonstrated that aphids situated on a mature, non-importing leaf can cause translocate from a younger source leaf to move into the older host leaf. The results appear to support the concept of mass flow of translocate along a pressure gradient to a region of lower turgor in the sieve tubes.

The effect of sink metabolism and the control of translocation is discussed more fully in Chapter 11, Section B, III.

II. Onset of Exporting Capacity

1. Time Course

During development, the leaf passes from a state of importing to one of exporting. WEBB and GORHAM (1964) observed that transition starts when the leaf reaches 40% of the final petiole length and is complete by 60%, a 24- to 36-h period. TURGEON and WEBBER (1973) reported that a developing leaf of *Cucurbita pepo* L begins to export assimilate when it is about 35% expanded. The ability to export was found to move basipetally down the leaf in squash, tobacco and sugar beet. FELLOWS and GEIGER (1974) observed that the 7th leaf of sugar beet began to load assimilate into minor veins at 25% final laminar length (% FLL), started to export at approximately 35% FLL and was completely converted to exporting state by approximately 50% FLL. The changeover occurred during a 24- to 36-h period. The failure to translocate or carry out phloem loading did not result from a lack of the translocate species in the leaf (KÖCHER and LEONARD, 1971).

2. Causal Factors and Preparatory Events

Ultrastructural studies by FELLOWS and GEIGER (1974) reveal that structural maturation occurred gradually in advance of the start of phloem loading. Attainment of structural maturity appeared to be preparatory to the beginning of phloem loading and export in a given region of the leaf. Phloem loading was a necessary but not sufficient factor for the onset of export. Following the start of phloem loading, as revealed by whole-leaf autoradiography, the osmotic pressure of the se-cc complexes in the developing leaf region increased. It appeared that transport from the region began when the osmotic pressure surpassed a threshold value, presumably reversing the osmotic gradient from a pattern characteristic of a sink to that of a source. Data from studies of onset of export support the view that phloem loading indeed motivates the mass flow of assimilate from the source region. This topic of development of export capability is developed in Chapter 10.

III. Relationship between Photosynthesis and Translocation

1. Photosynthesis as a Source of Assimilate and Energy for Phloem Loading

Previous workers have investigated relationships between photosynthesis and translocation including the role of the former in supplying assimilate, its potential as a source of the energy that drives translocation as well as the feed-back control of photosynthesis which may be exerted by translocation. A number of workers have concluded that light has no effect on translocation other than increasing photosynthetic carbon fixation, but some still suggest photosynthetic phosphorylation is able to enhance translocation. HARTT (1965) proposed a theory of phototranslocation based on her observation that basipetal translocation in detached sugarcane leaves saturated at very low light intensity while photosynthesis did so only at a much higher intensity. The effect was thought to be the result of cyclic photophosphorylation supplying ATP for the translocation process. Data showing light stimulation of translocation rates led PLAUT and REINHOLD (1969) to suggest that ATP formed in non-cyclic photophosphorylation increases translocation possibly by promoting phloem loading. SERVAITES and GEIGER (1974) found no increase in the rate of translocation when the light intensity was increased from 2,000 to 7,200 ft-c if the assimilation rate was kept constant by lowering the CO_2 concentration sufficiently. Increasing oxygen concentration while adjusting net photosynthesis to a constant value by varying CO_2 concentration also failed to increase translocation. It appears that some product of photosynthesis rather than ATP from photophosphorylation is limiting translocation under the conditions of the experiments. This conclusion seems reasonable in view of the low rate of ATP utilization estimated to be used for phloem loading (Table 1, entries 10 to 12).

Using a ^{11}C-labeling technique, MOORBY et al. (1974) found a rapid adjustment of translocation velocity to changes in illumination. The speed of translocation out of the fed leaf approximately doubled when the plants were illuminated. When plants were transferred to darkness there was an immediate decrease in the speed of translocation of approximately 20 percent in maize, with a decrease of approximately 1 cm min^{-1} over the next 20 h. The authors consider it unlikely that these changes resulted from a change in assimilate concentration in the leaves. Considering the translocation source as the se-cc complexes of the minor veins it is possible that a rapid change in the loading rate might be responsible for the observed changes in translocation velocity although direct involvement of photophosphorylation cannot be ruled out by their data.

2. Correlation between Photosynthesis and Translocation Rates

A number of studies have shown that translocation rates are a direct function of photosynthesis rate. The relationship is probably caused by the dependence of translocation on a supply of assimilate. As was discussed previously, translocation rates show saturation as the concentration of exogenous sucrose, supplied to the free space, is increased. It seems possible that translocation rates might also show saturation at high photosynthesis rates. By increasing the light intensity, HABESHAW (1969) found saturation of translocation at a rate of approximately 125 μg C/min dm^2 in sugar beet. The leaves at that time were exporting approximately 87% of the carbon fixed. SERVAITES and GEIGER (1974), using younger sugar beet leaves, found no saturation with translocation rates of 50μg C min^{-1} dm^{-2}. Net photosynthesis was varied from 0 to 60 mg CO_2 h^{-1} dm^{-2} by adjusting CO_2 concentration, light intensity and oxygen concentration. The rate of translocation of photosynthate out of the leaf was a linear function of the net photosynthesis rate; the slope of the curve was 0.18 (translocation rate *vs.* net photosynthesis rate). Under conditions of sufficient sink demand translocation seemed to be limited by the availability of translocate rather than ATP derived by photophosphorylation. It may be that the younger leaves did not divert sufficient assimilate to phloem loading to reach the saturation point. Also, by adjustment of the free space sugar concentration or by some other compensating mechanism, membrane transport may not be limiting. Hence a saturation curve for phloem uptake is not observed until photosynthesis rates are increased to a very high rate. Further study of the problem is needed to obtain a more definitive answer to this issue.

In some manner, the proportion of assimilate which is exported from a leaf is rather closely regulated. TERRY and MORTIMER (1972) reported that approximately 75% of the net assimilate is exported in a mature sugar beet leaf. SERVAITES and GEIGER (1974) found that a 60%-expanded sugar beet leaf exported approximately 20% of the assimilate over a very wide range of rates. Sucrose accumulation in the source leaf was only about 4% of the sucrose export rate. The mechanism which determines the proportion of photosynthate which undergoes phloem loading is not known; elucidation will probably require a more detailed knowledge of short distance transit through membranes and free space prior to loading.

EDELMAN et al. (1971) present evidence for chloroplast permeation by sucrose which suggests the presence of facilitated transport through the chloroplast membrane. It is possible that exit from the chloroplast or mesophyll cells may provide a means of regulating free-space concentration of translocate species. BASSHAM et al. (1968) observed a control over the exit of intermediate compounds from isolated photosynthesizing chloroplasts. The pattern appeared to be adapted to metabolic requirements. A control of metabolic pathways may determine the proportion of the assimilate converted to the translocate species.

A number of workers have reported that increased source-leaf assimilate concentration, resulting from inhibition of translocation, can limit assimilation in the source (KING et al. (1967); HABESHAW, 1973). In an extensive review, NEALES and INCOLL (1968) concluded that the mechanism of control of photosynthesis by translocation, if it exists, is not known. LIU et al. (1973) found a strong correlation between the rate of translocation and photosynthesis in two cultivars of bean, which differed in their photosynthetic efficiency. They postulated that translocation is one of the important physiological factors controlling varietal differences in photosynthetic efficiency. Although a correlation is noted and both varieties translocated approximately the same proportion of assimilate, neither evidence for a strong causal relationship nor a mechanism is presented. Generally, convincing evidence that inhibition of translocation produces a decrease in photosynthesis is wanting and further work is needed on this question.

The relationship between translocation and plant productivity needs systematic study. Plants vary considerably in the proportion of assimilates exported during photosynthesis (HOFSTRA and NELSON, 1969a). It is not clear under what conditions source-region factors exert an overriding control over translocation and under what conditions the sink is most important for determining phloem-loading rates. Present indications are that phloem-loading capacity is not rate-limiting and so does not lower productivity under field conditions.

Of more practical interest is an understanding of factors which control the proportion of assimilate which is loaded and translocated. The simple presence or absence of sugars able to be translocated is not the whole answer. As the mechanism of phloem loading becomes clearer it should be possible to design better experiments to study the relationship between phloem loading and productivity.

E. Summary

Phloem loading is the process by which major translocated substances are selectively and actively delivered to sieve tubes in the source region prior to translocation. Several studies have demonstrated that the gradients of sugars including those which can be translocated are not favorable to entry of these assimilates into the phloem by diffusion. An active phloem loading process is required.

Several lines of evidence support the participation of phloem loading as an integral part of the translocation process. By autoradiography, accumulation of labeled assimilate in the minor veins can be shown. Osmotic pressure measurements of the cellular contents of the sieve tubes of minor vein phloem reveal that solutes accumulate to a level considerably higher than their level in the mesophyll. Selectivity of uptake and the involvement of energy metabolism point to active uptake as a part of the phloem loading process.

Structurally, the minor veins are ideally suited to the uptake of solutes during phloem loading. The extensiveness and small diameter of the minor vein phloem network offer a large surface which is only 2 to 3 mesophyll-cell diameters away from the cells supplying assimilate. Companion cells, rich in cytoplasmic organelles and, in some species, modified to be transfer cells, appear to be physiologically connected to the sieve tubes in the minor vein phloem.

Several lines of evidence indicate the involvement of the leaf free space in the transfer of sugars from the mesophyll prior to phloem loading. Exogenous sucrose supplied to the free space at 10 to 20 mM is selectively and actively loaded into the minor vein phloem at rates which are of the same order as those for assimilate produced by photosynthesis. Labeled sucrose produced by photosynthesis can be trapped by unlabeled sucrose solution applied to the free space. The sharp concentration boundary at the plasma membrane of the sieve element-companion cell complex indicates that this membrane is the site of active uptake from the free space during phloem loading.

The composition of the sieve tube contents is controlled by the selective uptake process of phloem loading, but also is produced in part by the differential permeability of the plasma membrane of the sieve element-companion cell complex and the compartmentalization of metabolites in the source leaf. The basis of selectivity during phloem loading is not established. Although selective active transport is a part of the process, directed metabolic conversion in the phloem of the minor vein may also contribute to establishing the pattern of sugars found in the phloem.

Evidence from a number of studies indicates that sucrose is not hydrolyzed during or prior to loading in the source leaf but is hydrolyzed during the unloading process in the sink. Whether the latter pattern is of general occurrence cannot be stated at present.

The phloem loading process must be capable of establishing a high concentration ratio and high flux rates to account for observed data. The requirement for a high vectorized flux is satisfied by the energy-requiring nature of phloem loading. Loading is promoted by supplying ATP exogenously and is inhibited by application of metabolic inhibitors. Kinetic studies reveal saturation of phloem loading by increasing concentrations of exogenous sucrose, suggesting active, carrier-mediated transport during phloem loading. The lower saturation-isotherm seems to be able to account for the highest rates of translocation observed.

Phloem loading appears to be capable of generating solute concentrations of the magnitude needed to account for the patterns of osmotic pressure and turgor observed in translocating plants. Models of translocation systems based on mass flow add theoretical support for movement of assimilate by bulk flow along a pressure gradient. The motive force in these models is the difference between the free energy of the water surrounding the sieve tubes and the lower free energy of the water inside them. Both the "push" at the source end and the "pull" of the water exiting in the sink end determine the movement of translocated assimilates according to this view.

During development, a leaf passes from the state of being a net importer to that of being an exporter of assimilate. This change moves from the apex of the leaf to its base over a period of several days. Events such as opening of sieve pores and degeneration of sieve-tube contents appear to prepare for the initiation of export. The buildup of osmotic pressure in the sieve element-companion cell complex of the minor vein phloem to a point sufficient to produce export seems to be the critical event triggering export.

Photosynthesis provides the assimilate which is translocated but a further role as a major source of energy for phloem loading is less clear. While light does stimulate the rate of translocation, experimental data seem to indicate that photosynthetic phosphorylation normally does not limit the rate of export from a leaf. The proportion of assimilate which is exported appears to be under close control by an as yet unknown mechanism.

The relationship between photosynthesis, translocation and plant productivity is in need of further study, especially in view of the need to increase crop productivity.

References

AMAR, L., REINHOLD, L.: Loss of membrane transport ability in leaf cells and release of protein as a result of osmotic shock. Plant Physiol. **51**, 620–625 (1973).

ARNOLD, W.N.: The selection of sucrose as the translocate of higher plants. J. Theoret. Biol. **21**, 13–20 (1968).

BARCLAY, G.F., FENSOM, D.S.: Passage of carbon black through sieve plates of unexcised *Heracleum sphondylium* after micro-injection. Acta Botan. Neerl. **22**, 228–232 (1973).
BASSHAM, J.A., KIRK, M., JENSEN, R.G.: Photosynthesis by isolated chloroplasts. I. Diffusion of labeled photosynthetic intermediates between isolated chloroplasts and suspending medium. Biochim. Biophys. Acta **153**, 211–218 (1968).
BAUER, L.: Zur Frage der Stoffbewegungen in der Pflanze mit besonderer Berücksichtigung der Wanderung von Fluorochromen. Planta **42**, 362–451 (1953).
BEDNARZ, R.M., RASMUSSEN, H.P.: CO_2-fixation sites in leaves of maize and oats. J. Exptl. Botany **23**, 415–421 (1972).
BEITLER, G.A., HENDRIX, J.E.: Stachyose: an early product of photosynthesis in squash leaves. Plant Physiol. **53**, 674–676 (1974).
BIELESKI, R.L.: Accumulation of phosphate, sulfate and sucrose by excised phloem tissues. Plant Physiol. **41**, 447–454 (1966).
BONNER, J., VARNER, J.E.: Plant biochemistry. New York: Academic Press 1965.
BOYER, J.S.: Nonstomatal inhibition of photosynthesis in sunflower at low leaf water potentials and high light intensities. Plant Physiol. **48**, 532–536 (1971).
BREVEDAN, E.R., HODGES, H.F.: Effects of moisture deficits on ^{14}C translocation in corn (*Zea mays* L.). Plant Physiol. **52**, 436–439 (1973).
BRIARTY, L.G.: Repeating particles associated with membranes of transfer cells. Planta **113**, 373–377 (1973).
BROVCHENKO, M.I.: On the movement of sugars from the mesophyll to the conducting bundles in sugar-beet leaves. Soviet Plant Physiol. **12**, 270–279 (1965).
BROVCHENKO, M.I.: Some proofs of the splitting of sucrose during its movement from mesophyll into the fine bundles of sugar beet leaves. Soviet Plant Physiol. **14**, 352–359 (1967).
BROVCHENKO, M.I.: Sucrose hydrolysis in free space of leaf tissues and localization of invertase. Soviet Plant Physiol. **17**, 24–30 (1970).
CATALDO, D.A.: Vein loading: the role of the symplast in intercellular transport of carbohydrate between the mesophyll and the minor veins of tobacco leaves. Plant Physiol. **53**, 912–917 (1974).
CATALDO, D.A., CHRISTY, A.L., COULSON, C.L.: Solution flow in the phloem. II. Phloem transport of THO in *Beta vulgaris*. Plant Physiol. **49**, 690–695 (1972b).
CATALDO, D.A., CHRISTY, A.L., COULSON, C.L., FERRIER, J.M.: Solution flow in the phloem. I. Theoretical considerations. Plant Physiol. **49**, 685–689 (1972a).
CHOPOWICK, R.E., FORWARD, D.F.: Translocation of radioactive carbon after the application of ^{14}C alamine and $^{14}CO_2$ to sunflower leaves. Plant Physiol. **53**, 21–27 (1974).
CHRISTY, A.L., FERRIER, J.M.: A mathematical treatment of Münch's pressure-flow hypothesis of phloem translocation. Plant Physiol. **52**, 531–538 (1973).
COULSON, C.L., CHRISTY, A.L., CATALDO, D.A., SWANSON, C.A.: Carbohydrate translocation in sugar beet petioles in relation to petiolar respiration and adenosine 5′-triphosphate. Plant Physiol. **49**, 919–923 (1972).
CRAFTS, A.S.: Movement of viruses, auxins and chemical indicators in plants. Botan. Rev. **17**, 203–284 (1951).
CRAFTS, A.S., CRISP, C.E.: Phloem transport in plants. San Francisco: Freeman and Co. 1971.
CURTIS, O.F., ASAI, G.N.: Evidence relative to the supposed permeability of sieve tube cytoplasm. Am. J. Botany **26**, 165–175 (1939).
CURTIS, O.F., SCOFIELD, H.T.: Comparison of osmotic concentrations of supplying and receiving tissue and its bearing on the Münch hypothesis of the translocation mechanism. Am. J. Botany **20**, 502–513 (1933).
DOWNTON, W.J.S., HAWKER, J.S.: Enzymes of starch and sucrose metabolism in *Zea mays* leaves. Phytochemistry **12**, 1551–1556 (1973).
EDELMAN, J., SCHOOLAR, A.I., BONNER, W.B.: Permeability of sugar-cane chloroplasts to sucrose. J. Exptl. Botany **22**, 534–545 (1971).
ESAU, K.: Plants, viruses. Viruses, and insects. Cambridge, Mass: Harvard Univ. 1961.
ESAU, K.: Minor veins in Beta leaves: structure related to function. Proc. Am. Phil. Soc. **111**, 219–233 (1967).
ESAU, K.: Cytology of sieve elements in minor veins of sugar beet leaves. New Phytologist **71**, 161–168 (1972).
ESAU, K., CRONSHAW, J., HOEFERT, L.L.: Relation of beet yellows virus to the phloem and to movement in the sieve tube. J.Cell Biol. **32**, 71–87 (1967).

ESAU, K., HOEFERT, L.L.: Cytology of beet yellows virus infection in *Tetragonia*. II. Vascular elements in infected leaf. Protoplasma **72**, 459–476 (1971).

ESAU, K., HOEFERT, L.L.: Ultrastructure of sugar beet leaves infected with beet western yellows virus. J. Ultrastruct. Res. **40**, 556–571 (1972)

ESCHRICH, W.: Biochemistry and fine structure of phloem in relation to transport. Ann. Rev. Plant Physiol. **21**, 193–214 (1970).

EVERT, R.F., ESCHRICH, W., EICHORN, S.E.: P-protein distribution in mature sieve elements of *Cucurbita maxima*. Planta **109**, 193–210 (1973).

EVERT, R.F., YOUNG, J.H.: Solution flow in tubular semi-permeable membranes. Planta **107**, 279–300 (1972).

FELLOWS, R.J., GEIGER, D.R.: Structural and physiological changes in sugar beet leaves during sink to source transition. Plant Physiol. **54**, 877–885 (1974).

FIFE, J.M., PRICE, C., FIFE, D.C.: Some properties of phloem exudate collected from root of sugar beet. Plant Physiol. **37**, 791–792 (1962).

FINKELMAN, I., REINHOLD, L.: Studies on the uptake and release of sugars by segments of sunflower hypocotyl. I. The effect of 2,4-dinitrophenol on the uptake of fructose. Israel J. Botany **12**, 97–105 (1963a).

FINKELMAN, I., REINHOLD, L.: Studies on the uptake and release of sugars by segments of sunflower hypocotyl II. The effect of 2,4-dinitrophenol on the release of sugars and on the apparent free space of the tissue. Israel J. Botany **12**, 106–113 (1963b).

FISCHER, A.: Studien über die Siebröhren der Dicotylenblätter. Akademie der Wissenschaften, Leipzig. Berichte **37**, 245–290 (1885).

FISHER, D.B.: Kinetics of C-14 translocation in soybean. II. Kinetics in the leaf. Plant Physiol. **45**, 114–118 (1970).

FISHER, D.B.: Some quantitative and qualitative observations on the distribution of sieve-tube contents. Plant Physiol. **47** (suppl.) 41 (1971).

FORD, J., PEEL, A.J.: The movement of sugars into the sieve elements of bark strips of willow. I. Metabolism during transport. J. Exptl. Botany **7**, 607–619 (1967).

GARDNER, D.C.J., PEEL, A.J.: Transport of sugars into the sieve elements of willow. Phytochemistry **10**, 2621–2625 (1971).

GARDNER, D.C.J., PEEL, A.J.: Some observations on the role of ATP in sieve tube translocation. Planta **107**, 217–226 (1972).

GARRARD, L.A., HUMPHREYS, T.E.: Effect of hydrogen ion concentration on sucrose leakage from corn scutellum slices: evidence for two kinds of sucrose pools within the slice. Phytochemistry **10**, 243–253 (1971).

GAYLER, K.R., GLASZIOU, K.T.: Physiological functions of acid and neutral invertases in growth and sugar storage in sugar cane. Physiol. Plantarum **27**, 25–31 (1972).

GEIGER, D.R., CATALDO, D.A.: Leaf structure and translocation in sugar beet. Plant Physiol. **44**, 45–54 (1969).

GEIGER, D.R., GIAQUINTA, R.T., SOVONICK, S.A., FELLOWS, R.J.: Solute distribution in sugar beet leaves in relation to phloem loading and translocation. Plant Physiol. **52**, 585–589 (1973).

GEIGER, D.R., MALONE, J., CATALDO, D.A.: Structural evidence for a theory of vein loading of translocate. Am. J. Botany **58**, 672–675 (1971).

GEIGER, D.R., SOVONICK, S.A., SHOCK, T.L., FELLOWS, R.J.: Role of free space in translocation in sugar beet. Plant Physiol. **54**, 892–898 (1974).

GEIGER, D.R., SWANSON, C.A.: Evaluation of selected parameters in a sugar beet translocation system. Plant Physiol. **40**, 942–947 (1965).

GIAQUINTA, R.T., GEIGER, D.R.: Mechanism of inhibition of translocation by localized chilling. Plant Physiol. **51**, 372–377 (1973).

GIESE, A.A.: Cell physiology, 4th ed. Philadelphia: Saunders Co. 1973.

GIFFORD, R.M., BREMNER, P.M., JONES, D.B.: Assessing photosynthetic limitation to grain yield in a field crop. Australian J. Agri. Res. **24**, 297–307 (1973).

GLASZIOU, K.T., GAYLER, K.R.: Sugar accumulation in sugarcane. Role of cell walls in sucrose transport. Plant Physiol. **49**, 912–913 (1972).

GUNNING, B.E.S., PATE, J.S.: "Transfer cells". Plant cells with wall ingrowths, specialized in relation to short-distance transport of solutes—their occurrence, structure and development. Protoplasma **68**, 107–133 (1969).

GUNNING, B.E.S., PATE, J.S., BRIARTY, L.G.: Specialized "transfer cells" in minor veins of

leaves and their possible significance in phloem translocation. J. Cell Biol. **37**, C7–C12 (1968).
HABERLANDT, G.: Physiological plant anatomy. London: Macmillan 1914.
HABESHAW, D.: The effect of light on the translocation from sugar beet leaves. J. Exptl. Botany **20**, 64–71 (1969).
HABESHAW, D.: Translocation and the control of photosynthesis in sugar beet. Planta **110**, 213–226 (1973)
HAMMEL, H.T.: Measurement of turgor pressure and its gradient in the phloem of oak. Plant Physiol. **43**, 1042–1048 (1968).
HAREL, S., REINHOLD, L.: The effect of 2,4-dinitrophenol on translocation in the phloem. Physiol. Plantarum **19**, 634–643 (1966).
HARTT, C.E.: Light and translocation of C^{14} in detached blades of sugar-cane. Plant Physiol. **40**, 718–724 (1965).
HATCH, M.D., GLASZIOU, K.T.: Direct evidence for translocation of sucrose in sugarcane leaves and stems. Plant Physiol. **39**, 180–184 (1964).
HAWKER, J.S.: The sugar content of cell walls and intercellular spaces in sugar-cane stems and its relation to sugar transport. Australian J. Biol. Sci. **18**, 959–969 (1965).
HAWKER, J.S., HATCH, M.D.: Mechanism of sugar storage by mature stem tissue of sugarcane. Physiol. Plantarum **18**, 444–453 (1965).
HENDRIX, J.E.: Translocation of sucrose by squash plants. Plant Physiol. **52**, 688–689 (1973).
HIGINBOTHAM, N.: The mineral absorption process in plants. Botan. Rev. **39**, 15–69 (1973).
HO, L.C., MORTIMER, D.C.: The site of cyanide inhibition of sugar translocation in sugar beet leaf. Can. J. Botany **49**, 1769–1775 (1971).
HOFSTRA, G., NELSON, C.D.: A comparative study of translocation of assimilated ^{14}C from leaves of different species. Planta **88**, 103–112 (1969a).
HOFSTRA, G., NELSON, C.D.: The translocation of photosynthetically assimilated ^{14}C in corn. Can. J. Botany **47**, 1435–1442 (1969b).
HUMPHREYS, T.E.: Sucrose leakage from excised maize scutella. Phytochemistry **11**, 1311–1320 (1972).
HUMPHREYS, T.E., GARRARD, L.A.: The storage of exogenous sucrose by corn scutellum slices. Phytochemistry **7**, 701–713 (1968).
HUMPHREYS, T.E., GARRARD, L.A.: Sucrose leakage from the maize scutellum. Phytochemistry **10**, 2891–2901 (1971a).
HUMPHREYS, T.E., GARRARD, L.A.: Sucrose leakage from the maize scutellum: evidence for the participation of the phloem. Phytochemistry **10**, 981–995 (1971b).
JARVIS, P., HOUSE, C.R.: Evidence for symplastic ion transport in maize roots. J. Exptl. Botany **21**, 83–90 (1970).
JOY, K.W., ANTCLIFF, A.J.: Translocation of amino-acids in sugar beet. Nature **211**, 210–211 (1966).
KENNEDY, J.S., MITTLER, T.E.: A method of obtaining phloem sap via mouth-parts of aphids. Nature **171**, 528 (1953).
KING, R.W., WARDLAW, I.F., EVANS, L.T.: Effect of assimilate utilization on photosynthetic rate in wheat. Planta **77**, 261–276 (1967).
KÖCHER, H., LEONARD, O.A.: Translocation and metabolic conversion of ^{14}C-labeled assimilates in detached and attached leaves of *Phaseolus vulgaris* L. in different phases of leaf expansion. Plant Physiol. **47**, 212–216 (1971).
KRIEDEMANN, P., BEEVERS, H.: Sugar uptake and translocation in the castor bean seedling. I. Characteristics of transfer in intact and excised seedlings. Plant Physiol. **42**, 161–173 (1967a).
KRIEDEMANN, P., BEEVERS, H.: Sugar uptake and translocation in the castor bean seedling. II. Sugar transformations during uptake. Plant Physiol. **42**, 174–180 (1967b).
KURSANOV, A.L.: Metabolism and the transport of organic substances in the phloem. Advan. Botan. Res. **1**, 209–278 (1963).
KURSANOV, A.L., BROVCHENKO, M.I.: Effect of ATP on the entry of assimilates into the conducting system of sugar beets. Soviet Plant Physiol. **8**, 211–217 (1961).
KURSANOV, A.L., BROVCHENKO, M.I.: Sugars in the free space of leaf plates: their origin and possible involvement in transport. Can. J. Botany **48**, 1243–1250 (1970).

KURSANOV, A.L., BROVCHENKO, M.I., BUTENKO, E.P.: Transformation of sugars absorbed by the leaf tissues of sugar beets. Soviet Plant Physiol. **14**, 684–691 (1967).

KURSANOV, A.L., SOKOLOVA, S.V., TURKINA, M.V.: Hexokinase in conducting tissues of sugar beet and its possible connection with transport of sugars through cell membranes. J. Exptl. Botany **21**, 30–39 (1970).

LEHNINGER, A.L.: Active transport across membranes. In: Biochemistry, p. 605–627. New York: Worth 1970.

LEONARD, R.T., HODGES, T.K.: Characterization of plasma membrane-associated adenosine triphosphatase activity of oat roots. Plant Physiol. **52**, 6–12 (1973).

LINASK, J., LATIES, G.G.: Multiphasic absorption of glucose and 3-0-methyl glucose by aged potato slices. Plant Physiol. **51**, 289–294 (1973).

LIU, P., WALLACE, D.H., OZBUN, J.L.: Influence of translocation on photosynthetic efficiency of *Phaseolus vulgaris*, L. Plant Physiol. **52**, 412–415 (1973).

MARETZKI, A., THOM, M.: The existence of two membrane transport systems for glucose in suspensions of sugarcane cells. Biochem. Biophys. Res. Commun. **47**, 44–50 (1972).

MOSS, D.N., RASMUSSEN, H.P.: Cellular location of CO_2 fixation and translocation of metabolites. Plant Physiol. **44**, 1063–1068 (1969).

MÜNCH, E.: Die Stoffbewegungen in der Pflanze. Jena: Fischer 1930.

NEALES, T.F., INCOLL, L.D.: The control of leaf photosynthesis rate by the level of assimilate concentration in the leaf: a review of the hypothesis. Botan. Rev. **34**, 107–125 (1968).

NELSON, C.D.: The translocation of organic compounds in plants. Can. J. Botany **40**, 757–770 (1962).

NOBEL, P.S.: Light-induced changes in the ionic content of chloroplasts in *Pisum sativum*. Biochim. Biophys. Acta **172**, 134–143 (1969).

NOBEL, P.S.: Plant and cell physiology. San Francisco: Freeman Co. 1970.

PATE, J.S., GUNNING, B.E.S.: Vascular transfer cells in angiosperm leaves. A taxonomic and morphological survey. Protoplasms **68**, 135–156 (1969).

PATE, J.S., GUNNING, B.E.S.: Transfer cells. Ann. Rev. Plant Physiol. **23**, 173–196 (1972).

PEEL, A.J., FORD, J.: The movement of sugars into sieve elements of bark strips of willow. II. Evidence for two pathways from the bathing solution. J. Exptl. Botany **19**, 370–380 (1968).

PENNELL, G.A., WEATHERLEY, P.E.: On the mechanism of sugar uptake by floating leaf disks. New Phytologist **57**, 326–339 (1958).

PLAUT, Z., REINHOLD, L.: The effect of water stress on (^{14}C) sucrose transport in bean plants. Australian J. Biol. Sci. **18**, 1143–1155 (1967).

PLAUT, Z., REINHOLD, L.: Concomitant photosynthesis implicated in the light effect on translocation in bean plants. Australian J. Biol. Sci. **22**, 1105–1111 (1969).

PORTER, H.K., MAY, L.H.: Metabolism of radioactive sugars by tobacco leaf disks. J. Exptl. Botany **6**, 43–63 (1955).

PRISTUPA, N.A.: Redistribution of radioactive assimilates in the leaf tissues of cereals. Soviet Plant Physiol. **11**, 38–42 (1964).

QURESHI, F.A., SPANNER, D.C.: The influence of dinitrophenol on phloem transport along the stolon of *Saxifraga sarmentosa*. Planta **111**, 1–12 (1973).

REINHOLD, L., SHTARKSHALL, R.A., GANOT, D.: Transport of amino acids in barley leaf tissue. J. Exptl. Botany **21**, 926–932 (1970).

ROECKL, B.: Nachweis eines Konzentrationshubs zwischen Palisadenzellen und Siebrohren. Plant **36**, 530–550 (1949).

SACHER, J.A., HATCH, M.D., GLASZIOU, K.T.: Sugar accumulation cycle in sugar cane. III. Physical and metabolic aspects of cycle in immature storage tissues. Plant Physiol. **38**, 348–354 (1963).

SAUTER, J.J., ITEN, W., ZIMMERMANN, M.H.: Studies on the release of sugars into the vessels of sugar maple (*Acer saccharum*). Can. J. Botany **51**, 1–8 (1973).

SCHOOLAR, EDELMAN, J.: The site and active nature of sucrose secretion from sugar-cane leaf tissue. J. Exptl. Botany **22**, 809–817 (1971).

SERVAITES, J., GEIGER, D.R.: Effects of light intensity and oxygen on photosynthesis and translocation in sugar beet. Plant Physiol. **54**, 575–578 (1974).

SHIROYA, M.: Comparison of upward and downward translocation of ^{14}C from a single leaf of sunflower. Plant Physiol. **43**, 1605–1610 (1968).

SHUEL, R.W.: Studies of nectar secretion in excised flowers. II. The influence of certain growth regulators and enzyme inhibitors. Can. J. Botany **37**, 1167–1180 (1959).

SMITH, R.C., EPSTEIN, E.: Absorption by shoot tissue: Technique and first findings with excised leaf tissue in corn. Plant Physiol. **39**, 338–341 (1964).

SOVONICK, S.A.: GEIGER, D.R., FELLOWS, R.J.: Evidence for active phloem loading in the minor veins of sugar beet. Plant Physiol. **54**, 886–891 (1974).

SPITZER, N.C.: Low resistance connections between cells in the developing anther of lily. J. Cell Biol. **45**, 565–575 (1970).

STEWART, C.R., BEEVERS, H.: Gluconeogenesis from amino acids in germinating castor bean endosperm and its role in transport to the embryo. Plant Physiol. **42**, 1587–1595 (1967).

SWANSON, C.A., EL-SHISHINY, E.D.H.: Translocation of sugars in the concord grape. Plant Physiol. **33**, 33–37 (1958).

TAMMES, P.M.L., VONK, C.R., VAN DIE, J.: Studies on phloem exudation from *Yucca flaccida* Haw. XI. Xylem feeding of ^{14}C-sugars and some other compounds, their conversion and recovery from the phloem exudate. Acta Botan. Neerl. **22**, 233–237 (1973).

TERRY, N., MORTIMER, D.C.: Estimation of the rates of mass carbon transfer by leaves of sugar beet. Can. J. Botany **50**, 1049–1054 (1972).

TRIP, P.: Sugar transport in conducting elements of sugar beet leaves. Plant Physiol. **44**, 717–725 (1969).

TRIP, P., NELSON, C.D., KROTKOV, G.: Selective and preferential translocation of ^{14}C-labeled sugars in white ash and lilac. Plant Physiol. **40**, 740–747 (1965).

TROUGHTON, J.H., MOORBY, J., CURRIE, B.G.: Investigations of carbon transport in plants. I. The use of carbon-11 to estimate various parameters of the translocation process. J. Expt. Botany **25**, 684–694 (1974).

TURGEON, R., WEBB, J.A.: Leaf development and phloem transport in *Cucurbita pepo*: transition from import to export. Planta **113**, 179–191 (1973).

TURKINA, M.V.: Sucrose absorption by plant conducting tissues. Soviet Plant Physiol. **8**, 523–528 (1961).

TURKINA, M.V., SOKOLOVA, S.V.: Sucrose transport across the cell membranes of vascular tissue. Soviet Plant Physiol. **14**, 425–433 (1967).

TURKINA, M.V., SOKOLOVA, S.V.: Membrane transport of sucrose in plant tissue. Soviet Plant Physiol. **19**, 912–919 (1972).

TYREE, M.T.: The symplast concept. A general theory of symplastic transport according to the thermodynamics of irreversible processes. J. Theoret. Biol. **26**, 181–214 (1970).

ULLRICH, W.: Zur Wirkung von Adenosintriphosphat auf den Fluoresceintransport in den Siebrohren. Planta **57**, 713–717 (1962).

VICKERY, R.S., MERCER, F.V.: The uptake of sucrose by bean leaf tissue. I. The general nature of the uptake. Australian J. Biol. Sci. **17**, 338–347 (1964).

VICKERY, R.S., MERCER, F.V.: The uptake of sucrose by bean leaf tissue. II. Kinetic experiments. Australian. J. Biol. Sci. **20**, 565–574 (1967).

WANNER, H.: Phosphataseverteilung und Kohlenhydrattransport in der Pflanze. Planta **41**, 190–194 (1952).

WARDLAW, I.: Phloem transport: physical, chemical or impossible. Ann. Rev. Plant Physiol. **25**, 515–539 (1974).

WEATHERLEY, P.E.: On the uptake of sucrose and water by floating leaf disks under aerobic and anaerobic conditions. New Phytologist **54**, 13–28 (1955).

WEATHERLEY, P.E., PEEL, A.J., HILL, G.P.: The physiology of the sieve tube. Preliminary experiments using aphid mouth parts. J. Exptl. Botany **10**, 1–16 (1959).

WEBB, J.A., GORHAM, P.R.: Translocation of photosynthetically assimilated ^{14}C in straight-necked squash. Plant Physiol. **39**, 663–672 (1964).

WHITESELL, J.H., HUMPHREYS, T.E.: Sugar uptake in the maize scutellum. Phytochemistry **11**, 2139–2147 (1972).

WOLOSIUK, R.W., PONTIS, H.G.: Evidence of the existence of two forms of sucrose synthetase. FEBS Letters **16**, 237–240 (1971).

WU, A., THROWER, L.B.: Translocation into mature leaves. Plant Cell Physiol. (Tokyo) **14**, 1225–1228 (1973).

WYLIE, R.B.: Relations between tissue organization and vein distribution in dicotyledon leaves. Am. J. Botany **26**, 219–225 (1939).

WYLIE, R.B.: The role of the epidermis in foliar organization and its relations to the minor venation. Am. J. Botany **30**, 273–280 (1943).

YAMAMOTO, T., SEKIGUCHI, S., NOGUCHI, M.: The translocation of photosynthetic products from mesophyll into midrib in tobacco plant. III. The transformation of translocated ^{14}C-sugars in the veins. Plant Cell Physiol. (Tokyo) **11**, 367–375 (1970).

ZIMMERMANN, M.H.: Translocation of organic substances in trees. I. The nature of the sugars in the sieve-tube exudate of trees. Plant Physiol. **32**, 288–291 (1957).

ZIMMERMANN, M.H.: Transport in the phloem. Ann. Rev. Plant Physiol. **11**, 167–190 (1960).

ZIMMERMANN, M.H.: Translocation velocity and specific mass transfer in the sieve tubes of *Fraxinus americana*. L. Planta **84**, 272–278 (1969).

ZIMMERMANN, M.H., BROWN, C.L.: Trees: Structure and function, p. 244–254. Berlin-Heidelberg-New York: Springer 1971.

18. Radial Transport in Rays

W. HÖLL

A. Introduction

The vascular tissue of most woody stems functions for a limited time only. In most species the sieve tubes of the phloem are active in assimilate transport for only one growing season. The xylem also functions for a limited time. In ring-porous trees water conduction takes place primarily in the youngest growth ring; most vessels of older growth rings are embolized and in some species, such as *Robinia pseudoacacia* L., filled with tyloses. On the other hand, phloem and xylem parenchyma cells, which function as storage tissue, remain alive and functional for many years. Most of these cells are therefore not in direct contact with functional sieve elements and vessels. The ray parenchyma cells have evolved to transport nutrients and water radially between phloem and xylem. The histological construction of rays differs greatly within gymnosperms and dicotyledonous stems and is characteristic for various taxonomic groups.

This chapter discusses the structural organization of rays and the physiology of solute exchange with axial vascular tissue. Much more information is available on xylem rays than those of phloem. Attention is therefore focused mainly on xylem rays.

B. Structural Organization of Rays

I. General

The rays in the xylem of perennial plants (excluding arborescent Monocotyledons) are classified as primary or secondary on the basis of their origin. Primary rays are continuous with the pith or with the primary xylem. They originate either between the primary vascular bundles or from the fascicular region. In gymnosperms rays are initially two or three cells high. Increase in ray height is brought about variously by fusion of rays, increase in size of initials or transverse anticlinal division. With the exception of the rays of Gnetales, the rays of the gymnosperms are uniseriate, i.e. one cell-layer thick. The first cells of the primary ray in gymnosperms are stretched radially (for detailed references see BRAUN, 1970). In contrast the primary rays of dicotyledons are usually very high at the time of initiation, made up of several superimposed rows of cells, often more than one cell wide. As the diameter of the stem increases, new rays are formed. These secondary rays arise in the cambium from fusiform initials. The problem of secondary ray development has been studied for about one hundred years (see the literature cited by BRAUN, 1970).

Secondary rays are initiated in one of the following ways (see KOZLOWSKI, 1971 for the literature): 1. A segment cut off at the tip of a fusiform initial may be reduced to one or several ray initials. 2. A ray initial may be cut off the side of a fusiform initial; it may become shortened before conversion to one or two ray initials. 3. An entire fusiform initial may be subdivided to produce a vertical series of ray initials. In a fourth, relatively unimportant type, ray initials derive from radial plates (radially arranged sheets of parenchymatous tissue characteristic of Pinaceae).

Some investigators (e.g. BRAUN, 1955) stated that most secondary rays of gymnosperms originate by division of the ends or sides of fusiform initials. On the other hand, most secondary rays of *Chamaecyparis* and *Thuja* are derived by segmentation of fusiform initials and only a few from divisions of the ends or sides (see KOZLOWSKI, 1971). In dicotyledons all three types of ray development are common.

The young ray initials soon develop radial cell walls, to produce an uniseriate ray. Multiseriate rays, characteristic for most dicotyledons, develop from uniseriate rays, a process accompanied by an increase in size of ray initials and by cell division. It is followed by growth of daughter cells or by ray fusion (see KOZLOWSKI, 1971). Most ray initials are orientated axially, but some become procumbent (i.e. radially elongated) when anticlinal cell divisions occur. New secondary rays are formed between two older rays. The ray density is thus approximately maintained as the stem circumference increases (BANNAN, 1955).

In some species ray cells of the phloem respond to an increase in circumference by dilatation. This conspicuous phenomenon is characterized by either tangential extension of ray cells or more commonly by an increase in number of cells in tangential direction (for further details the reader is referred to ESAU, 1969). One of the best known examples of phloem ray dilatation is that of *Tilia*. In other species phloem parenchyma proliferates but ray tissue does not.

II. Structural, Cytological and Physiological Differentiation of Rays in Gymnosperms

The rays of gymnosperms are composed either of parenchyma cells alone (e.g. *Abies alba* MILL.) or of parenchyma cells and tracheids. In contrast with parenchyma cells, ray tracheids lack a living protoplast. Besides this, the two cell types have different pits: tracheids have small bordered pits, while those of parenchyma cells are simple pits. With the exception of *Abies, Keteleeria, Pseudolarix,* and occasionally *Sequoia* and most Cupressaceae, ray tracheids occur regularly in all Pinaceae (see ESAU, 1965). Ray tracheids may occur singly or in series at the margins of a ray or interspersed among the layers of parenchyma cells.

The cell wall organization of tracheids has been examined by optical and electronmicroscopy (see literature cited by HARADA, 1965). Ray tracheids have lignified secondary walls partly of considerable thickness. In the light microscope one can see that the walls of ray tracheids of some conifers possess projections in the form of bands extending across the lumen of the cell. Electronmicroscopic investigations have established the existence of an additional structure, the so-called warty layer (LIESE, 1965). This sculptured layer covers the lumen side of the tertiary wall. This structure is not restricted to tracheids of gymnosperms, however, it occurs also in hardwoods, arborescent monocotyledons (Liese, 1957) and even in herbaceous plants (Liese and Ledbetter, 1963).

Ray tracheids are often discontinuous within the Pinaceae, parenchyma cells may be inserted at the border of annual rings (Huber, 1949). Liese and Bauch (1967) demonstrated that the total area of ray tracheids and the ratio of ray tracheids to ray parenchyma varies greatly within conifers. In *Pinus sylvestris* L. for instance the ratio is 1:1, whereas for *Picea abies* (L.) Karst. it is 1:4, consequently the velocity of radial movement of a dye solution in air-dried wood of *Pinus* was found to be 5 times faster than that of air-dried wood of *Picea*. Thus, experimental results strongly support the idea that radial permeability in conifers depends largely on the presence of ray tracheids.

The differentiation of conifer rays into tracheids and parenchyma cells occurs during ray development (see Wodzicki and Brown, 1973). In early stages of ontogeny, primary and secondary rays are made up of parenchyma cells or tracheids alone. According to Braun (1955), tracheids are the only cells in newly developing secondary rays in *Pinus sylvestris* L. The rays become heterogeneous when four cell rows high. The rows of parenchyma cells increase in number by differentiation of initials, which move into the center during their marginal expansion. So far only tracheids have formed but cells now develop as parenchyma. In conifers, ray tracheids and ray parenchyma comprise 1–2% by weight of the wood (Hoffmann and Timell, 1972a). Ray parenchyma cells have living protoplasts in the sapwood zone. In the Taxodiaceae, Araucariaceae, Taxaceae, Podocarpaceae, Cupressaceae and Cephalotaxaceae they possess only primary walls. Ray parenchyma cells of the members of *Pinaceae* have secondary walls. Balatinecz and Kennedy (1967) showed that in pines of the diploxylon group the ray parenchyma cell walls lignify only during heartwood formation. However, Bamber and Davies (1969) confirmed this for *Pinus radiata* D. Don. Bauch et al. (1974), using histochemical tests, microautoradiography and UV-microspectrophotometry, demonstrated that ray cells of haploxylon pines and some other coniferous species lignify in the cambial zone.

Hoffmann and Timell (1972a) separated tracheids and ray cells from red pine (*Pinus resinosa* Ait.) by a screening technique and determined both lignin and polysaccharide content in the two cell types. The results of their findings (Table 1) indicate differences in the chemical composition of ray cells and tracheids. The structural organization of ray cells seems to change, when normal wood is transformed to

Table 1. Chemical composition of ray cells and tracheids of red pine (*Pinus resinosa* Ait) in percent (Hoffmann and Timell, 1972a)

Component	Ray cells	Tracheids
Cellulose	35	42
Lignin	40	27
Galactomannans	9	18
β-1,3-Glucan (laricinan)	2	–
Xylan	11	10
Pectin	2	1
Other polysaccharides	1	2

compression wood. However, information concerning the structure of rays in compression wood is often contradictory. Some investigators agree that compression wood contains more ray cells in a given volume than does normal wood (KENNEDY, 1970). On the other hand, TIMELL (1972) found no differences between rays of normal and rays of compression wood in seven tree species investigated. Red pine was an exception, however, with both the individual ray cells and the entire ray notably larger in compression than in normal wood. Although there are anatomical differences in both types of wood, the ray cells in compression wood of this species are chemically indistinguishable from those of normal wood (HOFFMANN and TIMELL, 1972b). Axial tracheids in normal and compression wood, however, differ significantly in their chemical composition.

Judging by the metabolic activity of ray parenchyma cells, the cytological changes which occur during the aging of these cells are important. Several investigators have studied the cytological and histochemical changes in ray cells in radial direction of stems. These investigations were mostly performed to obtain fundamental information on the mechanism of heartwood formation.

FREY-WYSSLING and BOSSHARD (1959), following a light microscopic investigation of nuclei, mitochondria, and reserve materials in ray parenchyma cells, reported a gradual degradation of ray parenchyma cells with increasing distance from the cambium. Japanese investigators confirmed these findings (HIGUCHI et al., 1964; FUKAZAWA and HIGUCHI, 1965, 1966; NOBUCHI and HARADA, 1968). They studied the variation in shape, volume, DNA and RNA content of the ray parenchyma nuclei from the cambium to the heartwood. The volume and slenderness ratio of nuclei of coniferous trees decreased gradually within about 1–3 annual rings from the cambium. In both trees with colored and non-colored heartwood, nuclei containing DNA disappeared at the boundary between intermediate wood and heartwood. The amount of RNA, which is closely related to protein synthesis, was higher in ray cells near the cambial zone of coniferous trees investigated (*Cryptomeria japonica* D. DON, *Chamaecyparis obtusa* SIEB. et ZUCC., *Thujopsis dolabrata* SIEB. et ZUCC., and *Pinus densiflora* SIEB. et ZUCC.). In the innermost sapwood and intermediate wood, RNA was virtually absent. NEČESANÝ (1966) demonstrated that in ray parenchyma cells of *Pinus sylvestris* L. the osmotic value as well as the velocity of vacuole staining with neutral red decreased with increasing trunk depth.

From these findings, using histological, histochemical, and physicochemical methods, it is concluded that the pattern of metabolism of ray parenchyma cells in gymnosperms changes from cambial to the inner sapwood through necrobiotic or catabiotic processes.

On the other hand, however, more recent investigations indicate that the metabolic activity of ray cells in gymnosperms changes during the course of a year. During the dormant season, respiration (SHAIN and MACKAY, 1973) and ethylene production (SHAIN and HILLIS, 1973) were highest in the transition zone located between sapwood and heartwood in stems of *Pinus radiata* D. DON. This enhanced metabolic activity is related closely to heartwood formation. The activities of various enzymes apparently changed from the cambial zone inward somewhat inconsistently. Some enzyme activities increased in the zone between sapwood and heartwood, whereas others decreased progressively from the outside of the stem inward. In *Pinus* and *Larix* the activity of peroxidase increased markedly in the innermost sapwood (LAIRAND, 1963). KONDO (1964) demonstrated that enzymes which hydrolyze sucrose and oxidize catechol show an enhanced activity in the intermediate zone.

At present it seems to be likely that the aging of ray parenchyma cells in gymnosperms is not necessarily accompanied by a successive loss of vitality. Depending on the time of the year, ray cells of the innermost sapwood probably play an important role in the biosynthesis of heartwood constituents.

III. Structural, Cytological and Physiological Differentiation of Rays in Dicotyledons

In general the secondary xylem and phloem of most dicotyledons are more complex than the respective tissues in gymnosperms. This complexity is also true for rays. The histological construction of rays in dicotyledons differs greatly from one species to another and is thus of taxonomic importance. Although most dicotyledons typically contain only parenchyma cells in the rays (for exceptions see CHATTAWAY, 1948, 1951) they can be heterogeneous in nature. Rays composed of either procumbent or upright cells alone are called homogeneous (or homocellular). In genera which possess procumbent and upright cells (which can occur in various combinations), the rays are referred to as heterogeneous (or heterocellular).

Investigations of various types of wood rays suggest three stages of organization with the characteristic "contact-isolation-differentiation" (BRAUN and DEN OUTER, 1964; BRAUN, 1965, 1967; BRAUN et al., 1967, 1968). This work has been summarized by BRAUN (1970). The differentiation of rays into "contact cells" with large pits to the vessel elements and central rows of "isolation cells" without conspicuous pits to the vessels is of considerable physiological importance (see Fig. 1). The contact cells, which are often elongated axially (upright cells) are believed to serve in nutrient exchange between vessels and ray cells, while the isolation cells which are mostly procumbent, play an essential role in radial transport (see below).

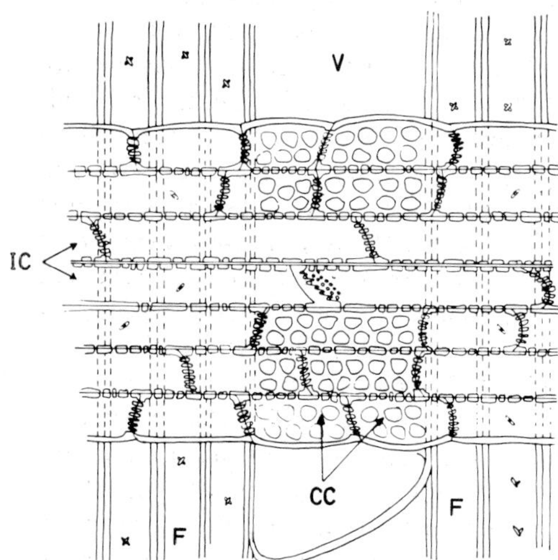

Fig. 1. Differentiation in xylem rays of *Populus* in radial view. Upper and lower rows of ray cells are "contact cells" (*CC*) which are connected with vessels (*V*) *via* large pits. Central rows of cells are "isolation cells" (*IC*). *F* fibers (SAUTER, 1966a)

The organization of ray parenchyma cell walls of dicotyledons has been investigated by polarizing microscopy, X-ray diffraction (see literature cited by HARADA, 1965) and electronmicroscopy (see literature cited by PREUSSER et al., 1961). In electronmicrographs of ultrathin transverse sections of procumbent ray parenchyma cells three layers could be distinguished in the cell wall, the primary and outermost layer of the secondary wall ($P+S_1$), and successive layers of the secondary wall (S_2 and S_3). An additional layer, described as S_4 (HARADA, 1962) is regarded as a layer of a cytoplasmatic substance. The layer S_2 is, as in axial xylem cells, the thickest part of the cell wall. There seem to be no significant differences in the cell wall structure between axial and radial parenchyma cells in angiosperms.

As in the case of gymnosperms there are conflicting data concerning cytological and metabolic changes in rays of dicotyledons with increasing distance from the cambium. Staining the nuclei of ray parenchyma cells of various hardwoods with Feulgen reagent or haemalum, FREY-WYSSLING and BOSSHARD (1959) reported that with increasing distance from the cambium transformation of the nuclei could be observed. Their shape and their capacity to accumulate haemalum stain changes and, at the heartwood boundary they lose the nucleolus. The reducing capacity of the mitochondria was tested in rays of both soft- and hardwoods by FREY-WYSSLING and BOSSHARD (1959). When proceeding inwards along the ray, the time needed for the reduction of the dye Janus green increased, and long before the heartwood boundary was reached, the reducing capacity of mitochondria and (or) sphaerosomes disappeared. From these findings the authors concluded that the aging of ray cells is accompanied by a diminished respiratory activity. FAHN and ARNON (1963) reported that nuclei in ray parenchyma cells of *Tamarix aphylla* (L.) KARST. change in shape and disintegrate with increasing distance from the cambium. The surface of the nucleus first becomes irregular in form, thereafter the nuclei lose their staining properties, and in a final stage of degeneration chromatin bodies are dispersed in the cell lumen.

On the other hand, CHATTAWAY (1949, 1952) stated that the ray cells play an active role in the process of heartwood formation. She suggested that the production of tannins in ray cells increased prior to their death. HUGENTOBLER (1965) who investigated seven genera of hardwoods, found that with the beginning of the dormant period, the nuclei of ray cells at the sapwood-heartwood boundary showed a maximum in size. During the summer months, however, this maximum in nuclear size is restricted to the cambial region. HUGENTOBLER'S suggestion that the ray cells at sapwood-heartwood boundary show enhanced metabolic activity depending on time of year was confirmed by later investigations. ZIEGLER (1968) demonstrated that some water-soluble vitamins occur in highest concentration at the heartwood boundary, and HÖLL and LENDZIAN (1973) measured a respiration maximum in the innermost sapwood tissue in a black locust tree, felled during winter. Although these authors investigated whole tissue homogenates, one can presume that most of the vitamin content and respiratory activity are restricted to ray cells.

Enhanced metabolic activity of ray cells at the heartwood boundary requires considerable intracellular organization. This view is contrary to the findings of FREY-WYSSLING and BOSSHARD (1959) and other investigators. According to SHAIN and HILLIS (1973), however, it is possible that organelles in this tissue might have escaped observation. It is difficult to obtain properly fixed samples of transition zone material for ultrastructural examination. Further investigation of the specific cytological and metabolic changes during heartwood formation of both hard- and softwood ray parenchyma cells are therefore still needed. Since this process certainly represents a sink for precursor substances, it is of great importance in the discussion of radial transport in rays.

C. Storage in Rays

I. Stored Material

According to the most conspicuous reserve material in parenchyma cells, we distinguish between "starch trees" and "fat trees" (FISCHER, 1891). There are some striking correlations between the nature of stored material and vessel arrangement in the wood. SINNOTT (1918), using histochemical techniques, found that ring-porous species are always starch trees. As yet no explanation could be given for this rule. Trees with narrow rays may be in either group, but those with compound rays usually store starch. SINNOTT also found several genera which store fat as well as starch in the rays during the winter season, he therefore classified trees into three groups depending on the types of food reserve (see also KRAMER and KOZLOWSKI, 1960).

Fats are important reserve material because they contain more energy per unit weight than do carbohydrates or proteins. The heat of combustion of 1 g of fat is 9.3 kg-calories while that of carbohydrates is only 5.1 kg-calories. Since most of the early workers regarded materials which were stainable with fat reagents or extractable with organic solvents as "true" fats, data expressing fat content in percent must be interpreted cautiously. Extracts from wood and phloem tissue include such compounds as waxes, sterols and phospholipids in addition to true fats. When ether extracts of the wood of *Tilia cordata* MILL. and *Robinia pseudoacacia* L. were fractionated by means of thin layer chromatography triglycerides were found to contribute up to 70 and 20% respectively (HÖLL and POSCHENRIEDER, unpublished).

It is well known that ray cells of roots—even in fat trees—contain little or no fat but rather starch as reserve material. ZIEGLER (1964) considered two possible reasons for this observation; either roots are unable to synthesize large amounts of reserve fats or they are not exposed to environmental conditions which cause extensive fat production. Since he could not find sufficient biochemical differences between root and stem wood, he suggested that the significant factor is the environment, especially temperature, to which stems and roots are exposed. This was confirmed by his observation that during the particularly long and cold winter of 1962–63 during which roots of *Tilia vulgaris* were exposed to temperatures below 0° C, for several months, the ray cells of these roots showed the same extensive and exclusive fat accumulation.

Accumulated reserve material in ray cells changes qualitatively as well as quantitatively with increasing distance from the cambium. It is well known that starch grains in ray parenchyma cells disappear towards the inner zones of the stem. Rays in the heartwood contain, if at all, only insignificant amounts of starch (see DIETRICHS, 1964). Besides starch depletion, there seems to be a qualitative change in the nature of starch radially. Starch isolated from peripheral annual rings of *Robinia pseudoacacia* L. showed, as iodine complex, a typical amylose absorption spectrum, while starch from the innermost sapwood tissue showed an amylopectinate spectrum (HÖLL, 1972). In contrast to the depletion of starch with increasing age of the ray parenchyma cells, the fat content in the innermost region is higher than in the peripheral younger wood zones. In *Tilia cordata* MILL., lipid content rises from 4.4 to 6.8% towards the central part of the trunk, without any significant change in its composition (HÖLL and POSCHENRIEDER, unpublished). On the other hand changes in composition of lipid material in radial direction seem to occur in both heartwood-forming dicotyledons and gymnosperms. Sapwood and heartwood of *Cryptomeria japonica* D. DON. showed different patterns of fatty acids (HIGUCHI et al., 1969). In *Robinia pseudoacacia* L., the saponifiable lipid fraction of heartwood showed higher amounts of unsaturated and longer-chained fatty acids than the comparable fraction obtained from the sapwood (HÖLL and POSCHENRIEDER, unpublished). The physiological meaning of the occurrence of energy-rich fat and fatty acids in ray cells of heartwood, commonly regarded as a dead tissue, is still obscure.

The innermost sapwood zone of some tree species is not only characterized by changes in metabolism as described above, but also by a change from storage products to secondary compounds, which are formed during heartwood formation. Chemical pathways leading to the synthesis of heartwood extractives were summarized by HILLIS (1968).

It is widely acknowledged that extractives found in ray parenchyma cells are synthesized from intermediates of sugar breakdown in primary metabolism (e.g. HIGUCHI et al., 1969; HILLIS and HASEGAWA, 1963). From acetyl coenzyme A, two pathways lead to formation of two classes of extractives, one to malonyl-CoA and thence to fatty acids, and the other to acetoacetyl-CoA and isoprenoid derivatives (e.g. terpenoids, steroids, etc.). Some woods contain extractives that are largely formed from pyruvate. The shikimic acid- prephenic acid pathway leads to formation of C_6, C_6C_1, C_6C_2, C_6C_3 phenolic compounds. Several groups of heartwood extractives (e.g. flavonoids, stilbenes, isoflavonoids) are produced from a combination of acetate and shikimic acid pathway (see KOZLOWSKI, 1971). For a more detailed description of biosynthetic processes leading to the formation of various extractives, the reader is referred to HILLIS (1962).

Heartwood ray cells adjoining a vessel often contain crystals of characteristic form (CHATTAWAY, 1953). Some tree species even contain considerable amounts of calcium carbonate in their heartwood (see review by SANDERMANN, 1956). In ray cells of secondary phloem the crystals often occur mainly in the outermost and marginal cells. They are usually more abundant in the older tissue, for crystal deposition is often associated with sclerification, that is, crystal-containing cells accompany those that develop secondary lignified walls (see ESAU, 1969). Electron-microscopic investigation has shown that young ray parenchyma cells in the secondary phloem of *Pinus strobus* L. often contain far more tannin than do mature cells (MURMANIS and EVERT, 1967).

Amounts of trace elements are not significantly different in sapwood and heartwood (WAZNY and WAZNY, 1964). One must remember, however, that the detection methods in most cases are not sufficiently sensitive to establish such differences.

II. Seasonal Variations

One of the first investigators to study the seasonal sequence of storage materials in trees was Hartig (1858). He reported that reserve materials in early spring began to be dissolved first in twigs: mobilization then proceeded basipetally into the roots. In contrast, deposition began in the roots and extended distally up through the stem into twigs. Since Hartig's contribution, numerous papers have discussed the phenomenon of filling and clearing of storage tissue. Only the more recent findings are discussed in this chapter, the older literature has been reviewed by Kramer and Kozlowski (1960) and Kozlowski and Keller (1966).

In the above-ground organs of seven to eight year old poplars, Sauter (1966a) found the following seasonal changes in starch content of woody rays in different parts of the stem:

1. A maximum content in early autumn, shortly after leaf abscission (September, October),
2. A period of increasing dissolution of starch in late autumn and winter (November, December),
3. A minimum content in winter (January, February),
4. Resynthesis of starch at the end of dormancy (February, March, April),
5. A maximum in early spring (March, April),
6. Dissolution of starch during the period of bud-swelling and unfolding of leaves (April),
7. A minimum of starch content after the unfolding of leaves at the beginning of the vegetation period (April, May),
8. A period of starch deposition during the growing season (May to September).

During the mobilization period in spring, the upper parts of the stem show a different behavior as compared to the lower parts. Ray cells in the lower parts of poplar stems dissolve their starch reserves earlier than upper parts. The cell rows of rays which are isolated from the vessels (isolation cells) dissolve starch earlier and deposit starch later than the cell-rows which are connected with the vessels *via* contact cells. From these findings, Sauter concluded that contact cells play an important part in exchange reactions of substances (see below). In a later paper, Sauter (1967) showed that changes in starch content can be induced by a temperature change. Sections of conifers and deciduous trees in deep dormancy, when subjected to different temperatures, showed the following changes in starch content:

1. At 0° C starch was dissolved in most parenchyma of wood and bark, at +5° C it was resynthesized, and at higher temperatures redissolved.
2. In most trunks, which were brought immediately from deep dormancy to +20° C, first starch synthesis then starch dissolution took place.
3. The velocity of starch synthesis in ray parenchyma of different tree species at constant temperatures (+5° and +10° C) varied.
4. In contrast to other genera, ray cells of *Quercus, Fraxinus* and *Larix* showed no significant starch degradation at lower temperatures.
5. In contrast with other ray cells, Strasburger cells in the phloem rays of conifers and contact cells in the wood rays of deciduous trees show an increased physiological activity.

6. In the rays of *Betula* and *Populus,* cell rows which are isolated and those which are connected by contact-cells with the vessels show a different pattern in starch dissolution, revealing again a physiological differentiation within the ray parenchyma.

From his findings. SAUTER concluded that during winter dormancy, temperature is an important factor influencing mobilization and dissolution of starch under *in vivo* conditions. JEREMIAS (1964) suggested that with decreasing temperature in winter, respiratory intensity is lowered leading to a decrease in acidity of the tissue, thus activating starch-degrading enzymes. A rise in temperature, on the other hand, leads to enhanced respiration and the resulting acid conditions favor starch synthesis. In contrast to this hypothesis, SAUTER (1967) demonstrated a starch degradation at higher temperatures. It is thus obvious that the filling and clearing of ray cells with reserve materials is a quite complex process, which certainly involves endogenous factors such as growth regulators (see KULL, 1972).

A minimal starch content in phloem ray cells during the cold period was confirmed by electronmicroscopic investigations. MURMANIS and EVERT (1967) showed that during March small starch granules began to appear in the plastids of phloem ray cells of *Pinus strobus* L. During April, May and June the starch grains were large, often filling the plastids almost entirely. The amount of starch increased and reached a maximum during May and June. At the beginning of July the starch content was still high, but towards the end of that month it shows a marked decrease. In January starch was completely absent.

So far little information has been obtained by modern analytical techniques (e.g. gas chromatography) on the changes in fat content during the course of a growing season. Accumulation of fat in ray cells of poplar first established by ISHIBE (1935) was studied in more detail by JEREMIAS (1968). KULL and JEREMIAS (1972) investigated the fatty acid composition of the saponifiable lipids from barks of *Populus balsamifera* L. during the course of a year. Seventeen different fatty acids were found, twelve of them could be measured quantitatively at monthly intervals. Palmitic, oleic, linolic and linolenic acid were found in considerable amounts. During the spring another acid, possibly margarinic acid predominated. During winter, the concentration of unsaturated acid, linolenic and especially linoleic, increased. The increase in the amount of unsaturated fatty acids during the cold period might influence frost hardiness. The authors investigated whole bark tissue, conclusions on statements in ray cells are therefore only indirect.

D. Movement of Assimilates in Rays

I. General

According to their presence (in voluminous secondary tissues), their radial extension through bark and wood, and their anatomical structure (living cells with numerous pits) the rays are radial translocation tissues between the xylem and the phloem. More direct evidence that rays function as translocation tissue is provided by the fact that living cells which become disconnected from ray cells die. An instructive example of this statement was cited by ZIEGLER (1964). In some gymnosperms, single ray cells die if they are isolated on the inside of "stretched" secondary rays.

ZIEGLER (1965) used isotopes to investigate radial transport in rays. When leaves of *Fagus sylvatica* L. and *Prunus avium* L. were fed with $^{35}SO_4^{--}$ radioactivity was found in the phloem and xylem rays. Radial transport velocity of ^{14}C-glucose migration in ray cells of *Robinia pseudoacacia* L. was considerably higher than could be accounted for by mere diffusion (ZIEGLER, 1965).

HIGUCHI et al. (1969) investigated the sites of biogenesis of heartwood compounds and obtained strong evidence that sugars, especially sucrose, are translocated through the ray cells to the sapwood-heartwood boundary. Similar results were obtained earlier by HASEGAWA and SHIROYA (1967) who administered labeled sucrose to the cambial region of a *Prunus yedoensis* tree and found radioactivity in the inner parts of the trunk. Several findings indicate that the assimilate loading process requires metabolic energy (cf. ZIMMERMANN and BROWN, 1971), but the sites at which energy is provided are unknown. Using cytochemical methods, SAUTER and coworkers demonstrated in a series of investigations the sites of certain enzymatic activities in phloem and xylem rays. This work is discussed below.

II. Loading and Unloading of Rays *via* Strasburger Cells

Strasburger (1891) described "albuminous cells" (Strasburger cells) which seem to be specialized cells in the bark of gymnosperms. In most genera they are localized both in the axial system and at the margins of the rays. In the Pinaceae, Strasburger cells are almost exclusively erect cells at the margins of the phloem rays. Because of their close contact with both sieve cells and procumbent ray cells it has been suggested that the Strasburger cells are mediators between the axial assimilate transport and the radial translocation in the bark rays. ZIEGLER and HUBER (1960) were the first to demonstrate phosphatase activity in the Strasburger cells in the needles of gymnosperms.

Using cytochemical staining reactions and cytoenzymatic reactions, SAUTER and BRAUN (1968b) investigated the phloem rays of *Larix decidua* Mill. both during the growing period and during dormancy. The Strasburger cells differ from the erect and procumbent phloem ray parenchyma cells mainly in their connections to the sieve cells, in the absence of starch and in the extraordinary high activity of acid phosphatases. Both the absence of starch and the high phosphatase activity are restricted to times of considerable assimilate translocation and to zones of the phloem with active conducting sieve cells. Fig. 2 demonstrates the cytophysiologi-

---

Fig. 2A–C. Structural organization and functional differentiation of a phloem ray of *Larix decidua* Mill. during the growing season. (A) pit connections, (B) occurrence of starch, (C) activity of acid phosphatase within the different cell types of the phloem ray. The same cells are shown in (A), (B) and (C). The phloem ray consists of the following three cell types: procumbent ray parenchyma cells (*PPC*), which lack contact with sieve cells, contain starch, are long-lived and show little phosphatase activity; erect (upright) ray parenchyma cells (*EPC*), functionally similar to the *PPC*; and Strasburger cells (StC_{1-3}). *SC* sieve cells, *APP* axial phloem parenchyma. Zones 1–3 indicate successively older phloem tissue, with the cambium on the far right. For further details see text. (From SAUTER and BRAUN, 1968b)

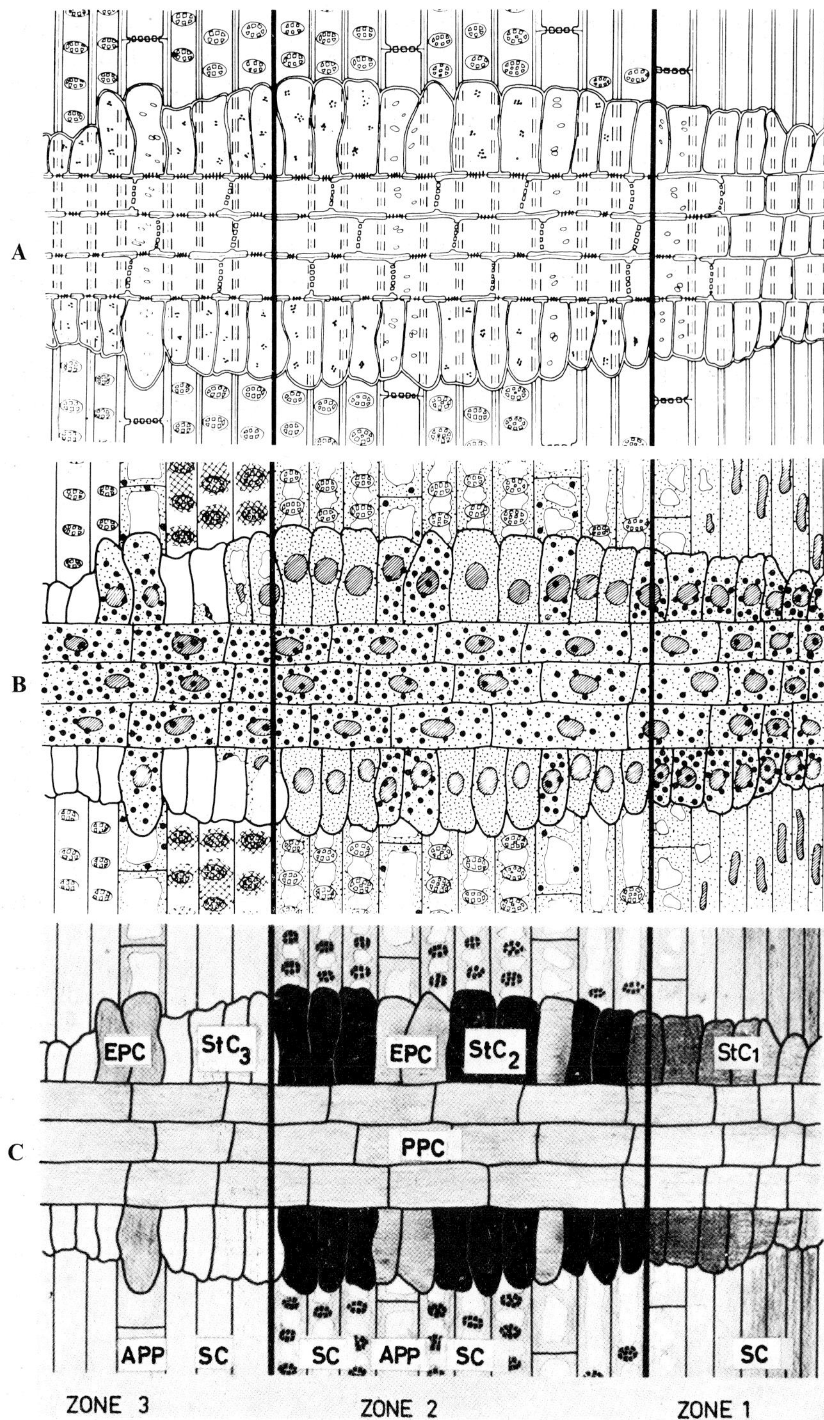

Fig. 2A–C. Legend see opposite page

cal differentiation of the Strasburger cells during the course of a growing season: during the summer, in Zone 1 with young nucleated sieve cells, Strasburger cells are rich in cytoplasm, contain more or less starch and show a low activity in acid phosphatase. In the adjacent Zone 2 with active, non-nucleated sieve cells, Strasburger cells have less dense cytoplasm, their starch is dissolved and they show an extraordinary high phosphatase activity. In this zone sieve cells show also a remarkable increase in phosphatase activity, localized mainly in the sieve areas. Since the activity of acid phosphatase is dramatically raised in tissues which are involved in translocation processes (see below), it can be assumed that this enzyme - plays a role in loading and unloading of sieve elements. In the next older layer Zone 3, both sieve cells and Strasburger cells are dead while other ray cells function as storage tissue.

In a later paper, SAUTER and BRAUN (1972) demonstrated that specific enzymes of respiration, phosphorylation and dephosphorylation exhibit a maximum of activity in Strasburger cells at times of active translocation. Enhanced alcohol dehydrogenase activity indicated that aerobic as well as anaerobic respiration seem to play a role. Increased metabolic activity was measurable only in Strasburger cells which were in close contact with sieve cells. The authors concluded that Strasburger cells function as shuttles controlling the exchange of material between ray and sieve cells. Moreover high metabolic activity might control long-distance translocation of assimilates in two ways; by an active energy-requiring uptake with carbohydrate secretion, and by the supply of energy for the translocation mechanism in the sieve cells themselves.

III. Possible Mechanism of Radial Transport in Rays

Although it is quite obvious that rays are indeed translocatory tissues, very little factual information is available about the mechanism of transport in them. SAUTER (1966b) suggested that phosphatase plays a role in transcellular sugar transport, because its activity in ray parenchyma cells of poplar is low during the dormant period and increases during periods of intensive radial transport (mobilization of starch in spring, starch deposition in summer). This remarkably increased phosphatase activity is mainly restricted to the tangential cell walls which must be passed by the assimilates. SAUTER (1966b) suggested that acid phosphatase participates actively in the intercellular and transcellular transport of carbohydrates by dephosphorylation (high-phosphatase activity) and phosphorylation (low-phosphatase activity) processes which seem to be localized at the ends of the ray cells. Possibly the phosphorylating step at one end of the ray cell is necessary to combine the sugar molecule with a "carrier". Dephosphorylation after migration into the neighboring cell would then require the splitting of the sugar-carrier complex. It is still unknown whether this hypothesis is correct or if the phosphorylated sugars migrate as such *via* cytoplasmatic connections from one cell to the next. SAUTER also pointed out that at times of intensive radial transport, the enhanced phosphatase polarity could significantly increase the transcellular sugar transport. Due to the phosphatase activity a steep sugar concentration gradient (enrichment of free sugars at one pole of the cell after dephosphorylation, removal of free sugars at the other cell pole *via* phosphorylation) could be built up. In phosphorylation and dephosphory-

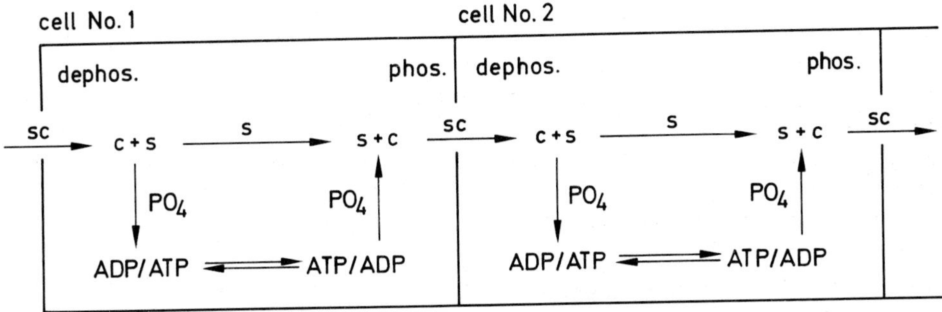

Fig. 3. Model of carbohydrate translocation in ray cells. *phos.* phosphorylation, *dephos.* dephosphorylation, *s* sugar, *sc* sugar-carrier complex, $s \rightarrow s$ transcellular sugar transport by activated diffusion and $c \rightarrow c$ intercellular transport by carrier mechanism (SAUTER, 1966b)

lation reactions the ATP/ADP-system surely plays an important role. This might explain the frequent observation that the carbohydrate translocation is ATP dependent. SAUTER's model of carbohydrate transport in ray cells is shown in Fig. 3.

The pronounced polarity in intracellular localization of acid phosphatase during periods of radial transport was also established in ray cells of the coniferous genera *Pseudotsuga, Abies* and *Pinus* (SAUTER and BRAUN, 1968a). It was always the cambium-facing end of the cells in both xylem and phloem rays which showed the high enzyme activity. In the same tissue section, the polarity in the phloem ray cells is thus opposite to that found in wood ray cells. As far as SAUTER's (1966b) proposal of phosphorylation is concerned, this phenomenon is enigmatic, because phosphatase activity is located on the "wrong" side of the cell wall.

Phosphatase may indeed play a role in carbohydrate translocation in rays, but the understanding of radial transport depends with certainty upon numerous additional parameters which must be investigated in the future. Improved instrumentation and a better understanding of the nature of biological membranes has recently given new information about cell-to-cell transport, but so far only in lower and herbaceous plants. The interested reader is referred to comprehensive reviews (e.g. KOTYK and JANÁČEK, 1970; LÜTTGE, 1973).

IV. Exchange of Carbohydrates between Rays and Vessels

In trees such as *Acer, Betula, Carpinus, Alnus, Populus* etc. considerable amounts of sugars have been found in the vessel sap in early spring. In addition to the radial transport of carbohydrates along rays from the phloem into the xylem and *vice versa,* exchange seems to occur between the rays and the vessels. The mediators of this exchange are specialized "contact cells" (see above).

Investigating eight- to fifteen-year-old trees of *Betula populifolia* MARCH. and *Populus tremuloides* MICHX., SAUTER (1972) found that starch begins to disappear gradually from contact cells shortly before and continues during the period when buds swell, and still later from isolation cells. This period of activity of the contact cells coincides with the time during which sugars appear in the vessel sap. Parallel to the dissolution of starch in contact cells, phosphatase activity in these cells in-

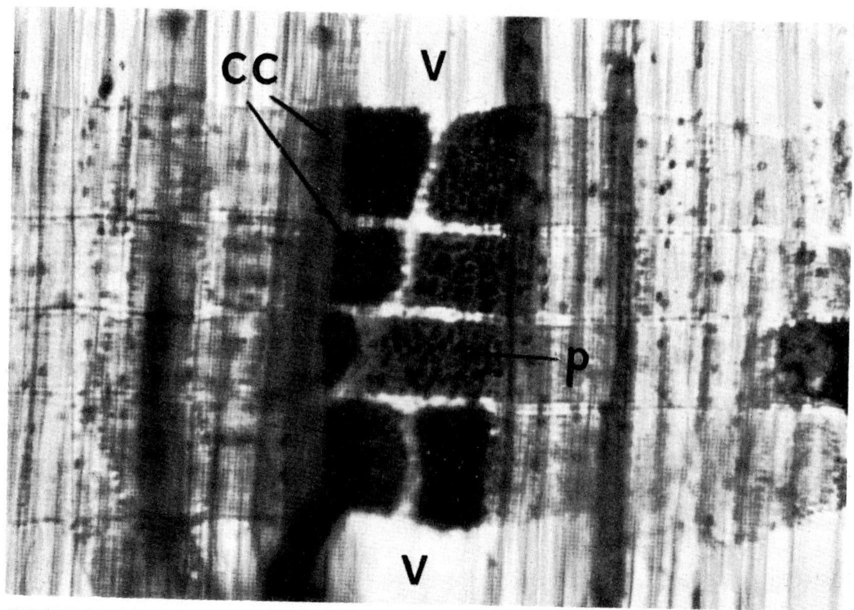

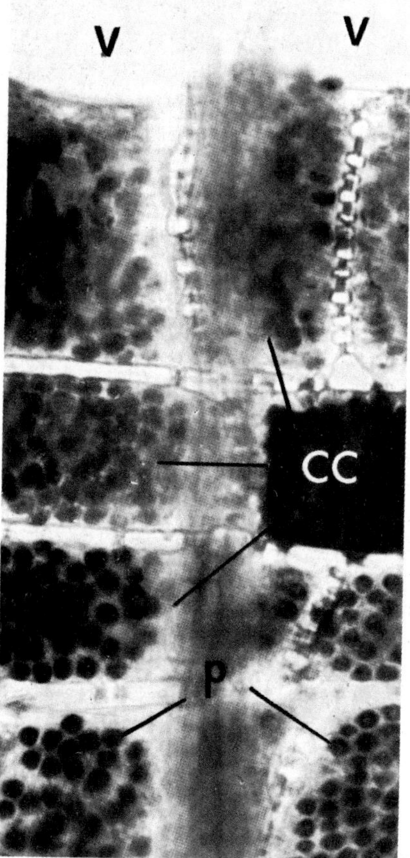

▲

Fig. 4. Cytochemical test for acid phosphatases in a ray of *Betula populifolia* Marsh. when starch dissolves in contact cells and sugar appears in the vessel sap (end of April). The contact cells (*cc*) show greatly increased phosphatase activity on the pits (*p*) that face the vessels (*v*). Incubation period 5 h. ×750 (SAUTER, 1972)

Fig. 5. Cytochemical demonstration of high phosphatase activity on pits (*p*) of contact cells (*cc*) facing the vessels (*v*) in *Betula populifolia* Marsh. during starch mobilization within contact cells. Incubation period 5 h. ×1,400 (SAUTER, 1972)

creased. No increased activity of this enzyme, however, was measurable in isolation cells. At the time when the breakdown of starch was well under way, the most distinctive reaction appeared in the large pits between cells and vessels (see Figs. 4 and 5). Phosphatase activity on these pits increased further and reached a maximum when starch in contact cells had been completely dissolved. Enhanced activity of NAD-dependent isocitrate dehydrogenase, succinate dehydrogenase and alcohol dehydrogenase in contact cells indicated their high metabolic activity. Later SAUTER et al. (1973) demonstrated that the amount of sucrose released into the vessels in isolated stem segments of sugar maple (*Acer saccharum* MARSH.) is temperature dependent. Sugar release was inhibited by p-chloromercuribenzoate. Quantitative measurements indicated that sugar release into vessels is 10 to 30 times faster than the calculated diffusion rates. Thus, biochemical and cytochemical findings suggest that the contact cells are the specific sites of sugar release into vessels and that their metabolism is involved in this process. However, details of the mechanism of sugar release are still unknown.

E. Summary

In both gymnosperms and dicotyledons, rays are composed of cell types differing in structure and function. In most gymnosperms, xylem rays are differentiated into living procumbent parenchyma cells and dead ray tracheids. The ray tracheids function as radial water conducting elements. In gymnosperms most ray parenchyma cells have lignified secondary walls. The process of lignification occurs either in the cambium region or during heartwood formation. Cell walls of ray parenchyma cells have a higher lignin and lower cellulose content than axial tracheids. Reports concerning the metabolic activity in ray cells of increasing age are contradictory in both gymnosperms and dicotyledons. Prior to their death at the heartwood boundary there seems to be a phase of enhanced metabolic activity. In dicotyledons there are two types of ray cells, "contact cells", usually upright, with pit-connections to vessels, and "isolation cells" usually procumbent and lacking direct contact with the vessels. The most conspicuous reserve materials in rays are starch and fats; they occur either alone or in combination. Ray parenchyma cells in roots do not normally store fat even in "fat storing" trees. Rays in heartwood contain insignificant amounts of starch but fat seems to be present in considerable concentrations. Heartwood rays often contain large amounts of secondary substances. Reserve materials exhibit seasonal fluctuations: in winter, starch content is minimal. Starch is deposited during the growing season and reaches a maximum in early autumn. During cold periods the concentration of unsaturated fatty acids increases. Strasburger cells (=albuminous cells) appear to play a role in the exchange of carbohydrates between ray cells and sieve cells. During times of translocation these cells exhibit a very high activity of acid phosphatase. This enzyme is also detectable in sugar-secreting contact cells and during times of assimilate transport at the tangential walls of isolation cells. It is presumed that phosphatases participate in inter- and trans-cellular transport of carbohydrates by phosphorylation and dephosphorylation processes. Ray cells involved in exchange of carbohydrates with vessels show enhanced respiration. Respiratory inhibitors depress secretion from ray cells into the vessels.

References

Balatinecz, J.J., Kennedy, R.W.: Maturation of ray parenchyma cells in pine. Forest Prod. J. **17**, 57–64 (1967).

Bamber, R.K., Davies, G.W.: Lignification of ray parenchyma cell walls in the wood of *Pinus radiata* D.Don. Holzforschung **23**, 83–84 (1969).

Bannan, M.W.: The vascular cambium and radial growth in *Thuja occidentalis* L. Can. J. Botany **33**, 113–138 (1955).

Bauch, J., Schweers, W., Berndt, H.: Lignification during heartwood formation: Comparative study of rays and bordered pit membranes in coniferous woods. Holzforschung **28**, 86–91 (1974).

Braun, H.J.: Beiträge zur Entwicklungsgeschichte der Markstrahlen. Botan. Stud. **4**, 73–131 (1955).

Braun, H.J.: Zelldifferenzierung im Holzstrahl. Ber. Deut. Botan. Ges. **77**, 355–376 (1965).

Braun, H.J.: Entwicklung und Bau der Holzstrahlen unter dem Aspekt der Kontakt-Isolations-Differenzierung gegenüber dem Hydrosystem. I. Das Prinzip der Kontakt-Isolations-Differenzierung. Holzforschung **21**, 33–37 (1967).

Braun, H.J.: Funktionelle Histologie der sekundären Sproßachse. I. Das Holz: Encyclopedia of plant anatomy, vol. IX, part 1. Berlin-Stuttgart: Gebrüder Borntraeger 1970.

Braun, H.J. den Outer, R.W.: Die unterschiedlichen Beziehungen der Holzstrahlen zum Hydrosystem als wesentliches Differenzierungsprinzip. I. Die einschichtigen Strahlen. Z. Botan. **52**, 539–571 (1964).

Braun, H.J., Wolkinger, F., Böhme, H.: Entwicklung und Bau der Holzstrahlen unter dem Aspekt der Kontakt-Isolations-Differenzierung gegenüber dem Hydrosystem. II. Die Typen der Kontakt-Holzstrahlen. Holzforschung **21**, 145–153 (1967).

Braun, H.J., Wolkinger, F., Böhme, H.: Entwicklung und Bau der Holzstrahlen unter dem Aspekt der Kontakt-Isolations-Differenzierung gegenüber dem Hydrosystem. III. Die Typen der Kontakt-Isolations-Holzstrahlen und der Isolations-Holzstrahlen. Holzforschung **22**, 53–60 (1968).

Chattaway, M.: The wood anatomy of the *Proteaceae*. Australian J. Sci. Res. **1**, 279–302 (1948).

Chattaway, M.: The development of tyloses and secretion of gum in heartwood formation. Australian J. Sci. Res. **2**, 227–240 (1949).

Chattaway, M.: Morphological and functional variations in the rays of pored timbers. Australian J. Sci. Res. **4**, 12–27 (1951).

Chattaway, M.: The sapwood-heartwood transition. Australian Forest. **16**, 25–34 (1952).

Chattaway, M.: The occurrence of heartwood crystals in certain timbers. Australian J. Botany **1**, 27–38 (1953).

Dietrichs, H.H.: Chemisch-physiologische Untersuchungen über die Splint-Kern-Umwandlung der Rotbuche (*Fagus sylvatica* Linn.). Ein Beitrag zur Frage der Holzverkernung. Mitt. Bundesforschungsanst. Forst- u. Holzwirtschaft Nr. 58 (1964).

Esau, K.: Plant anatomy, 2nd ed. New York: John Wiley and Son 1965.

Esau, K.: The phloem. Encyclopedia of plant anatomy, vol. V, part 2. Berlin-Stuttgart: Gebrüder Borntraeger 1969.

Fahn, A., Arnon, N.: The living wood fibres of *Tamarix aphylla* and the changes occurring in them in transition from sapwood to heartwood. New Phytologist **62**, 99–104 (1963).

Fischer, A.: Beiträge zur Physiologie der Holzgewächse. Jahrb. Wiss. Bot. **22**, 73–160 (1891).

Frey-Wyssling, A., Bosshard, H.H.: Cytology of the ray cells in sapwood and heartwood. Holzforschung **13**, 129–137 (1959).

Fukazawa, K., Higuchi, T.: Studies on the mechanism of heartwood formation. II. Some observations on the nucleus and DNA content in the ray parenchyma cell. J. Japan Wood Res. Soc. **11**, 196–201 (1965).

Fukazawa, K., Higuchi, T.: Studies on the mechanism of heartwood formation. IV. RNA content in the ray parenchyma cell. J. Japan Wood Res. Soc. **12**, 221–226 (1966).

Harada, H.: Electronmicroscopy of ultrathin sections of beech wood (*Fagus crenata* Blume). J. Japan Wood Res. Soc. **8**, 252–258 (1962).

Harada, H.: Ultrastructure of angiosperm vessels and ray parenchyma. In: Cellular ultrastructure of woody plants (ed. W.A. Côté, Jr.), p. 235–249. Syracuse: Syracuse University Press 1965.

Hartig, Th.: Über die Bewegung des Saftes in den Holzpflanzen. Botan. Z. **16**, 329–335 (1858).

Hasegawa, M., Shiroya, T.: Translocation and transformation of sucrose in the wood of *Prunus yedoensis*. IUFRO 14th Congress Munich (1967).

Higuchi, T., Fukazawa, K., Nakashima, S.: Studies on the mechanism of heartwood formation. I. Histochemistry of the wood tissue. J. Japan Wood Res. Soc. **10**, 235–241 (1964).

Higuchi, T., Onda, Y., Fujimoto, Y.: Biochemical aspects of heartwood formation with special reference to the site of biogenesis of heartwood compounds. Wood Res. Bull. Wood Res. Inst. Kyoto Univers. **48**, 15–30 (1969).

Hillis, W.E. (ed.): Wood extractives and their significance to the pulp and paper industries. New York: Academic Press 1962.

Hillis, W.E. (ed.): Chemical aspects of heartwood formation. Wood Sci. Technol. **2**, 241–259 (1968).

Hillis, W.E., Hasegawa, M.: The formation of polyphenols in trees. I. Administration of ^{14}C-glucose and subsequent distribution of radioactivity. Phytochemistry **2**, 195–199 (1963).

Hoffmann, G.C., Timell, T.E.: Polysaccharides in ray cells of normal wood of red pine (*Pinus resinosa*). Tappi **55**, 733–736 (1972a).

Hoffmann, G.C., Timell, T.E.: Polysaccharides in ray cells of compression wood of red pine (*Pinus resinosa*). Tappi **55**, 871–873 (1972b).

Höll, W.: Stärke und Stärkeenzyme im Holz von *Robinia pseudoacacia* L. Holzforschung **26**, 41–45 (1972).

Höll, W., Lendzian, K.: Respiration in the sapwood and heartwood of *Robinia pseudoacacia*. Phytochemistry **12**, 975–977 (1973).

Huber, B.: Zur Frage der anatomischen Unterscheidbarkeit des Holzes von *Pinus sylvestris* L. und *Pinus nicricans* Host. mit Betrachtungen über heterogene Markstrahlen. Forstwiss. Zentr. **68**, 456–468 (1949).

Hugentobler, U.: Zur Cytologie der Kernholzbildung. Vierteljahresschr. Naturforsch. Ges. Zürich **110**, 321–342 (1965).

Ishibe, O.: The seasonal changes in starch and fat reserves of some woody plants. Mem. Coll. Sci. Kyoto Imp. Univ. Ser. B **11**, 1–53 (1935).

Jeremias, K.: Über die jahresperiodischbedingten Veränderungen der Ablagerungsform der Kohlenhydrate in vegetativen Pflanzenteilen. Botan. Stud. **15**, 1–96 (1964).

Jeremias, K.: Die Veränderungen des Fettgehaltes in den Rinden der Pappelsorten Oxford, Rochester und Androscoggin im Verlaufe eines Jahres. Mitt. Ver. forstl. Standortsl. u. Forstpflzüchtg. **18**, 95–97 (1968).

Kennedy, R.W.: An outlook for basic wood anatomy research. Wood Fiber **2**, 182–186 (1970).

Kondo, T.: On the wood enzyme. J. Japan Wood Res. Soc. **10**, 43–48 (1964).

Kotyk, A., Janáček, K.: Cell membrane transport. New York-London: Plenum Press 1970.

Kozlowski, T.T.: Growth and development of trees, vol. II. New York-London: Academic Press 1971.

Kozlowski, T.T., Keller, Th.: Food relations of woody plants. Botan. Rev. **32**, 293–382 (1966).

Kramer, P.J., Kozlowski, T.T.: Physiology of trees. New York: McGraw-Hill 1960.

Kull, U.: Wirkungen von Wuchsstoffen auf Speicherung und Stoffwechsel in vegetativen Pflanzenteilen. Bot. Stud. **19**, Jena: Gustav Fischer 1972.

Kull, U. Jeremias, K.: Die Fettsäurezusammensetzung der verseifbaren Lipide aus Rinden von Populus balsamifera im Jahresgang. Z. Pflanzenphys. **68**, 55–62 (1972).

Lairand, D.E.: About the cytochemistry of wood elements. Drev. Vysk. **1**, 1–11 (1963).

Liese, W.: Zur Struktur der Tertiärwände bei den Laubhölzern. Naturwissenschaften **44**, 240–241 (1957).

Liese, W.: The warty layer. In: Cellular ultrastructure of woody plants W.A. Côté, Jr., (ed.), p. 251–269. Syracuse University Press 1965.

Liese, W., Bauch, J.: On the anatomical causes of the refractory behavior of spruce and douglas fir. J. Inst. Wood Sci. **19**, 3–14 (1967).

Liese, W., Ledbetter, M.: On the occurrence of a warty layer in the vascular cells of plants. Nature **197**, 201–202 (1963).

Lüttge, U.: Stofftransport der Pflanzen. Berlin-Heidelberg-New York: Springer 1973.

MURMANIS, L., EVERT, R.F.: Parenchyma cells of secondary phloem in *Pinus strobus*. Planta **73**, 301–318 (1967).

NEČESANÝ, V.: Die Vitalitätsveränderung der Parenchymzellen als physiologische Grundlage der Kernholzbildung. Holzforsch. Holzverwert. **4**, 61–65 (1966).

NOBUCHI, T., HARADA, H.: Electronmicroscopy of the cytological structure of the ray parenchyma cells associated with heartwood formation of sugi (*Cryptomeria japonica* D.Don). J. Japan Wood Res. Soc. **14**, 197–202 (1968).

PREUSSER, H.-J., DIETRICHS, H.H., GOTTWALD, H.: Elektronenmikroskopische Untersuchungen an Ultradünnschnitten des Markstrahlparenchyms der Rotbuche — *Fagus sylvatica* L. Holzforschung **15**, 65–75 (1961).

SANDERMANN, W.: Holzinhaltsstoffe, ihre Chemie und Biochemie. Naturwissenschaften **53**, 513–525 (1966).

SAUTER, J.J.: Untersuchungen zur Physiologie der Pappelholzstrahlen. I. Jahresperiodischer Verlauf der Stärkespeicherung im Holzstrahlenparenchym. Z. Pflanzenphysiol. **55**, 246–258 (1966a).

SAUTER, J.J.: Untersuchungen zur Physiologie der Pappelholzstrahlen. II. Jahresperiodische Änderungen der Phosphataseaktivität im Holzstrahlparenchym und ihre mögliche Bedeutung für den Kohlenhydratstoffwechsel und den aktiven Assimilattransport. Z. Pflanzenphysiol. **55**, 349–362 (1966b).

SAUTER, J.J.: Der Einfluß verschiedener Temperaturen auf die Reservestärke in parenchymatischen Geweben von Baumsproßachsen. Z. Pflanzenphysiol. **56**, 340–352 (1967).

SAUTER, J.J.: Respiratory and phosphatase activities in contact cells of wood rays and their possible role in sugar secretion. Z. Pflanzenphysiol. **67**, 135–145 (1972).

SAUTER, J.J. BRAUN, H.J.: Enzymatic polarity in ray parenchyma cells of conifers in spring. Z. Pflanzenphysiol. **58**, 378–381 (1968a).

SAUTER, J.J., BRAUN, H.J.: Histologische und cytochemische Untersuchungen zur Funktion der Baststrahlen von *Larix decidua* Mill., unter besonderer Berücksichtigung der Strasburger-Zellen. Z. Pflanzenphysiol. **59**, 420–438 (1968b).

SAUTER, J.J., BRAUN, H.J.: Cytochemische Untersuchung der Atmungsaktivität in den Strasburger-Zellen von *Larix* und ihre Bedeutung für den Assimilattransport. Z. Pflanzenphysiol. **66**, 440–458 (1972).

SAUTER, J.J., ITEN, W., ZIMMERMANN, M.H.: Studies on the release of sugar into the vessels of sugar maple (*Acer saccharum*) Can. J. Botany **51**, 1–8 (1973).

SHAIN, L., HILLIS, W.E.: Ethylene production in xylem of *Pinus radiata* in relation to heartwood formation. Can. J. Botany **51**, 1331–1335 (1973).

SHAIN, L., MACKAY, J.F.G.: Seasonal fluctuation in respiration of aging xylem in relation to heartwood formation in *Pinus* radiata. Can. J. Botany **51**, 737–741 (1973).

SINNOTT, E.W.: Factors determining character and distribution of food reserve in woody plants. Botan. Gaz. **66**, 162–175 (1918).

STRASBURGER, E.: Über den Bau und die Verrichtung der Leitungsbahnen in Pflanzen. Jena: Gustav Fischer 1891.

TIMELL, T.E.: Beobachtungen an Holzstrahlen im Druckholz. Holz, Roh-Werkstoff **30**, 267–273 (1972).

WAZNY, H., WAZNY, J.: Über das Auftreten von Spurenelementen im Holz. Holz, Roh-Werkstoff **22**, 299–304 (1964).

WODZICKI, T.J., BROWN, C.L.: Cellular differentiation of the cambium in the *Pinaceae*. Botan. Gaz. **134**, 139–146 (1973).

ZIEGLER, H.: Storage, mobilization and distribution of reserve material in trees. In: The formation of wood in forest trees M.H. ZIMMERMANN (ed.), p. 303–320. New York: London: Academic Press 1964.

ZIEGLER, H.: Use of isotopes in the study of translocation in rays. In: Isotopes and radiation in soil-plant nutrition studies, p. 361–370. Vienna: International Atomic Energy Agency 1965.

ZIEGLER, H.: Biologische Aspekte der Kernholzbildung. Holz, Roh-Werkstoff **26**, 61–68 (1968).

ZIEGLER, H., HUBER, F.: Phosphataseaktivität in den „Strasburger-Zellen" der Koniferennadeln. Naturwissenschaften **47**, 305–306 (1960).

ZIMMERMANN, M.H., BROWN, C.L.: Trees: Structure and function. Berlin-Heidelberg-New York: Springer 1971.

19. Exchange of Solutes between Phloem and Xylem and Circulation in the Whole Plant

J.S. Pate

A. Introduction

Two main pathways exist for transport of solutes in the vascular plant. One of these comprises the cytoplasmic continuum (symplast) of the plant, including cell-to-cell transfer over short distances *via* plasmodesmata and over longer distances through the sieve elements of the phloem. The predominant direction of flux within this system is usually from photosynthetically active structures which serve as bulk sources of concentrated solutes such as carbohydrate, to sink regions of various kinds in which these solutes are consumed in growth or in the establishment of new reserves. The second pathway constitutes the extra-protoplasmic compartment (apoplast) of the plant, consisting in particular of the mass flow of water, ions and certain organic solutes upwards from the root in the xylem to transpiring surfaces of the shoot system.

The overall necessity for a continual exchange of solutes between these living and non-living compartments should be obvious. However, in certain regions of the plant, solute interchange of this kind occurs most intensively and becomes intimately linked with long-distance transport in the xylem and phloem and hence with the nourishment of the organs which these conducting systems serve. These situations comprise the subject matter of this chapter. One example is the fate of solutes arriving in mature foliar organs from the root in the xylem, and the possibility of their being absorbed from the apoplast of the leaf, loaded onto the phloem and then passed back out of the leaf along with photosynthate in the translocation stream. Other examples relate to root and stem, including the abstraction or addition of solutes by cells bordering the transpiration pathway, and the cycling of solutes through roots, from the descending phloem stream back to the ascending stream of the xylem.

The plan of the chapter is to deal first with anatomical and ultrastructural features concerned with xylem-phloem interchange of solutes, then to deal in detail with the physiology of such processes as they occur in specific donor or acceptor organs of the plant, and finally to consider exchange phenomena in relation to the overall mobility and circulatory profiles of specific ions or nutrient elements within the whole plant.

B. Structural Considerations Relating to Phloem-Xylem Exchange of Solutes

In plants where xylem and phloem become differentiated in vascular tissue these two systems invariably accompany one another into virtually every ramification of the vascular network. Only in the finest ultimate branches of leaf veins, and in specialized structures like nectaries, hydathodes, haustoria and certain regions of seeds and fruits can vascular traces be found consisting of either only xylem or only phloem elements, implying that throughout its length, vascular tissue provides an extensive and uninterrupted potential for solute exchange between xylem and phloem. The proximity of the two types of conducting elements varies considerably with location in the plant body. In the vascular bundles of ferns and monocotyledons and in the primary vasculature of gymnosperms and dicotyledons, xylem tissue may abut directly against phloem tissue, and, as sometimes occurs in leaf veins, only one parenchymatous layer may separate one type of element from another. But in those herbaceous dicotyledons and woody forms which undergo secondary thickening, a cambium eventually separates xylem from phloem so that several layers of young, undifferentiated cells must be traversed by symplastic or apoplastic routes before exchange between conducting channels can be mediated. The numerous experiments conducted by PEEL (see Chapter 7) and other workers on phloem-xylem fluxes in shoot segments of willow reveal that these intervening layers do not act as any real barrier to cross-transfer of many solutes, but it is still likely that the more intimate connections between xylem and phloem existing in the leaf-vein network provide an easier and quantitatively more important opportunity for exchange of solutes. Also, it must be remembered that solutes running the gauntlet of intraveinal retrieval systems will finally reach cell walls of the mesophyll cells, and if absorbed into these same cells may be ferried back out of the leaf by a symplastic route *via* the phloem. This is unlikely to apply, of course, to those few species in which an endodermis (eg. certain *Plantaginaceae*, TRAPP, 1932) or a suberized lamella (e.g. certain grasses, O'BRIEN and CARR, 1970) impedes apoplastic transfer from the free space of the vein to that of the remainder of the leaf.

Although intraveinal exchange and the longer route for solutes between xylem and phloem *via* the mesophyll may be extremely important in the physiology of leaves, other regions of the plant, notably the nodes, would appear to possess great potential for exchange, not only within specific elements of the network but also between quite different vascular pathways. The complex ramifications of vascular tissue in nodes of monocotyledons are a case in point, although experimental evidence for transport of this kind within them is lacking.

In certain plants the parenchyma cells of the vascular strands become transformed in a unique manner by the intrusion into their protoplasts of irregular ingrowths of cellulosic wall material. This type of cell, first described for the minor veins of a leaf (*Vicia*) by ZIEGLER, 1965, and for the xylem parenchyma of a stem (*Pinus*) by WOODING and NORTHCOTE (1965), is now known to occur quite commonly throughout the plant kingdom, not only in vascular tissues, but also in reproductive organs and specialized structures such as haustoria, hydathodes, root nodules, nectaries, salt glands etc. (see GUNNING and PATE, 1969; PATE and GUNNING, 1972). The "transfer cell", with its greatly increased plasmamembrane surface and high concentration of mitochondria and endoplasmic reticulum in the region of the wall ingrowths, (see WOODING, 1969) is believed to represent a module which, when strategically located in regions of the plant engaging in intensive short-distance transport of solutes, can operate at high efficiency in the exchange of solutes between apoplastic and symplastic compartments of a tissue. Acting in some situations as sink tissue for secretion from the symplast, in others as loading points to the symplast for dilute apoplastic solutes, its wall-membrane apparatus would seem capable of handling a variety of solutes ranging from inorganic ions to organic solutes such as amino acids and amides (PATE and GUNNING, 1972). Recent measurements of rates of flux across plasmamembranes of transfer cells suggest that they can indeed function most effectively in transmembrane flux of solutes. A recent measurement of their activity for xylem loading of legume nodules with products of nitrogen fixation suggests a flux of 24 p moles amino acid sec^{-1} cm^{-2}, a rate high within the range of values for this type of activity by plant cells, and obviously a very high relative rate on a tissue volume basis, bearing in mind the elevated surface: volume ratio of its constituent transfer cells (see GUNNING et al., 1974). Possibly, as suggested by PATE and GUNNING, 1972, standing osmotic gradients can be generated within the wall ingrowth, thus accelerating transport to and from the adjacent plasmamembrane, whilst the presence of a Mg^{++}-activated ATPase in membrane lining the ingrowths (MAIER and MAIER, 1972) and the demonstration of a special pattern of repeating particles in the same region of the plasmamembrane of the transfer cell (BRIARTY, 1973) suggest that the membrane areas associated with ingrowths may be specially equipped for purposes of transport.

Sometimes, as very commonly occurs in the nodes of ferns, gymnosperms and many families of monocotyledons and dicotyledons (GUNNING et al., 1970; O'BRIEN and ZEE, 1971; ZEE and O'BRIEN, 1971) transfer cells flank the xylem of leaf traces or the phloem of the margin of the gaps in the vasculature caused by the departure of such traces. The strategy of this positioning is possibly to facilitate the withdrawal of solutes from the conducting elements and their conduction to meristematic tissue subtended at the node, particularly at an early stage in development before the apex or axillary bud has differentiated its own vascular supply. Microautoradiographic evidence has been obtained in support of this view (PATE et al., 1970).

More relevant to present consideration of solute exchange between xylem and phloem are the transfer cells of leaf veins, particularly those bridging sieve and xylem elements. As far as we are aware, minor vein transfer cells are almost entirely restricted to certain families of dicotyledons, and, in these, particularly to herbaceous members (PATE and GUNNING, 1969). Four types are recognized in the minor vein, one, the commonest, a modified companion cell, another, quite common type, a modified phloem parenchyma cell, and two other rarer types, modified xylem parenchyma or bundle sheath cells. Present singly or in combination it is suggested that they function collectively in the retrieval of solutes from the free space (apoplast) of the minor vein, and hence, in the symplastic transfer of this class of solute to the sieve elements. In leaves of certain species (eg. certain members of the Compositae, see PATE and GUNNING, 1969) all four types of transfer cell develop so that virtually every intercellular boundary within the minor vein carries a complement of wall ingrowths. The net result of this is that the apoplast-symplast interface of the vein is some 4–8 times larger than it would be were only smooth-walled cells of similar dimensions present (see Fig. 1).

One is tempted to conclude that an apparatus of this nature might well allow substantial amounts of the solutes arriving in the xylem to be absorbed and passed to the phloem and exit from the leaf without ever reaching the termini of the veins. However, although the wall ingrowth of minor vein transfer cells has been shown to be accessible to electron-dense tracers and their protoplasts to be capable of taking up ^{3}H-leucine fed to leaves through the transpiration stream (GUNNING et al., 1968; GUNNING and PATE, 1969), the importance of intraveinal transfer of

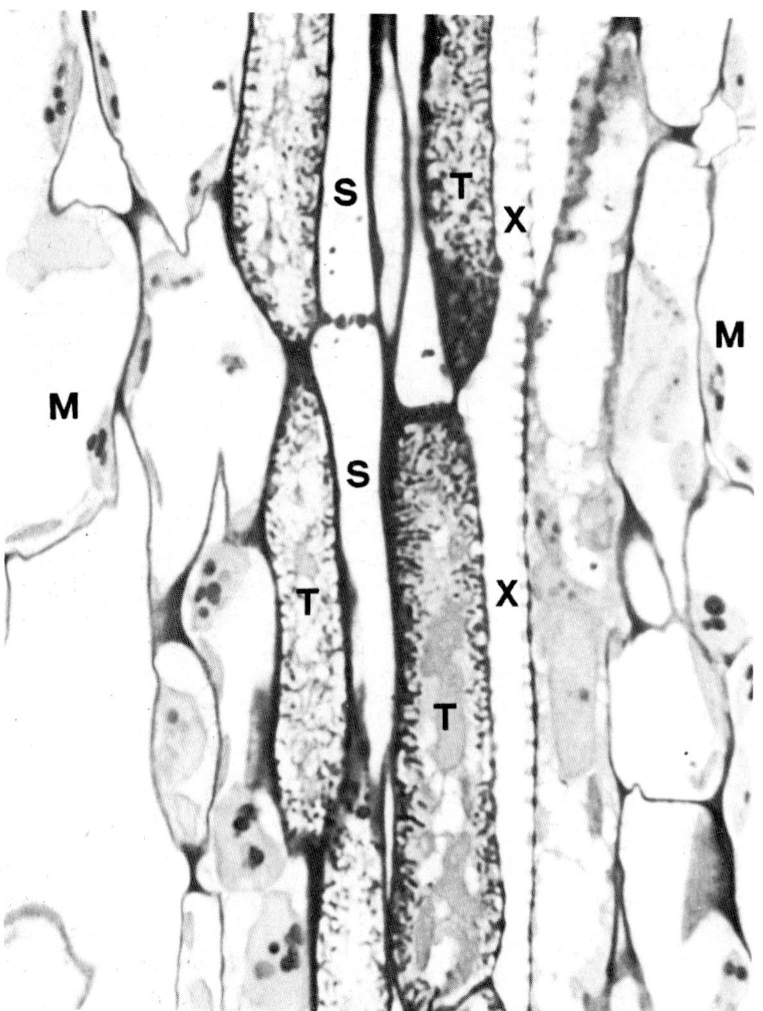

Fig. 1. Longitudinal section through part of a minor vein of a leaf of *Pulicaria* spp., showing transfer cells (*T*), bridging the gap between sieve elements (*S*) and xylem elements (*X*). Leaf mesophyll cells marked *M* ($\times$2,200). (1 micron section of material embedded in glycol methacrylate. Toluidine blue stain with Periodic acid-Schiff Reagent counterstain to reveal cellulose wall ingrowths of transfer cells. Material prepared and photographed by Professor B.E.S. GUNNING and author)

xylem-delivered materials to the phloem has still to be assessed relative to that possible through the longer route *via* the mesophyll cells (see PATE and GUNNING, 1972).

The structural information described so far and the physiological implications which it carries can be conveniently summarized in diagrammatic form as shown in Fig. 2. In this the basic working parts of the plant are reduced to a mature leaf, stem, root and growing structure of the shoot, the latter representing bud, meristem, young leaf or developing reproductive structure. Principal interchange points between xylem and phloem carry the notation I, regions of loading or unloading of long distance-transport channels the symbols L and U respectively, whilst regions marked A suggest areas specializing in the absorption and assimilation of raw materials from the environment and hence, ultimately, in the replenishment of solutes in long-distance transport channels. The diagram also shows where transfer cells may be located, the positioning of the wall ingrowths on these being represented and the presumed direction of net solute flux across them being designated by means of arrows. Elements of this working model are considered in turn in the sections which follow.

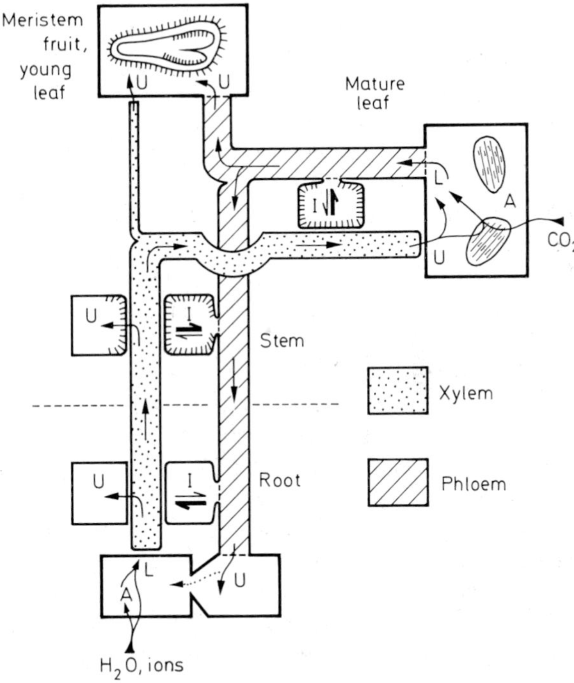

Fig. 2. Diagram showing basic elements of circulatory system of the plant. Principal interchange points between xylem and phloem labeled *I*, regions of loading and unloading of transport channels labeled *L* and *U* respectively, areas specializing in assimilation of raw materials labeled *A*. Possible location of transfer cells is given, the positioning of wall ingrowths on these being marked. Directions of flux of solutes indicated by arrows

C. Solutes Present in the Xylem and Their Origin in the Root

Investigators have used two basically different techniques to recover fluids from the xylem. One, applicable principally to herbaceous species, utilizes sap exuding from xylem under root pressure from plants cut at or near the base of their shoots. Efforts are usually made to restrict collection periods to a minimum and so avoid complications due to starvation reactions in the detopped root, but it is still likely that contamination of sap might occur from cells damaged at the cut surface, or even that phloem contents might be exuded along with those from xylem. Nevertheless, root bleeding is widely believed to offer a fairly pure and representative sample of what normally moves upwards in the transpiration stream (see BOLLARD, 1960; PATE, 1971). Of course, solute concentrations in bleeding sap are likely to be much higher than in the xylem of an intact, actively transpiring plant.

A second technique is to extract by suction the "tracheal" sap from solid shoots or woody twigs. Here, if samples are taken high up a shoot, they are likely to be not fully representative of what originally left the root, since during passage through the lower parts of the shoot, solutes are quite likely to be withdrawn or added by cells lining the xylem pathway. Also, vacuum extraction suffers the disadvantage that compartments outside the functioning xylem may release solutes (ANDERSSEN, 1929; HARDY and POSSINGHAM, 1969). It is not surprising to find, therefore, that where tracheal sap and root bleeding sap have been collected from the same plant, quite substantial qualitative and quantitative differences in composition have been observed (MORRISON, 1965; HARDY and POSSINGHAM, 1969).

Xylem fluids recovered by either of these methods are of acidic reaction (pH 5.4–6.5) (see FIFE et al., 1962; SHELDRAKE and NORTHCOTE, 1968; HALL et al., 1971), and have relatively low levels of dry matter (0.05–0.4% w/v), most of this in inorganic form. Major inorganic cations present are K^+, Ca^{++}, Mg^{++}, Na^+, often in that order of decreasing concentration, whilst the main inorganic anions recorded are usually $PO_4^{\equiv}$, Cl^-, $SO_4^=$, and, in certain species, NO_3^- (see analyses of JACOBY, 1965; WALLACE and PATE, 1967; JONES and ROWE, 1968). The presence in xylem sap of boron (HUSA and MCILRATH, 1965), copper, zinc, manganese and iron (e.g. see Table 1), suggest that these micronutrients are mobile in the transpiration stream. Iron in chelated form as citrate has been recorded (SCHMID and GERLOFF, 1961; TIFFIN, 1970; CLARK et al., 1973) and this has been suggested to overcome problems in transport of this element at high levels of phosphate and calcium (see BOLLARD, 1960). Sulphur may be present in organic form as methionine, cysteine and glutathione (PATE, 1965) although this is a small fraction in comparison with the free sulphate of the xylem. Phosphorus is also usually present predominantly as inorganic phosphate (see BIELESKI, 1973), but in some species up to 25% of the xylem phosphorus may be organic, principally as phosphorylcholine (TOLBERT and WIEBE, 1955; MAIZEL et al., 1956).

Carbohydrate is usually recorded as being absent or present in only trace amounts in the xylem sap of herbaceous species, but this is not true of some woody species where, at certain seasons, up to 0.3–0.4% of sugars may be recovered from tracheal or bleeding sap (see OLOFINBOBA, 1969; HARDY and POSSINGHAM, 1969). In the sugar maple (*Acer saccharum*) sugars are commonly 2.2–4.8% (TAYLOR, 1956). SAUTER et al., 1973, have suggested that the late winter maximum in sucrose concentration in the xylem results from mobilization of carbohydrate from ray tissues.

Organic acids are found commonly in xylem of herbaceous species (see KURSANOV, 1961) but usually the major organic fraction is nitrogenous, amides and amino acids predominating in most species, alkaloids and ureides in others (see literature reviewed by PATE, 1971, 1973).

Special importance attaches to the mobility of growth substances in xylem. Cytokinin-like activity in xylem sap of woody and herbaceous species has been widely reported (eg. KENDE, 1965; CARR and BURROWS, 1966; BURROWS and CARR,

1969; YOSHIDA et al., 1971) and in one recent instance (HALL, 1973 for *Acer saccharum*) a specific cytokinin, N^6-(Δ^2-isopentenyl) adenosine, has been identified in xylem. Gibberellin-like activity has also been recorded in several instances for xylem fluids (eg. PHILIPS and JONES, 1964; CARR et al., 1964; SKENE, 1967; JONES and LACEY, 1968; SELVENDRAN and SABARATNAM, 1971). In willow (*Salix*) abscisic acid is suspected to be present in xylem (BOWEN and HOAD, 1968).

The origin of solutes recovered from xylem is not always easy to determine. Apart from the possibilities of contamination and exchange with surrounding tissues, specific fractions of a given solute might arise from any one or more of the following:

1. *Uptake from the environment and immediate release in unchanged form to the xylem.*

Obviously the bulk of the inorganic ions in xylem of plants growing in a medium rich in nutrients is likely to originate in this manner, as has been proven in many studies using radioisotopes.

2. *Uptake from the environment, metabolic transformation in root cells, and release of products to the xylem.*

Organic phosphorus and organic sulphur compounds can arise in this fashion, as shown in $^{32}PO_4^{\equiv}$ feeding studies of willow (*Salix*) by MORRISON (1965), and $^{35}SO_4^{=}$ feeding studies of pea (*Pisum*) by PATE (1965), but probably the most important activities in this connection relate to nitrogen. In plants fed with ammonium, most, or all, is converted to organic form, often amide or ureide, before entering the xylem; in nitrogen-fixing nodulated plants the same applies; and, in those species possessing a root-located nitrate reductase system, all, or a major fraction of the nitrate entering the root may be converted to organic form before release to the transpiration stream (see PATE, 1971, 1973). Proof that it is currently assimilated nitrogen which is involved is readily obtained in ^{15}N feeding studies (eg. IVANKO, 1971; OGHOGHORIE and PATE, 1972) and the ease and rapidity with which the amino compounds of the xylem can have their carbon labeled with ^{14}C after shoots have been fed with $^{14}CO_2$ (PATE, 1962), suggest that recently translocated carbohydrate is involved in their biosynthesis, especially in herbaceous plants which do not carry large root reserves for such purposes.

3. *Release from tissues of the root.*

The fact that detopped root systems continue to bleed inorganic ions from their xylem for some time after removal to distilled water (ANDEL, 1953; WEATHERLEY, 1969) suggests that mobilizable pools of solutes can be called upon for xylem transport during starvation stress. Also, in starved or non-starved roots, senescing and differentiating cells might release autolytic or catabolic products to the xylem, processes considered likely to account for the appearance in xylem of hydrolytic enzymes (SHELDRAKE and NORTHCOTE, 1968) and certain amino fractions not readily labeled in ^{14}C feeding experiments (PATE, 1962).

4. *Cycling of solutes translocated to the root in the phloem and transferred to xylem with or without further metabolism.*

It is probable that substantial fractions of the K^+, $PO_4^{\equiv}$, and $SO_4^{=}$ present in the xylem relate to this category since tracer studies have suggested that these ions flow quite freely through the phloem-xylem pathways of the plant (BIDDULPH et al., 1958; BIDDULPH, 1959; HARTT and KORTSCHAK, 1965). Organic solutes such as organic acids, and certain nitrogenous solutes may behave similarly, although the evidence here is not so clear cut, it being especially difficult to distinguish true recycling from new synthetic activity of the root. Similar problems apply when considering the origin of growth substances in xylem, as discussed in several articles on this subject (eg. PHILIPS and JONES, 1964; SITTON, ITAI, KENDE, 1967; SITTON, RICHMOND, VAADIA, 1967; WAISEL and SHAPIRA, 1971; CROZIER and REID, 1971).

D. Exchange of Xylem Solutes with the Shoot Axis and Interchange with Shoot Phloem

When solutes of various kinds are fed to plants through their roots or to cut shoots through the transpiration stream it is frequently observed that a quite substantial amount of the applied solute is abstracted laterally into shoot tissues and never reaches the centers of transpiration in the foliar organs. This feature can be readily demonstrated by collecting tracheal sap or bleeding sap at different levels of a shoot and showing that sap from higher regions of the shoot is considerably more dilute than that collected nearer the root (PATE et al., 1964; COOPER et al., 1972). The lateral uptake process is in some way selective since certain solutes can be shown to exhibit a steeper down-gradient in xylem concentration up the stem than do others. At the same time certain solutes may appear to increase in concentration as the xylem stream ascends, (eg. sucrose in grapevine (*Vitis vinifera*), HARDY and POSSINGHAM, 1969; glutamine in groundsel (*Senecio vulgaris*), PATE et al., 1970), suggesting that the very cells withdrawing solutes might, at the same time, also be selectively releasing other kinds of solutes to the xylem.

A particularly good example of selectivity in uptake from xylem relates to sodium. Ion uptake studies and ^{22}Na feeding experiments show that this ion is taken up rapidly by upper parts of roots (SHONE et al., 1969) and lower regions of shoots (JACOBY, 1965; WALLACE et al., 1965) a mechanism which RAINS (1969) suggests as preventing toxic levels of sodium reaching the transpiring leaves.

The physiology of the uptake of solutes by stems from xylem has been studied both for inorganic ions fed to whole shoots (eg. $^{45}Ca^{++}$ studies in *Phaseolus* by BIDDULPH et al., 1961) and for amino acids percolated through stem segments (VAN DIE and VONK, 1967), for tomato (*Lycopersicon*), HILL-COTTINGHAM and LLOYD-JONES (1968, 1973a, b, c) for apple (*Malus*). A two-phase exchange system is suggested, first a reversible adsorption at physical binding sites on vessel and parenchyma walls in the xylem, and, second, an essentially irreversible and metabolically-operated accumulation, presumably by living cells bordering the xylem elements. The latter process can apparently discriminate between D- and L-forms of an amino acid, and ^{14}C-labeling studies have shown that if an amino acid is taken up it can be metabolized to form related amino compounds (HILL-COTTINGHAM and LLOYD-JONES, 1973a) or broken down so that $^{14}CO_2$ is released from the fed segment of stem (VAN DIE and VONK, 1967).

Histoautoradiography of the fate in stems of xylem-fed ^{3}H-labeled substrates shows that xylem parenchyma may be involved in the initial uptake (WOODING and NORTHCOTE, 1965) and that other cells considerably distant from the xylem can also benefit (eg. the outer cortex cells of *Pisum* stems (PATE and O'BRIEN, 1968) or the undifferentiated plumule cells of a *Senecio* seedling (PATE et al., 1970).

Since cambial and phloem cells can also be shown to become labeled after xylem feeding of a stem (PATE and O'BRIEN, 1968) the possibility is suggested of retranslocation from the fed stem *via* the phloem. VAN DIE (1963), PATE et al. (1965) and JOY and ANTCLIFF (1966) have all demonstrated effects attributable to this class of activity in experiments using ^{14}C-labeled amino acids, but the more convincing evidence of xylem to phloem transfer comes from studies on segments of woody shoots of *Salix* in which labeled organic materials fed to the xylem or cambium surface are subsequently recovered in the honeydew or stylet exudate of aphids feeding on nearby phloem. In this manner FORD and PEEL (1967) showed transfer of ^{14}C-labeled sugars, GARDNER and PEEL (1971) transfer of ^{14}C-aspartic and -glutamic acids, ESCHRICH (1968) and HOAD et al. (1971) transfer of ^{14}C-indole acetic acid. Some of these radiosubstrates appeared largely in unchanged form in the phloem, others appeared to have been extensively metabolized before or during transfer so that other labeled substances also appeared in the phloem exudate. The same experimental system has been used to demonstrate xylem to phloem transfer of $PO_4^{\equiv}$, K^+ and other ions. But calcium ions failed to cross from xylem to phloem even when the xylem was perfused with 100 mM Ca^{++}; Na^+ never entered the phloem as freely as did K^+ (PEEL, 1963; HOAD and PEEL, 1965).

The impression must not be left that interchange in stems is always a one-way process from xylem to phloem. After leaves are fed with $^{14}CO_2$ a substantial (up to 49%) cross transfer of ^{14}C-assimilates from stem phloem to xylem, and hence to the transpiration stream, has been suggested by several investigators (eg. BIDDULPH and CORY, 1965; HARDY and POSSINGHAM, 1969). In grapevine, HARDY, 1969, suggests that after $^{14}CO_2$ feeding of a leaf, selective transfer to the xylem stream of ^{14}C-labeled glutamine and malic acid takes place, but that these substances are subsequently withdrawn from the transpiration stream higher up the stem and there metabolized to other substances. Two-way traffic of ^{14}C-labeled gibberellic acid and ^{14}C-kinetin is suggested from the experiments of BOWEN and WAREING (1969). Labeled substrate was applied to bark or xylem and recovered respectively in either aphid honey dew or in tracheal sap, but, of course, as with other experiments using exogenously applied radiosubstrates, the results indicate that a diffusion pathway or, at best, a translocation pathway, exists, not necessarily one which operates in nature. Caution must obviously be exercised in interpretation, particularly if the radiosubstrate in question is not a proven constituent of the experimental plant and is being applied by a means or through a route not normally available or utilized in the intact system.

E. Solutes Present in the Phloem and Their Origin in Leaves

Space is devoted elsewhere in this volume to describing the use of aphids or stem incision techniques for tapping the phloem of plants (see Chapters 3, 6, 7 and 8), and detailed information may be found there relating to the nature of the substances present in phloem sap obtained by these methods. Since attention is being focused here on circulation of solutes, comments will be largely restricted to an evaluation of the basic differences between xylem and phloem fluids and the relevance of such information to the possible transfer of dissolved materials from the transpiration to translocation streams during the normal functioning of the leaf.

Phloem sap is of more alkaline reaction (pH 7.8–8.4) and of much higher dry-matter content (15–25% w/v) than xylem sap (ZIEGLER, 1968). Sucrose is usually the main carbohydrate, though galactose-based oligosaccharides and sugar alcohols may also be present (ZIMMERMANN, 1957, 1969; MEYER-MEVIUS, 1959; KLUGE, 1967; ZIEGLER, 1968). Carbohydrate at a concentration of 5–30% w/v usually accounts for 80–90% of the dry matter of the sap. Amino acids and other nitrogenous solutes are also usually present at higher concentration (up to 1% w/v) in phloem than in xylem, and, unlike xylem sap, phloem sap may contain quite high levels of protein, particularly if obtained by stem or bark incision techniques (see MACROBBIE, 1971). This protein may well represent non-mobile, structural constituents displaced by pressure release after cutting (KOLLMANN, DÖRR and KLEINIG, 1970; WALKER and THAINE, 1971), and since inorganic ions or organic solutes might well be bound onto this protein its release might introduce to the sample of phloem sap substances really not representative of the normal translocation stream.

Organic acids may be major anions of phloem sap, particularly malate (HALL and BAKER, 1972), and growth substance activity has been detected in honey dew of aphids, aphid stylet sap or sap obtained by stem cutting (see HOAD and BOWEN, 1968; HALL and BAKER, 1972, for gibberellins; HOAD et al., 1971, and HALL and BAKER, 1972, for auxins; HALL and BAKER, 1972, and PHILIPS and CLELAND, 1972, for cytokinins; BOWEN and HOAD, 1968, and HOAD, 1973, for abscisic acid). Since the species of growth substances involved are not necessarily the same as those recovered in xylem, and since few, if any, comparisons have been made of growth substance complements of xylem and phloem of the same plant at the same stage of development, the relationships between the species of substances moving in the two transport channels remains in doubt.

Several inventories of inorganic cations and anions have been made for phloem exudates notably those of MOOSE (1938) for *Beta vulgaris*, TAMMES (1958) for *Arenga saccharifera*, TAMMES and VAN DIE (1964) for *Yucca flaccida*, and KIMMEL (1962) for a variety of tree species. The range of concentrations recorded (see MACROBBIE, 1971) are generally much higher than in xylem, this being particularly so for potassium, the major cation, which can reach concentrations of up to 2% w/v in phloem (PEEL and WEATHERLEY, 1959). Exceptions are afforded by Ca^{++}, NO_3^-, $SO_4^=$, and the element boron, which are often present in only trace amounts, if detectable at all, in phloem, though freely mobile in the xylem. However, in the case of calcium, mobility in the phloem of certain species is suggested from its presence in quite high amounts in phloem sap (see Table 1). Possibly the best evidence of mobility in phloem comes from its detection in honey dew and stylet exudates of aphids (see Chapter 6).

Since few detailed comparisons of xylem and phloem sap from the same species are available, it is difficult to comment generally on the relative abilities of specific ions or nutrient elements to be loaded onto phloem after arriving in leaves through the xylem. Comparisons for legumes (see Table 1) show that many nutrient elements are apparently present at many times the concentration in phloem than in xylem, suggesting the existence of quite effective and selective cross-transfer mechanisms if xylem be considered as the major catchment for these phloem mobile ions. TAMMES and VAN DIE (1966) have used the relationship between concentration of a given element in phloem exudate and its concentration in leaves as an index of phloem mobility. Values for *Yucca* ranged from 0.9 for potassium as the most "mobile"

Table 1. Comparisons of phloem and xylem sap composition in two species of annual lupin [Data from PATE et al. 1974, 1975; J.F. LONERAGAN, W.J. SIMMONS and J.S. PATE (unpublished)]

	Lupinus albus		*Lupinus angustifolius*	
	Xylem sap (Tracheal)	Phloem sap (Fruit bleeding)	Xylem sap (Tracheal)	Phloem sap (Fruit bleeding)
$mg\ ml^{-1}$				
sucrose	*	154	*	171
amino acids	0.70	13	2.6	15
$\mu g\ ml^{-1}$				
potassium	90	1,540	180	1,820
sodium	60	120	50	101
magnesium	27	85	8	140
calcium	17	21	73	64
iron	1.8	9.8	1.0	7.0
manganese	0.6	1.4	0.4	0.6
zinc	0.4	5.8	0.7	5.5
copper	T	0.4	T	0.2
nitrate	10	*	31	T
pH	6.3	7.9	5.9	8.0

* = not present in detectable amount. T = present in trace amount.

element to 0.01 for calcium as the least "mobile". Wide differences in element mobility are also reflected in ratios of specific ions in the phloem, K : Na and Mg : Ca ratios being noticeably higher in phloem sap than elsewhere in the plant (EHRHARDT, 1965; MACROBBIE, 1971).

As mentioned above for solutes of the xylem, it is no easy matter to determine with certainty the origin of solutes translocated away from leaves in the phloem. However, certain generalizations appear to hold true:

1. Solutes such as sugars, amino acids and organic acids which accept ^{14}C readily in $^{14}CO_2$ feeding studies and are then shown to be translocated away from the leaf or, better still, can be recovered in labeled form in phloem exudates, are obviously likely to represent primary products of photosynthesis. As KURSANOV (1961, 1963) and his collaborators have shown not all photosynthetic products enter the phloem readily. In *Rheum rhaponticum* (rhubarb) leaves, for example, sucrose is loaded onto the phloem but monosaccharides are not; of organic acids serine, alanine, and threonine appear to be translocated more easily than are aspartic acid and proline. Undoubtedly species differ widely in this respect, the unusually high amounts of ^{14}C-serine in translocated products of young soybean leaves fed with $^{14}CO_2$ being a case in point (NELSON, 1962).

2. Organic solutes present in quantity in phloem but not, apparently, in xylem, and which are not readily labeled in short-term photosynthesis experiments, are obviously likely to originate in leaves, but not as a direct result of photosynthesis. The B vitamins of phloem sap (ZIEGLER and ZIEGLER, 1962) and the nucleotides (ATP, GTP) present in it (KLUGE and ZIEGLER, 1964; GARDNER and PEEL, 1969;

HALL and BAKER, 1972) fall into this category. BECKER et al. (1971) have suggested from experiments in which phloem sap was incubated with $^{32}PO_4^{\equiv}$ that ATP and other organic substances containing phosphate may be synthesized within the sieve tubes, although this does not rule out the possibility of these same substances also forming in leaves prior to loading of the phloem (see BIELESKI, 1969, 1973).

3. Elements, present predominantly in inorganic form in xylem but mainly in organic form in phloem are obviously likely to have been assimilated by synthetic processes in the leaf. For example, the organic sulphur of phloem sap is likely to derive from reduction of incoming $SO_4^{=}$, although definitive labeling experiments are not available in this connection. Similarly, a substantial amount of the organic nitrogen of phloem is likely to derive from nitrate reduction in the leaf, as can be shown by feeding $^{15}NO_3$ to shoots *via* the xylem and subsequently recovering ^{15}N almost exclusively in organic form, principally as amide, in the phloem (PATE et al., 1975, data for *Lupinus albus*). The conversion of nitrate to amino compounds in the leaf of *Lupinus* can be so effective that even when shoots are fed through the xylem with extremely high levels of nitrate only trace amounts of free nitrate carry over to the phloem; amino compounds, by contrast, reach very high levels in the phloem under such circumstances (PATE et al., 1975).

4. In circumstances where an inorganic or organic solute is present in quantity in both xylem and phloem direct transfer in unchanged form from xylem to phloem is to be anticipated, either through intraveinal recycling, or *via* the mesophyll cells. This undoubtedly applies to several inorganic cations, eg. K^+, Mg^{++}, and also, to certain nitrogenous substances. For instance, in *Acer*, allantoic acid and allantoin are major constituents of both xylem and phloem, and the same applies to citrulline in *Alnus*, and asparagine in *Lupinus* (see ZIEGLER and SCHNABEL, 1961; PATE, 1971). In *Spartium junceum* feeding of ^{14}C-asparagine through the xylem leads to this compound being transferred unchanged to phloem sap, whereas if ^{14}C-aspartic acid is presented in a similar manner most of the ^{14}C subsequently recovered from phloem sap is attached to compounds other than aspartic acid. In this species asparagine is a major sap amino compound, whereas aspartic acid is only a minor one (PATE et al., 1975).

5. During leaf senescence the content of many mineral elements falls. P, N, K, Cl, and Mg decrease most noticeably, whilst other elements—Ca, Mn, Zn, Fe and B are lost only slightly, if at all (see studies of HES, 1958; HUMPHRIES, 1958; OLAND, 1963; HARTT and KORTSCHAK, 1965; MCILRATH, 1965). At such times the phloem is likely to be particularly rich in these mobilized materials, as witnessed for nitrogen in the substantial rise in amino acid levels in phloem sap of woody species coincident with natural or induced senescence of the leaves (PEEL and WEATHERLEY, 1959; ZIMMERMANN, 1969). In herbaceous species the onset of flowering may signal extensive mobilization from leaves, as shown, for example for *Trifolium subterraneum* in the ^{65}Zn feeding studies conducted by MILLIKAN et al., 1969.

F. Transport to Centers of Growth or Storage in the Shoot

Fruits, meristems, buds, young leaves and storage organs such as stem tubers have several features in common. They are all heavily dependent, if not entirely so, on outside sources of nutrients; they are relatively ineffective in capturing water through transpirational activity; they possess, especially early in growth, considerable volumes of undifferentiated tissues quite distant from the nearest functional vascular elements; and they accumulate high levels of organic and inorganic solutes and ergastic substances. This combination of attributes suggests that phloem transport as opposed to xylem transport features prominently in their nutrition, a conclusion which has been consistently supported by many writers on the subject (eg. MÜNCH, 1930; WIERSUM, 1966; MILTHORPE and MOORBY, 1969; ZIMMERMANN, 1969). Items in support of this contention are not difficult to find:

1. The dry weight of fruits is quite close to that of phloem sap (ZIMMERMANN, 1969; CRAFTS and CRISP, 1971), and assuming that a fruit gains from the phloem by mass (pressure) flow it could conceivably obtain all of its requirements for water by this route. Indeed, ZIEGLER (1963), has suggested that at certain times in its growth a fruit might receive an excess of water through its phloem, this engendering back flow to the shoot through the xylem of the fruit stalk.

2. Using data on levels of phosphorus in xylem and in buds and rates of water uptake by these same buds on breaking dormancy in spring BURSTRÖM (1948) has calculated that this element arrives faster in the buds of *Carpinus* and *Betula* than would be possible were the xylem the sole source of phosphorus. The suggested source of phosphorus to the bud is that released to the xylem from storage parenchyma in the stem. The phosphorus is then suggested to be removed from the xylem, passed in concentrated form to the phloem, and thence delivered to the bud (BURSTRÖM, 1948).

3. The low calcium content of young fruits of apple and tomato (WIERSUM, 1966) and of potato tubers (MOORBY, 1968) and the high K:Na ratio of young leaves of barley (GREENWAY et al., 1965) match what is generally known of phloem-sap composition. Similarly endospermic fluids are generally low in calcium (SMITH, 1973). Later in development, however, seeds can accumulate quite large amounts of this element combined in phytate (EASTWOOD and LAIDMAN, 1968; GUARDIOLA and SUTCLIFFE, 1972; HOFSTEN, 1973) suggesting that calcium becomes phloem-mobile as fruits mature, that xylem transport becomes more effective, or that some unconventional transport process provides calcium to the fruit (see also evidence from aphids in Chapter 6). In the older fruit, where the embryo comes into close contact with cellular endosperm, perisperm or endothelium, there is the possibility of contact exchange of cations with the parent tissues, as is also possible through the suspensor of the embryo. It is perhaps relevant that in these situations transfer cells may be developed, these being suggested to be particularly adept in ferrying solutes across the cytoplasmic discontinuities which exist between tissues of parent and embryo (PATE and GUNNING, 1972, and Fig. 2).

4. $^{14}CO_2$ feeding studies of foliar organs adjacent to fruits demonstrate a heavy commitment on the part of a blossom leaf to its subtended fruits (eg. LINCK and SUDIA, 1962, for *Pisum;* KIPPS and BOULTER, 1973, for *Vicia faba*). *Pisum* seeds gain approximately two-thirds of their carbon from photosynthesis at their blossom node and at least one-fifth of their nitrogen from that present in the shoot before flowering (FLINN and PATE, 1970; PATE and FLINN, 1973), half of the K requirement of a young barley leaf derives from the older leaf below it (GREENWAY and PITMAN, 1965), and large amounts of the N, P and K required by developing potato tubers apparently comes from the haulm (MOORBY, 1968). In all of these and many other studies of the nutritional balance of plants in vegetative growth or at reproduction

(e.g. see WILLIAMS, 1955) mobilization of materials through the phloem is likely to be the operative avenue of transport.

5. The time course of labeling of organs of a fruiting shoot of *Pisum,* fed *via* the xylem with ^{15}N-labeled nitrate, demonstrates that the bulk of the isotope is delivered first to the leaves and stem, but that after a lag of several hours the labeling of seeds rises exponentially (LEWIS and PATE, 1973). This is consistent with the concept that leaves process and retranslocate in concentrated form to other sinks, materials which they receive in their transpirational activity.

6. Electron-probe microanalyzer studies of fruit stalks of *Pisum* by LÄUCHLI (1968) provide evidence that long-distance transport of K, P, and even Ca takes place through the phloem. The presence of the latter element in phloem, though not necessarily in mobile form, is demonstrated by its specific association with callose (LÄUCHLI, 1972).

Despite the quantitative importance of phloem transport to fruits and young organs there is ample evidence that the small amount of xylem transport which does take place may still have a vital role to play in the delivery of elements which are only sparingly mobile in the phloem. ^{45}Ca feeding studies on a variety of fruits indicate that import of this element occurs almost exclusively in the xylem (WIERSUM, 1966; STÖSSER, 1970) and that where xylem flow to the fruit is restricted, nutritional disorders associated with critically low levels of calcium are manifest (eg. bitter pit of apple, blossom-end rot of tomato, WIERSUM, 1966). Underground organs, eg. potato tubers (MOORBY, 1968) and geocarpic fruits have obvious problems in this connection, studies of HARRIS, 1949; BLEDSOE et al., 1949; and WIERSUM, 1951, proving conclusively that the calcium requirement of the developing peanut fruit (*Arachis hypogaea*) is not adequately met by transport through the fruit stalk, but must be supplemented by absorption by the fruit from the medium with which it is in contact. If the latter is deficient in calcium, fruits fail to develop properly. Parallel situations are to be encountered in the nutrition of young leaves. For instance MICHAEL et al. (1969) report that tobacco plants grown in a humid atmosphere show boron deficiency in their developing leaves. Presumably the high humidity discourages flow in the xylem, the effective avenue of transport for this element.

Obviously much has still to be learned about the transport of materials into growing organs, particularly how the flows of solutes in xylem and phloem are interrelated and regulated throughout development, and how, for example, in seeds the final stages in transport across the investments surrounding the embryo are mediated. Detailed anatomical and ultrastructural studies must be made if physiological data on nutrient fluxes are to be properly interpreted.

G. Solute Transport and Circulation in the Whole Plant

For a solute to be completely exchangeable and miscible within tissues and to be freely mobile in the circulatory pathways of the plant it would have to satisfy several rather exacting physiological criteria. It would have to be:

1. Capable of free movement in the xylem,
2. Capable of unrestricted movement at high concentration in the phloem,

3. Cycled efficiently through the root from the downward phloem stream back to the ascending xylem stream,
4. Cycled efficiently through mature leaves, i.e. in through the xylem and out again in the phloem,
5. Not subject to metabolic transformation before or during transport,
6. Readily exchangeable with existing cellular pools of the same solute on arrival in a tissue or organ,
7. Barred from metabolic incorporation into macromolecules or from irreversible adsorption upon such molecules,
8. Recovered with efficiency from senescent tissues and freely redistributed from these sites to growing parts of the plant.

Of all the major solutes found in plants the potassium ion probably comes closest to meeting all eight of the above requirements. Its extremely low involvement, if any, in organic linkage, its rapid cycling through leaves, even those not fully grown (GREENWAY and PITMAN, 1965), its unusually high concentration in vascular tissues and the ease with which it can be leached from leaf surfaces during rain (TUKEY, 1970), all bear witness to its extreme mobility and exchangeability in plant tissues. The same might also be said of the sodium ion were it not that it appears to be taken up and held more avidly by plant roots, to be more actively withdrawn from the xylem of stems, and to enter the phloem much less effectively than does potassium (see earlier Sections).

The other major nutrient ions absorbed by roots apparently fall far short of achieving a mobility equal to that shown by potassium, and in most instances it is possible to single out specific criteria from the above list which are not properly met and which therefore constitute major barriers to free circulation of the ion within the plant body. With nitrate and sulphate capture by assimilatory centers in roots and/or leaves is the obvious impediment to ion mobility, the phloem being loaded not with the free ion but with products of its reduction. The latter products are particularly susceptible to incorporation into macromolecules of low turnover rate, such as protein, meaning that further cycling beyond sites of delivery in the phloem is likely to be curtailed. The patterns of labeling described for ^{35}S by BIDDULPH et al. (1958) for *Phaseolus* and for ^{15}N by OGHOGHORIE and PATE (1972) for *Pisum*, suggest that failure of the elements in question to cycle through roots, from translocation stream back again to the xylem, prevents rapid mixing of pools of these elements in root and shoot systems. Phosphate, another ion subject to a certain amount of metabolism before or during transport, appears to be able to cycle through roots more freely, and, indeed, it has been suggested that on an average a given P atom, presumably still attached to phosphate, may undergo several daily cycles between shoot and root of a herbaceous plant like *Phaseolus* (see BIDDULPH, 1959). Nevertheless, it is still likely that significant proportions of the organic and inorganic phosphorus in transport channels will be drawn off into reservoirs of phosphate esters and macromolecules containing this element (see BIELESKI, 1973).

Other nutrient elements, assumed to move principally in ionic form are iron, chlorine, copper, manganese, molybdenum, cobalt, zinc and magnesium. Of these magnesium and chlorine are generally regarded as being mobile, the remainder probably only of intermediate mobility (see BROWN et al., 1965; HENKENS and JONGMAN, 1965; MILLIKAN et al., 1969; EPSTEIN, 1972). However, leaf-feeding experiments using radionuclides can lead to equivocal results since factors such as ability to be absorbed through the stomata or cuticular surfaces of the leaf, method of presentation, dose rate, general nutrient status of the plant, photosynthetic activity and age of leaf at time of treatment, can all affect general accessibility of a substrate to loading sites for phloem (eg. see comments of EDDINGS and BROWN, 1967, regarding $^{59}Fe^{+++}$ absorption by leaves, and the contradictory findings regarding ^{28}Mg mobility in *Phaseolus* of BUKOVAC, TEUBNER and WITTWER, 1960, and STEUCEK and KOONTZ, 1970).

Finally, while still dealing with mobility of inorganic substances consideration must be given to two elements, calcium and boron, both of which are widely accepted to be virtually immobile, or, at best, only conditionally mobile, in phloem. Because no suitable isotopic form of boron exists and analytical techniques for its assay in small quantities in plant tissue are difficult, very little is known about its transport in plants. Lack of mobility in phloem is suggested by the experiments of SCHOLZ (1960) using isolated rooted leaves of tobacco. Feeding boron to one half of a divided root system, uptake of boron by the leaf was observed, and hence, one would suggest, xylem mobility of the element, but no evidence whatever was obtained of retranslation from the leaf back to the untreated half of the root system. However, OERTLI and RICHARDSON (1970) have suggested that a leaf's apparent inability to translocate boron is not caused by any inaccessibility of the element to the sieve elements, but rather that after being loaded onto the phloem and translocated to the main veins of the lamina and leaf stalk it is lost back again to the xylem and so swept back again into the leaf. A recycling mechanism of this sort would effectively prevent long-distance transport of the element.

The situation regarding calcium is more satisfactory, largely because a suitable radio-isotope (^{45}Ca) is available for tracer work and spectrophotometric techniques can be readily used for its assay. Like boron, it is xylem-mobile, though as a divalent cation it is likely to become readily adsorbed on immobile anions in cell walls and other compartments of vascular and non-vascular tissues. Though many experiments of short duration using xylem or leaf-fed ^{45}Ca have shown calcium to be virtually completely excluded from the phloem (eg. see BUKOVAC and WITTWER, 1957; BIDDULPH et al., 1958; other studies have shown that a measure of mobility may be expressed, provided that calcium continues to arrive in sufficient quantity during the feeding period or that the calcium status of the plant is high at the time of feeding (MILLIKAN and HANGER, 1965, 1967; RINGOET et al., 1968). Moreover, in long-term studies using ^{45}Ca, lasting several weeks (HART and KORTSCHAK, 1965), or seasons (FERREL and JOHNSON, 1956) radioactivity has been traced into new plant growths, produced long after the administration of the isotope. Nevertheless, mobility in the phloem never appears to reach high proportions, as gauged by the generally low level of the element in phloem sap, and in structures served primarily by the phloem (see earlier discussion on fruits), and by the low efficiency of its withdrawal from organs during senescence.

Turning to transport of organic solutes, one rarely encounters situations where a solute moves freely in xylem and phloem and appears to satisfy the other criteria relating to mobility and miscibility listed at the beginning of this section. Instead, the rationale for distribution of organic solutes seems to be one of directly linking specific sources with specific sinks, with no back flow of solute from receptor tissues into wider circulatory pathways. The high concentration of sugars and other assimilates in phloem, but almost total absence of these compounds from xylem offers obvious evidence of this principle, and the same probably applies to many organic phosphorus and sulphur compounds, to β vitamins, and to certain amino acids, and, as mentioned earlier, to specific growth substances. However, exceptions to this rule are to be found, particularly among nitrogen-containing solutes. Alkaloids, amides and ureides, for example, appear to move freely and unchanged between xylem and phloem, can accumulate in quantity in all tissues of a plant, and equilibrate rapidly with newly assimilated nitrogen. In herbaceous plants these nitrogen-rich molecules become prominent during the assimilatory phase of the plant cycle but once reproduction starts may become progressively withdrawn from the circulatory system and utilized as sources of nitrogen for protein synthesis in seeds (see LEWIS and PATE, 1973). Whilst circulating within the plant between root and leaf it is conceivable that they might exercise a regulatory function in the control of rates of assimilation and utilization of other related amino compounds (see PATE, 1971, 1973).

Whatever the general pattern of transport and metabolism of an element within plants as a whole, there is no doubt that considerable variations exist between species and that these may have subtle and still poorly appreciated implications in respect of a plant's ability to adapt to and grow within a particular environment. Differences between and within species in efficiency of uptake of specific nutrients, or in efficiency with which species utilize specific nutrients once they have entered the plant are well described for both native and agriculturally important plants (eg. see EPSTEIN, 1972). In respect specifically of transport, the study of calcium movement from roots of calcicole and calcifuge species (BOUSQUET, 1971), the recent study of xylem transport of iron in maize genotypes efficient or inefficient in utilization of this element (CLARK et al., 1973), and the studies of specific behavior in respect of calcium translocation by MILLIKAN and HANGER (1965, 1967) give some indication of the breadth of variation likely to exist in this quarter. Study has now reached the stage where the general pattern of species behavior in transport of many kinds of solutes is sufficiently well known for limits to be set around what might be regarded as "normal" behavior for a plant, enabling the experimenter to engage profitably in study of species differences, and, on encountering an unusual performance in respect of some transport attribute, to attempt to ascribe to it adaptive significance. There is no doubt that a most challenging and fruitful field lies within this area of investigation, its very nature being of special benefit to the better understanding of plant nutritional relationships in both natural and agricultural environments.

H. Summary

This chapter deals with a quantitatively important, yet much neglected physiological activity of plants, namely the role of the mature organs of the shoot in processing and redistributing the many classes of solutes which arrive continuously from the roots in the transpiration stream. The essence of this activity is the passage of solutes, directly or indirectly, from xylem to phloem, and, thereby, from sites in receipt of xylem fluids to weakly transpiring structures dependent largely on phloem for their nourishment. Both the shoot axis and the mature leaves appear to be capable of xylem to phloem transfer, and the cellular pathways and structures involved, and the solute specificity in this form of transport receives attention in the chapter. The leaf exports through its phloem photosynthate and solutes mobilized from reserves as well as materials originating from the xylem, and the significance of all of these classes of commodities is considered when dealing with the nutrition of centres of growth or storage.

The significance of xylem-phloem interchange in the circulatory system of the plant and in the eventual nourishment of meristems and fruits is dealt with in a final, integrative section to the chapter. Dissolved substances are seen to differ greatly in their mobility within the plant, case histories for certain ions, organic solutes and nutrient elements being provided to illustrate the structural and physiological features of the transport pathways which may facilitate or impede the circulation of specific solutes.

References

ANDEL, O.M. VAN: The influence of salts on the exudation of tomato plants. Acta Botan. Neerl. **2**, 445–521 (1953).

ANDERSSEN, F.G.: Some seasonal changes in the tracheal sap of pear and apricot trees. Plant Physiol. (Lancaster) **4**, 459–476 (1929).

BECKER, D., KLUGE, M., ZIEGLER, H.: Der Einbau von $^{32}PO_4^{\equiv}$ in organische Verbindungen durch Siebröhrensaft. Planta **99**, 154–162 (1971).

BIDDULPH, O.: Translocation of inorganic solutes. In: Plant physiology, vol. 2. Plants in relation to water and solutes (ed. F.C. STEWARD), chap. 6, p. 553–603. New York: Academic Press 1959.

BIDDULPH, O., BIDDULPH, S., CORY, R., KOONTZ, H.: Circulation patterns for phosphorus, sulfur, and calcium in the bean plant. Plant Physiol. (Lancaster) **33**, 293–300 (1958).

BIDDULPH, O., CORY, R.: Translocation of C^{14}-metabolites in the phloem of the bean plant. Plant Physiol. (Lancaster) **40**, 119–129 (1965).

BIDDULPH, O., NAKAYAMA, F.S., CORY, R.: Transpiration stream and ascension of calcium. Plant Physiol. (Lancaster) **36**, 429–436 (1961).

BIELESKI, R.L.: Phosphorus compounds in translocating phloem. Plant Physiol. (Lancaster) **44**, 497–502 (1969).

BIELESKI, R.L.: Phosphate pools, phosphate transport, and phosphate availability. Ann. Rev. Plant Physiol. **24**, 225–252 (1973).

BLEDSOE, R.W., COMAR, C.L., HARRIS, H.C.: Absorption of radioactive calcium by the peanut fruit. Science **109**, 329–330 (1949).

BOLLARD, E.G.: Transport in the xylem. Ann. Rev. Plant Physiol. **11**, 141–166 (1960).

BOLLARD, E.G., BUTLER, G.W.: Mineral nutrition of plants. Ann. Rev. Plant Physiol. **17**, 77–112 (1966).

BOUSQUET, U.: Absorption et migration du calcium chez une espèce calcifuge et une espèce calcicole. Compt. Rend. **272**, 1768–1771 (1971).

BOWEN, M.R., HOAD, G.V.: Inhibitor content of phloem and xylem sap obtained from willow (*Salix viminalis*) entering dormancy. Planta **81**, 64–70 (1968).

BOWEN, M.R., WAREING, P.F.: The interchange of ^{14}C-kinetin and ^{14}C-gibberellic acid between the bark and xylem of willow. Planta **89**, 108–125 (1969).

BRIARTY, L.G.: Repeating particles associated with membranes of transfer cells. Plant **113**, 373–375 (1973).

BROWN, A.L., YAMAGUCHI, S., LEAL-DIAZ, J.: Evidence for translocation of iron in plants. Plant Physiol. (Lancaster) **40**, 35–38 (1965).

BUKOVAC, M.J., TEUBNER, F.G., WITTWER, S.H.: Absorption and mobility of magnesium-28 in the bean (*Phaseolus vulgaris*). Proc. Am. Soc. Hort. Sci. **75**, 429–434 (1960).

BUKOVAC, M.J., WITTWER, S.H.: Absorption and mobility of foliar-applied nutrients. Plant Physiol. (Lancaster) **32**, 428–435 (1957).

BURROWS, W.J., CARR, D.J.: Effects of flooding the root system of sunflower plants on the cytokinin content in the xylem sap. Physiol. Plantarum **22**, 1105–1112 (1969).

BURSTRÖM, H.: The rate of the nutrient transport to swelling buds of trees. Physiol. Plantarum **1**, 124–135 (1948).

CARR, D.J., BURROWS, W.J.: Evidence of the presence in xylem sap of substances with kinetin-like activity. Life Sci. **5**, 2061–2077 (1966).

CARR, D.J., REID, D.M., SKENE, K.G.M.: The supply of gibberellins from the root to the shoot. Planta **63**, 382–392 (1964).

CLARK, R.B., TIFFIN, L.O., BROWN, J.C.: Organic acids and iron translocation in maize genotypes. Plant Physiol. (Lancaster) **52**, 147–150 (1973).

COOPER, D.R., HILL COTTINGHAM, D.G., SHORTHILL, M.J.: Gradients in the nitrogenous constituents of the sap extracted from apple shoots of different ages. J. Exptl. Botany **23**, 247–254 (1972).

CRAFTS, A.S., CRISP, C.E.: Phloem transport in plants. San Francisco: Freeman 1971.

CRAFTS, A.S., LORENZ, O.A.: Composition of fruits and phloem exudate of cucurbits. Plant Physiol. (Lancaster) **19**, 326–337 (1944).

CROZIER, A., REID, D.M.: Do roots synthesize gibberellins? Can. J. Botany **49**, 967–975 (1971).

EASTWOOD, D., LAIDMAN, D.L.: Mineral translocation in germinating wheat grain. Biochem. J. **109**, 9–10 (1968).

EDDINGS, J.L., BROWN, A.L.: Absorption and translocation of foliar applied iron. Plant Physiol. (Lancaster) **42**, 15–19 (1967).

EHRHARDT, P.: Die anorganischen Bestandteile des Honigtaues von *Megoura viciae* Buckt. Experentia **21**, 472–473 (1965).

EPSTEIN, E.: Mineral nutrition of plants: Principles and perspectives. New York: Wiley 1972.

ESCHRICH, W.: Translokation ^{14}C-markierter Assimilate im Licht und im Dunkeln bei *Vicia faba*. Planta **70**, 99–124 (1966).

ESCHRICH, W.: Translokation radioaktivmarkierter Indolyl-3-Essigsäure in Siebröhren von *Vicia faba*. Planta **78**, 144–157 (1968).

FERREL, W.K., JOHNSON, F.D.: Mobility of ^{45}Ca after injection into Western Pine. Science **124**, 364–365 (1956).

FIFE, J.M., PRICE, C., FIFE, D.C.: Some properties of phloem exudate collected from root of sugar beet. Plant Physiol. (Lancaster) **37**, 791–792 (1962).

FLINN, A.M., PATE, J.S.: A quantitative study of carbon transfer from pod and subtending leaf to the ripening seeds of the field pea (*Pisum arvense* L.). J. Exptl. Botany **21**, 71–82 (1970).

FORD, J., PEEL, A.J.: The movement of sugars into the sieve elements of bark strips of willow. I. Metabolism during transport. J. Exptl. Botany **18**, 607–619 (1967).

GARDNER, D.C.J., PEEL, A.J.: ATP in sieve-tube sap from willow. Nature **222**, 774 (1969).

GARDNER, D.C.J., PEEL, A.J.: Metabolism and transport of ^{14}C-labeled glutamic and aspartic acids in the phloem of willow. Phytochemistry **10**, 2385–2387 (1971).

GREENWAY, H., GUNN, A., PITMAN, M.G., THOMAS, D.A.: Plant response to saline substrates. VI. Chloride, sodium and ptassium uptake and distribution within the plant during ontogenesis of *Hordeum vulgare*. Australian J. Biol. Sci. **18**, 525–540 (1965).

GREENWAY, H., PITMAN, M.G.: Potassium retranslocation in seedlings of *Hordeum vulgare*. Australian J. Biol. Sci. **18**, 235–247 (1965).

GUARDIOLA, J.L., SUTCLIFFE, J.F.: Transport of materials from cotyledons during germination of the garden pea (*Pisum sativum* L.). J. Exptl. Botany **23**, 322–337 (1972).

GUNNING, B.E.S., PATE, J.S.: "Transfer Cells" plant cells with wall ingrowths, specialized in relation to short distance transport of solutes—their occurrence, structure and development. Protoplasma **68**, 107–133 (1969).

GUNNING, B.E.S., PATE, J.S., BRIARTY, L.G.: Specialized "Transfer Cells" in minor veins of leaves and their possible significance in phloem translocation. J. Cell Biol. **37**, C7–12 (1968).

GUNNING, B.E.S., PATE, J.S., GREEN, L.W.: Transfer cells in the vascular system of stems: Taxonomy, association with nodes, structure. Protoplasma **71**, 147–171 (1970).

GUNNING, B.E.S., PATE, J.S., MINCHIN, F.R., MARKS, I.: Quantitative aspects of transfer-cell structure in relation to vein loading in leaves and solute transport in legume nodules. Symp. Soc. Exptl. Biol. **28**, 87–126 (1974).

HALL, R.H.: Cytokinins as a probe of developmental processes. Ann. Rev. Plant Physiol. **24**, 415–444 (1973).

HALL, S.M., BAKER, D.A.: The chemical composition of *Ricinus* phloem exudate. Planta **106**, 131–140 (1972).

HALL, S.M., BAKER, D.A., MILBURN, J.A.: Phloem transport of ^{14}C-labeled assimilates in *Ricinus*. Planta **100**, 200–207 (1971).

HARDY, P.J.: Selective diffusion of basic and acidic products of CO_2 fixation into the transpiration stream in grapevine. J. Exptl. Botany **20**, 856–862 (1969).

HARDY, P.J., POSSINGHAM, J.V.: Studies on translocation of metabolites in the xylem of grapevine shoots. J. Exptl. Botany **20**, 325–335 (1969).

HARRIS, H.C.: The effect on the growth of peanuts of nutrient deficiencies in the root and the pegging zone. Plant Physiol. (Lancaster) **24**, 150–161 (1949).

HARTT, C.E., KORTSCHAK, H.P.: Radioactive isotopes in sugar cane physiology. Proc. 12th I.S.S.C.T. Congress, Puerto Rico, p. 647–662 (1965).

HENKENS, CH.H., JONGMAN, E.: The movement of manganese in the plant and the practical consequences. Neth. J. Agr. Sci. **13**, 392–407 (1965).

HES, J.W.: Leaf fall and excretion. Acta Botan. Neerl. **7**, 278–281 (1958).

HILL-COTTINGHAM, D.G., LLOYD-JONES, C.P.: Relative mobility of some organic nitrogenous compounds in the xylem of apple shoots. Nature **220**, 389–390 (1968).

HILL-COTTINGHAM, D.G., Lloyd-Jones, C.P.: Seasonal variations in absorption and metabolism of carbon-14-labeled arginine in intact apple stem tissue. Physiol. Plantarum **29**, 35–44 (1973a).

HILL-COTTINGHAM, D.G., LLOYD-JONES, C.P.: Metabolism of carbon-14-labeled arginine, citrulline and ornithine in intact apple stems. Physiol. Plantarum **29**, 125–128 (1973b).

HILL-COTTINGHAM, D.G., LLOYD-JONES, C.P.: A technique for studying the adsorption, absorption and metabolism of amino acids in intact apple stem tissue. Physiol. Plantarum **28**, 443–446 (1973c).

HOAD, G.V.: Effect of moisture stress on abscisic acid levels in *Ricinus communis* L. with particular reference to phloem exudate. Planta **113**, 367–372 (1973).

HOAD, G.V., BOWEN, M.R.: Evidence for gibberellin-like substances in phloem exudate of higher plants. Planta **82**, 22–32 (1968).

HOAD, G.V., HILLMAN, S.K., WAREING, P.F.: Studies on the movement of indole auxins in willow (*Salix viminalis* L.) Planta **99**, 73–88 (1971).

HOAD, G.V., PEEL, A.J.: Studies on the movement of solutes between the sieve tubes and surrounding tissues in willow. I. Interference between solutes and rate of translocation measurements. J. Exptl. Botany **16**, 433–451 (1965).

HOFSTEN, A. VAN: X-ray analysis of microelements in seeds of *Crambe abyssinica*. Physiol. Plantarum **29**, 76–81 (1973).

HUMPHRIES, E.C.: Entry of nutrients into the plant and their movement within it. Proc. Fertil. Soc. **48** (1958).

HUSA, J.G., MCILRATH, W.J.: Absorption and translocation of boron by sunflower plants. Botan. Gaz. **126**, 186–194 (1965).

IVANKO, S.: Metabolic pathways of nitrogen assimilation in plant tissue when ^{15}N is used as a tracer. In: Nitrogen-15 in soil plant studies. Int. Atom. Energy Ag. Vienna (1971).

JACOBY, B.: Sodium retention in excised bean stems. Physiol. Plantarum **18**, 730–739 (1965).

JONES, O.P., LACEY, H.J.: Gibberellin-like substances in the transpiration stream of apple and pear trees. J. Exptl. Botany **19**, 526–531 (1968).

JONES, O.P., ROWE, R.W.: Sampling the transpiration stream in woody plants. Nature **219**, 403 (1968).

JOY, K.W., ANTCLIFF, A.J.: Translocation of amino-acids in sugar beet. Nature **211**, 210–211 (1966).

KENDE, H.: Kinetin-like factors in the root exudate of sunflowers. Proc. Natl. Acad. Sci. U.S. **53**, 1302–1307 (1965).

KIMMEL, C.: Über das Vorkommen anorganischer Ionen in Siebröhrensäften und den Transport von Salzen im Phloem. Diss. tech. Hochsch. Darmstadt (1962).

KIPPS, A., BOULTER, D.: Carbon transfer from the blossom node leaf to the fruit of *Vicia faba*. New Phytologist **72**, 1293–1298 (1973).

KLUGE, H.: Untersuchungen über Kohlenhydrate und Myo-inosit in Siebröhrensäften von Holz. Doctoral Dissertation, Darmstadt Technical University (1967).

KLUGE, M., ZIEGLER, H.: Der ATP-gehalt der Siebröhrensäfte von Laubbäumen. Planta **61**, 167–177 (1964).

KOLLMANN, R., DÖRR, I. KLEINIG, H.: Protein filaments—structural components of the phloem exudate. Planta **95**, 86–94 (1970).
KURSANOV, A.L.: The transport of organic substances in plants. Endeavour **20**, 19–25 (1961).
KURSANOV, A.L.: Metabolism and the transport of organic substances in the phloem. Advances in Botanical Research, vol. 1, p. 209–278. London: Academic Press 1963.
LÄUCHLI, A.: Untersuchungen mit der Röntgen-Mikrosonde über Verteilung und Transport von Ionen in Pflanzengeweben. II. Ionentransport nach Früchten von *Pisum sativum*. Planta **83**, 137–149 (1968).
LÄUCHLI, A.: Translocation of inorganic solutes. Ann. Rev. Plant Physiol. **23**, 197–218 (1972).
LEWIS, O.A.M., PATE, J.S.: The significance of transpirationally derived nitrogen in protein synthesis in fruiting plants of pea (*Pisum sativum* L.). J. Exptl. Botany **24**, 596–606 (1973).
LINCK, A.J., SUDIA, J.W.: Translocation of labeled photosynthate from the bloom node leaf to the fruit of *Pisum sativum*. Experientia **18**, 69–70 (1962).
MACROBBIE, E.: Phloem translocation. Facts and mechanisms. A comparative survey. Biol. Rev. **46**, 429–481 (1971).
MAIER, K., MAIER, U.: Localization of beta-glycerophosphatase and Mg^{++}-activated adenosine triphosphatase in a moss haustorium, and the relation of these enzymes to the wall labyrinth. Protoplasma **75**, 91–112 (1972).
MAIZEL, J.V., BENSON, A.A., TOLBERT, N.E.: Identification of phosphoryl choline as an important constituent of plant saps. Plant Physiol. (Lancaster) **31**, 407–408 (1956).
MCILRATH, W.J.: Mobility of boron in several dicotyledonous species. Botan. Gaz. **126**, 27–30 (1965).
MEYER-MEVIUS, U.: Vorkommen und Transport von Kohlenhydraten und Stickstoffverbindungen in den pflanzlichen Leitungsbahnen. Flora (Jena) **147**, 553–594 (1959).
MICHAEL, G., WILBERG, E., KOUHSIAHI-TORK, K.: Durch hohe Luftfeuchtigkeit induzierter Bormangel. Z. Pflanzenernähr. Düng. Bodenk. **122**, 1–3 (1969).
MILLIKAN, C.R., HANGER, B.C.: Effects of chelation and of certain cations on the mobility of foliar-applied ^{45}Ca in stock, broad beans, peas and subterranean clover. Australian J. Biol. Sci. **18**, 211–226 (1965).
MILLIKAN, C.R., HANGER, B.C.: Redistribution of ^{45}Ca in *Trifolium subterraneum* L. and *Antirrhinum majus* L. Australian J. Biol. Sci. **20**, 1119–1130 (1967).
MILLIKAN, C.R., HANGER, B.C., BJARNASON, E.N.: The mobility of ^{65}Zn in *Trifolium subterraneum* L. and *Antirrhinum majus* L. Australian J. Biol. Sci. **22**, 311–320 (1969).
MILTHORPE, F.L., MOORBY, J.: Vascular transport and its significance in plant growth. Ann. Rev. Plant Physiol. **20**, 117–138 (1969).
MOORBY, J.: The influence of carbohydrate and mineral nutrient supply on the growth of potato tubers. Ann. Botany (London) **32**, 57–68 (1968).
MOOSE, C.A.: Chemical and spectroscopic analysis of phloem exudate and parenchyma sap from several species of plants. Plant Physiol. (Lancaster) **13**, 365–380 (1938).
MORRISON, T.M.: Xylem sap composition in woody plants. Nature **205**, 1027 (1965).
MÜNCH, E.: Die Stoffbewegungen in der Pflanze. Jena 1930.
NELSON, C.D.: The translocation of organic compounds in plants. Can. J. Botany **40**, 757–770 (1962).
O'BRIEN, T.P., CARR, D.J.: A suberized layer in the cell walls of the bundle sheath of grasses. Australian J. Biol. Sci. **23**, 275–287 (1970).
O'BRIEN, T.P., ZEE, S.Y.: Vascular transfer cells in the vegetative nodes of wheat. Australian J. Biol. Sci. **24**, 207–217 (1971)
OERTLI, J.J., RICHARDSON, W.F.: The mechanism of boron immobility in plants. Physiol. Plantarum **23**, 108–116 (1970).
OGHOGHORIE, C.G.O., PATE, J.S.: Exploration of the nitrogen transport system of a nodulated legume using ^{15}N. Planta **104**, 35–49 (1972).
OLAND, K.: Changes in the content of dry matter and major nutrient elements of apple foliage during senescence and abscission. Physiol. Plantarum **16**, 682–694 (1963).
OLOFINBOBA, M.O.: Seasonal variations in the carbohydrates in the xylem of *Antiaris africana*. Ann. Botany (London) **33**, 339–349 (1969).
PATE, J.S.: Root exudation studies on the exchange of ^{14}C-labeled organic substances between the roots and shoot of the nodulated legume. Plant Soil **17**, 333–356 (1962).
PATE, J.S.: Roots as organs of assimilation of sulfate. Science **149**, 547–548 (1965).
PATE, J.S.: Movement of nitrogenous solutes in plants. In: Nitrogen-15 in soil-plant studies. Int. Atom. Energy Ag. Vienna (1971).

PATE, J.S.: Uptake, assimilation and transport of nitrogen compounds by plants. Soil Biol. Biochem. **5**, 109–119 (1973).

PATE, J.S., FLINN, A.M.: Carbon and nitrogen transfer from vegetative organs to ripening seeds of field pea (*Pisum arvense* L.). J. Exptl. Botany **24**, 123–145 (1973).

PATE, J.S., GUNNING, B.E.S.: Vascular transfer cells in Angiosperm leaves. A taxonomic and morphological survey. Protoplasma **68**, 135–156 (1969).

PATE, J.S., GUNNING, B.E.S.: Transfer Cells. Ann. Rev. Plant Physiol. **23**, 173–196 (1972).

PATE, J.S., GUNNING, B.E.S., MILLIKEN, F.F.: Function of transfer cells in the nodal regions of stems, particularly in relation to the nutrition of young seedlings. Protoplasma **71**, 313–334 (1970).

PATE, J.S., O'BRIEN, T.P.: Microautoradiographic study of the incorporation of labeled amino acids into insoluble compounds of the shoot of a higher plant. Planta **78**, 60–71 (1968).

PATE, J.S., SHARKEY, P.J., LEWIS, O.A.M.: Phloem bleeding from legume fruits—A technique for study of fruit nutrition. Planta **120**, 229–243 (1974).

PATE, J.S., SHARKEY, P.J., LEWIS, O.A.M.: Xylem to phloem transfer of solutes in fruiting shoots of legumes, studied by a phloem bleeding technique. Planta **122**, 11–26 (1975).

PATE, J.S., WALKER, J., WALLACE, W.: Nitrogen-containing compounds in the shoot system of *Pisum arvense* L. II. The significance of amino acids and amides released from nodulated roots. Ann. Botany (London) **29**, 475–493 (1965).

PATE, J.S., WALLACE, W., VAN DIE, J.: Petiole bleeding sap in the examination of the circulation of nitrogenous substances in plants. Nature **204**, 1073–1074 (1964).

PEEL, A.J.: The movement of ions from the xylem solution into the sieve tubes of willow. J. Exptl. Botany **14**, 438–447 (1963).

PEEL, A.J., WEATHERLEY, P.E.: Composition of sieve-tube sap. Nature **184**, 1955–1956 (1959).

PHILLIPS, D.A., CLELAND, C.F.: Cytokinin activity from the phloem sap of *Xanthium strumarium* L. Planta **102**, 173–178 (1972).

PHILLIPS, I.D.J., JONES, R.L.: Gibberellin-like activity in bleeding sap of root systems of *Helianthus annuus* detected by a new dwarf pea epicotyl assay and other methods. Planta **63**, 269–278 (1964).

RAINS, D.W.: Cation absorption by slices of stem tissue of bean and cotton. Experientia **25**, 215–216 (1969).

RINGOET, A., SAUER, G., GIELINK, A.J.: Phloem transport of calcium in oat leaves. Planta **80**, 15–20 (1968).

SAUTER, J.J., ITEN, W., ZIMMERMANN, M.H.: Studies on the release of sugar into the vessels of sugar maple (*Acer saccharum*). Can. J. Botany **51**, 1–8 (1973).

SCHMID, W.E., GERLOFF, G.C.: A naturally occurring chelate of iron in xylem exudate. Plant Physiol. (Lancaster) **36**, 226–231 (1961).

SCHOLZ, G.: Über die Translokation des Bors in Tabak-Blattstecklingen mit geteilten Wurzelsystemen. Flora (Jena) **148**, 484–488 (1960).

SELVENDRAN, R.R., SABARATNAM, S.: Composition of the xylem sap of tea plants (*Camellia sinensis* L.). Ann. Botany (London) **35**, 679–682 (1971).

SHELDRAKE, A.R., NORTHCOTE, D.H.: Some constituents of xylem sap and their possible relationship to xylem differentiation. J. Exptl. Botany **19**, 681–689 (1968).

SHONE, M.G.T., CLARKSON, D.T., SANDERSON, J.: The absorption and translocation of sodium by maize seedlings. Planta **86**, 301–314 (1969).

SITTON, D., ITAI, C., KENDE, H.: Decreased cytokinin production in the roots as a factor in shoot senescence. Planta **73**, 296–300 (1967).

SITTON, D., RICHMOND, A., VAADIA, Y.: On the synthesis of gibberellins in roots. Phytochemistry **6**, 1101–1105 (1967).

SKENE, K.G.M.: Gibberellin-like substances in root exudate of *Vitis vinifera*. Planta **74**, 250–262 (1967).

SMITH, J.G.: Embryo development in *Phaseolus vulgaris*. Plant Physiol. (Lancaster) **51**, 454–458 (1973).

STEUCEK, G.L., KOONTZ, H.V.: Phloem mobility of magnesium. Plant Physiol. (Lancaster) **46**, 50–52 (1970).

STÖSSER, R.: Autoradiographische Lokalisierung von ^{45}Calcium im Xylem bei Fruchtstielen von *Prunus avium* L. Z. Pflanzenphysiol. **4**, 387–392 (1970).

TAMMES, P.M.L.: Micro- and macro-nutrients in sieve-tube sap of palms. Acta Botan. Neerl. **7**, 233–234 (1958).

TAMMES, P.M.L., VAN DIE, J.: Studies on phloem exudation from *Yucca flaccida* Haw. I. Some observations on the phenomenon of bleeding and the composition of the exudate. Acta Botan. Neerl. **13**, 76–83 (1964).

TAMMES, P.M.L., VAN DIE, J.: Studies on phloem exudation from *Yucca flaccida* Haw. IV. Translocation of macro- and micro-nutrients by the phloem sap Stream. Proc. Kaninkl. Ned. Akad. Wetenschap. **69**, 655–659 (1966).

TAYLOR, F.H.: Variation in sugar content of maple sap. Vermont Agr. Expt. Stat. Bull. **587**, 1–39 (1956).

TIFFIN, L.O.: Translocation of iron citrate and phosphorus in xylem exudate of soybean. Plant Physiol. (Lancaster) **45**, 280–283 (1970).

TOLBERT, N.E., WIEBE, H.: Phosphorus and sulfur compounds in plant xylem sap. Plant Physiol. (Lancaster) **30**, 499–504 (1955).

TRAPP, G.: A study of the foliar endodermis in the Plantaginaceae. Trans. Roy. Soc. Edinburgh **17**, 523–546 (1932).

TUKEY, H.B.: The leaching of substances from plants. Ann. Rev. Plant Physiol. **21**, 305–324 (1970).

VAN DIE, J.: Pathways of translocation and metabolic conversions of root-absorbed ^{14}C (U) L-glutamic acid in tomato plants. Acta Botan. Neerl. **12**, 269–280 (1963).

VAN DIE, J., VONK, C.R.: Selective and stereo-specific absorption of various amino acids during xylem translocation in tomato stems. Acta Botan. Neerl. **16**, 147–152 (1967).

WAISEL, Y., SHAPIRA, Z.: Functions performed by roots of some submerged hydrophytes. Israel J. Botany **20**, 69–77 (1971).

WALKER, T.S., THAINE, R.: Proteins and fine structural components in exudate from sieve tubes in *Cucurbita pepo* stems. Ann. Botany (London) **35**, 773–790 (1971).

WALLACE, A., HEMAIDAN, N., SUFI, S.M.: Sodium translocation in bush beans. Soil Sci. **100**, 331–334 (1965).

WALLACE, W., PATE, J.S.: Nitrate assimilation in higher plants with special reference to the cocklebur (*Xanthium pennsylvanicum* Wallr.) Ann. Botany (London) **31**, 213–228 (1967).

WEATHERLEY, P.E.: Ion movement within the plant and its integration with other physiological processes. In: Ecological aspects of the mineral nutrition of plants (ed. I.H. RORISON). Oxford: Blackwells 1969.

WIERSUM, L.K.: Water transport in the xylem as related to calcium uptake by groundnuts (*Arachis hypogoea* L.) Plant Soil **3**, 160–169 (1951).

WIERSUM, L.K.: Calcium content of fruits and storage tissue in relation to the mode of water supply. Acta Botan. Neerl. **15**, 406–418 (1966).

WILLIAMS, R.F.: Redistribution of mineral elements during development. Ann. Rev. Plant Physiol. **6**, 25–42 (1955).

WOODING, F.B.P.: Absorptive cells in protoxylem: association between mitochondria and the plasmalemma. Planta **84**, 235–238 (1969).

WOODING, F.B.P., NORTHCOTE, D.H.: An anomalous wall thickening and its possible role in the uptake of stem-fed tritiated glucose by *Pinus pinea*. J. Ultrastruct. Res. **12**, 463–472 (1965).

YOSHIDA, R., ORITANI, T., NISHI, A.: Kinetin-like factors in the root exudate of rice plants. Plant Cell Physiol. (Tokyo) **12**, 89–94 (1971).

ZEE, S.Y., O'BRIEN, T.P.: Vascular transfer cells in the wheat spikelet. Australian J. Biol. Sci. **24**, 35–49 (1971).

ZIEGLER, H.: Der Ferntransport organischer Stoffe in den Pflanzen. Naturwissenschaften **50**, 177–186 (1963).

ZIEGLER, H.: Die Physiologie pflanzlicher Drüsen. Ber. Deut. Botan. Ges. **78**, 466–477 (1965).

ZIEGLER, H.: L'abeille et la fleur. II. Le miel 1. La Sève des tubes criblés. In: Traité de Biologie de L'Abeille, vol. 3, p. 207–217. Paris: Masson et Cie. 1968.

ZIEGLER, H., SCHNABEL, M.: Über Harnstoffderivate im Siebröhrensaft. Flora (Jena) **150**, 306–317 (1961).

ZIEGLER, H., ZIEGLER, I.: The water-soluble vitamins in the sieve-tube sap of some trees. Flora (Jena) **152**, 257–278 (1962).

ZIMMERMANN, M.H.: Translocation of organic substances in trees. I. The nature of the sugars in the sieve-tube exudates of trees. Plant Physiol. (Lancaster) **32**, 288–291 (1957).

ZIMMERMANN, M.H.: Translocation of nutrients. In: The physiology of plant growth and development M.B. WILKINS (ed.). Maidenhead, England: McGraw Hill 1969.

Appendix I:
Flow of Biological Fluids through Non-Ideal Capillaries

T.R.F. Nonweiler

Flow through biological capillaries is frequently not ideal in terms of the simple physical relations one might wish. In this section equations are provided so that flow characteristics can be studied with reasonable accuracy in such non-ideal situations. These range from sap flow through sieve tubes of varying dimensions to flow through the tapered bore of an excised aphid stylet. Some precautionary notes are included concerning the rheological properties of biological fluids in such systems.

The best-known theoretical result relating to the flow of a viscous fluid in a tube is that of Hagen and Poiseuille. It can be expressed in various ways: most suited to our present purposes, we can state it as a relation connecting the rate of change of pressure (p) with distance (x) along the axis of a long horizontal tube of circular cross-section (radius r) filled with a fluid of dynamic viscosity η flowing steadily and slowly at a volumetric rate Q per unit time. With this notation, the Hagen-Poiseuille law is:

$$\frac{dp}{dx} = -8\eta Q/\pi r^4 \tag{1}$$

the negative sign denoting that the pressure falls downstream. It is a supplementary result that the velocity distribution across the tube is parabolic, with a maximum speed on the axis, and (by hypothesis) zero velocity at the walls of the tube.

The result can readily be generalized to tubes of any given cross-section; we then write

$$\frac{dp}{dx} = -k\eta Q/Am^2 \tag{2}$$

where A is the cross-sectional area, and m is the mean hydraulic radius of the tube, defined as its cross-sectional area divided by its perimeter. Further, k is a coefficient dependent only on the shape (but not the absolute dimensions) of the cross-section: evidently if it is circular, then $A = \pi r^2$ and

$$m = (\pi r^2)/(2\pi r) = r/2$$

so that, from Eq. (1), we see that $k = 2$. In principle, it is possible to estimate the value of k for any shape of cross-section; in practice, the calculation is difficult, except for particular shapes. Thus, for example, for an elliptic cross-section of eccentricity e, it can be shown that

$$k = 4/(1 + \sqrt{1 - e^4}) \tag{3}$$

so that k varies from 2 for a circle ($e = 0$) to 4 for a completely flattened ellipse ($e = 1$). But the value of $k = 2$ remains a good approximation unless the eccentricity is large:

for example, if $e=0.5$, Eq. (3) gives the value of $k=2.03$. For tubes of rectangular section, k varies from 1.78 for a square to 3 corresponding to a narrow slit.

A further generalization is possible by supposing that the tube is inclined, rather than horizontal; if its axis (in the direction of flow) makes an angle Φ with the downward vertical, then

$$\frac{dp}{dx} = \rho g \cos \Phi - k \eta Q / A m^2 \tag{4}$$

where ρ is the fluid density, and g is the acceleration due to gravity. Placing the driving pressure gradient term dp/dx as zero in this equation reveals that there is of course a flow through an inclined tube due to gravity, even when there is no pressure difference to drive it. (Similarly, though gravity exerts a pressure on a liquid in a sealed vertical tube, if the tube is opened, then during the free-fall flow the pressure falls to zero.)

As a consequence of the assumptions on which Eq. (4) is based, all the terms on the right-hand side are constants, and therefore so also would be the pressure gradient; accordingly, the left-hand side could be replaced by a pressure difference between two positions on the axis of the tube divided by the distance between them, and in this way the appearance of a differential equation is avoided. However, the form of this equation is applicable, without serious loss in accuracy, beyond the strict limits imposed in its derivation, including conditions such that the terms on the right-hand side are variable. It will be our purpose here to examine its range of validity relevant to the present context, assuming for this purpose that the tube is circular in cross-section, and that the fluid is a liquid.

We first enquire what is meant by the assumption in the derivation of the Hagen-Poiseuille relation that the rate of volume flow (Q) is "small". Of relevance here is the value of the Reynolds Number

$$R = \rho Q / \eta r = Q / \nu r \tag{5}$$

where ν is the kinematic viscosity ($=\eta/\rho$). This is a dimensionless number, and if its value is above about 1,000 the flow becomes turbulent (i.e. composed of small eddies) and Eq. (1) is then inapplicable; below this critical condition the flow is said to be *laminar*. There is no doubt, in the present context, where the values of R are likely to be between 1 and 10, that the flow would be laminar.

A similar condition affects the dependence of the flow upon the state of the internal surface of the tube. If there are excrescences (of height ε) or hairs (of diameter ε) then these can create turbulence if (ε/r) exceeds about $3/R$; but clearly this condition does not apply at very low Reynolds Numbers even if the tube surface is not smooth.

For such slow flows as we envisage here, it is permissible to apply the results to the flow through curved tubes (so that the inclination Φ in Eq. (4) may possibly vary along the tube with the distance x). If the radius of curvature of the tube axis is c (say) then the pressure gradient is reduced by a fraction $10^{-8} R^4 (r/c)^2$, and this will be seen to be negligible at low Reynolds Number, even if the tube is tightly coiled.

The requirement that the tube is long is introduced in deriving Eq. (1) to ensure that the local disturbance at the inlet and outlet to the tube is unimportant. Although this disturbance depends on the geometry of the tube close to its ends, any effect will be unimportant provided that (r/l) is small compared with $1/R$, where l is the total length of the tube. Alternatively, this will be seen to imply that $(Q/\nu l)$ is small compared with unity, and there is no doubt of this in the present context, where therefore inlet and exit effects can be ignored.

A similar consideration applies to the possibility of extending the Hagen-Poiseuille relation to tubes having a cross-section which varies along the tube. Provided that the value of (dr/dx), which is the tangent of the conical angle of convergence (or divergence) of the tube, is numerically small compared with $1/R$, then Eq. (1) applies with r interpreted as variable with distance (x) along the tube. If the tube radius changes gradually along the axis, then (dr/dx) will be numerically less than (r/l), so that as before this condition will be met if $(Q/\nu l)$ is small compared with unity.

Likewise, if $(Q/\nu l)$ is small, Eq. (4) can be applied to tubes whose cross-section varies along the tube. Assuming then that the terms on the right-hand side of Eq. (4) are variable with x, we may integrate it most easily by noting that

$$\cos\Phi = -dh/dx$$

where h is the height of the tube axis at a distance x along the tube. Then

$$p_0 - p_l = \rho g(h_l - h_0) + kQ\eta \int_0^l (1/Am^2)\,dx \tag{6}$$

where the subscripts 0 and l denote conditions at respectively the positions $x=0$ (upstream), and $x=l$ (downstream) along the tube. In particular if the tube contracts or diverges linearly (that is, if it is shaped as the frustum of a cone) then Eq. (6) becomes

$$p_0 - p_l = \rho\, g(h_l - h_0) + kQ\eta\, l(A_l + A_0 + \sqrt{A_0 A_l})/(3A_0 A_l m_0 m_l) \tag{7}$$

where, as noted earlier, k is approximately 2 for a roughly circular cross-section, and l is the length of the tube.

These results will also apply to unsteady flows, where the pressure difference (and so the volume flow) varies with time, provided it does not do so too rapidly. In fact, there will be a time lag between cause and effect, but this is of order r^2/ν which is likely to be so short a time that, in the present context, it may be ignored. However it should be borne in mind that in starting the flow, before the tube is filled, forces due to surface tension may be important.

In both Eqs. (5) and (6) it is assumed that the dynamic viscosity is a constant, and generally η only varies significantly due to a change in temperature of the fluid. However, it should be noted that the Hagen-Poiseuille law assumes that the fluid is "Newtonian"—that is, that the viscosity is independent of the rate of shear in the fluid, or its duration, as is so for water. In practice, a fairly wide category of fluids do not behave in this way.

A large group of liquids have an apparent viscosity which varies with time: those (including the much-studied colloidal liquids) in which viscosity is reduced with duration of stress are said to be *thixotropic*, and others in which it increases with duration are termed *rheopectic*. If it happens that the time scale of this phenomenon is short compared with the duration of time occupied by a particle of fluid in moving through the tube (which is of order lA/Q) then the dynamic viscosity appropriate to the fully mobile state may be applicable.

Fluids for which the effective viscosity is reduced under severe rates of shear are said to be *pseudo-plastic* (clay, milk and blood come into this category): those in which it increases are termed *dilatent*, and aqueous solutions of rice starch or sugar (in high concentration) exhibit this property. For such liquids an effective viscosity can be defined which depends upon the mean rate of shear, (Q/Am), but unless the dependence is of minor importance in determining the viscosity, there is no justification for applying the Hagen-Poiseuille relation to the flow. An analysis of such problems will be found in textbooks dealing with the subject of rheology.

Appendix II:

On the Simultaneous Movement of THO, ^{14}C-Sucrose, and $^{32}PO_4$ in the Sieve-Tubes of Willow

M.T. TYREE and M.H. ZIMMERMANN

PEEL et al. (1969) performed experiments on 12 cm-long bark strips of willow (*Salix viminalis*). The bark strips were fixed to polythene tubes which were divided into two compartments, each compartment having its own window through which two areas of the cambial surface could be irrigated with different solutions. The "cold" side was irrigated with 2 ml sec^{-1} of distilled water, and the "hot" side was irrigated with 2 ml sec^{-1} solution containing THO, ^{14}C-sucrose and $^{32}PO_4$. In one experiment (Table 3, PEEL et al., 1969) two severed aphid stylets were located on the bark strip — one on the hot and the other on the cold side. During the eight-hour time course of the experiment, measurable quantities of ^{14}C-sucrose and $^{32}PO_4$ were collected from both stylets; THO was detected only on the hot side (18,000 cpm/µl of exudate).

From these and other experiments PEEL et al. (1969) concluded that THO is relatively immobile in sieve tubes and therefore this constituted evidence against mass flow of solution. We propose to show that the failure to detect THO was due to lateral diffusion of THO out of the sieve tube, a possibility dismissed by PEEL et al. (1969).

When the bark strip has no aphid stylets it seems that the rate of movement of THO into the cold side is the same for living and dead tissue (Table 4, PEEL et al., 1969). When an aphid stylet is present in the cold zone the exudation rate in one case was 0.94 µl hr^{-1}, for willow sieve tubes of radius $r = 1.15 \times 10^{-3}$ cm this corresponds to an average sap velocity $v = 6.28 \times 10^{-2}$ cm sec^{-1} (226 cm h^{-1}) if the stylet is supplied only from one side (or half the velocity if the stylet is supplied equally from both sides). These data suggest that rapid mass flow occurs only in the sieve tubes pierced by the stylet. This permits us to assume a very large volume outside the transporting sieve tube, and it probably justifies the assumption of negligible THO concentrations outside the active sieve tube. Under these conditions we can apply Eq. (42) (TYREE and DAINTY, Chapter 16, p. 386), to give the concentration of THO in the cold stylet exudate, C, in terms of the concentration of THO in the hot stylet exudate, C^*. We have

$$C/C^* = \exp\left(-\frac{2P^*}{r}\frac{s}{v}\right)$$

where P^* = the water permeability of the sieve-cell membrane, r = the sieve tube radius (1.15×10^{-3} cm), s = the distance between the cold stylet and the end of the hot side (4.5 cm), and v = the average sap velocity (6.28×10^{-2} cm sec^{-1}).

P^* for plant cell membranes ranges at most from a high of 10^{-2} cm sec^{-1} to a low of 10^{-4} cm sec^{-1}. Given these values the ratio C/C^* ranges from $< 10^{-99}$ to 3.7×10^{-6}. The most likely value of P^* for MÜNCH pressure flow in trees is $> 6 \times 10^{-4}$ cm sec^{-1} (TYREE et al., 1974); This gives a value of $C/C^* < 3 \times 10^{-33}$. Thus we would expect the THO concentration in the cold stylet exudate to be well below the detectable level. This analysis could be refined to include the diffusional resistance encountered by THO in the water beyond the sieve-cell membrane, but this is likely to be small. Even if the radial path length is 1 mm (= to the half-thickness of the bark) the overall permeability of the membrane—extracellular water path would still be greater than 10^{-4} cm sec^{-1}.

References

PEEL, A.J., FIELD, R.J., COULSON, C.L., GARDNER, D.C.J.: Movement of water and solutes in sieve tubes of willow in response to puncture by aphid stylets. Evidence against a mass flow of solution. Physiol. Plantarum **22**, 768–775 (1969).

TYREE, M.T., CHRISTY, A.L., FERRIER, J.M.: A simpler iterative steady state solution of Münch pressure-flow systems applied to long and short translocation paths. Plant Physiol. (Lancaster) **54**, 589–600 (1974).

Appendix III:

List of Sugars and Sugar Alcohols in Sieve-Tube Exudates

M.H. ZIMMERMANN and H. ZIEGLER

The following list of sieve-tube sugars and sugar alcohols is primarily based upon two, as yet unpublished, surveys. One of these was carried out by M.H. ZIMMERMANN, the other by H. KLUGE, both with HARTIG's incision method (cf. p. 59). The list could easily have been expanded by including additional published data on sieve-tube exudate analyses and tracer studies. In the latter case, it would be difficult to draw the line between reporting results and interpreting them, because moving and stationary tracers are not easily distinguished. Since published results are discussed in several chapters (e.g. Chapters 3, 7, 8, etc.), we did not duplicate these efforts.

The main purpose of publishing this list is the fact that it covers about one hundred dicotyledonous families and more than five hundred species. The striking grouping of sugars within given families makes the list taxonomically interesting and also useful to workers for the selection of experimental species with particular sugar combinations. Another interesting point is that certain sugars appear only at a given time of the year in some species. Thus raffinose-type sugars may appear in the spring before the leaves are out and be nearly absent during summer and fall. This confirms findings reported by G.P. HILL for *Tilia americana* with the aphid stylet method [J. Exptl. Bot. **13**, 144–151 (1962)].

Reference numbers 1–9, following the plant name, indicate place and date of collection, as follows:

1. Samples collected at the Harvard Forest and Harvard Black Rock Forest, September 1956 [see Plant Physiol. **32**, 288–291 (1957)].
2. Atkins Garden of Harvard University, Soledad near Cienfuegos, Cuba, December 1959 and January 1960.
3. Fairchild Tropical Garden, Miami, Florida, Easter week 1961.
4. Harvard Forest, Petersham, Massachusetts, August 1960.
5. Botanic Garden, Technical University, Darmstadt, Germany, July 22–August 1, 1964.
6. Botanic Garden, Technical University, Darmstadt, Sept. 16–Oct. 31, 1964 and October 1965.
7. Botanic Garden, Technical University, Darmstadt, April 2–22, 1965.
8. Jardin des Plantes, University of Montpellier, France, May 5–12, 1965.
9. Botanic Garden "Mar y Murtra", Blanes, Costa Brava, Spain, May 15–June 2, 1965.

Analyses marked by reference numbers 1–4 were made by M.H. ZIMMERMANN. Exudate samples were spotted on Whatman No. 1 filter paper in the field and separated on three different chromatograms. Two of these were run with n-butanol: acetic acid: water, 3:3:2 (v/v) for 24 h and developed with resorcinol-HCl and aniline-oxalic acid respectively. The third was run in n-butanol: acetic acid: water, 6:1:1 (v/v) for 72 h to give better resolution for sugar alcohols, and developed with $AgNO_3$-NaOH. A number of species were analyzed repeatedly at different times and/or from different individual trees, but unless results differed markedly, only one entry is given. In a few cases where only a very small quantity of exudate could be obtained only one or two chromatograms could be prepared.

Analyses marked by reference numbers 5–9 were carried out by H. KLUGE during the course of her work towards a Ph.D. degree under the guidance of H. ZIEGLER at the Technical University in Darmstadt. Her trip to France and Spain was made possible by a grant from the Carlos Faust Foundation. Samples were either frozen immediately after collection and stored at −22° C before chromatography, or spotted on filter paper (SCHLEICHER-SCHÜLL 2043b) in the field. The partitioning solvent most often used was n-butanol:dimethyl-formamide:water, 2:1:1 (v/v) and the developing solution $AgNO_3$-NaOH.

Both authors estimated concentrations roughly by the size of the spots on the filter paper, whereby quantities are expressed as follows:

++++ ca. 20–30% (w/v) sucrose equivalent
+++ ca. 10–20% (w/v)
++ ca. 2–10% (w/v)
+ ca. 0.5–2% (w/v)
tr trace (ca. 0.1–0.5%)

Estimated quantities are meant as guidelines only, and the concentrations indicated by the two authors are not strictly comparable. ZIMMERMANN did not analyze for myo-inositol, absence of this substance from his reports does not necessarily mean absence in the species. $AgNO_3$-NaOH brings out numerous fainter spots on chromatograms of many species. Some of these remained unidentified.

The sugars and derivatives are: S = sucrose, R = raffinose, St = stachyose, V = verbascose, Aj = ajugose, M = D-mannitol, So = sorbitol, Du = dulcitol, I = myoinositol.

List of Exudates

	Ref.	S	R	St	V	Aj	M	So	Du	I
Aceraceae										
Acer circinatum Pursh.	6	++++	+	+						
Acer ginnala Maxim.	6	++++		+						
Acer lobelii Ten.	6	++++	tr							tr
Acer mono Maxim.	6	++++	+							
Acer monspessulanum L.	6	++++								
Acer negundo L.	6	++++	tr							tr
	8	++++		tr						+
Acer obtusatum Kit.	6	++++	tr	tr						tr
Acer pensylvanicum L.	1	+++	tr							
Acer platanoides L.	6	++++	+	tr						
Acer rubrum L.	4	+++								
Acer rufinerve Sieb. et Fucc.	6	++++	+							tr
	7	+++	+	tr						+
Acer saccharum Marsh.	6	++++	+							
	4	+++								
Acer velutinum Boiss. *var. vanvosxemii* Rehd.	6	++++								
Anacardiaceae										
Anacardium excelsum Skeels	2	+++	tr	tr						
Anacardium occidentale L.	2	+++								
Astronium balansae Engl.	3	+++	tr							
Astronium graveolens Jacq.	2	+++	tr	tr						
Cotinus coggygria Scop.	6	++++	+	++	+					+
Dracontomelon edule Skeels	2	+++	tr	tr						
Mangifera indica L.	2	++								
Pistacia lentiscus L.	8	+++	+							+
Schinus dependens Orteg	8	++++	+	+						tr
Schinus molle L.	9	++++	++	+						+
Schinus terebinthifolius Raddi	9	++++	+	++						+
Sorindeia juglandifolia Planch.	2	+++	tr							
Spondias cytherea Sonn.	2	+++	tr							

Annonaceae							
Annona bullata A. Rich.	2	+ + +	tr	tr			
Annona glabra L.	2	+ + +	tr	tr			
Annona macrocarpa Barb.	2	+ + +	tr	tr			
Annona muricata L.	2	+ + +	tr	tr			
Annona squamosa L.	2	+ + +	+				
Cananga odorata Hook. f. et Thoms.	2	+ + +	tr	tr			
Apiaceae (*Umbelliferae*)							
Bupleurum fruticosum L.	9	+ + +		tr			tr
Apocynaceae							
Alstonia macrophylla Wall. et G. Don	2	+ +	tr	tr			
Kopsia fruticosa (Ker) A. DC	2	+ +	+ +	tr			
Nerium oleander L.	8	+ + +	+ +	+	+		+
Aquifoliaceae							
Ilex aquifolium L. *cv. crispum*	8	+ + +		+			+
Ilex cassine L.	2	+ + +	tr	+			
Ilex ciliospinosa Loes.	7	+ + + +	+	+			
Araliaceae							
Brassaia actinophylla F. Muell.	2	+ + +					
Silibertia arborea	2	+ + +					
Asteraceae (Compositae)							
Artemisia canariensis Michx.	9	+	tr				tr
Euryops spec.	9	+	+				+
Berberidaceae							
Mahonia aquifolium Nutt.	8	+ +	+				+
Betulaceae (see *Corylaceae*)							
Bignoniaceae							
Campsis radicans Seem.	9	+ +	+	+ +			+
Catalpa bignonioides Walt.	9	+ + +	+	+ + +	+	tr	+
Catalpa longissima (Jacq.) Sims	3	+	+	+ + +			
Jacaranda sagraeana DC.	2	+	+ + +	+ +			
Spathodea campanulata P. Beauv.	3	+ +	+ +	+ + +			

List of exudates (continued)

	Ref.	S	R	St	V	Aj	M	So	Du	I
Spathodea nilotica Seem.	2	tr	+	+++						
Stereospermum kunthianum Cham.	2	++	++	+++						
Tabebuia berteri Britton	2	+++	+	+++						
Tabebuia glomerata Urban	2	+++	tr	+++	tr					
Tabebuia heterophylla Britt.	2	++	+	+++	tr					
Tabebuia leucoxyla P. DC.	2	+	+	++						
Tabebuia pallida Miers.	2	++	+	+++	tr					
Tabebuia speciosa Standley	2	++	+	+++						
Bombacaceae										
Bombacopsis quinata Dugand	2	+++								
Ochroma bicolor Rowlee	2	++								
Ochroma lagopus Sw.	2	+++								
Pachira rosea (?)	2	+								
Pseudobombax ellipticum (HBK.) Dugand	2	+++								
Boraginaceae										
Cordia abyssinica R. Br.	2	+++								
Cordia angiocarpa A. Rich.	2	+++								
Cordia dichotoma Forst. f.	2	+++								
Cordia glabra Cham.	3	+++								
Cordia myxa L.	3	++								
Ehretia thyrsiflora Nakai	8	+	tr							tr
Gerascanthus nitida	2	+++								
Gerascanthus obliqua	2	+++								
Gerascanthus superba	2	+++								
Gerascanthus tremula	2	+++								
Buddleiaceae										
Buddleia albiflora Hemsl.	6	++	+++	++++	+					+
Buddleia allemifolia Maxim.	6	++	+++	++++	+					+
Buddleia davidii Franch.	6	++	+++	++++	tr					+
	7	++++	++	+++	+					+
	6	++	+++	++++	+	tr				+
	7	+++	+++	++++	+	tr				+
	8	+++	+++	++++	+	tr				+

Buddleia lindleyana Fortune	9	+++	+++	++++	+		++
Buddleia salvifolia Lam.	9	++	+	++	+		+
Burseraceae							
Bursera serrata Colebr.	2	+++	tr				
Bursera simaruba (L.) Sarg.	2	+++					
Buxaceae							
Buxus sempervirens L.	6	++++	+++	+++	+		++
	7	++++	+	++	+	tr	+
	8	++++	++	++	+	tr	tr
Caesalpiniaceae							
Bauhinia candicans Benth.	2	+++					
Bauhinia malabarica Roxb.	2	+++					
Bauhinia megalandra Griseb	2	+++					
Bauhinia variegata L.	2	++++					
Bauhinia variegata L. *var. candida* Roxb.	9	+++		tr			+
Brownea coccinea Jacq.	2	++++					
Brownea grandiceps Jacq.	2	+++					
Brownea macrophylla Linden	2	+++					
Caesalpinia acutifolia Johnst.	2	+++					
Caesalpinia melanocarpa Grieseb.	2	++++					
Caesalpinia paucijuga Benth.	2	+++					
Caesalpinia vesicaria Lam.	2	+++					
Cercis siliquastrum L.	6	++++					tr
Cassia grandis L.f.	2	+++					
Cassia siamea Lam.	2	+++					
Cassia spectabilis DC.	2	+++					
Colvillea racemosa Bojer	2	+++					
Erythrophloeum guineense G. Don	2	+++					
Gleditschia fera Merr.	2	++++					
Gleditschia sinensis Lam.	6	++++					
Haematoxylum campechianum L.	2	+++					
Hymenaea courbaril L.	2	+++					
Intsia bijuga Ktze.	2	++++					
Lysidice rhodostegia Hance	2	+++					
Peltophorum africanum Sond.	2	++++					
Peltophorum dasyrachis Kurz	2	+++					

List of exudates (continued)

	Ref.	S	R	St	V	Aj	M	So	Du	I
Phyllocarpus septentrionalis Donn.-Smith	2	+++								
Saraca declinata Miq.	2	++++								
Saraca indica L.	2	+++								
Calycanthaceae										
Calycanthus occidentalis Hook. et Arn.	9	+++	+	+						++
Caprifoliaceae										
Kolkwitzia amabilis Graebn.	6	++++	++	+	tr					+
Lonicera fragrantissima Lindl. et Paxt.	9	+	++	tr						+
Viburnum lantana L.	8	+++	++	+						++
Viburnum tinus L.	9	+++	+++	tr						tr
Casuarinaceae										
Casuarina equisetifolia Forst.	3	+++								
Celastraceae										
Catha edulis Forsk.	2	+	tr	+++	tr					
Celastrus orbiculata Thunb.	7	++	+	+	tr				+++	tr
Elaeodendron quadrangulatum Reiss. in Mart.	3	+	tr	+++	tr					
Elaeodendron xylocarpum DC	3	++	tr	+++	tr					
Euonymus japonica Thunb.	8	+++	+	+	+				++++	tr
Euonymus latifolia Scop.	7	+	++	++					+++	tr
Euonymus oxyphylla Mig.	6	++	++	+++	tr				++++	+
Euonymus sanguinea Loes.	7	+++	+++	++++	+				+++	+
Cercidiphyllaceae										
Cercidiphyllum japonicum Sieb. et Zucc.	6	++++	++	+						tr
Cistaceae										
Cistus purpureus Lam.	9	+	tr							tr
Clethraceae										
Clethra acuminata Michx.	6	++++	++++	++++	+					+

Cneoraceae							
Cneorum tricoccum L.	9	+ + +	tr	tr	tr		+
Combretaceae							
Buchenavia capitata Eichl.	2	+ + +	+	tr			
Combretum spec.	3	+ +	+ +	+ +			
Laguncularia racemosa Gaertn. f.	3	+ + +				+ + +	
Terminalia angustifolia Jacq.	2	+ + +	+	+ +	tr		
Terminalia arjuna Bedd.	2	+ + +	+ +	+	tr	+ +	
Terminalia bellerica Roxb.	2	+ + + +	+	tr			
Terminalia catappa L.	2	+ + +	+	+			
Terminalia chebula Retz.	2	+ + +	+ + +	tr		+	
Terminalia edulis Blanco	2	+ +	+ +	+			
Terminalia mülleri Benth.	3	+ + +		+			
Terminalia myriocarpa Heurck et Muell.-Arg.	3	+ +	+ + +	tr		?	
Terminalia oliveri Brandis	2	+ +	+ + +	+	tr	+ + +	
Terminalia superba Engl. and Diels.	2	+ + +	+ +	+	tr		
Compositae (see *Asteraceae*)							
Coriariaceae							
Coriaria myrtifolia L.	8	+ + +	+	+			tr
Cornaceae							
Aucuba japonica Thunb.	8	+ + +	tr	tr			+
Cornus mas L.	6	+ + + +	+	+			tr
Cornus officinalis Sieb. et Zucc.	6	+ + + +	+	+			tr
Corylaceae (= Betulaceae)							
Alnus glutinosa Gaertn.	6	+ + + +	+ +	+ +			tr
Alnus × *roehnei* Call.	6	+ + + +	+	+			tr
Betula fruticosa Pall.	6	+ + + +	+ + +	+ +	+		+
Betula lenta L.	4	+ +					
Betula lutea Michx.	4	+ +					
Betula papyrifera Marsh.	4	+ + +					
Betula populifolia Marsh.	4	+ + +					
Carpinus betulus L.	6	+ + + +	+	tr			tr
Corylus avellana L.	6	+ + + +	+ +	+ +			tr

List of exudates (continued)

	Ref.	S	R	St	V	Aj	M	So	Du	I
Dichapetalaceae										
Tapura cubensis Gris.	2	+++	tr	+						
Dilleniaceae										
Dillenia indica L.	2	++	tr	+						
Dillenia philippinensis Rolfe.	2	++	tr	tr						
Ebenaceae										
Diospyros Kaki L. f.	8	++++	+		+(?)					++
Diospyros maritima Blume	2	+++		tr						
Diospyros mespiliformis Hochst.	2	++++								
Diospyros virginiana L.	6	+++	+++	++	+					+
Elaeagnaceae										
Elaeagnus angustifolia Don.	6	++++	tr	tr						tr
	9	++++	+	tr	tr(?)					tr
Hippophaë salicifolia Don.	6	++++	tr							tr
Elaeocarpaceae										
Muntingia calabura L.	2	+++								
Ericaceae										
Arbutus unedo L.	8	+++		tr						+
Rhododendron houlstonii Hemsl. et Wils	6	+++	++	+						
Euphorbiaceae										
Alchornea cordifolia Müll. Arg.	2	+++								
Aleurites moluccana Willd.	2	+++								
Aleurites trisperma Blanco	2	++++								
Andrachne colchica Fisch. et Men.	8	+++		tr	tr					tr
Antidesma bunius (L.) Spreng.	2	+	+++	tr						
Antidesma platyphyllum H. Mann.	2	tr	+	tr						
Antidesma venosum E. Mey. ex Tul.	3	+	tr							
Bridelia monoica Merrill	2	+++								

Drypetes lateriflora (SW) Krug et Urban	2	+++			
Pera bumeliaefolia Griseb.	2	+++			
Phyllanthus emblica L.	2	+++			
Phyllanthus grandiflorus L.	6	++	+++	+	+
Ricinus communis L.	9	++++	+++(?)	tr	+
Sapium luzonicum Merr.	2	+++			
Sapium sebiferum (L.) Roxb.	2	+++			
Fabaceae (= *Papilionaceae*)					
Amorpha fruticosa L.	9	+++	tr	tr	tr
Anagyris foetida L.	8	++++	tr		+
Atelaia apetala Griseb.	2	+++			
Butea frondosa Roxb.	2	+++			
Caragana arborescens Lam.	6	++++			
Centrolobium ochroxylon Rose	2	+++			
Cladrastis lutea U. Koch	6	++++			
	8	++			
Dalbergia assamica Benth.	2	+++			
Dalbergia cochinchinensis Pierre	2	+++			
Dalbergia melanoxylon Guill. and Perr.	2	+++			
Dalbergia retusa Hemsl.	2	+++			
Dalbergia sissoo Roxb.	2	+++			
Erythrina berteroana L.	2	++			
Erythrina grisebachii Urb.	2	++			
Erythrina monosperma Gaudich.	2	++			
Erythrina senegalensis DC.	2	++			
Erythrina variegata L.	2	++			
Halimodendron halodendron Voss.	6	++++			
Hebestigma cubense (HBK.) Urban	2	+++			
Laburnum anagyroides Med.	8	+++	tr		tr
Lonchocarpus punctatus HBK.	2	+++			
Lonchocarpus violaceus Kunth	2	+++			
Ormosia calavensis Azaola	2	+++			
Ormosia monosperma Urb.	2	+++			
Piscidia piscipula Sarg.	2	++++			
	3	++++			
Platymiscium pinnatum (Jacq.) Dugand	2	+++			

List of exudates (continued)

	Ref.	S	R	St	V	Aj	M	So	Du	I
Pongamia pinnata (L.) Merrill	2	+++								
Pterocarpus officinalis Jacq.	2	+++								
Robinia hispida L.	8	++								tr
Robinia luxurians Sihn.	6	++++								tr
Robinia pseudoacacia L.	4	+++								
	6	++++								tr
Spartium junceum L.	9	+++								tr
Fagaceae										
Castanea dentata Borkh.	1	+++	tr							
Castanea sativa Mill.	6	++++	tr	tr						tr
Castanea spec.	4	+++								
Fagus japonica Maxim.	6	++++		tr						
Fagus orientalis Lipsky	6	++++	tr	tr						
Fagus sylvatica L.	6	++++		tr						
Fagus sylvatica L. *var. pendula* Loud.	6	++++		+						
Fagus sylvatica L. *var. purpurea – pendula* Rehd.	6	++++		tr						
Fagus sylvatica L. *var. laciniata* Vignet	6	++++	tr	+						
Quercus alba L.	4	+++								
	6	++++	+	+						+
Quercus bicolor Willd.	6	++++	tr	tr						+
Quercus borealis Michx. *var. maxima* Ashe	6	++++	+	tr						+
Quercus × *bushii* Sarg.	6	++++	tr	tr						+
Quercus castaneaefolia C.A. Mey.	6	++++	tr	tr						+
Quercus cerris L.	6	++++	+	tr						+
Quercus × *exacta* Trel. (*Q. imbricaria* × *Q. palustris*)	6	++++	tr	tr						+
Quercus frainetto Ten.	7	+++	+	++	tr	tr(?)				+

Quercus grosseserrata Rehd. et Wils.	6	++++	tr	+		+
Quercus ilex L.	8	++++				+
Quercus imbricaria L.	6	++++	tr	tr		+
Quercus lusitanica Lam.	8	++				tr
Quercus macranthera Fisch. et Mey.	6	++++	tr	tr		+
Quercus macrocarpa Michx.	6	++++	tr	tr		+
Quercus marilandica Muenchh.	6	++++	tr	tr		+
Quercus palustris Muenchh.	6	++++	+	tr		+
Quercus pontica K. Koch.	6	++++	tr	tr		tr
Quercus prinus L.	1	++++				
	6	+++	tr	tr		+
Quercus robur L.	6	++++	tr	+		tr
Quercus rubra L.	4	+++				
Flacourtiaceae						
Caloncoba brevipes Gilg.	2	+++	+	+		
Dovyalis hebecarpa Warb.	2	+++				
Flacourtia indica (Burm. f.) Merr.	2	+++	tr	tr		
Flacourtia inermis Roxb.	3	+++	+	+		
Flacourtia fangomas Stend.	2	+++	+	+		
Hydnocarpus alpina Wight.	2	+++				
Hydnocarpus anthelminthicus Pierre	2	+++				
Hydnocarpus wightiana Bl.	2	+++	tr			
Zuelania guidonia Britt and Millsp.	2	+++	tr	+		
Garryaceae						
Garrya elliptica Dougl.	8	++	+			+
Hamamelidaceae						
Corylopsis veitchiana Bean	7	+++	+++	++	+	+
Liquidambar styraciflua L.	6	++++	++	+		tr
Parrotia persica C.A. Mey.	6	++	tr	tr		tr
Hernandiaceae						
Hernandia sonora L.	3	+++				

List of exudates (continued)

	Ref.	S	R	St	V	Aj	M	So	Du	I
Hippocastanaceae										
Aesculus hippocastanum L.	6	++++	tr	tr						tr
Aesculus turbinata Bl.	6	++++	tr	tr						tr
Hypericaceae (=*Guttiferae*)										
Clusia rosea Jacq.	3	+++								
Garcinia oblongifolia Champ.	2	+++								
Juglandaceae										
Carya glabra Sweet.	6	++++	+++	+++						++
Carya illinoensis K. Koch.	6	++++	++	++	tr					++
Carya laciniosa Loud.	6	++++	+++	+++	tr	tr				++
Carya ovata K. Koch.	6	++++	+++	++	tr					++
	7	+++	+++	++	tr					+
Carya tomentosa Nutt.	6	++++	++	++						+
Juglans cinerea L.	4	+++								
Juglans nigra L.	9	++++	+	tr	tr?					tr
Juglans regia L.	6	++++	+	++	tr?					+
Pterocarya fraxinifolia Spach.	6	++++	+	+	tr?					+
Lamiaceae (=Labiatae)										
Rosmarinus officinalis L.	9	++	++(?)	+						++
Salvia grahami Benth.	9	++	tr	++	tr					+
Lardizabalaceae										
Holboellia latifolia Wall.	8	+++	++	tr	tr					+
Lauraceae										
Cinnamomum camphora Nees and Eberm.	8	+++	+		+					++
Laurus nobilis L.	8	++++	+	tr						+
Miscanteca triandra Mez.	2	++++								
Persea americana Mill.	3	+++								
Sassafras albidum Nees.	6	+++	tr	+						tr
Lecythidaceae										
Lecythis zabucaja Aubl.	2	+++								

Leguminosae						
(see *Caesalpiniaceae, Fabaceae, Mimosaceae*)						
Lythraceae						
Lagerstroemia indica L.	8	+++	+++	+	tr	tr
Magnoliaceae						
Liriodendron tulipifera L.	1	+++	tr	tr		
Magnolia grandiflora L.	9	+	tr			tr
Magnolia kobus D.C.	6	++++		+	tr	+
Malpighiaceae						
Byrsonima crassifolia Luman ex Griseb.	2	+++				
Lophanthera lactescens Ducke	2	++	tr	+		
Malvaceae						
Abutilon spec.	9	+++	tr		tr?	tr
Hibiscus elatus DC.	2	+++				
Hibiscus syriacus L.	9	+++	tr		tr?	tr
Montezuma speciosissima (Moc. and Sessé) DC.	3	+++				
Meliaceae						
Aglaia montana C. DC.	2	+++		+++		
Carapa guianensis Aubl.	2	+++	+	+		
Cedrela toona Roxb.	2	+++	tr	tr		
Khaya nyasica (Stapf) Baker	2	+++	+	+		
Khaya senegalensis Juss.	2	+++	tr	tr		
Melia azedarach L.	9	++++	+	+		+
Swietenia candollei Pittier	2	+++	tr	tr		
Swietenia humilis Zucc.	2	+++	tr	tr		
Swietenia macrophylla King	2	+++	tr	tr		
Swietenia mahagoni Jacq.	2	+++	tr			
Trichilia odorata Andr.	6	+++	+	++	tr	tr
Melianthaceae						
Melianthus comosus Vahl.	9	+++		tr?		+
Melianthus major L.	9	++++		tr	tr	tr

List of exudates (continued)

	Ref.	S	R	St	V	Aj	M	So	Du	I
Mimosaceae										
Acacia baileyana F.V.M.	9	+++		tr	tr					tr
Acacia melanoxylon R.Br.	9	+++								+
Acacia retinodes Schlecht.	9	+++								+
Adenanthera microsperma Teijsm and Binn	3	+++								
Albizzia julibrissin Durazz.	9	++++								tr
Parkia javanica Merr.	2	+++								
Pithecellobium dulce Benth.	2	+++								
Pithecellobium filicifolium Benth.	2	++								
Monimiaceae										
Peumus boldus Mol.	8	+								tr
Moraceae										
Artocarpus communis J.R. and G. Forster	2	+++								
Ficus carica L. (mixed with latex)	6	++++	+++	++	tr					+
	8	++++	+	+	tr?					++
Ficus spec.	2	+++								
Morus alba L.	6	++++	+	++	tr					+
Moringaceae										
Moringa oleifera Lam.	2	+++								
Myrsinaceae										
Ardisia humilis	3	++++	tr							
Jacquinia armillaris	3	+++								
Jacquinia keyensis Mez	3	+++								
Myrtaceae										
Acca sellowiana Burret	8	+++	++	+						tr
Anamomis simpsonii Small	3	+++	++							
Callistemon lanceolatus Sw.	9	++	++	tr	tr					+

Calyptranthes decandra Gr.	2	+++	+++	tr				
Eucalyptus globulus Labill	9	+++	+++	+				++
Eucalyptus naudiniana F. Muell.	2	+++	+	tr				
Eucalyptus saligna Sm.	2	++	++					
Eucalyptus viminalis Labill.	9	++++	+++	+				tr
Eugenia atropunctata Steud.	2	+++		tr				
Eugenia axillaris Willd.	2	+++	+++	tr				
Eugenia buxifolia Willd.	2	+++	+++					
Eugenia edulis Benth. and Hook. f.	2	+++	+++	tr				
Eugenia malaccensis L.	2	+++	tr	++				
Eugenia uniflora L.	2	+++	+++	tr				
Eugenia uvalha Cambess.	2	+++	+++	+				
Melaleuca leucadendron L.	3	++	++	tr				
Pimenta officinalis Lindl.	2	+++		tr				
Pimenta racemosa J.W. Moore	2	+++	tr	tr				
Psidium friedrichsthalianum (Berg) Ndzu.	2	+++	+++	tr				
Psidium guajava L.	2	+++	++	tr				
Psidium guineense Sw.	2	+++	++	tr				
Psidium molle Bertol.	2	+++	+++	tr				
Syzygium lineatum Merr. and Perry	2	+++		tr				
Nyctaginaceae								
Bougainvillea glabra Choisy	9	+++		tr				+
Nyssaceae								
Nyssa sylvatica Marsh.	1	+++	tr					
Oleaceae								
Fraxinus americana L.	1	++	++	+++	tr		+++	
	6	+	++	+++	+		++	+
Fraxinus excelsior L.	6	++	++	+++	tr		++++	tr
Fraxinus oregona Nutt. *var. glabra*	6	++	++	+++	+		+++	+
Fraxinus ornus L.	5	++	++	+++	++	tr	++++	tr
	6	++	++	+++	+		++++	+
	8	+++	++	++++	++		+++	+
Fraxinus oxycarpa Willd.	6	++	++	+++	+		++++	+
Jasminum heterophyllum Roxb.	9	++		+			+++	tr

List of exudates (continued)

	Ref.	S	R	St	V	Aj	M	So	Du	I
Jasminum nudiflorum Lindl.	8	+ +	tr	+	+		+ + +			tr
Ligustrum japonicum Thunb.	8	+	+	+ + +	+ +		+ + +			tr
Olea europaea L.	9	+ + +	+	+ + +	tr		+ + + +			+
Phillyrea decora Boiss. et Bal.	8	+	tr	+			+ +			tr
Phillyrea latifolia L.	8	+ +	+	+ +			+ + +			tr
Syringa julianae Schr	6	+ +	+ +	+ + +	+		+ + +			+
Syringa pubescens Turcz.	7	+ +	+	+ + +	tr		+ + +			tr
Syringa vulgaris L.	7	+ + +	+ +	+ + + +	+		+ + +			+
	6	+ +	+ +	+ + +	+		+ + +			tr
	8	+ + + +	+ + +	+ + + +	+ + +	+	+ + +			+ +
	2	+ +	+ +	+ + +	tr		+ + +			
Onagraceae										
Hauya spec.	2	+ +	+ + +	+ +						
Oxalidaceae										
Averrhoa carambola L.	2	+ + +								
Papilionaceae (see **Fabaceae**)										
Pittosporaceae										
Pittosporum heterophyllum Franch.	8	+		tr						tr
Pittosporum pentandrum	3	+ + +								
Pittosporum rhombifolium Cunn.	3	+ + +								
Pittosporum undulatum Vent.	9	+ +	tr?	+						+ +
Polygalaceae										
Polygala virgata Thunb.	9	+	tr							tr
Polygonaceae										
Coccoloba floridana Meissn.	3	+ + +								
Coccoloba grandifolia Jacq.	2	+ + +								
Coccoloba retusa Gris.	2	+ + +								
Coccoloba uvifera Jacq.	2	+ + +								
Ruprechtia coriacea (L.) Karst.	3	+ + +								
Triplaris americana Vahl.	2	+ + +								

Proteaceae							
Grevillea robusta A. Cunn.	2	+++					
	9	++++	+				tr
Prunoideae							
Osmaronia cerasiformis Greene	7	++	tr	tr		++++	tr
Prunus amygdalus Batsch. var. *amara* Focke	9	++++	++	+		+++	++
Prunus amygdalus Batsch × ?	8	+++	tr	tr	tr	++++	+
Prunus laurocerasus L.	8	+++	+	tr		++	+
Prunus mahaleb L.	6	+++		tr		++++	tr
Prunus padus L.	6	+++	++	++		++++	+
	7	+++		tr		+++	tr
Prunus pensylvanica L. f.	4	++				++	
Prunus serotina Ehrh.	4	+++				++	
Prunus serrulata Lindl. cv. Kanzan	6	+++		tr		++++	tr
Prunus virginiana L.	4	+++				++	
Punicaceae							
Punica granatum L.	8	++++	+++	+++			+
Rhamnaceae							
Colubrina ferruginosa Brongn.	3	+++					
Colubrina reclinata Brongn.	2	+++	+	tr			
Paliurus aculeatus Lam.	9	++++	+				+
Rhamnus cathartica L.	1	+++	tr	tr			
	4	+++					
	6	++++	tr	tr			tr
Zizyphus jujuba Lam.	2	+++					
Rosaceae (Chrysobalanoideae)							
Licania rigida Benth.	2	+++	tr	tr			
Parinarium macrophyllum Sabine	2	++					
Rosaceae (Pomoideae)							
Cotoneaster bullata Bois.	7	++	+	tr	tr	+++	+
Cotoneaster hupehensis Rehd. et Wils.	6	+++	tr			++++	tr
Cotoneaster wardii W.W. Sm.	6	+++		tr		++++	tr
Crataegus monogyna Jacq.	6	+++	++	+		++++	+

List of exudates (continued)

	Ref.	S	R	St	V	Aj	M	So	Du	I
Malus × *zumi* Rehd. *var. calocarpa* Rehd.	6	++	+	tr				+++		tr
Mespilus germanica L.	6	+++	tr	tr	tr			++++		+
Photinia serrulata Lindl.	8	++	tr					++++		tr
Pyracantha coccinea Roem.	7	+	tr	tr				+++		tr
Pyrus malus L.	4	+++						+		
Sorbus aucuparia L.	8	+++	tr	tr				++++		+
Sorbus × *hybrida* L.	6	+++	++	+				+++		+
Stranvaesia davidiana Decne.	6	+++	tr	tr				++++		tr
Rosaceae (Rosoideae)										
Rosa camua L.	7	++++	tr	tr	tr					+
	6	++++	+	+	tr					
Rosa "New Dawn"	6	++++		+						+
Rubus thibetanus Franch.	6	++++	+	+						+
Rubiaceae										
Calycophyllum candidissimum (Vahl) DC	2	+++	tr	tr						
Nauclea orientalis L.	3	+++								
Posoqueria latifolia (Lam.) R. and Sch.	2	+++								
Randia dumetorum Lam.[a]	2	tr		tr			?			
Rondeletia brachycarpa C. Wright[a]	2	tr	tr	tr						

[a] These low quantities could possibly be due to dilutions with latex, gum, or some other liquid.

	Ref.	S	R	St	V	Aj	M	So	Du	I
Rutaceae										
Aegle marmelos (L.) Correa	2	++++								
Casimiroa edulis Llav. et Lex	2	+++	tr	tr						
Citrus aurantium L. *var. Bigaradia*	9	+++	++		tr					++
Citrus dulcamara Souza	2	+++								
Citrus hystrix DC.	2	+++								
Citrus macroptera Montr.	2	++++								
Citrus medica L. *var. limonum* Wight et Arn.	9	+	+?							+

Clausena lansium (Lour.) Skeels	2	+++	tr	+		
Evodia daniellii Hamsl.	6	++++	+	++		+
Evodia henryi Dode	6	++++	+	+	tr	tr
Poncirus trifoliata Raf.	8	+	tr			tr
Ptelea serrata Small.	6	++++	tr	++	tr	tr
Ptelea trifoliata L.	8	++++	tr	tr		+
Ptelea trifoliata L. *var. mollis Torr.* et Gray	6	++++	tr	++		tr
Zanthoxylum elephantiasis Macf.	2	+++	tr	++		
Zanthoxylum martinicense DC.	2	+++	tr	++		
Salicaceae						
Populus candicans Ait.	6	++++	+	+		+
Populus × euro-americana Fornd.	6	++++	+	+		+
Populus grandidentata Michx. × P. tremula L.	6	++++	+	+	tr	+
Populus simonii Carr.	8	++++	++	+	+?	+
Populus tremuloides Michx.	4	++++	tr			
	1	+++	tr	tr		
	6	+++	+	tr		+
Populus Wilsonii Schneid.	6	++++	+	+		+
Salix acutifolia Willd.	6	++++	+	+		tr
Salix alba L.	6	++++	+	+		tr
Salix alba L. *var. chermesina* Hartig	6	++++	+	+		tr
Salix alba L. *var. tristis* Rehd.	6	++++	+	tr		tr
Salix aurita L.	6	++++	+	+		tr
Salix daphnoides Vill. *var. pomeranica* Koch	6	++++	+	+		tr
Santalaceae						
Santalum album L.	2	+++				
Sapindaceae						
Allophylus cominia (L.) Sw.	2	++++				
Blighia sapida Koenig	2	++				
Dodonea triguetra Andr.	8	+++	tr	tr		+
Euphoria longana Lam.	2	+++				
Harpullia cupanioides Roxb.	3	++++				
Koelreuteria formosana Hayata	2	+++				

List of exudates (continued)

	Ref.	S	R	St	V	Aj	M	So	Du	I
Koelreuteria paniculata Laxm. *var. apiculata* Rehd.	6	++++								
Litchi chinensis Sonn.	2	+++								
Sapindus saponaria L.	2	+++								
Sapindus trifoliatus L.	2	+++								
Sapotaceae										
Bumelia obovata DC.	2	++++								
Bumelia tenax Willd.	8	++	+							tr
Chrysophyllum cainito L.	3	+++								
Dipholis montana Gr.	2	++++								
Dipholis salicifolia (L.) A. DC.	2	++++								
Lucuma salicifolia HBK.	2	+++								
Lucuma serpentaria HBK.	2	+++								
Sideroxylon foetidissimum Jacq.	2	+++								
Saxifragaceae										
Escallonia macrantha Hook. et Arn.	9	++		+?						+
Escallonia sp.	9	++	tr	tr?	tr					++
Philadelphus sp.	7	+	tr	+						tr
Scrophulariaceae										
Paulownia tomentosa Steud.	8	++++	+++	++++	++	tr				+
Simarubaceae										
Picrodendron baccatum Kr. and Urban	2	+++								
Simaruba glauca DC.	3	++								
Solanaceae										
Datura arborea L.	9	+		tr						
Solanum giganteum Jacq.	9	++								+
Sonneratiaceae										
Duabanga sonneratioides Buch.-Ham.	2	++								
Spiroideae										
Exochorda giraldii Hesse	6	+++	tr					++++		+

Physocarpus amurensis Max.	7	+++	tr	+		++	tr
Sorbaria arborea Schn. *var. subtomentosa* Rehd.	6	+++	+	tr		++++	tr
Spiraea henryi Hemsl.	6	+++	+	tr	tr	++++	tr
Spiraea veitchii Hemsl.	6	+++	+	tr	tr	+++	tr
Staphyleaceae							
Staphylea colchica Steven	8	+++	++	tr	tr		+
Staphylea pinnata L.	7	+	tr	tr			tr
Sterculiaceae							
Pterocymbium tinctorium Merr.	2	+++					
Sterculia lanceolata Blume	3	++++					
Sterculia platanifolia L.	8	+	tr				tr
Sterculia quadrifida R. Br.	2	+++					
Sterculia tragacantha Mind.	2	+++					
Styracaceae							
Halesia monticola Sarg.	6	++++	+	+			+
Tamaricaceae							
Tamarix gallica L.	6	++++		tr			tr
	8	+++					tr
Tamarix pentandra Pall.	8	+++					+
Thymeleaceae							
Daphne caucasica Pall.	6	++					tr
Tiliaceae							
Belotia grewiaefolia A. Rich.	2	++					
Tilia americana L.	1	+++	+	+			
	6	++++	++	++			+
Tilia × blechiana Dieck.	6	++++	++	++	tr		+
Tilia cordata Mill	6	++++	+	+			+
(leaves not yet developed)	7	++++	++	++	+		+
Tilia × euchlora Koch.	6	++++	tr	+			tr
	8	++++	+	+			+
Tilia × europaea L.	6	++++	++	++			tr
Tilia mongolica Maxim.	6	++++	++	+			tr

List of exudates (continued)

	Ref.	S	R	St	V	Aj	M	So	Du	I
Tilia olivieri Szysz.	6	++++	++	+	tr					+
Tilia petiolaris DC.	6	++++	++	++	tr					+
(leaves not yet developed)	7	++++	+++	++	tr					+
Tilia platyphyllos Scop.	6	++++	+	+						+
(leaves partly developed)	7	++++	+++	+++	+					+
Ulmaceae										
Celtis australis L.	9	++++	++++	+	tr					++
Celtis occidentalis L.	6	++++	+	+						+
Holoptelea integrifolia Planch.	2	+++	tr	tr						
Ulmus americana L.	4	+++	tr							
	1	+++	++	++						
Ulmus carpinifolia Gled.	6	++++	++	++						+
Ulmus pumila L.	6	++++	+++	++	+					+
Zelkova carpinifolia K. Koch.	5	++++	tr	tr						tr
Zelkova serrata Makino	6	++++	tr	tr						tr
Umbelliferae (see **Apiaceae**)										
Verbenaceae										
Callicarpa arborea Roxb.	2	++	+	+++	+					
Citharexylum fruticosum L.	2	++	++	+++	tr					
Clerodendron trichotomum Thunb.	6	+++	+++	++++	+					+
Clerodendron tuberculatum A. Rich.	2	+++	+	++						
Record Run		+	+	++						
Cornutia grandiflora (Schecht. and Cham.) Schauer	3	tr	tr	+++	tr					
Gmelina arborea Roxb.	2	++	++	+++	tr					
Gmelina asiatica L.	2	++	++	+++	tr					
Petitia domingensis Jacq.	2	tr	+	+++	tr					
Tectona grandis L.	2	tr		+++	tr					
Vitex agnus-castus L.	8	+++	+	+						+
Vitex altissima Linn.	2	+	tr	+++						
	2	++		+++						

Vitex cymosa Bert.	2	++	++	++	+	
Vitex gigantea HBK.	2	+	+	++	tr	
Vitex parviflora A. Juss.	2	+++	tr	+++	tr	
Vitex quinata F.N. Williams	2	++	++	+++		
Vitaceae						
Leea alata Edgew.	2	+++				
Parthenocissus henryana Diels et Gilg.	8	++	tr	+	tr	tr
Parthenocissus tricuspidata Planch. *var. veitchii* Rehd.	6	++++	+++	++	+	tr
Tetrastigma voinerianum Pierre ex Gagnep	9	+				+
Zygophyllaceae						
Bulnesia arborea Engl.	3	+++				

Author Index

Page numbers *in italics* refer to the bibliography

Subject Index

Italic page numbers indicate illustrations

Encyclopedia of Plant Physiology, New Series

Edited by A. Pirson
and M.H. Zimmermann

The well-known and successful **Encyclopedia of Plant Physiology**, conceived three decades ago by **W. Ruhland**, was concluded in 1967 with the publication of the last of the 18 volumes. The **Encyclopedia** is still an important reference work useful for both research and teaching.

But plant physiology has continued to develop and considerable advances have been made since the publication of the **Encyclopedia.** Biochemical and biophysical methods, and the methods of modern molecular biology in particular, continue to stimulate research.

Extensive discussions between **Springer-Verlag** and numerous scientists resulted in the concept of the **Encyclopedia of Plant Physiology, New Series,** – under the editorship of **A. Pirson,** Göttingen, and **M.H. Zimmermann,** Harvard. The volumes of the **New Series** are dedicated to special topics, they will be smaller and less expensive, and thus will appear within a shorter publication time. For more extensive areas multiple but largely self-contained volumes are planned, and editors of related volumes will maintain close contact with each other. The **New Series** will be written entirely in English and each volume will be edited by editors who are experts in the fields concerned.

The editors and the publisher hope that the **Encyclopedia of Plant Physiology, New Series** – will in time build up a comprehensive, modern treatise covering the whole field of plant physiology. Such a work will stimulate collaboration among specialists of different disciplines, offer detailed information for teaching at university level, and enable graduate students to find their way into the current research areas of any field.

Volumes to be published in the near future:

Vol. 2: **Transport in Plants II**
Edited by U. Lüttge and M.G. Pitman
With a Foreword by R.A. Robertson
With contributions by numerous experts.
Part A: **Cells**

Part B: **Tissues and Organs**

Vol. 3: **Transport in Plants III**
Intracellular Transport and Exchange Mechanisms
Edited by U. Heber and C.R. Stocking

Vol. 4: **Physiological Plant Pathology**
Edited by R. Heitefuss and P.H. Williams

Springer-Verlag
Berlin Heidelberg New York

Membrane Transport in Plants

Editors: U. Zimmermann, J. Dainty

Contents: Thermodynamics and Electrochemistry of Membrane Transport. – Water Transport and Osmotic Processes. – Electrical Properties of Membranes. – Solute Transport in Algae and Cell-suspension Cultures. – Transport in Isolated Chloroplasts. – ATPases and Transport. – Kinetics of Transport. – Transport in Organs of Higher Plants. – Regulating Factors in Membrane Transport.

This book contains the proceedings of the 'International Workshop on Membrane Transport in Plants', held in February 1974 at the Nuclear Research Center, Jülich (FRG). The Papers cover a broad spectrum of topics in plant physiology, including the thermodynamics of transport processes, water relations, primary reactions of photosynthesis, hormonal regulation, phytochrome interaction with membranes, and the more conventional aspects of membrane transport. The aim was to bring advanced modern concepts of membrane transport to the attention of biologists and to give physical chemists an understanding of complex biological systems.

D. Hess

Plant Physiology

Molecular, Biochemical, and Physiological Fundamentals of Metabolism and Development
Springer Study Edition

Contents: Control of Character Formation by Nucleic Acids. – Photosynthesis. – Carbohydrates. – Biological Oxidation. – Fats. – Terpenoids. – Phenols. – Amino Acids. – Alkaloids. – Porphyrins. – Cell Division. – Differential Gene Activity as Principle of Differentiation. – Regulation. – Polarity and Unequal Cell Division as Fundamentals of Differentiation. – Cell Elongation. – The Formation of Seeds and Fruits. – Germination. – The Vascular System. – Flower Formation.

An elementary introduction to the metabolic and developmental physiology of higher plants from the point of view of molecular biology. The outstanding feature of the text is that equal weight is given to metabolism and development.

Springer-Verlag Berlin Heidelberg New York